Ce-7-9427

Elements
of
Radio

FOURTH EDITION

ELEMENTS

OF

RADIO

By

ABRAHAM MARCUS

and

WILLIAM MARCUS

PRENTICE-HALL, INC.
Englewood Cliffs, N.J.

ELEMENTS OF RADIO
Fourth Edition
Marcus and Marcus

Other Prentice-Hall books in this series

Radio Projects, by Abraham Marcus
Radio Servicing, Theory and Practice, by Abraham Marcus
Elements of Television Servicing, by Marcus and Gendler
Basic Electricity, by Abraham Marcus

DEDICATION

To the thousands of men and women who patiently and painstakingly helped answer the myriad of questions that swirled through our heads we gratefully dedicate this book.

Some of these men and women we had the pleasure of meeting in person. Others we knew only as a name on a book or a signature to a magazine article. But through speech or through the printed word, each helped to transmit our common heritage, our civilization.

We fondly hope that in some slight measure we do likewise, and thus repay, in small part, the debt we owe our teachers.

ABRAHAM MARCUS
WILLIAM MARCUS

ABOUT

THIS

BOOK

The organization of this book has evoked a good deal of curiosity, and an explanation is in order. The subject matter seems to fall into three general categories. These are:

1. Electrical theory.
2. The radio transmitter.
3. The radio receiver.

Some authors have arranged their books as follows:

1. Electrical theory. The assumption is that before the student can learn radio theory he first must know electrical theory.
2. The radio transmitter. This is predicated on the fact that, before a signal can be received, a signal must be transmitted.
3. The radio receiver.

This order seems logical to the author, but is it logical to the student?

There is a maxim in pedagogy that you must teach from the known to the unknown. That is, material must be presented in light of what the student already knows. In this way the transition to the new is made easy, especially if the steps are small and in proper sequence.

With the above in mind, let us see what happens to the sequence of topics. To the average beginner the electrical theory represents a mass of abstract principles and laws, generally without meaning or reality, that must be memorized. As for the radio transmitter, hardly a beginner has even seen one.

The only thing that has any reality or familiarity for him is the radio receiver that he has seen and handled in his home.

Accordingly, he should learn first how the radio receiver operates. So important is this that the first part of this book is devoted entirely to the receiver.

Of course, it would be absurd to attempt to explain to the beginner the operation of the modern superheterodyne receiver at the very beginning of the book. The simple crystal receiver is chosen as embodying all the basic principles of any receiver.

To insure a complete understanding of this simple receiver, the device of the spiral is adopted in presenting the subject matter. Thus at the first cycle an extremely elementary explanation of the radio is presented—tuning, detection, and reproduction. The next turn around covers the same ground but at a slightly higher level. And so on through the various cycles.

But at each level, the complete radio receiver is presented. By this means, the student's interest is maintained. Also, at each stage, set construction is presented so that the student can see the result of the theoretical concepts of that stage in concrete form.

Having mastered an understanding of the simple crystal receiver, the student is led on to more advanced sets by being confronted with problems he must solve. Thus, the drawbacks of the crystal detector lead to the development of the vacuum-tube detector. To eliminate the nuisance of headphones requires the audio-frequency amplifier. Our search for sensitivity leads us to the radio-frequency amplifier. And so on. Note that this is how the science of radio actually developed.

Another *must* is the elimination, as far as possible, of all formulas and mathematics. Too often a formula is substituted for an explanation. We must remember that what is perfectly clear to the engineer may not be so clear to the student. Thus this first part does not contain a single formula.

The second part of this book is devoted to electrical theory, transmitters, and more advanced aspects of radio. It is hoped that the student will be sufficiently enthusiastic and curious to continue beyond the first part. But even if he is not, it must be remembered that each part is a complete unit in itself.

Teaching Devices

To make the textbook a useful tool of instruction, several devices approved by most progressive teachers are included:

1. *Problems* are set up as questions at the beginning of each chapter.
2. Paragraphs are introduced by *boldface captions*.
3. A *glossary* appears at the end of each chapter.
4. A set of *questions* and *problems* accompanies each chapter.
5. A complete program of classroom *demonstrations* is provided at the end of the text.
6. Useful *tables of data* are grouped in the *Appendix*.
7. The *drawings* are large and more than usually profuse. They are definitely directed toward explanation — not for adornment.
8. A *Table of Contents* may be used as a guide to weekly planning of work.
9. A detailed index for easy reference will be found at the end of the book.

The Time Allotment

The book is designed for a one-year course. Experience with classes has shown that each part may serve for about one semester when one period per day, five times a week is the schedule.

Methods and Equipment

It is recommended that all principles be introduced and investigated as a problem or difficulty; that the principles be demonstrated by the teacher; and that one period or more per week be given to practical wiring, testing, soldering, and measurement by the students in the laboratory. The facilities of the school will determine the amount of individual laboratory work that can be done. But it is believed that any instructor with the ordinary equipment in physics and with the addition of the parts salvaged from one or more radio sets can carry out most of the demonstrations listed in the back of the book.

THE AUTHORS

TABLE

OF

CONTENTS

PART I

PART II

Elements
of
Radio

Part I

1

History of Communication

| PROBLEM. *How has man improved his means of communication since time began?*

Sound Signals. Ever since man could make a sound, he has attempted to transmit messages over ever-increasing distances. A shout may have been the first "long-distance transmission." Man soon learned that greater distances could be spanned by beating with a club on a hollow tree. Even today, a fairly effective system of drum-beat communication exists among primitive tribes.

Sight Signals. Another ancient method of message transmission involves the sense of sight. From hand-waving, men progressed, thousands of years ago, to the waving of flags, the use of puffs of smoke, of fires, of lanterns, of the heliograph—a device whereby sunlight is reflected by mirrors and flashed over considerable distances.

All the above methods of communication suffer from one common fault: they are useful only over comparatively short distances, a few miles at best.

The Telegraph. Nevertheless, it was not until the nineteenth century that better means of communication were devised. In 1832, Samuel F. B. Morse invented the electric telegraph. By sending an electrical impulse along a wire, he operated an electromagnet at the end of the line. This electromagnet attracted a bar of iron, causing an audible click. By means of a code, these clicks were translated into letters and words.

This was a big step forward. No longer was man bound by the limits of sight and hearing. Wires could be strung for many miles, and the electrical impulses could be sent through them at the incredible speed of nearly 186,000 miles per second! In 1866, the first message was sent from America to Europe by means of a telegraph cable beneath the Atlantic Ocean.

The Telephone. In 1875, another stride forward was taken when Alexander Graham Bell invented the telephone. Now, sound could be converted into electricity at the transmitting end of the line, sent through wires at the same tremendous speed as in the telegraph, and reconverted into sound at the receiving end of the line. Thus, the very spoken word was sent by wire over hundreds and thousands of miles!

Wireless Telegraph—Radio. Marvelous advances though they were, the telephone and telegraph fell short of meeting the demands which our ever-expanding civilization put upon them. Wires could not be strung everywhere. Explorers and ships at sea were cut off from communication with home and one another. The balloon, and later the airplane, required some means of communication that did not entail stringing wires from sender to receiver. Clearly, a wireless telegraph and a wireless telephone were needed.

Like all great inventions, neither the wireless telegraph nor the wireless telephone (or radio, as we now call them both) was the product of any one man's activity. Many men from many lands contributed their shares before the radio came into being.

Nearly a quarter of a century before the first radio wave was produced intentionally, an English scientist, James Clerk Maxwell, by means of an elaborate mathematical formula, proved the possibility of producing the radio wave. This was in 1864. His contribution was the theory of electromagnetic waves.

Radio Communication. In 1888, Heinrich Rudolf Hertz, a young German of Frankfort, succeeded in transmitting the first radio wave across a room and picking up this wave signal on an extremely crude type of receiver.

Then followed six years of activity during which a large number of scientists each contributed something new or improved what was already known. These experiments finally led to the wireless telegraph, the first practical radio system. This was invented by Guglielmo Marconi, a young Italian, in 1895. With his system, Marconi was able to send and receive messages for several miles without any intervening wires. In 1901, Marconi succeeded in spanning the Atlantic Ocean.

Here, indeed, was the way to the solution of one of the needs of the twentieth century—a system of communication over long distances without interconnecting wires.

SUMMARY

In this chapter we have learned that man has improved his means of communication gradually. The probable steps in this progress have been successively: sound, light, electrical signal in wires, and finally signals sent and received through space by radio.

QUESTIONS AND PROBLEMS

1. What were the shortcomings of primitive means of communication?
2. What needs of daily life made wired systems of electrical communication inadequate?
3. Who first proved mathematically the possibility of producing the radio wave? When? What is the name of his theory?
4. Who first produced an elementary radio transmitter and receiver? When?
5. Who invented the first practical radio system? When? What was this system called?

2

Wave Motion

PROBLEM. *What are the characteristics of a wave?*

Water Waves. Radio communication, we are told, travels in *waves*. We must therefore try to understand what a wave is. If you drop a pebble into a pond of still water, *ripples* or *waves* are created and travel away from the splash in ever-widening circles.

Fig. 2-1. *A stone thrown into a still pond causes ripples. These travel in ever-widening circles from the point of disturbance.*

If you examine these waves, you can see how they are formed and how they travel. The falling pebble, when it strikes the water, pushes some water away from its path, forming a sort of cavity, or hollow, in the pond. The displaced water is forced above the normal level of the pond in a circular wall around the cavity.

4

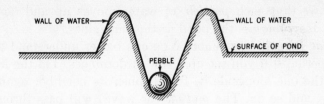

Fig. 2-2. *A sectional view of the pond shows the cavity and wall of water formed by the falling pebble.*

The weight of the water causes this circular wall to collapse, to fall—and when it falls, it goes past and below the original level of the pond. This falling water, like the falling pebble, in turn displaces some more water, thereby causing another circular wall to be built up a little distance from the original cavity. This rising and falling continues on and on. The building up and collapsing of the walls of water cause the wave to travel away from the original hollow made by the pebble. Because of the resistance to movement of the water, each wall is a little lower than the one before it and when it falls it descends a little less below the surface of the pond.

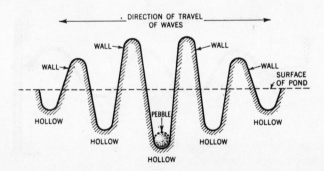

Fig. 2-3. *This sectional view of the pond shows the series of circular walls and hollows formed by the falling pebble.*

Place a small piece of cork on the surface of the pond a little distance from where you drop the pebble. As the ripples reach the cork, it bobs up and down but does not travel on with the wave.

This shows that each *particle* of water moves up and down but does not travel across the pond as the wave does.

What Travels in a Wave? You can better understand this behavior, perhaps, if you set up a row of dominoes. Tip the first one against the one alongside it. It will push its neighbor against the next one, and so on. The *motion* (or wave) will pass through the entire row, but each domino will travel only a short distance.

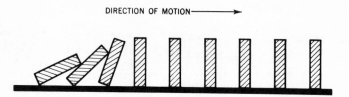

Fig. 2-4. *A row of dominoes illustrates wave motion.*

It is the *energy,* or motion, of the falling domino that travels, not the dominoes. Similarly, in the case of the water wave, the particles of water do not travel across the pond: it is the energy of the falling wall of water alone that travels.

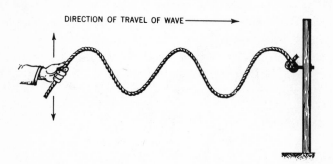

Fig. 2-5. *Illustrating wave motion with a rope.*

Obtain a fairly heavy rope about fifteen feet long. Fasten one end to a post. Now, move the free end up and down. The rope seems to travel towards the post, but the rope itself is not traveling. You can see that because the free end is no nearer the post now than before. Each particle of rope is moving merely up and down.

It is the *energy* or *wave* that is traveling through the rope from the end in your hand to the end fixed to the post.

In these examples, the water, the dominoes, and the rope are each called the *medium*. The particles of the medium move a very short distance. *It is the energy or motion traveling through the medium from particle to particle that we call the wave.*

Wavelengths. Let us look more closely at the ripples in the pond. Recall that the pebble forms a hollow in the pond and builds

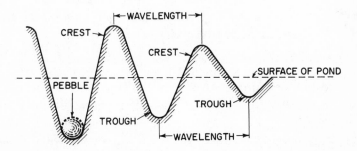

Fig. 2-6. *What is meant by wavelength is shown in this sectional view of a pond into which a pebble has been thrown.*

up a wall surrounding that hollow; when this wall falls it makes a hollow with a wall next to it, and so on. Note that the walls and hollows alternate—that is, first there is a wall, then a hollow, then a wall, and so on. The top of the wall is called the *crest* of the wave; the bottom of the hollow is called the *trough*. The dis-

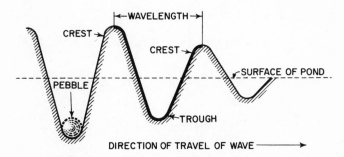

Fig. 2-7. *In this sectional view of the pond, the heavy line shows the path of the wave going through one cycle.*

tance between one crest of a wave and the next crest (or between one trough and the next trough) is called the *wavelength*.

At the seashore, you may see waves whose lengths vary from a few feet to about a half mile. You may set up a rope wave whose length varies from several inches to several feet.

The series of changes in the water surface in going one wave length are called a *cycle*. This means the changes from one crest through the trough and to the next crest, or from one trough through a crest and down to the next trough.

Frequency and Amplitude. The number of *cycles* in a given unit of *time* is called the *frequency*. Thus, an ocean wave may have a frequency of about two cycles per minute. This means that the wave will travel through two cycles in one minute.

If you examine the water ripples again, you may notice another interesting thing about them. The larger the pebble you drop, or the more force with which you throw it, the deeper is the hollow produced and the higher the wall of water set up. The depth of the trough beneath the normal level of the pond or the height of the crest above it is called the *amplitude* of the wave. Note that the amplitude of a wave depends upon the force producing it.

Another interesting fact is the *speed* with which a wave passes through a medium. *Since the wave travels from particle to particle in the medium, the type of medium makes a difference in the speed with which a given kind of wave will pass through it.*

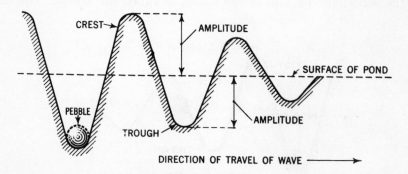

Fig. 2-8. *This sectional view of the pond illustrates what is meant by amplitude. Notice that in this kind of wave the amplitude decreases as the wave travels further away from the point of disturbance.*

SUMMARY

A *wave* is energy traveling through a medium by means of vibrations transmitted from particle to particle.
The *amplitude* (of a water wave) is the height of the crest of a wave above, or depth of the trough below, the surface of the medium at rest.
The *wavelength* is the distance between one crest of a wave and the next crest, or between one trough and the next trough.
A *cycle* is the series of changes from normal that are produced as the wave travels in going one wavelength.
The *frequency* is the number of cycles in a given unit of time.
The *speed* with which the wave travels depends upon the nature of the *medium*.

QUESTIONS AND PROBLEMS

1. Describe what happens when a stone is thrown into a pond.
2. What is meant by a wave?
3. By means of a diagram, describe what is meant by wavelength.
4. What is meant by a cycle? What is the relationship between cycles and frequency?
5. Upon what does the amplitude of a wave depend?
6. What determines the speed with which a wave travels through a medium?
7. Make a diagram of a series of water waves. Label the following: wavelength, amplitude.
8. How may energy be made to travel from one place to another?

3

Light, Heat, and Radio Waves

| PROBLEM. *How do light, heat, and radio waves travel?*

Light Waves. See if you can get an electric-light bulb of the vacuum type. These bulbs are becoming scarce because it has been found that electric-light bulbs do their work better if filled with a gas, like nitrogen. You may still get the vacuum-type bulb in a large electrical supply store. Screw the bulb into the electric-light socket and turn the switch. *Light waves,* which are a type of energy, travel from the hot filament to our eyes. Scientists tell us that light is energy traveling by means of waves.

Now, since a vacuum surrounds the hot filament, what is the medium that carries the light waves? What is the medium that carries the light waves from the sun to the earth? The reason we ask these questions is that scientists say that the space between the earth and sun is empty, or, in other words, is a vacuum.

A Convenient Medium for Waves in Vacuum. To get around the difficulty, scientists were forced to assume that a medium existed, and they called this medium *ether.* (Note that this ether is not the same as the gas the doctor gives you when he wants to put you to sleep.) Ether, as scientists use the word, is what remains in space when all substance or matter, as we know it, has been taken away. This so-called ether is the medium that transmits the light waves across a vacuum; hence it is called *luminiferous* (that is, light-carrying) *ether.**

*The idea of an *ether* was proposed in the latter part of the seventeenth century by Sir Isaac Newton and given prominence by Christian Huygens, the Dutch physicist, who discovered polarized light. There is no proof that ether does or

Experiments have shown that the light wave travels through ether at the enormous *speed* of 186,000 miles (300,000,000 meters) per second. The *frequency* (that is, the number of cycles per second) of light waves varies from 375 million million to 750 million million cycles, and their *wavelength* varies from approximately 15 to 30 millionths of an inch (0.000015 to 0.000030 inch).

Heat Waves. Now touch the outside of the "burning" electric-light bulb. It is hot. How did *heat,* another type of wave energy, get across the vacuum in the bulb? How do the heat waves sent out by the sun reach the earth?

The heat wave, like the light wave, travels through the ether. Like the light wave, its *speed* is 186,000 miles per second. The *frequency* of heat waves varies from 750,000 million to 375 million million cycles per second; hence their *wavelengths* vary from approximately one hundredth to 30 millionths of an inch (0.01 to 0.000030 inch).

Waves that move in ether are known as *ether waves.* Light and heat are two forms of energy that travel by ether waves.

The Metric System. At this point, it should be explained that scientists prefer the *metric* to the *English system* for the measurement of length. Under the English system, you know that

12 inches = 1 foot
3 feet = 1 yard
1760 yards = 1 mile

In the metric system, the unit of length is the *meter,* which is slightly more than a yard long (39.37 inches). The prefix *deka-* means ten, *hecto-* means hundred, *kilo-* means thousand, and *mega-* means million. Similarly, *deci-* means a tenth (1/10), *centi-* means a hundredth (1/100), *milli-* means a thousandth (1/1000), and *micro-* means a millionth (1/1,000,000).

Thus, a *kilometer* means 1000 meters, and a *millimeter* means 1/1000 of a meter. Other examples follow:

10 millimeters (mm) = 1 centimeter (cm)
10 centimeters = 1 decimeter (dm)
10 decimeters = 1 meter (m)
10 meters = 1 dekameter (dkm)
10 dekameters = 1 hectometer (hm)
10 hectometers = 1 kilometer (km)

---

does not exist. Some scientists prefer to ignore it. However, since *ether* is a convenient label for the idea of a medium by which all forms of radiant energy (heat, light, radio) are transmitted, it will be used in this text.

The relationship between the metric and English systems can be seen from the following table:

1 inch = 2.54 centimeters
39.37 inches = 1 meter
0.62 mile = 1 kilometer

The prefixes used in the metric system for length are also used to measure other values. Thus, 1000 cycles per second becomes a *kilocycle* (kc), and 1,000,000 cycles per second, a *megacycle* (mc). Hence when we say that the frequency of light waves varies from 375 million millions (375,000,000,000,000) to 750 million millions (750,000,000,000,000) of cycles per second, we may express these numbers as from 375,000,000 megacycles to 750,000,-000 megacycles.

We have taken time out to explain the metric system because you will constantly come across this system of measurement in your scientific studies. As a matter of fact, the frequency of the radio waves from the various broadcasting stations are usually listed in kilocycles (1000 cycles). Thus, the frequency of station WOR, New York, is 710 kc (710,000 cycles) per second.*

Other Forms of Energy. For the light and heat types of ether waves, special organs of our bodies act as *receivers*. However, other forms of energy are transmitted through the ether; we cannot detect these with any of our unaided senses. We must, therefore, devise special instruments that can change such forms of energy to types which it is possible for our senses to perceive.

To see the effect of one such type of energy, balance a magnetic needle on a pivot and near it suspend a coil of about 25 turns of No. 18 insulated copper wire. Then pass the current from a dry cell through the coil, and observe that the magnetic needle is sharply deflected. *Energy from the coil of wire passes to the magnetic needle.* To show that it is not the air which transmits the energy, place the whole apparatus under a bell jar and pump out the air. Once again pass the current of electricity through the coil. Again the magnetic needle is deflected. The energy is transmitted across the vacuum.

---

* Often when indicating frequency, the term "per second" is omitted, and thus 710 kc per second is merely written as 710 kc, "per second" being understood.

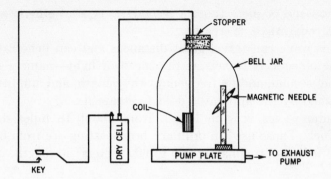

Fig. 3-1. *This apparatus shows that electric current flowing through a coil of wire will set up a magnetic field around that coil. This field is created even though the coil is surrounded by a vacuum.*

For want of a better explanation, we again fall back upon the ether and assume that it is the medium which transmits the energy. We say that when an electric current passes through a wire it sets up a *magnetic field* in the ether around that wire.

Note that this magnetic field, unlike the light and heat waves, cannot be received by our senses. Accordingly, we use the magnetic needle to detect this field, and thus to change its energy to a form which our senses can receive. The energy of the magnetic field is changed to the *motion* of the needle; we can see motion.

All these ether waves are "wireless" waves: they do not depend upon metallic wires to transmit their energy. Because of this fact, these waves may be used to communicate between places where it is not possible to string wires, as between an airplane and the ground. Light waves, as we well know, have been used for communications. To a lesser degree, so have heat waves and magnetic fields.

Radio Waves. Light waves travel in straight lines and cannot penetrate many kinds of materials. Substances through which light cannot pass are called *opaque*. Because of this, the curvature of the earth and such intervening objects as houses, trees, hills, and the like, limit the range of this method of communication.

As for heat waves, they are too readily absorbed by surrounding objects to permit them a large range.

The magnetic field is effective for only a very short distance. If, however, the key in Figure 3-1 is opened and closed very rapidly (ten thousand or more times a second), a type of ether wave new to us, a *radio* wave, is created.

This wave can travel great distances and can penetrate non-metallic objects. It travels at the speed of light—namely 186,000 miles per second, and its frequency, wavelength, and amplitude are determined by the apparatus used to create it.

Radio waves vary in length from about 18 miles down to 1/250 inch. Those used in ordinary broadcasting are from 656 feet to 1968 feet (approximately 200 to 600 meters) in length.

SUMMARY

The following principles have been discussed in this chapter:

1. Certain forms of radiant energy are transmitted by ether waves. Some of these forms are light, heat, and radio waves.
2. The idea of a medium called *ether* has been assumed for practical reasons, although not proven.
3. Radiant energy travels through the ether with a speed of 186,000 miles, or 300,000,000 meters, per second.
4. The lengths of the waves are determined by the vibration frequency of the source of the waves. The ranges are:

    Visible light waves............0.00004 to 0.00008 cm
    Heat waves.................0.00008 to 0.04 cm
    Radio waves.................0.01 cm to 30 km

5. The length of an ether wave is found by dividing 300,000,000 meters by the number of vibrations (or cycles) per second.

GLOSSARY

Ether: The medium, permeating all space, which is *supposed* to carry such forms of energy as light, heat, and radio waves. There is no proof that ether does or does not exist.
Ether Wave: A wave of energy which uses ether as a medium.
Heat Wave: An ether wave whose wavelength lies between 0.00008 and 0.04 cm.
Light Wave: An ether wave whose wavelength lies between 0.00004 and 0.00008 cm.
Magnet: A bar of iron, steel, or other material, or a coil of wire carrying an electric current that has the property of attracting to it pieces of iron, steel, or other magnetic substances.
Radio Wave: An ether wave whose length lies between 0.01 cm and 30 km.

QUESTIONS AND PROBLEMS

1. In what ways are radio, heat, and light waves similar? In what ways do they differ?
2. What is unusual about the medium of a radio wave?
3. At what velocity do light and radio waves travel?
4. Define and give examples of ether waves.
5. For what ether waves are our bodies receivers? For which are our bodies insensitive and in need of special receivers?
6. Why can the magnetic field of an electromagnet not be used to send wireless messages in a practical manner?
7. Identify the mathematical prefixes: *kilo-, mega-, milli-, micro-*. Give examples of how they are used.

4

A Simple Radio Receiving Set

> **PROBLEM 1.** *What are the four essential parts of the radio receiver?*
>
> **PROBLEM 2.** *What is the function of each part?*

It will be helpful in our study of the principles of radio to ₄ learn at the start that every radio receiver, no matter how complex or involved, consists of only four essential parts. They are:

1. The *antenna-ground system,* which collects the radio waves.

2. The *tuner,* which selects the radio wave (or station) to be received, and rejects all others.

3. The *reproducer,* the device which changes the energy of the radio wave to a form which our senses can perceive.

4. The *detector,* which changes the energy of the radio wave to a form whereby it can operate the reproducer.

This holds true for all receiving sets, from the simplest crystal set to the most complex television receiver. Everything else in the receiver is merely a refinement of these four essentials.

WHAT IS THE PURPOSE OF THE ANTENNA-GROUND SYSTEM?

The Antenna. Suppose we string a copper wire so that one end is up in the air and the other end is connected to ground. Radio waves sent out by a broadcasting station, striking this wire, will set up an *electrical pressure,* or *voltage,* along the wire. This pressure will cause a small electrical current to flow up and down the wire. We now have the beginning of our receiver, the *antenna-ground system*. With this system, we collect radio waves. All receivers must have an antenna-ground system, which may be external and connected to the set by wires or may be contained in the set itself in the form of a number of loops of wire.

To prove that this antenna-ground system is necessary to the receiver, connect up a regular broadcast receiver with an external antenna (sometimes called *aerial*) and ground. Tune in a station and then disconnect the antenna and ground. The station dies away.*

WHAT IS THE FUNCTION OF A TUNER?

Resonance. All radio receivers must have some method of separating the station desired from all other stations broadcasting at the same time. The apparatus that does this is called the *tuner*. Since each station sends out radio waves of a different frequency, the tuner must select the frequency desired and reject all others.

To understand how this is done you must first learn about *resonance*.

Place a number of drinking glasses of different size, shape, and thickness upon a table. Strike each with a pencil. Observe that each glass gives off a different tone. The vibrating glasses set up air waves, which reach our ears and are interpreted as *sound*. The different tones are caused by the different frequencies of these air waves. This means that the glasses, too, are vibrating at different frequencies. The frequency at which an object will vibrate when struck depends upon its material, size, shape, and thickness. This frequency is called the *natural frequency* of the object.

Resonance with a Pendulum. From a nail, suspend a small weight at the end of a string about a yard long. You now have a pendulum. Start the pendulum swinging gently. You will note that it swings a certain number of times per minute. That number is the natural frequency of that particular pendulum. Wait till it is swinging gently. Now, every time the pendulum reaches the end of its swing, give it a very light tap. You will soon have your

---

* The station may be faintly received even after the antenna and ground are disconnected, because the wires in the set itself act as a very inefficient antenna and ground. A receiver that has no built-in loop antenna should be used here.

pendulum swinging violently to and fro. Note that you must tap the pendulum at the exact instant it reaches the peak of its swing if you wish to increase that swing. If you tap it too soon or too late, the pendulum will slow down. The increased energy of the swing came from the tapping. Therefore, to obtain the maximum transfer of energy from the tapping to the pendulum, the *frequency of the tapping must be equal to the natural frequency of the pendulum.* The tapping is in *resonance* with the swing of the pendulum.

Resonance with Tuning Blocks. Here is another experiment you may perform. Obtain two tuning blocks of similar frequency, say, 256 vibrations per second, which corresponds to the note we call middle C on the piano. A tuning block is a bar of steel so designed that it will vibrate at a certain frequency when struck. This bar is mounted on a hollow wooden block which amplifies the note produced.

Place these blocks about 10 feet apart. Now, strike one of them vigorously: it will give off its note, middle C. Place your hand on the block you struck to stop its vibrations. You will continue to hear the note, although a good deal fainter. Bring your ear near the second block. The sound will be coming from it, although you did not strike it. Place your hand on the second block. The sound stops.

Let us see what happened. When you struck the first block, it was set vibrating at its natural frequency of 256 vibrations per second. The vibrating bar set up air waves at that same frequency. These air waves struck the second block. Since the frequency of the air waves was the same as the natural frequency of this second block, the energy of the air waves was transferred to the block, and it was set in vibratory motion. The second block thereupon set up air waves of its own, and it was these waves you heard when you stopped the vibrations of the first block. We say that the two blocks are in *resonance* with each other.

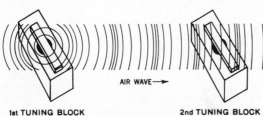

AIR WAVE→

1st TUNING BLOCK   2nd TUNING BLOCK

Fig. 4-1. *Air waves sent out by the first tuning block strike the second one and set it vibrating.*

Repeat this experiment, using two tuning blocks of different frequency, say, one at 256, or middle C, and the other at 288, or D. This time you get no sound from the second block because the air waves are not vibrating at the natural frequency of the second block, and therefore, there is no transfer of energy. These blocks are *not in resonance* with each other.

So you see that you have here a means of selecting only a certain frequency and rejecting all others. All you have to do is to construct your receiving block so that it is in *resonance* with the frequency you wish to receive. It will vibrate only when air waves of that frequency hit it, but not at any other frequency.

Resonance in a Radio Receiver. In our radio receiver, we use the same principle that was shown by the tuning blocks. Assume that three stations A, B, and C are broadcasting simultaneously at frequencies of *a*, *b*, and *c*, respectively. If you wish to receive Station A, you adjust your tuner so that the natural frequency of your receiver is the same as the frequency *a* of the radio wave from station A. The receiver now is in resonance with the radio wave from station A, and the energy of the radio wave is transferred to the receiver. Since stations B and C are not in resonance with the receiver, the energy of the radio waves sent out by these stations is rejected, and we do not hear them.

WHAT IS THE FUNCTION OF THE REPRODUCER?

Need for a Reproducer. So far, we have been able to catch or collect the radio waves by means of the antenna-ground system and to select the station (or frequency) we desire by means of the tuner. But we still cannot hear or see the electric currents which have been set up in our receiver. What we now need is some device which will change this electric current to a form of energy that we can hear or see. This device is called the *reproducer.*

Using copper wire, hook up a telephone transmitter, a telephone receiver, and some dry cells as shown in Figure 4-2.

The Telephone as a Reproducer. The electric current flows from the dry cells through the copper wire, through the telephone transmitter, then from the transmitter through the copper wire, through the telephone receiver, and then through the copper wire back again to the dry cells. We call this an *electrical circuit.*

When you speak into the telephone transmitter, the sound waves hitting it cause it to act like a gate, allowing more or less electric current to flow through the circuit. A fluctuating electric current is thus set flowing in the circuit. At the other end of the line, in the telephone receiver, this fluctuating electric current causes a metallic diaphragm to fluctuate (move back and forth) in step with the current. This movement of the diaphragm causes the air next to the diaphragm to move back and forth, setting up air waves: we hear these air waves as sound. Since the air waves that hit the transmitter move the same way as the air waves set up by the diaphragm of the receiver, you hear the same sound as was spoken into the transmitter. The telephone receiver is a *reproducer*.

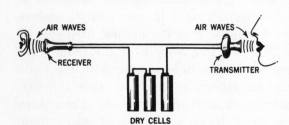

Fig. 4-2. *Hookup of a telephone transmitter, telephone receiver, and dry cells shows air waves, striking the transmitter, are heard as sound coming from the receiver.*

Now, remember that radio waves set up an electric current in an antenna-ground system, as we discovered earlier. Hence, it would seem that all you have to do to hear a radio message from a distant station is to lead this electric current through the tuner and into some type of telephone receiver.

But not so fast. Some electric currents cannot operate the telephone receiver. The current that the radio wave sets up in your antenna-ground system is of this type; so it is necessary to change it to current of a type that will operate the reproducer.

WHAT IS THE FUNCTION OF THE DETECTOR?

The Detector. The change of current from one type to another can be accomplished in a number of ways. The simplest way, perhaps, is to compel the current to pass through a certain type of mineral such as *galena*. This passing changes the antenna-ground current into a current type that will operate the telephone receiver and make it possible to hear the radio wave as sound. Such a device, which changes the electric current set up by the radio wave into a form that will operate the reproducer, is called a *detector*.

SUMMARY

Here, then, is your complete radio receiver. First of all is the **antenna-ground system,** which collects the radio waves. Next comes the **tuner,** which selects the station or radio wave desired and rejects all the others. Then comes the **detector,** which changes the form of the electric current set up by the radio wave into a form that will operate the **reproducer** and, in turn, produces the sound we hear.

GLOSSARY

Antenna-Ground System: The wire system which picks up radio waves and across which the radio wave produces an electrical pressure.
Detector: The device to change the electrical currents, which are produced in a receiver by radio waves, into electrical currents which can operate the reproducer.
Natural Frequency: The frequency at which a body will vibrate if kept free from outside interference.
Reproducer: A device, such as a telephone receiver, that changes electric currents to a form which affects our senses and is usually experienced as sound.
Resonance: The condition of two vibrating bodies when the natural frequency of one body is equal to the frequency of the other vibrating body. In the radio receiver, when the natural frequency of the tuner is the same as the frequency of the transmitting station, the two are in resonance.
Tuner: The device in a radio receiver which selects a radio wave of a certain frequency and rejects all others.
Voltage: An electrical pressure which tends to make an electric current flow.

QUESTIONS AND PROBLEMS

1. What are the four essentials of all radio receivers?
2. What effect is produced when a radio wave sweeps across an antenna-ground system?
3. Explain the function of a tuner in a radio receiver.
4. In what manner does resonance of the tuner relate the receiver to the radio wave of a station?
5. Upon what factors does the natural frequency of the tone of a drinking tumbler depend?
6. Why must a reproducer be used in a radio receiver?
7. Why must a receiver have a detector?

THE LOVETT SCHOOL

5

The Antenna-Ground System

PROBLEM 1. *How is a simple antenna set up?*

PROBLEM 2. *How is the antenna connected to the ground?*

Before we continue our study, let us have clearly in mind what we are trying to do. According to the plan of this book, we propose to take up the problems of radio in the following order:

1. *What* are the parts of a radio receiving set?
2. *How* are these parts connected and how do they work?
3. *Why* do the parts function as they do?

We have learned that the radio wave, striking the antenna, sets up an electric pressure, called an *electromotive force* (abbreviated emf) which causes a small electric current to flow up and down the antenna-ground system. Because this current is extremely small, it is necessary to construct your antenna-ground system as efficiently as possible, and you must be sure that you do not waste this current once it is set flowing.

The Antenna. First of all, there is the antenna or aerial. For ordinary broadcast reception, the simplest type of antenna consists of a single strand of wire about 75 feet long. This wire should be of No. 12 or No. 14 gauge copper, and may be either insulated or bare. It should be raised as high above ground as is practical, and should be kept clear of all obstructions, especially metal. *Insulators* should be attached to both ends of the wire to prevent the small currents from leaking off. Insulators are substances that do not conduct electricity. Common examples of insulators are glass, porcelain, bakelite, and hard rubber. If a power line or a trolley wire runs nearby, your antenna should be installed at right angles to that line or wire.

The Lead-In. After the antenna comes the *lead-in,* which is a piece of wire similar to the antenna. It is connected at one end to the antenna and at the other end to the receiving set. If possible, the antenna and lead-in should be made of one piece of wire. But if you should have to join one piece of lead-in wire to another, or to the antenna, be sure to scrape the two pieces clean with a knife or sandpaper. Then twist one wire securely around the other. For best results, this joint should be soldered. Finally, wrap friction tape around the joint to prevent the air from corroding it.

The lead-in should be kept at least 6 inches away from all walls and other surrounding objects. It is usually brought in through a window, and, to avoid the necessity of drilling a hole in the frame, the lead-in is cut, and a flexible window strip is inserted. This window strip lies flat under the window frame and permits the window to be opened and closed without disturbing the installation.

From the inside end of the window strip, connect an insulated copper wire to the post on your radio set marked *ANT.* or *AERIAL.* For best results, the lead-in should be about 25 feet in length, from the antenna to your radio set.

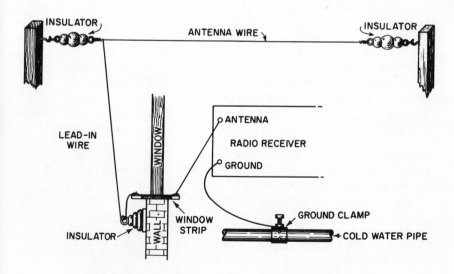

Fig 5-1. *Diagram of the antenna-ground system.*

The Ground. Finally, there is a *ground* connection.* The best connection for a ground, if one is available, is a cold-water pipe. Next best is a radiator or any other pipe which goes to the ground. Gas pipes should *never* be used as grounds. Scrape the paint off the pipe where you plan to make the connection. Then wrap a number of turns of bare copper wire tightly around the cleaned part.

Better yet, get a ground clamp designed for this purpose, and attach it onto the pipe at the point selected. Then run a piece of insulated copper wire from your ground connection to the post marked *GROUND* or *GND* on your radio set. This wire should be about No. 18 gauge and should be as short as possible.

When we draw a diagram of our radio set, we use symbols to signify the various parts. The symbol used for the antenna and lead-in is Y or Ψ , and that used to signify a ground is $\downarrow$.

It should be understood that the antenna-ground system just described is a very simple type. In a later chapter, some other types better adapted to certain purposes will be discussed.

---

* *Ground* is a technical term used in radio work, and refers to a part of a circuit which is directly connected either to the earth or to the metallic base of some device. In an automobile, one terminal of the battery is connected to the steel frame of the car: this is a *ground*. Hence, in the automobile, there is only one wire leading to a lamp or other fixture, the circuit being completed by connecting it through the frame.

SUMMARY

1. The *antenna-ground system* consists of three parts: the *antenna or aerial,* the *lead-in* wire, and the *ground.*
2. The function of this system is to receive and capture some of the radio waves being sent out by broadcasting stations.

GLOSSARY

Aerial or Antenna: An elevated conductor, usually of copper, insulated from its supports and the ground, and connected to the receiving set by the lead-in wire.

Conductor: Any substance, usually a metal wire, through which a current of electricity can flow freely.

Ground: A water pipe, or some such arrangement, by which the receiving set makes contact with the earth. See also footnote, p. 23.

Insulator: Any substance through which a current of electricity cannot flow freely.

Lead-in: An insulated wire connecting antenna to receiving set.

SYMBOLS

Υ or Ψ Antenna and lead-in.

$\perp$ Ground.

QUESTIONS AND PROBLEMS

1. Describe the structure of a simple type of antenna system.
2. What is meant by an insulator? Give examples.
3. With what precautions must antennas near trolleys or power wires be set up?
4. What precautions must be taken in setting up a lead-in?
5. What is the best length for a lead-in?
6. What objects may best be used to make good contact with ground?
7. Draw the symbols for an antenna and lead-in; for a ground.
8. How should the ground connection be installed?
9. Describe the complete installation of an antenna, giving size, materials, and other details.

6

The Tuner

PROBLEM 1. *What are the principles of a tuning system?*

PROBLEM 2. *What do we mean by inductance and capacitance?*

You have already learned that the tuner selects the desired radio station by adjusting the natural frequency of the receiver so that it is in *resonance* with the transmitter frequency. Let us see what determines the natural frequency of the receiver.

Examination of the tuner shows that it consists of two parts —a coil of wire called an *inductor* and an electrical device known as a *condenser* or *capacitor*. This coil and capacitor produce certain electrical effects upon the current flowing through them. We call the electrical effect of the coil *inductance* and that of the capacitor, *capacitance*. We will discuss these effects later in the book, but for the present, it will be enough to say that the values of inductance and capacitance determine the natural frequency of the tuner, even as the size and weight of a tuning block determine its natural frequency.

Inductance. The device that provides the *inductance* consists of a coil of wire wound around a tube, which is usually made of cardboard or bakelite. Its electrical value depends on:

1. The number of turns or loops of wire.

2. The length of the coil.

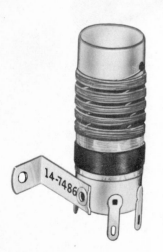

Fig. 6-1. *Air-core inductor.*

26

3. The diameter of the tube on which it is wound.

4. The core of the coil. This is the material inside the tube. The two most common materials for the core are air and iron. Air-core coils are usually used for the tuner.

The unit for measurement of inductance is the *henry* (h) or the *millihenry* (mh). (Chap. 32.) The millihenry is one one-thousandth of a henry. The symbol for inductance devices, or *inductors,* having cores of air or iron, is:

AIR CORE   IRON CORE

We can vary the value of our inductance by changing one or more of the four factors listed above. The symbol for a variable inductor is any of the following:

Whenever we desire to represent inductance in an electrical formula or equation, we use the letter L

Capacitance. The *capacitance* in a tuner is provided by a device called a capacitor.* This capacitor is made of two or more metal plates facing one another and separated by some substance which will not conduct electricity. This substance is called a *dielectric* and usually consists of air, paper, mica, oil, or glass. The plates are usually made of brass, tin foil, or aluminum. The electrical value of a capacitor depends on:

1. The total area of the plates facing one another.

2. The material of the dielectric.

3. The thickness of the dielectric (or distance between plates).

The unit of measure of capacitance is the *farad* (f). For radio purposes, we usually use the *microfarad* (μf), which is one one-millionth of a farad, and the *micromicrofarad* ($\mu\mu$f), which is one one-millionth of a microfarad (Chap. 33). Sometimes, when the *mu* (μ) is not available in type, the small letter *m* is used instead.

---

* Although the term *condenser* has been widely used, present-day usage favors the term *capacitor.*

–A–   –B–

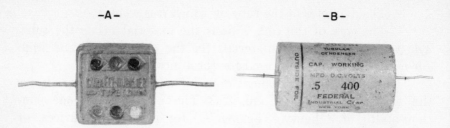

Fig. 6-2. *Fixed capacitor. A—Mica capacitor.*
B—Paper capacitor.

Thus, *microfarad* may appear as mf and *micromicrofarad,* as mmf.
The symbol for the capacitor is ⊥

 We can vary the value of our capacitor by changing one or
more of the three factors listed above. The most convenient
method is that of changing the area of the plates facing one another. This is done by making one plate or set of plates rotary and
the other plate or set of plates stationary. All the stationary plates
are joined together, giving the effect of one large stationary plate.
The same is done with the rotary plates. The rotary plates move
in and out between the stationary plates. Thus, the more the rotary
plates are moved in between the stationary plates, the greater the
area of the plates facing one another, and the greater the capacitance of the capacitor. Variable capacitors generally use air as a
dielectric.

 The symbol for a variable capacitor is ⌗

Whenever we desire to represent capacitance in an electrical formula or
equation, we use the letter *C*.

 The Tuning Circuit. If, by means
of wire, you connect a coil and a variable capacitor as shown in Figure
6-4, you create a tuning circuit. When
you apply a voltage (electrical pressure) across the coil or capacitor, you
cause an electrical current to flow
back and forth through the circuit.
We speak of such back-and-forth flow

Fig. 6-3. *Variable ca-*
pacitor.

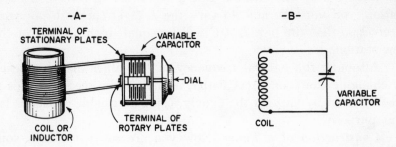

Fig. 6-4. *This hookup shows how a coil and a variable capacitor are connected to form the tuning circuit. A is the pictorial method of showing the circuit, and B is the schematic method using symbols.*

of current as *oscillations*. These oscillations are more fully discussed in Chapter 12.

The natural frequency of the oscillations in this circuit is determined by the product of the values of inductance L and capacitance C ($L \times C$ or LC).

The transmitting station uses a capacitor-and-coil hookup similar to the one we have just described to generate the radio wave it sends out. The frequency of its wave is determined by the $L \times C$ of the transmitting set. Should the $L \times C$ of the transmitting station equal the $L \times C$ of your receiver, your set will be in resonance (in tune) with the frequency of the radio wave from the transmitter. You will then receive only that station and no other.

Note that it is not necessary to have the same L and C in your receiving set as is in the transmitting station. It is enough that the product of L and C ($L \times C$) of your set be equal to the $L \times C$ of the transmitter. So, if we arbitrarily give a value of 4 to the L and 4 to the C of the transmitting station, the $L \times C$ of that station is 16. To bring your receiver in resonance with the transmitter (that is, to *tune* your set for reception), you may choose an L whose value is 2 and a C whose value is 8. Or else you may choose an L of 8 and a C of 2; or an L of 4 and a C of 4. In other words, you may choose any value of L and C whose product is equal to 16, the same as the $L \times C$ value of the transmitter.

Now, all this is very well if you wish to build a receiver that will receive only one station. But if you wish to receive another station, you must be able to vary the L or C (or both) of your receiver so that the new $L \times C$ will be equal to the $L \times C$ of the new station.

Although the natural frequency of the tuner may be varied by changing the L or C (or both), in most radio receivers, this is accomplished by varying the C only, using a variable capacitor for that purpose.

Construction of a Tuner. Now you are ready to build your tuner. Obtain a cardboard mailing tube about 2 inches in diameter and about 6 inches long. Upon this tube, wind 90 turns of No. 28 insulated copper wire so that the turns lie next to one another and form a single layer. This is your inductor.

Now obtain a variable capacitor whose maximum value is about 0.00035 microfarad (μf). Such a capacitor usually has from 17 to 21 plates, half rotary and half stationary. Connect one end of the coil to the rotary-plate terminal of the capacitor, and the other end of the coil to the stationary-plate terminal, as shown in Figure 6-4. You now have constructed your tuner.

SUMMARY

1. The *tuning system* consists of two essential parts: a *coil* of wire and a *capacitor.*
2. The coil provides the electrical effect known as *inductance.*
3. The capacitor provides the electrical effect known as *capacitance.*
4. The combined action of the inductance and the capacitance determines the *natural frequency* of the tuner.
5. The oscillations of electric current flowing in the tuner may be put in *resonance* with those of a broadcasting station by making the values of L (inductance) and C (capacitance) such that the product $L \times C$ is identical with the product $L \times C$ of the desired station.
6. *Tuning* usually is achieved by using a variable capacitor by which capacitance (C) can be given any desired value.

GLOSSARY

Capacitor (also known as *Condenser*): Two sets of metal plates separated by an insulator or dielectric.

Capacitor, Fixed: A capacitor whose plates are fixed, so that its electrical value cannot be changed.

Capacitor, Variable: A capacitor whose plates can be moved so that its electrical value can be changed at will.

Dielectric: An insulator placed between the plates of a capacitor.

Farad: The unit used to measure the electrical value of a capacitor.

Henry: The unit used to measure the electrical value of an inductor.

Inductor: A coil of wire wound on a form.

L × C: The product of the electrical values of the inductor and capacitor of the tuning circuit which determines its natural frequency.

Micro- (prefix): 1/1,000,000.

Micromicro- (prefix): 1/1,000,000,000,000.

Milli- (prefix): 1/1,000.

Oscillation: The to-and-fro surge of an electric current in a circuit.

SYMBOLS

⟋ꝏꝏꝏ⟍ Coil wound on nonmetallic core.

⟋ꝏꝏꝏ⟍ Coil wound on iron core.

Variable coil.

⊥ Fixed capacitor.

≠ Variable capacitor.

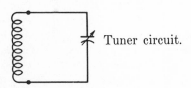 Tuner circuit.

QUESTIONS AND PROBLEMS

1. Upon what factors does the electrical value or inductance of a coil depend? Give the unit of inductance.
2. In what ways may the inductance of a coil be varied?
3. Describe the essential parts of all capacitors.
4. List several dielectric materials.

5. Upon what factors does the electrical value or capacitance of a capacitor depend?
6. Give the meaning of milli-, micro-, and micromicro-.
7. What is the most convenient method of varying the capacitance of the capacitor of a tuner?
8. Draw a tuner circuit showing the connections of the parts.
9. What factors determine the natural frequency of oscillations of a tuner circuit?
10. When will a receiver be in resonance with a particular transmitter?
11. Why is it not necessary for the physical size of the tuner at a broadcasting station to be the same as that of our receiver picking up that station?
12. How is the natural frequency of a tuner circuit varied in common practice?

7

The Reproducer

PROBLEM 1. *What are the principles of the repro-*
ducer?

PROBLEM 2. *How does a telephone receiver work?*

PROBLEM 3. *How does a loudspeaker work?*

Magnetism. To understand how the reproducer works, you must learn a few facts about magnetism and electromagnetism. Cut a circular disk of thin iron about 2 inches in diameter. Obtain a bar magnet and hold it near your iron disk. The magnet is surrounded by an invisible magnetic field of force which acts on the disk and pulls it towards the magnet.

Obtain a piece of soft-iron rod or bar stock about 1 inch in diameter and 2 inches long. Be sure it is not magnetized. Now wind upon it a coil of about 25 turns of No. 18 gauge insulated copper wire. Connect the ends of the coil to the post of a dry cell. When the current flows through the coil, the bar becomes a magnet: it has a magnetic field which will attract the iron disk just as did the bar magnet. When the current ceases to flow through the coil, the bar loses its magnetism. We call such a combination of a bar in a coil that is carrying current an *electromagnet*.

Magnetic Effect of a Varying Current. Mount the bar magnet upright on a board. Remove the soft-iron bar from the coil and slip the coil over the bar magnet. Above the magnet, and separated from it by about an inch, suspend your disk from a spring balance. This balance will show how much pull is being exerted on the disk.

Measure the pull which the bar magnet exerts on the disk. Connect the coil to the posts of a dry cell. The pull should increase, because you now have the double pull of the bar magnet and

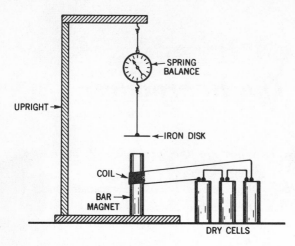

SPRING
BALANCE

UPRIGHT→

←IRON DISK

COIL→

BAR
MAGNET→

DRY CELLS

Fig. 7-1. *This apparatus is used to show that a varying electric current passing through an electromagnet exerts a varying pull on the iron disk.*

the electromagnet. (Should the pull decrease, reverse the connections to the dry cell.)

Now connect another dry cell *in series* with the coil. To connect this properly, disconnect the end of the coil from the outer post of the first dry cell. Connect this outer post to the center post of the second dry cell and connect the wire from the coil to the outer post of the second dry cell. Cells connected this way are *in series*.

You will observe that the pull is greater, which is to be expected, because using two dry cells in series increases the current and makes the electromagnet stronger. Now repeat, using three or more dry cells. As you add cells the pull becomes greater, because more current is flowing through the coil of the electromagnet. Reducing the number of dry cells reduces the current in the electromagnet coil, and the pull on the disk becomes weaker. If you pass a varying, or fluctuating, current through the coil, the pull on the disk will fluctuate in step with the current. Note that a steady current will not cause the disk to move: it will be pulled to a certain position and then will remain stationary as long as the current is steady.

Construction of a Telephone Receiver. Now get a telephone receiver and unscrew the cap. You will see a thin iron disk, called the *diaphragm*. Remove the diaphragm and you will see a coil of wire (the electromagnet coil) which is wound over the end of a bar magnet. The ends of the wires connecting the electromagnet pass out through the far end of the telephone receiver.

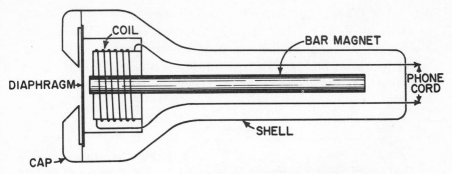

Fig. 7-2. *Construction of a telephone receiver.*

The bar magnet exerts a constant pull on the diaphragm. Since the diaphragm is held fast at its rim, it can only move inward toward the magnet at its center. The springiness of the diaphragm constantly tends to pull it back. When we add the pull of the electromagnet, the diaphragm bends inward much or little, depending upon the strength of the current flowing through the coil. You see then that a fluctuating current flowing through the coil causes the diaphragm to fluctuate in step with it.

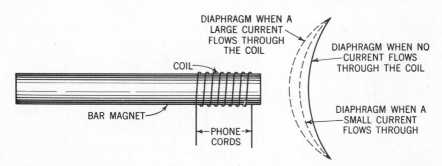

Fig. 7-3. *This diagram shows the positions of the diaphragm as a fluctuating current flows through the electromagnet of the phones. The bending of the diaphragm is greatly exaggerated in this drawing.*

Now look again at Figure 4-2. You will remember that the sound waves striking the telephone transmitter cause a fluctuating current to flow through the circuit. This current fluctuates in step with the sound waves. This current is sent through the electromagnet coil of the telephone receiver, and the diaphragm is thus made to fluctuate in step with the original sound waves. The moving diaphragm sets the air next to it in motion, and it is these air waves which hit our ear. Thus, we hear a sound which is the same as that which was spoken into the telephone transmitter.

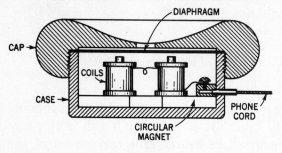

Fig. 7-4. *A sectional view of an earphone of the type used in radio receivers. Note how flat it is compared to the telephone receiver. The permanent magnet can be either circular or horseshoe shaped.*

For the sake of convenience, the earphones used for radio reception (called simply *phones*) are made flat. This flattening is accomplished by using a circular magnet instead of the long, straight one used in the telephone receiver. Usually, two of these phones are connected in series, one for each ear, and held in place with a metal band or spring that fits over the head.

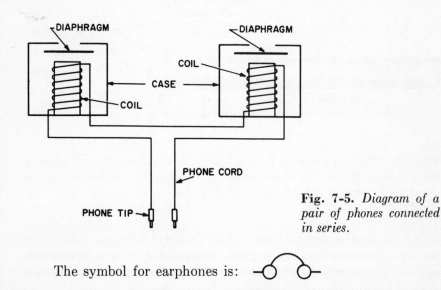

Fig. 7-5. *Diagram of a pair of phones connected in series.*

The symbol for earphones is:

The Magnetic Loudspeaker. You have seen that the moving diaphragms of the earphones set the air next to them in motion, and thus produce the sound you hear. If this sound were loud enough, you could lay the phones on the table and would not need to bother wearing them on your head.

If you were to make one of the diaphragms larger, it would move a greater quantity of air, and thus produce

Fig. 7-6. *A pair of headphones.*

a louder sound. For practical reasons, a diaphragm cannot be made very large, and so another scheme was developed. One end of a stiff wire is fastened to the center of the diaphragm. This wire now moves in and out in step with the diaphragm. To the other end of the wire a large paper cone is fastened. The fluctuating diaphragm moves the wire; the wire in turn moves the paper cone. This in turn sets a large amount of air in motion, creating a loud sound. By this means, we are able to do away with earphones. The device is called the *magnetic loudspeaker.*

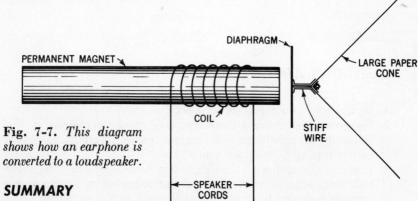

Fig. 7-7. *This diagram shows how an earphone is converted to a loudspeaker.*

SUMMARY

1. A coil of wire surrounding a core of soft iron becomes an **electromagnet** when an electric current passes through the coil.
2. The strength of the **magnetic field** (that is, its attractive force) increases when the current increases and decreases when the current decreases.

3. The *telephone receiver* is an application of the electromagnet. Sound entering the telephone transmitter produces a varying electric current. This varying current causes the electromagnet in the telephone receiver to have a varying magnetic strength. A metal *diaphragm* is pulled in and out as the current becomes stronger or weaker. This diaphragm produces sound waves in the air.

4. *Earphones* are telephone receivers with flat electromagnets.

5. *Loudspeakers* are comparable to telephone receivers in which the diaphragm is attached to a large cone. The cone sets in motion a larger amount of air, and hence gives a louder sound.

GLOSSARY

Diaphragm: A thin iron disk which is set vibrating by the flow of the electric current through the coil of the earphone. This disk causes the air to vibrate, thus creating sound waves.

Earphones or *Phones:* Two flat receivers, held on the head by a spring.

Electromagnet: A magnet made by electric current flowing through a coil of wire surrounding a core.

Loudspeaker: A reproducer which produces a loud, audible sound.

SYMBOLS

Earphones or phones.

Loudspeaker.

QUESTIONS AND PROBLEMS

1. How would you construct an electromagnet?
2. How may you increase the strength of an electromagnet?
3. Under what conditions will current passing through a set of earphones fail to produce sound?
4. Describe the action of the diaphragm of an earphone under the following series of events: no current followed by an increasing current, followed by a decreasing current in the earphone.
5. In what manner are the reproducers of a set of earphones connected?
6. How are dry cells connected in series?
7. How can the paper cone of a magnetic loudspeaker produce loud sounds?

8

The Detector

PROBLEM 1. *What is the electron theory?*

PROBLEM 2. *How is an alternating current changed to a pulsating direct current?*

PROBLEM 3. *How can we make a practical detector?*

In studying the antenna and tuner, you have learned that the radio wave, striking the antenna, sets up a voltage or electrical pressure in it which, in turn, causes a small current to flow in the receiver. But if you connect your phones to this circuit, as shown in Figure 8-1, you will hear nothing.

At this point a word might be said concerning *circuit diagrams*. These show how the various components are connected together. Symbols, instead of photographs or drawings of these components, are used and the lines between them indicate the connecting wires. Where two lines cross and connect together, a dot at the junction indicates this fact (+). If the lines cross, but do not connect, a loop is used (⌁).

What Is Electricity? To understand why the electrical current flowing in the receiver fails to operate the

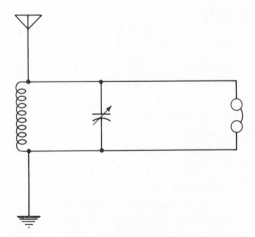

Fig. 8-1. *Diagram of the antenna-ground system and the tuner connected to a set of phones. This circuit will not work.*

39

phones, we must first consider the theory of electricity. Although scientists have succeeded in putting electricity to a great many uses, they do not know just what electricity is. It is one of the many forms of energy and may be changed into other forms such as heat, light, and motion. From a study of the behavior of an electric current and from a study of the methods of obtaining electrical effects, scientists have arrived at some theories about its nature.

Hypotheses, Theories, and Laws. When a scientist tries to explain one of nature's mysteries, he carefully examines all the facts he can obtain. He performs experiments to obtain more facts and then makes a guess that tries to explain all the facts. This guess is at first called a *hypothesis.* When more evidence is found to support the hypothesis, and other scientists generally accept it, the explanation is called a *theory.* After a time, someone may come along with proof which shows the theory to be true. We then call the explanation a *law.* Or someone else may come along with facts to show that the theory cannot be true. In the latter case, the theory may be modified to take the new facts into account or may be discarded entirely in favor of a new theory which tends to explain the new facts. Some scientific theories existed a great many years before they were proven to be true or false.

So it is with the electric current. Although we do not know what electric current is, the *electron theory* tries to explain it.

Types of Current. According to the electron theory (Chap. 29), an electric current consists of the movement of negatively charged minute particles, called *electrons.* Although some of these electrons will drift through a conductor like water flowing through a pipe, the main movement of the electrons consists in hitting their neighbors and by that means passing along the impulse of energy, which we call an electric current. The action is somewhat similar to that of the dominoes of Figure 2-4.

This impulse of energy travels at the rate of nearly 186,000 miles per second, or nearly the speed of light. When the electric current flows in one direction through the conductor, we say it is *direct current* (dc). If the current flows first in one direction and then reverses itself and flows back in the opposite direction, we say it is *alternating current* (ac). When an alternating current flows in one direction, stops, and then flows in the opposite direction, we say the current has gone through one *cycle.* The number of cycles per second is called the *frequency.*

Alternating Currents. The electricity used to light your house may be alternating current and have a frequency of 60 cycles per second. The current set flowing in your antenna-ground system by the action of the radio wave also is alternating current: its frequency is the same as the frequency of the radio wave. That is, it may vary from 10 kilocycles per second (kc) to 3,000,000 megacycles per second (mc). Electric current whose frequency falls within that range is said to be *radio-frequency alternating current.*

Now let us go back to our radio receiver. Let us assume that a broadcasting station sends out a radio wave whose frequency is 500 kc. This frequency we call *radio frequency* (rf). The radio wave hits our antenna and sets a current flowing in our antenna-ground system. This is an alternating current whose frequency is the same as that of the radio wave, namely, 500 kc (500 kc means that the current will change its direction of flow one million times per second). This, in turn, starts an alternating current of the same frequency flowing in the tuner. It is this current which you have applied to the phones in Figure 8-1.

Let us see what happens in the phones. For one one-millionth of a second, the current flows in one direction through the electromagnet of the phones. This causes the pull of the electromagnet to be added to that of the bar or permanent magnet. The diaphragm is, therefore, pulled a little closer to the magnet.

For the next one one-millionth of a second, the current reverses itself and is now flowing through the electromagnet coil in the opposite direction. Now the magnetism of the electromagnet is subtracted from that of the permanent magnet, and the total magnetic pull is less than before. The diaphragm starts to spring back. This process occurs every time the current reverses itself, which is once every millionth of a second.

Now, one one-millionth of a second is a very small interval of time, and no diaphragm is so sensitive that it can follow these changes. Every time the diaphragm begins to be pulled towards the magnet, the current reverses itself, and the pull is released. As a result, the diaphragm stands still, and you hear no sound.

Pulsating Currents. To overcome this difficulty, someone had a brilliant idea. Suppose we put in the circuit a gate which permits an electric current to flow only in one direction and not in the other. Now, let us see what happens to the radio-frequency alternating current in the circuit. For one one-millionth of a second, the current will flow through the gate. During the next one one-millionth of a second, the gate will block the current, and there will be no flow; then a flow in the same direction as the first; then no flow; and so on. The effect of the gate will be to permit a series of pulses of current to flow, all going in the same direction. These pulses of current will be separated by intervals when there is no flow. Each pulse and each interval will last only one one-millionth of a second.

Since the current now flows only in one direction, we call it *direct current*. Since it is not a steady flow, but consists of a series of pulses, we call it *pulsating direct current*.

Let us see what happens when the pulsating direct current flows into our phones. For one one-millionth of a second, the pull of the electromagnet is added to that of the permanent magnet, and the diaphragm starts to bend inward. For the next millionth of a second, the electromagnet will exert no pull, and the diaphragm will start to spring back. Before it can move back, however, the next pulse enters the electromagnet coil, and the diaphragm again receives the inward pull. As a result, the diaphragm receives a continuous inward pull. This pull varies in strength, in step with the variations of the signal strength. As a result, the diaphragm vibrates back and forth, thereby producing sound.

A Detector Is an Electrical Gate. The device used in radio which serves as a one-way gate is called a *detector*. Scientists have discovered that certain crystals like *carborundum* and the mineral *galena* have this peculiar property of permitting electric current to flow through them in one direction but practically no current in the other direction. We do not know precisely how this control is accomplished, but we have theories to explain it. It would not help our understanding of modern radio receivers, however, to enter at this point into a discussion of those theories.

Fig. 8-2. *This diagram shows the construction of a crystal detector.*

Crystal Detectors. One type of crystal commonly used for detectors is galena, a mineral compound consisting of lead and sulphur. Not every spot on the crystal, however, has this remarkable property of making the one-directional current. We must, therefore, use a fine wire to find the spots that will work. (If a fixed crystal, such as the *germanium* type, is used, no fine-wire adjustment is necessary.) The symbol for the crystal detector is: —▶︎|—

Making Your Set Work.
When you have hooked up your receiver with the crystal detector in series with the phones, you must move your fine wire (which is called a *catwhisker*) from spot to spot. When you find a spot where you hear a sound in the phones, leave the wire at that spot, and adjust the tuning control to produce maximum loudness of signal. You should avoid handling the crystal, since the grease from your fingers will interfere with its sensitivity. If your crystal becomes dirty, wash it in carbon tetrachloride to remove any grease.

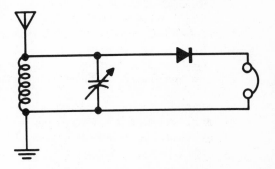

Fig. 8-3. *A diagram of the complete crystal receiver. Either the catwhisker or crystal side of the detector can be connected to the phones. This circuit will work.*

SUMMARY

Your complete radio receiving set, in its simplest terms, then, must have these parts which we have discussed: an **antenna** and **ground,** a **tuner** (an **inductor** and a **capacitor**), a **detector,** and a **reproducer** (phones). In Figure 8-3, these parts are arranged in proper relationship to one another. If you understand the symbols and connect the parts of your set according to this arrangement, you should be able to hear speech and music through the earphones.

GLOSSARY

Alternating Current (AC): An electric current in which the electrons periodically reverse their direction of flow.

Sixty-Cycle Alternating Current: An alternating current that changes direction 120 times a second, or goes through 60 cycles a second.

Radio-Frequency Alternating Current: An alternating current that changes direction thousands and even millions of times a second.

Catwhisker: The thin wire with which we hunt for a sensitive spot on the crystal.

Current, Electric: The flow of electrons through a conductor.

Detector: An electrical gate, or valve, permitting the flow of electrons in one direction but hardly or not at all in the other.

Direct Current (DC): An electric current in which the electrons constantly flow in one direction.

Pulsating Direct Current: A direct current that periodically changes in strength.

Electron: A minute, negatively charged particle.

Electron Theory: A theory which explains the nature of an electric current as electrons moving through a conductor.

Galena: A mineral crystal, a compound of lead and sulphur, used as a detector in the receiving set.

Voltage: The electrical pressure that causes electrons to flow in a conductor.

SYMBOLS

Crystal detector. ───▶▌───

QUESTIONS AND PROBLEMS

1. Briefly describe the nature of an electric current.
2. Draw the symbol for a crystal detector.
3. Describe direct current. Compare it with alternating current.
4. Give the relationship between the frequency and the cycles of an alternating current.
5. What is the frequency of alternating current in the home? How does its frequency compare with radio-frequency alternating currents?
6. What is the response of the diaphragm of a pair of earphones when radio-frequency alternating current is sent through the phones? Account for its behavior.
7. Describe the behavior of a pulsating direct current through a conductor.
8. Describe the action of a pulsating direct current which has been obtained from a radio-frequency alternating current by means of an electrical gate or detector, as the current passes into the phones.
9. What is the electrical action of a detector? Name two crystals used as detectors.
10. How do we manipulate a crystal used as a detector, and what must we do to take proper care of it?

9

Waveform

Did you ever visit a sick friend in a hospital? Did he, perhaps, point to the chart hung at the foot of his bed and say, "This is my temperature chart"? You examined the chart and saw on it a wavy line going up and down several times and finally—we hope—leveling out to a horizontal line. You know, of course, that the temperature did not travel over this scenic-railway type of path. This chart was merely a picture or diagram which showed how high your friend's temperature was at any given time of the day. We call such a chart a *graph*.

Graphs. The word *graph* means a drawing or a picture. Many kinds of graphs are used in science, mathematics, and economics. The most common kind of graph attempts to show, by a line called a *curve*, the course of events when two different conditions are changing. In the graph, Figure 9-1, the two conditions are time and temperature. The hours are marked from left to right on the horizontal line in equal spaces. The degrees of temperature are marked on the vertical line, with the lowest temperature at the bottom. The nurse reads the temperature of the patient each hour and makes a dot on the vertical line over the hour where the horizontal line from the observed temperature crosses it. For example,

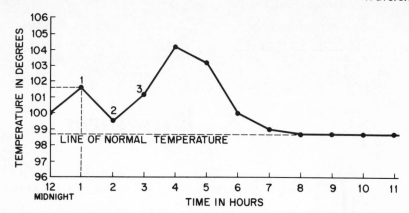

Fig. 9-1. *Temperature graph for your sick friend. The vertical part shows the degrees of temperature, and the horizontal part shows the time. By this means, we can find out what his temperature was at any particular time.*

the chart shows that at 1 A.M. the patient's temperature was 101.8° (dot No. 1); at 2 A.M. the temperature was 99.5° (dot No. 2). Thus each dot is the temperature at a certain hour. When the points or dots are connected by a continuous line, the course of the fever is pictured. This line or curve is called here the *temperature curve.*

Graph of Direct-Current Flow. We can draw such a chart or graph to show how electric current flows. First we draw a horizontal line and call it the *line of no-current flow.* When electric current flows in one direction, we call it *positive* and picture its path above the line of no-current flow. When electric current reverses itself and flows in the opposite direction, we call it *negative* and picture its path below the line of no-current flow. Thus, the path of a direct current is entirely above that line. If the current is a steady direct current, the picture of its flow starts at the line of no-current flow and very quickly rises above it to the maximum strength of the current (Fig. 9-2). It then continues to flow at a steady strength of current, and we picture it as a straight horizontal line until the instant when the current is cut off. At that point, the line drops down to zero, the line of no flow. The line we draw picturing that flow of current is called the *curve,* or *waveform.*

The strength of the current at any one instant of time is shown by the distance of the curve away from the line of no-current flow at that instant.

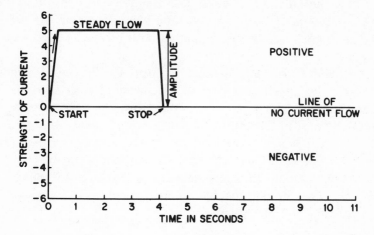

Fig. 9-2. *A graph of the curve or waveform of a steady direct current.*

Fluctuating Direct Current. A direct current may be either steady or fluctuating. If it is steady, the current strength, or maximum distance away from the line of no-current flow, is constant while the current is flowing, as shown in Figure 9-2. In the case of a fluctuating direct current, the current strength is different at different instants of time, as shown in Figure 9-3.

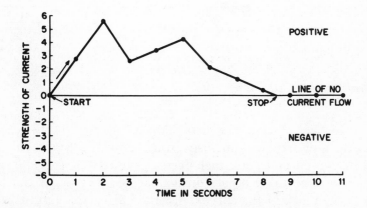

Fig. 9-3. *Graph of the curve or waveform of a fluctuating direct current. Note that the strength of the current may assume different values at different times.*

Note that in both Figures 9-2 and 9-3 the current is direct current—that is, it flows in only one direction. You can see this from the graphs by observing that in both cases the curves lie entirely above the line of no-current flow.

The Sine Curve for Alternating Current. We can also picture the flow of an alternating current by means of such a graph. The current strength starts from zero and rises to a maximum flow in one direction. Still flowing in that direction, it starts to decrease in strength until it again reaches the line of no-current flow. Then it flows to a maximum in the opposite direction (below the line), and decreases again until the zero line is reached. As you already know, the flow of current has gone through one cycle (p. 40). Then it starts and repeats all over again.

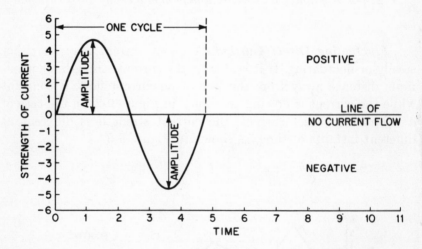

Fig. 9-4. *Graph of the curve or waveform of an alternating current. A curve whose current strength rises and falls in the smooth, even, and regular glide pictured here is called a* sine curve.

Note that during the first half of the cycle, the current strength increases continuously from zero to maximum in a smooth, regular glide, and then decreases to zero in the same, even way. The same thing occurs during the second half of the cycle (the bottom loop of the curve). A curve having this form is called a *sine curve* (Fig. 9-4). The distance from the line of no-current flow to the point of greatest current strength on either loop is called the *amplitude* of the curve.

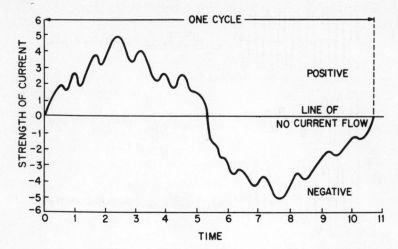

Fig. 9-5. *Graph of the curve or waveform of an alternating current. Notice that this curve is not smooth but irregular.*

The flow of alternating current does not always describe a smooth sine curve. The rise from zero to maximum may be irregular and varied. The decrease from maximum to zero may also be irregular and varied (Fig. 9-5).

Radio Waveforms. It would help you to better understand what takes place in your receiver, perhaps, if you were to examine the wave forms of the electrical currents flowing in the various parts.

Consider the waveform of the radio wave. It is the same as that of an alternating current—that is, the wave flows first in one direction and then in the other. Its range of frequency is from 10 kc to 3,000,000 mc. In the United States, standard broadcasting stations send out radio waves whose frequencies lie between 535 and 1,605 kc. This range is fixed by law, and each station is given a definite frequency to which it must always keep its station tuned.

The radio wave may take several different forms. For the moment, we are interested in three forms (Fig. 9-6). *First,* there is the wave whose form is that of a smooth sine wave and whose amplitude is constant throughout the entire wave. Such a wave is called a *continuous wave,* and is also known as a *carrier wave.*

Second, there is the wave whose form is that of a smooth sine wave but with the amplitudes of successive cycles decreasing gradually. Such a wave is called a *damped wave.*

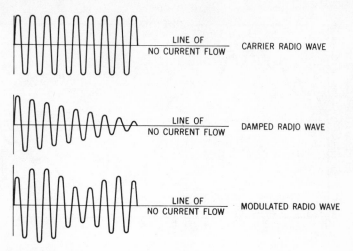

Fig. 9-6. *Graph of the waveforms of continuous, damped, and modulated radio waves. Note that in all three waves shown here the frequencies are the same. Only the amplitudes vary.*

Third, there is the wave whose form is that of a smooth sine wave but with the amplitudes of successive cycles varying irregularly. The waveform is obtained by combining the current that produces a continuous wave with a fluctuating direct or low-frequency alternating current at the broadcasting station. We call the resulting wave a *modulated carrier wave.* We say that the continuous or carrier wave is modulated by the fluctuating direct or low-frequency alternating current. The radio waves which carry speech and music through the ether are modulated carrier waves.

How the Modulated Wave Is Produced. To understand the method by which a fluctuating direct current modulates the carrier wave, examine Figure 9-7. First of all, sound striking the microphone at the broadcasting station sets up a fluctuating direct current. Meanwhile, in another part of the transmitting set, a continuous or carrier wave has been generated. Assume the frequency of this carrier wave to be 500 kc. The fluctuating direct current is now mixed with the carrier wave. The result is the modulated radio wave whose frequency is 500 kc, but whose amplitude variations correspond to the form of the fluctuating direct current. In some transmitters, the fluctuating direct current is converted into a low-frequency alternating current which, when mixed with the carrier current, produces a similar modulated radio wave.

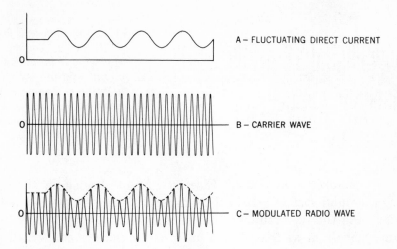

A – FLUCTUATING DIRECT CURRENT

B – CARRIER WAVE

C – MODULATED RADIO WAVE

Fig. 9-7. *This graph shows how a fluctuating direct current from the microphone modulates the carrier wave to produce the modulated radio wave that is broadcast by the transmitting station.*

In this way, we modulate the carrier wave by the electric currents set up by sound waves hitting the microphone at the transmitting station. The modulated radio wave is broadcast by the transmitter. It is the task of the radio receiver to collect this modulated radio wave and to separate the carrier wave from the electric currents impressed on it by the microphone. These impressed currents are the currents that operate our phones, and through their action we reproduce the original sound waves.

Waveform—Antenna-Ground System. You have already learned (p. 16) that when the modulated radio wave passes across the antenna of your receiving set, it sets up in the antenna-ground system an electrical pressure, or voltage, that causes an electric current to flow in that system. The greater the pressure, the greater the flow of current. This flow of current, therefore, conforms to the electrical pressure, which in turn conforms to the modulated radio wave. You can see, therefore, that the flow of current in the antenna-ground system will correspond to the waveform of the modulated radio wave. The current that flows in the antenna-ground system, then, is alternating current whose frequency is the same as that of the modulated radio wave (Fig. 9-8). The amplitude variations of this current, too, will correspond to the amplitude variations of the modulated radio wave.

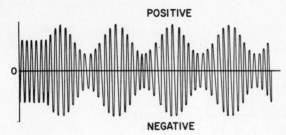

POSITIVE

0

NEGATIVE

Fig. 9-8. *This waveform of alternating current is set flowing in the antenna-ground system when the modulated radio wave shown in Figure 9-7-C passes across the antenna of the receiving set.*

Waveform—The Tuner. Electric current flowing in the antenna-ground system, you will recall, sets an electric current flowing in the tuning circuit of your receiver. This current takes the same waveform as that in the antenna-ground system, which in turn has taken the same waveform as that of the modulated radio wave. The current flowing in the tuner, then, is alternating current having the same frequency and amplitude variations as the current flowing in the antenna-ground system.

Waveform—The Detector. The crystal detector, you will remember, permits electric current to flow through it mostly in one direction. See if you can picture what happens to an alternating current as it attempts to flow through such a crystal.

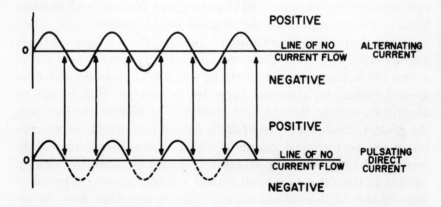

Fig. 9-9. *This graph shows how the crystal detector changes alternating current into pulsating direct current. The negative halves of the cycle which were stopped by the crystal detector are shown by the dotted lines. For practical purposes, we may disregard the small amount of curent flow in the negative direction.*

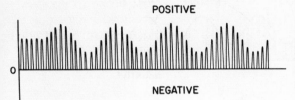

Fig. 9-10. *Graph of the waveform of pulsating direct current through the crystal detector. Note the action of the detector.*

First, the positive half of the cycle approaches the crystal and finds the "gate" wide open. That is, the positive part of the cycle can pass through the crystal. When the current reverses itself, the gate is shut, and no current can flow through. The current thus flows through with all its variaticns as long as it is going in one direction—that is, as long as it does not go below the line of no-current flow of our graph (Fig. 9-9). Everything in the graph below the line of no-current flow is wiped out. Our current now consists of a series of direct-current pulses, separated by gaps of no-current flow that represent the negative halves of the cycles which were stopped by the crystal. This is what is meant by a pulsating direct current.

We can now see what will happen to the alternating current of our tuner when it reaches the crystal detector. The current is changed from an alternating to a pulsating direct current, and the bottom halves of the cycles in the curve are wiped out. This, then, is what we mean by detection. The waveform picture is the same as that for the tuner, except that the half below the line of no-current flow is eliminated (Fig. 9-10).

Waveform—The Reproducer. The current flowing out of the crystal detector is now a series of direct-current pulses of varying amplitude. These variations of amplitude correspond to the curve described by the current that was set flowing by sound waves striking the microphone at the broadcasting station. If we again take our hypothetical radio station broadcasting at a frequency of 500 kc, each such direct-current pulse lasts for one one-millionth of a second and is separated from its neighbor by an interval of one one-millionth of a second when no current flows.

As you already know, the diaphragms of the phones cannot respond to a pulse of such short duration, but since each pulse is flowing in the same direction, a series, or train, of such pulses makes its effect felt. The result on the phones, then, is the same as

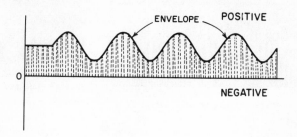

Fig. 9-11. *Graph of the waveform of fluctuating direct current through the phones. This waveform is indicated by the envelope, which has the same shape as the fluctuating direct current from the microphone in Fig. 9-7-A.*

if a continuous, but varying, direct current, equal to the average of all these pulses, were to pass through the coils. This waveform can be shown on the graph by joining the peaks of these pulses with a continuous line. We call such a line the *envelope* of the wave (Fig. 9-11). You will notice that this envelope has the same shape as the current set up by the microphone at the broadcasting station. We have succeeded in making the carrier wave take

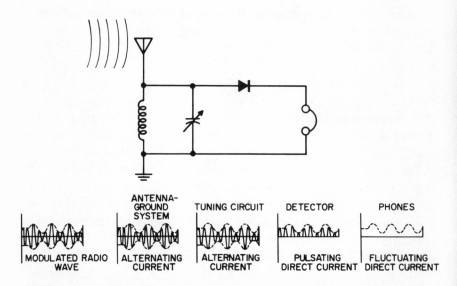

Fig. 9-12. *Hookup of a complete crystal receiver showing waveforms of electric currents flowing in the various parts.*

the form of the modulating current, and it is this modulating current, acting through our phones, that reproduces the sound originally created at the broadcasting station.

SUMMARY

1. A *graph* is a picture.
2. Graphs in scientific work usually show relations between two *variable* quantities.
3. The line which pictures the course of any event in a graph is called a *curve*.
4. The *sine curve* is the graph which shows the waveform of a simple alternating current.
5. Three forms of radio waves must be distinguished: *carrier* or *continuous* wave, *damped* wave, and *modulated carrier* wave.

GLOSSARY

Amplitude: In a graph picturing the flow of alternating current, the amplitude is the maximum distance from a point on the curve to the line of no-current flow.

Envelope: The line joining the peaks of the curve lying on one side of the zero line of the graph.

Fluctuating Direct Current: Direct current that is constantly changing in strength.

Graph: A diagram that pictures the instantaneous relationship between two varying factors; for example, temperature at a certain instant of time.

Modulation: The act of varying the amplitudes of a carrier wave by means of an alternating current of low frequency or by a fluctuating direct current.

Sine Curve: A graph indicating the smooth, continuous variations of current flowing in an alternating-current circuit.

Wave, Carrier: A continuous wave at radio frequency (very high frequency).

Wave, Continuous: A wave which has an equal amplitude for all cycles.

Wave, Damped: An alternating-current sine wave whose amplitude gradually and continuously decreases for each cycle.

Waveform: A graph showing changes of direct- and alternating-current flow with time.

Wave, Modulated Carrier: A carrier wave whose amplitude is continually varied as the result of mixing with an alternating current of low frequency or with a fluctuating direct current.

SYMBOLS

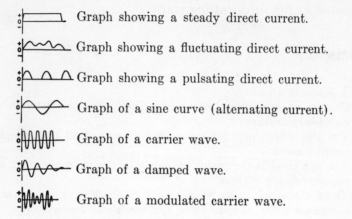

Graph showing a steady direct current.

Graph showing a fluctuating direct current.

Graph showing a pulsating direct current.

Graph of a sine curve (alternating current).

Graph of a carrier wave.

Graph of a damped wave.

Graph of a modulated carrier wave.

QUESTIONS AND PROBLEMS

1. What does a graph actually show?
2. Draw a graph of an alternating-current sine wave; of a steady direct current; of a pulsating direct-current.
3. For a sine curve, what fact would we know if we knew, at any one instant, the distance between the no-current line and the curve?
4. Draw the picture of an alternating current whose graph is not a sine curve.
5. In what particular electrical respect are radio broadcasting stations different?
6. Name three forms that a radio wave may take, and make a graph of each.
7. Describe briefly how the modulated radio wave is produced.
8. Describe the relationship between the modulated radio wave and the current in the antenna-ground system of a receiver.
9. Describe the waveform of the modulated carrier after it has gone through the crystal detector. Draw a graph of the waveform.
10. Describe what is meant by detection.
11. Why are phones unable to react to the current produced in the antenna-ground system, whereas they do respond to a detected radio-frequency current?
12. Draw the envelope of any modulated radio-frequency current graph. What does it represent?

10

The Antenna Coupler

PROBLEM 1. *What are the faults of a tuner having but one coil?*

PROBLEM 2. *What are the principles of a transformer?*

PROBLEM 3. *How do we use a transformer to correct the faults of our tuner?*

In continuing our study of radio, we shall follow the plan of pointing out certain faults and shortcomings of our simple sets. Then we shall explain the various methods of correcting these faults.

Faults of the Tuner. Let us study the tuner. The function of the tuning circuit is to select the wave of desired frequency and reject all others. Although the tuner you built does this job fairly well, it occasionally fails to separate two stations completely, especially if these stations are quite powerful, close to your home, and operate at approximately the same frequency. You then hear a fairly loud broadcast from one station and in the background, although a good deal weaker, the *signal* or program from another station.

Theoretically, the tuning circuit should pass only one frequency. But because some resistance to the flow of current is always present in the circuit, other frequencies creep in. When this resistance becomes too great, two stations may be heard at the same time.

Why We Hear Two Stations. We can draw a picture to represent this situation. In Figure 10-1, we have assumed that the station desired has a frequency of 1,000 kc. Let us assume also that there is no difference in the distance or power of the stations. Along the horizontal line, we have indicated successive frequencies

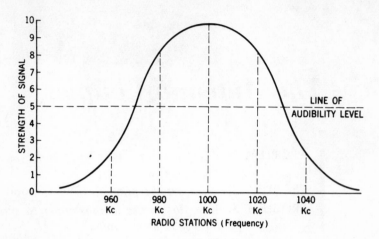

Fig. 10-1. *This graph or tuning curve shows what happens when a receiver tunes broadly. Note that unwanted radio stations at 980 and 1020 kc come in well above the line of audibility level. This means that three stations may be heard at the same time.*

from 960 to 1,040 kc. Along the vertical line we have indicated the loudness of the signal received. The height of the curve at any point then represents the loudness with which a signal of that particular frequency will be heard when your tuner is set for 1,000 kc. If the height at that frequency rises above the line marked "audibility level," the signal will be heard in the earphones. If it does not reach that level, the signal will be unheard and, therefore, will not interfere.

You will note from the graph in Figure 10-1 that this particular tuner will permit three stations to be heard simultaneously, the one we want at 1,000 kc and two unwanted ones at 980 and 1,020 kc. We say that such a set *tunes broadly.* We can remedy this by redesigning our tuner so it will have a tuning curve that will correspond to Figure 10-2. Note that now the strength of signal of every station except the one desired falls below the line of audibility level. Such a set, we say, *tunes sharply.*

Reducing Resistance in the Tuner. In practice, we accomplish the desired change by reducing the resistance of the tuning circuit. Examine again the circuit diagram of your crystal receiver in Figure 8-3. You will notice that the antenna-ground system is connected directly across the tuning circuit—that is, the antenna

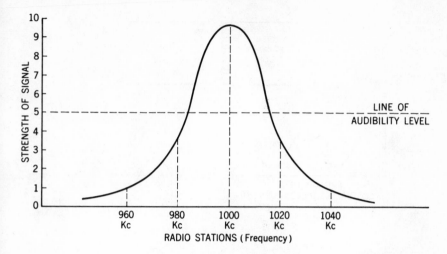

Fig. 10-2. *Graph or tuning curve for a sharply tuning receiver. Note that all unwanted radio stations fall below the line of audibility level.*

is connected to one end and the ground is connected to the other end. Thus, the resistances found in the antenna and ground circuits are added to those of the tuning circuit. This increase of resistance causes the tuner to tune broadly.

The ideal arrangement would be one where the electrical currents flowing in the antenna-ground system were transferred to the tuner, and yet the resistances of the antenna and ground circuits were kept out. The resistance of the tuning circuit then could be made very small, and much sharper tuning would result. This can be accomplished by means of a *transformer*.

What Is a Transformer? To see how this undesirable resistance is kept out, you must first learn what we mean by a *transformer*. You already know that when an electric current flows through a coil of wire, it sets up a magnetic field around this coil. When this magnetic field cuts across a conductor, it sets up an electrical pressure, or voltage, which in turn sets a current flowing, if there is a path through which it can flow.

We can have this magnetic field cut across a conductor in two ways: we can either have a stationary magnetic field set up by a steady direct current flowing through the coil and use a moving conductor, or we may have a moving magnetic field and a stationary conductor. This moving magnetic field can be pro-

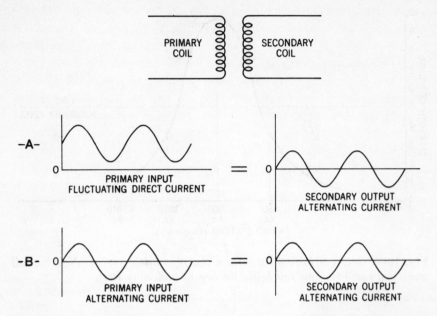

Fig. 10-3. *If a fluctuating direct current (**A**) or an alternating current (**B**) is sent into the primary of a transformer, the output from the secondary coil is always an alternating current.*

duced when either a fluctuating direct current or an alternating current passes through the coil. The magnetic field is built up and collapsed in step with the variations of current in the coil.

In the transformer, we have two stationary coils. We call one the *primary* and the other the *secondary*. We pass a fluctuating direct current or an alternating current through the primary coil. This current causes the magnetic field around the primary to fluctuate in step with it. This fluctuating magnetic field, cutting across the turns of the secondary coil, sets up an alternating electrical pressure that, in turn, causes an alternating current to flow in the secondary. This alternating current corresponds in form to the fluctuating direct current or the alternating current in the primary (Fig. 10-3).

Step-Up and Step-Down Transformers. Here is another interesting thing about a transformer. As you know, the fluctuating magnetic field cutting across the turns, or loops, of wire of the secondary coil sets up an electrical pressure, or voltage, in those loops. For low-frequency currents (up to about 15,000 cycles per second), an iron core is placed so that it passes through the primary and secondary coils. A magnetic field acts as though it prefers to pass through iron rather than through air. Thus, practically all the magnetic field is concentrated in the iron core. Since this iron core passes through both primary and secondary coils, the magnetic field around the primary coil is the same as that around the secondary coil. This means that if we have more loops in the secondary than in the primary coil, we obtain a greater total voltage in the secondary. If we have fewer loops in the secondary than in the primary, we obtain a smaller total voltage in the secondary coil. Thus, by varying the ratio between the number of turns of wire in the primary and secondary coils, we can

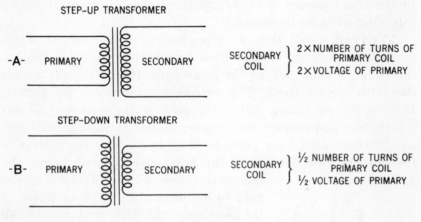

Fig. 10-4. *A—Step-up transformer.*
B—Step-down transformer.

get a greater or smaller voltage in the secondary coil. For example, if the secondary coil has twice the number of turns that are in the primary coil, the voltage in the secondary will be twice that in the primary coil. We call such a transformer a *step-up transformer*. If, however, the secondary winding has half the number of turns that are in the primary winding, the voltage set up in the secondary winding will be half the voltage in the primary. We call such a transformer a *step-down transformer* (See Fig. 10-4).

The Antenna Coupler. In dealing with radio-frequency currents (that is, alternating currents whose frequencies are the same

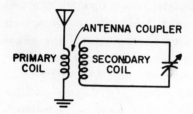

PRIMARY SECONDARY
COIL   COIL

Fig. 10-5. *Diagram showing how an antenna coupler or transformer is connected in the radio receiver. Note that the path of the antenna-ground system no longer passes directly through the tuning circuit.*

as those of the radio waves), iron-core transformers are seldom used because of the high loss of energy in the iron core. This means that an air core must be used, with the result that a very small amount of the primary field will cut across the turns of the secondary coil. The step-up or step-down effect of an iron-core transformer is not present. Fortunately, there is another way to obtain this effect at radio frequencies.

You will recall that we were seeking a method for transferring the electrical current from the antenna-ground system to the tuning circuit and, at the same time, permitting the tuning circuit to operate freely. The air-core transformer is the answer. If we make the tuning coil of the receiver the secondary of our transformer and connect the primary to the antenna-ground system, we have solved our problem (Fig. 10-5). Now the current in the primary (set flowing by the radio wave passing across the antenna) causes a little of the magnetic field to cut across the turns, or loops, of the secondary coil. This produces a small electrical pressure, or voltage, in those loops. When the secondary circuit is tuned to resonance with the incoming signal, this small voltage in the loops of the secondary coil produces a much larger voltage across the tuned circuit. This gives the same result as a step-up transformer. Since the tuned circuit is coupled magnetically (that is, linked by the magnetic field rather than by wire connections) to the antenna-ground circuit, it receives the desired electrical energy from the antenna-ground system without receiving its additional resistance.

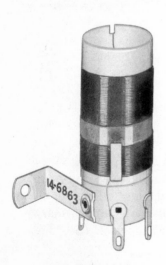

Fig. 10-6. *Antenna coupler.*

Such a transformer used at this point is called an *antenna coupler* or *transformer*. Through its use, we obtain sharper tuning —that is, we are able to keep out unwanted stations, since we have reduced the resistance of our tuning circuit.

To make such an antenna coupler, all you have to do is to wind upon the same tube on which you have your tuner coil an additional winding of about 15 turns of wire (the primary winding). Separate the two windings about ⅛ inch. Connect the lead-in from the antenna to one end of the primary winding and the ground to the other. Try reversing the antenna and ground connections to this winding to obtain best results. Your improved crystal receiver will now appear as in Figure 10-7.

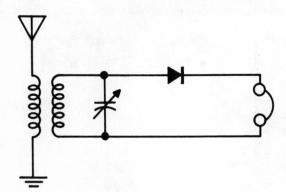

Fig. 10-7. *An improved crystal receiver, using an antenna coupler. This set will tune sharper than the one shown in Fig. 8-3.*

SUMMARY

1. One of the faults of the **tuner** consisting of a single coil is that it does not sharply separate different stations.
2. This fault may be partially corrected by an **antenna transformer.**
3. The transformer consists of two coils unconnected but wound upon the same core. In such a device, the magnetic field created by a current in one coil transfers the energy to the other coil. In the second coil the fluctuation in the current induced therein will follow the pattern of the current in the first coil.
4. In an iron-core transformer, the voltages in the primary and secondary coils have direct ratio to the ratio of the number of turns of wire in the coils.
5. An **antenna coupler** is an air-core transformer having the primary in the antenna circuit and the secondary in the tuner circuit.

GLOSSARY

Antenna Coupler: An air-core transformer used to couple the energy from the antenna-ground system to the tuning circuit.

Primary: The input coil of a transformer.

Resistance: The opposition a substance offers to the flow of electric current through it.

Secondary: The output coil of a transformer.

Transformer: An electrical device consisting of two separate, coils, insulated from each other, used to transfer electrical energy from one circuit to another.

Transformer, Step-Down: A transformer which develops a lower voltage across the secondary than the voltage impressed across the primary.

Transformer, Step-Up: A transformer which develops a higher voltage across the secondary than the voltage impressed across the primary.

Tuning, Broad: The simultaneous reception of several stations in a radio receiver.

Tuning, Sharp: The ability of a radio set to receive only one station at a time.

SYMBOLS

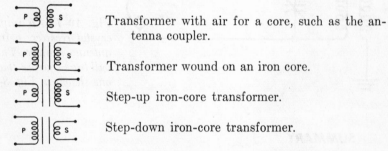

Transformer with air for a core, such as the antenna coupler.

Transformer wound on an iron core.

Step-up iron-core transformer.

Step-down iron-core transformer.

QUESTIONS AND PROBLEMS

1. What is the effect of resistance in a tuning circuit?
2. What response will be obtained from a receiver that tunes broadly?
3. What practical measure may we use to remove the resistance of the antenna and ground from the tuning circuit?
4. Under what circumstances will a moving magnetic field be produced about a stationary current-carrying conductor?
5. Describe the structure and operation of a transformer.
6. How may the voltage in the secondary of a transformer be made to vary from the voltage impressed across the primary?
7. Describe the type of transformer used as an antenna coupler.
8. Draw a diagram of a complete crystal receiver using an antenna coupler.

11

Electron Flow in the
Antenna-Ground System

PROBLEM 1. *How does a dry cell produce an electro-motive force?*

PROBLEM 2. *What are two kinds of alternating-current generators?*

PROBLEM 3. *How do electrons behave in the antenna-ground system?*

You have learned in our previous study that an electric current consists of a flow of electrons through a conducting forming a circuit. Let us see if this theory can throw some new light upon what happens in a radio receiver.

A Dry Cell Is an Electron "Pump". Look at a dry cell (Fig. 11-1). You will notice that it is a zinc can closed at one end. The other end is sealed with some insulator such as sealing wax or pitch. In the center of the sealing wax you will notice a binding post on a carbon rod. This post may be marked *POSITIVE* or +. At the same end of the cell, but fastened to the zinc, is a second binding post which may be marked *NEGATIVE* or −. The can is filled with certain chemicals.

The carbon rod in a dry cell is called the *positive pole* and the zinc is called the *negative pole*. It is customary to name the pole from which electrons leave the cell the negative pole. In general, the terminals of a battery or cell are called *poles* or *electrodes*.

You may not have heard it, but a dry cell is sometimes called an electron "pump." The chemical action inside the cell builds up a pressure of electrons. This pressure exists, even when no electrons are flowing. You can understand this if you think of a water faucet. The water behind the faucet is under a pressure even when the faucet is closed and no water is flowing. When the faucet is opened, the water flows out.

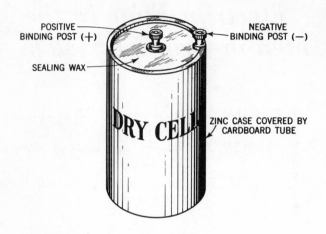

POSITIVE BINDING POST (+)

NEGATIVE BINDING POST (−)

SEALING WAX

DRY CELL

ZINC CASE COVERED BY CARDBOARD TUBE

Fig. 11-1. *The dry cell.*

So it is with the electrons in the dry cell. They accumulate at the negative pole, and thus produce a pressure. When a path is furnished them by connecting a conductor between the negative and positive posts of the dry cell, electrons will flow out of the negative post of the cell, through the conductor, and back into the positive post of the cell (Fig. 11-2).

Electromotive Force (EMF). The dry cell piles up electrons at the negative post and leaves a relative deficiency of electrons at the positive post. *When electrons are given a path to travel, they will always move from the place where they have been piled up to a place where there is a deficiency.* When electrons are in excess at a point, we say that point has a *negative charge*. When there is a deficiency, we say there is a *positive charge*. If given a path, then, electrons will flow from a point with a negative charge to a point with a posi-

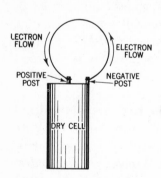

LECTRON FLOW

ELECTRON FLOW

POSITIVE POST

NEGATIVE POST

DRY CELL

Fig. 11-2. *The dry cell is a sort of pump that sends electrons streaming from the negative post to the positive post when a path is provided.*

tive charge. In other words, *electromotive force* (emf) is a pressure tending to make electrons move from a place where there are many electrons to a place where there are fewer electrons.

If two or more dry cells are connected in *series*—that is, with the positive post of one connected to the negative post of the other, the effect is as if two or more pumps were connected together. (Fig. 11-3A). The emf (or voltage) of the two cells is

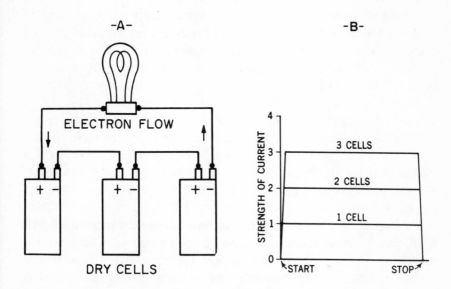

Fig. 11-3. *A—Three dry cells connected in a series.*
         B—A graph showing the flow of current from one, two, and three dry cells respectively.

equal to the sum of their voltages. This increased emf causes more electrons to flow through any given circuit in a period of time than does one cell.

Like Charges Repel; Unlike Charges Attract. *Another thing to remember about electrons is that they repel one another.* So, whereas electrons will be attracted to a point with a positive charge (a deficiency of electrons), they will be repelled from a point with a negative charge (an excess of electrons).

Since a dry cell can generate only a direct current, we have been considering the flow of electrons in one direction only. This kind of flow is called a *direct current* (*dc*). But if a pump could be devised that would cause electrons to flow first in one direction and then in the other, the current then would be called *alternating current (ac)*.

Alternating-Current Generators. We have no such battery, but we have another kind of "pump" to make current flow first in one direction and then in the other. It is called an *alternating-current (a-c) generator*. One form is the tremendous generator at the power house that supplies the current for our electric lights and electrical tools. The current is usually produced by passing conductors through magnetic fields. Each complete movement of a conductor through a magnetic field is called a *cycle,* and in each cycle the direction of the current changes twice. The stream of electrons pumped out by most a-c generators changes its direction of flow 120 times in a second. Hence, we call the electric current from such a generator a *60-cycle alternating current.*

Another modern pump to produce alternating current is the marvelous device called the *radio tube.* At the broadcasting station, one of these radio tubes sends out a stream of electrons which changes its direction of flow millions of times a second! We call this type of an electric current a *radio-frequency alternating current.*

Alternating Currents in the Antenna-Ground System. By this time, you know that the radio wave passing across your antenna causes an alternating current to flow up and down the antenna-ground system. The radio wave sets up an electrical pressure that causes the electrons to flow through the circuit. When electrons move back and forth through a circuit, we say that they *oscillate* in that circuit. See if you can picture how this takes place, by referring to Figure 11-4.

Here is the explanation. The radio wave, moving across the antenna-ground system, sets up for an instant a positive charge on the antenna and a negative charge on the ground of the system. The electrons, *which are present in the system at all times,* are set flowing *up* the antenna-ground system. These electrons flow from the ground, through the primary of the antenna coupler, through the lead-in wire, and on to the antenna wire. We show this flow on the graph in Figure 11-4-B.

The curve starts from point A on the line where the electrons are at a standstill and gradually increases its height (the quantity of electron flow in a given unit of time), until at B the

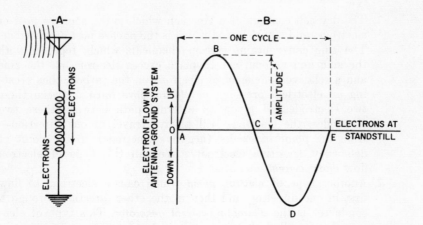

Fig. 11-4. *A—Electrons flow up and down the antenna-ground system.*
B—Graph showing one cycle of current flow in the antenna-ground
system.

electrons are flowing at their maximum quantity. Then these
electrons start to decrease, still flowing in the original direction,
until they reach a standstill at point C.

The radio wave has now reversed the direction of its electrical pressure. There is a negative charge on the antenna and a
positive charge on the ground of the antenna-ground system. The
electrons now change the direction of flow and stream *down*
the system to the ground.

On the graph, this direction change is shown where the curve
starts its bottom loop. The electrons, moving in the reversed direction, now increase their flow until they reach their maximum
at point D on the curve and then decrease to a standstill at
point E.

The electron flow has gone through one cycle. In one second,
there may be millions of such cycles corresponding to the frequency of the radio waves. We cannot show more than a few in
a graph, but we plan the graph so that it shows the frequency
by the time intervals along the horizontal line. The amplitude of
each of the graph loops, too, corresponds to the amplitude of each
loop in the current generated by the radio wave, as you have
learned in Chapter 9.

SUMMARY

1. The dry cell consists of a zinc can which is the **negative** post or electrode, and a carbon rod which is the **positive** post or electrode. The zinc can contains certain chemicals which, together with the zinc and carbon, act to place excess electrons on the zinc and a relative deficiency of electrons on the carbon, thus creating an electrical pressure, or **electromotive force,** between these two electrodes. If given an external path between these two electrodes, the electrons will always travel in one direction—from the point of excess (negative electrode) to the point of deficiency (positive electrode). We call this type of electron flow **direct current.**

2. Another type of **electron pump** which causes electrons to flow first in one direction and then in the other direction through a conductor is the **alternating-current generator.** This type of electron flow is called **alternating current.** As the electrons flow first in one direction and then reverse and flow in the other, we say that the alternating current has gone through one **cycle.** The number of cycles per second is called the **frequency.** Generators used to supply alternating current to our house lines usually have a frequency of 60 cycles per second.

3. Another type of alternating-current generator is the **radio tube.** This device is capable of generating alternating currents whose frequencies may be as high as millions of cycles per second. These radio tubes are used in radio broadcasting stations.

4. As the radio wave moves across the antenna of the receiver, it sets a high-frequency alternating current flowing in the antenna-ground system.

GLOSSARY

Alternating Current: A current that changes its direction of flow in a circuit because of the changing polarity of the applied voltage.
Sixty-Cycle Alternating Current: An alternating current that reverses its direction of flow through a circuit 120 times a second.
Radio-Frequency Alternating Current: Alternating current that makes thousands or millions of changes in the direction of current each second.
Cell: A chemical device used to generate an electron pressure or voltage.
Electromotive Force (emf): The electrical pressure, or voltage, that causes electrons to flow in a conductor.
Negative Charge: A region where there is an excess of electrons as compared with other regions.

Pole (or Electrode): Terminal of a cell or battery through which electrons leave or enter.

Series Connection of Cells: Cells connected from + to − to + to −, and so on, to supply a higher total voltage than that of any single cell.

SYMBOLS

A cell.

Several cells in series.

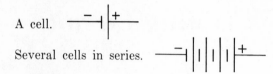

QUESTIONS AND PROBLEMS

1. In what direction will electrons always flow in a circuit?
2. What is the behavior of electrons toward positive charges? Toward other negative charges?
3. What is the effect on the total voltage of connecting several cells in series?
4. Why does a dry cell produce only direct current?
5. Describe by means of a graph the changes occuring in an alternating current.
6. Give two methods of creating an alternating current on a practical basis.
7. What are the characteristics of a 60-cycle alternating current?
8. Under what conditions are electrons said to oscillate?
9. Describe the electron oscillations set up by radio waves in the antenna-ground system of a receiving set.

12

Electron Flow in the Tuning Circuit

PROBLEM 1. *How are currents induced in conductors?*

PROBLEM 2. *What is the explanation of "charging" and "discharging" a capacitor?*

PROBLEM 3. *What is meant by self-induction?*

PROBLEM 4. *How are the oscillations of the tuning circuit produced?*

We have just learned that the radio wave sets our electrons moving up and down the antenna-ground system. We now want to see the effects of this alternating current upon the other parts of our receiver.

Why Induction Occurs. First of all, you should know* that (a) every electric current is accompanied by a magnetic field and (b) when this magnetic field cuts across a conductor or is cut through by a moving conductor, the result is an induced alternating voltage across the conductor.

Our antenna coupler is a combination of two unconnected coils so related that any alternating or fluctuating current in either one will set up, by induction, an alternating current in the other. The relationship of electromotive force, current, and rate of change, in one such induction coil, is known as *inductance,* or

---

* At this point the main principles of the induction coil and the methods of producing an induced current may be examined or demonstrated (Chap. 32).

72

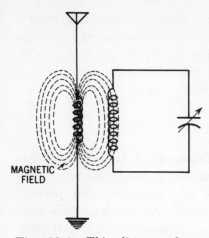

Fig. 12-1. *This diagram shows how the magnetic field around the primary of the antenna coupler cuts across the turns of the second-ary.*

in the case of two coupled coils, as *mutual inductance* (Chap. 32).

Here we have an explanation of how the electrical energy of the antenna-ground system is trans-ferred to the tuning circuit through the antenna coupler. The sequence of events is: (1) The radio wave sets up an alternating current in the antenna-ground system, of which the primary coil of the an-tenna coupler is a part. (2) This alternating current is accompanied by an alternating magnetic field. (3) This magnetic field cuts through the conductors in the sec-ondary coil of the antenna coupler. (4) Alternating currents in step with the radio waves are induced in the secondary coil. (5) These alternating currents, which are of radio frequency, flow through the tuning circuit. The frequency of the current set flowing in the tun-ing circuit is the same as that in the antenna-ground system. The variations in amplitude of each cycle likewise follow the variations in amplitude of the current in the antenna-ground system.

Fig. 12-2. *Diagram of the electrical charges and direction of electron flow in the antenna-ground system and tuning circuit during a half-cycle of current flow. During the next half-cycle, the charges and flow of electrons are reversed.*

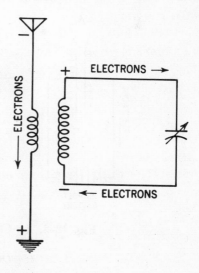

Now let us examine the electron flow in the tuning circuit. You will recall that this circuit consists of a capacitor and inductor connected together. We will examine each part separately, with special attention to the behavior of the electrons.

THE CAPACITOR

Charging and Discharging a Capacitor. A capacitor consists of two or more metal plates (or conductors) separated by a dielectric (or insulator). A conductor is a substance that permits electrons to flow through it quite easily. An insulator is a substance that does not permit electrons to flow through it readily.

Now obtain a capacitor whose capacitance is about one microfarad (1 μf) and connect it to a 45-volt battery for a few seconds. Disconnect the battery. By means of a piece of wire, connect one plate of the capacitor to the other. You will notice a spark jump from the end of the wire to the second plate of the capacitor just as you are about to touch them together.

This phenomenon is explained as follows: When you connected the battery to the capacitor (Figure 12-3-A), electrons were pumped into plate No. 2 of the capacitor from the negative post of the battery—that is to say, plate No. 2 received a *negative charge*. This negative charge tended to repel electrons from

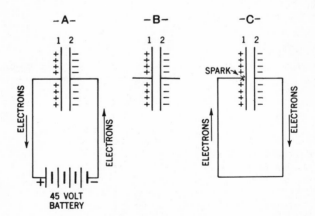

Fig. 12-3. *A—Charging a capacitor.*
B—A charged capacitor.
C—Discharging a capacitor.

plate No. 1. At the same time, the positive post of the battery drew away some of the electrons from plate No. 1 to satisfy its deficiency. Thus, a deficiency was created on plate No. 1 which means that a *positive charge* was placed there. The dielectric prevented the flow of electrons through the capacitor from plate No. 2 to plate No. 1. We call this process, *charging* a capacitor.

When you remove the battery and wires (Figure 12-3-B), the charges remained on the plates of the capacitor because there was no path over which the electrons could flow from the negative to the positive plate. Then you attached a wire to plate No. 2 of the capacitor (Figure 12-3-C). So great was the tendency of the electrons piled up on that plate to get over to plate No. 1 (where there was a deficiency of electrons), that they could not wait for the circuit to be closed, but actually jumped across the small gap just before you touched the end of the wire to plate No. 1. That was the spark you saw. This process is called *discharging* a capacitor.

The Discharge Is Oscillatory. But in their surge to get to plate No. 1, a good many more electrons rushed across than were necessary to make up for the deficiency. As a result, plate No. 1 had an excess of electrons, and plate No. 2 a deficiency of them. The charges were thus reversed. The electrons thereupon surged from plate No. 1 to plate No. 2. Again too many rushed across, and again the charges were reversed. These oscillations continued to become gradually weaker, and finally stopped.

You may understand this better by comparing the motion of the electrons to the behavior of a pendulum (Fig. 12-4). First, consider a pendulum at rest. The weight points straight down. Now raise the weight to one side. The force of gravity tends to bring the weight to its original position. Now release the weight. It rushes back to its original position, but overshoots the mark and swings on to the other side. Gravity thereupon pulls it down again. It rushes back toward the

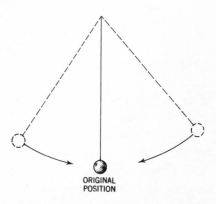

Fig. 12-4. *The movements of this pendulum illustrate oscillatory motion.*

lowest point, but again overshoots its mark. It makes many such swings, each one of less amplitude, before it finally comes to rest with the weight straight down.

The electrons in the capacitor, when discharging across a gap or through a conductor, surge back and forth many times before they come to rest. All this happens in a very small part of a second. We call this swinging of electrons back and forth an *oscillatory discharge*. The capacitance of the capacitor is a factor that determines the rate of oscillations.

SELF-INDUCTION

Our study of induction up to this point has been limited to showing how an electrical current, flowing in one coil, sets up a magnetic field that cuts across the turns of a second coil and causes a current to flow in the second coil. Now let us see what happens in the original coil.

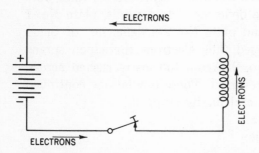

ELECTRONS

ELECTRONS

Fig. 12-5. *This hookup of coil, key, and battery illustrates self-induction.*

Counter Electromotive Force. Suppose you were to hook up a coil (such as your original tuner coil of 90 turns), a battery, and a key as shown in Figure 12-5. At the instant the key is closed, electrons start flowing from the negative post of the battery through the circuit in a counterclockwise direction, as shown by the arrows. The current flow causes a magnetic field to be built up around the coil. This magnetic field, at the instant it is formed, cuts across the turns of the coil itself, and sets up an electrical pressure (emf) in the coil which tends to start a second stream of electrons to flowing in the coil. This second electromotive force is only momentary and always is in a direction which *opposes* the original flow of electrons sent out by the battery. A *counter electromotive force* is said to have been induced in the coil. The effect is to reduce the amount of current which the battery can send through the coil.

After the key has been closed for a while, a steady direct current will flow through the coil. The magnetic field is now stationary. The counter electromotive force lasted only an instant, when the magnetic field was first formed. Now the original flow of electrons from the battery will pass through unhampered.

Self-Induction. As the key is opened, the magnetic field collapses. Again a changing magnetic field will cut across the turns of the coil and again it will induce a counter electromotive force in the coil. This time, the induced electromotive force will be in the original direction of electron flow, that is, counterclockwise. This momentary pressure now acts to oppose the stopping of the electron stream from the battery and thus it tends to keep the electrons flowing through the coil for a short interval of time after the key is opened.

In summary, the motion of electrons set up in the coil by a change in the magnetic field, at the moment the key is closed or opened, will always oppose the action of the battery. The phenomenon described above is known as *self-induction.* The *inductance* of a coil is the direct result of its self-induction. Both the size and the number of turns in a coil (that is, its "electrical size") affect its properties of inductance.

THE TUNING CIRCUIT

Joining the Capacitor and Coil. Now connect your capacitor to the coil. This is the tuning circuit. Let us study the diagram of this circuit in Figure 12-6.

Assume that a negative charge has been placed upon plate A of the capacitor and a positive charge upon plate B. Now the capacitor starts to discharge through the coil. Electrons surge from plate A through the coil, building up a magnetic field around it. The self-induction of the

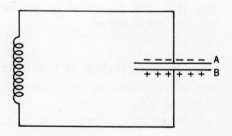

Fig. 12-6. *Tuning circuit, showing a charged capacitor.*

coil develops a counter electromotive force and slows down the number of electrons flowing through it to plate B. As a result of the oscillatory discharge of the capacitor, plate B now becomes a little more negative than plate A. Then the electron flow ceases. At that moment, the magnetic field around the coil collapses and induces an emf which pushes more electrons onto plate B. Thus, plate B becomes even more negative. Again the electron flow comes to a stop.

Then electrons surge from plate B towards plate A, and the situation repeats itself. It is really the electrical sizes of the capacitor and the coil together that determine the rate at which the electrons oscillate in the tuning circuit. Another way of saying this is that the electrical sizes of the capacitor and coil determine the *natural frequency* of the tuning circuit.

The question now arises, where does the capacitor get its charge?

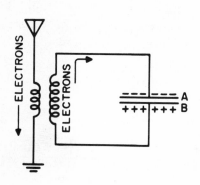

Examine Figure 12-7. You will notice that when electrons are flowing *down* the primary of the antenna coupler, they induce a voltage in the secondary which causes electrons to flow in the tuning circuit in a clockwise direction. This flow causes electrons to pile up on capacitor plate A and a deficiency of electrons results on plate B. Then, for an instant before reversing their direction, the electrons will cease moving in the primary of the antenna coupler. Nevertheless, at this instant, self-induction in the secondary of the coupler continues to pile up electrons on capacitor plate A.

Fig. 12-7. *This diagram shows how the capacitor got its charge.*

When the electron flow in the primary reverses itself, electrons begin to be piled up on plate B of the capacitor. So you see that the flow of electrons in the primary of the antenna coupler sets a stream of electrons oscillating in the tuning circuit. The frequency of this oscillation depends upon the frequency with which the electron flow in the primary reverses itself. This frequency in turn depends upon the frequency of the radio wave.

Resonance in the Tuning Circuit. But we must not forget the other stream of electrons set flowing in the tuning circuit by the discharging of the capacitor (pages 77-78). The frequency of this second oscillation depends, as you have seen, upon the electrical values of the coil and capacitor. Now, if these two sets of oscillations are in step, all is well, and they will work together. But should they be out of step, they will interfere with each other and quickly destroy all flow of electrons. If they are in step, we say that they are in *resonance*. We therefore select the proper values of inductance and capacitance to obtain a natural frequency for our tuning circuit that is in resonance with the frequency of the radio station we desire. Then oscillations caused by that station's wave are built up in our tuning circuit. Signals from stations of different frequencies cause oscillations that are out of step and they die away.

In practice, we usually keep the electrical size of the coil constant and vary the capacitance of the capacitor to place our tuning circuit in resonance with the radio station we wish to receive.

SUMMARY

1. The radio wave, passing across the antenna, starts an alternating current flowing in the antenna-ground system.
2. This alternating current causes a fluctuating magnetic field to be built up around the primary of the antenna coupler.
3. This magnetic field cuts across the loops of the secondary of the antenna coupler and sets an alternating current flowing in the tuning circuit, which is in step with the variations of the current flowing in the antenna-ground system.
4. Tuning is accomplished by the **inductance** of the secondary of the antenna coupler and the **capacitance** of the variable tuning capacitor. When the **natural frequency** of the tuning circuit is the same as the frequency of the alternating currents which the radio wave set flowing in the antenna-ground system, maximum transfer of electrical energy from the antenna-ground system to the tuning circuit takes place, and the oscillations of electrons in the tuning circuit are built up.

GLOSSARY

Capacitor: Two metal plates separated by a dielectric.
Inductance: The property of a coil whereby it tends to keep out a current coming in and, once in, to prevent it from discontinuing—in short, to oppose any current change through it.
Mutual Induction: The method by which electrical energy from one circuit is transferred to another by means of a moving magnetic field.
Oscillation: The movement of electrons back and forth through a circuit.

QUESTIONS AND PROBLEMS

1. What is the relationship between frequency of oscillation of electrons in the antenna-ground system and frequency of oscillation in the tuning circuit of a receiver?
2. Distinguish between an electrical conductor and an insulator. Give examples.
3. Give an electronic explanation (that is, in terms of electrons) of the charging of a capacitor.
4. Give an electronic explanation of the discharge of a capacitor.
5. Describe the chain of events occurring when a voltage (electromotive force) is applied across a coil.
6. Describe the chain of events occurring when the voltage applied across a coil is removed.
7. In what way does the coil of a tuning circuit serve to control the rate of discharge of the capacitor?
8. Give an electronic magnetic-field picture of a tuning circuit, showing how the coil and capacitor control the rate of oscillation of current in the tuning circuit.
9. "The receiver is in resonance with the radio wave." Electronically, what is meant by this statement?
10. Practically, how do we usually place our receiver in resonance with any broadcasting station? How else might we have done it?

13

Electron Flow in the Crystal Detector and Phones

> **PROBLEM 1.** *What are parallel circuits?*
>
> **PROBLEM 2.** *How do electrons behave in going from the tuning circuit to the detector and phones?*

Up to now you have seen a stream of electrons merrily oscillating through the tuning circuit many times each second. Now for the next step, let us see what happens in the detector and the phones of the receiver.

Parallel Circuits. Across the capacitor of the tuning circuit, connect a loop of wire as in Figure 13-1. When a stream of elec-

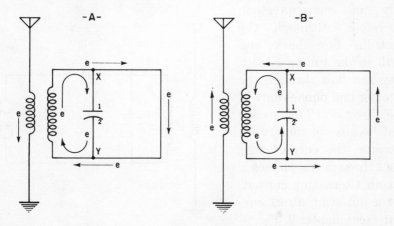

Fig. 13-1. *Parallel circuits. A—Flow of electrons during a half-cycle.*
B—Flow of electrons during the next half-cycle.

trons flows down the primary of the antenna coupler (Fig. 13-1-A), another stream is set flowing in a clockwise direction in the tuning circuit, and electrons are being piled up on plate No. 1 of the capacitor. At point X, however, the path divides, and some of the electrons are also pushed around through the loop of wire in the direction indicated, and back to the main stream at point Y.

Note that there are two paths for the electrons to follow—one through the tuner and the other through the loop of wire across the capacitor. We call a circuit in which the electrons have two or more paths through which they may flow simultaneously a *parallel,* or *shunt,* circuit.

When the flow of current reverses itself in the primary, it also reverses itself in the tuning circuit (Fig. 13-1-B). The stream of electrons divides at point Y, some flowing onto plate No. 2 of the capacitor while others flow through the loop of wire and rejoin the other electrons at point X. In other words, electrons flow through the loop of wire (the parallel circuit) in step with the flow of electrons in the tuning circuit.

The Crystal Detector and Phones in a Parallel Circuit. Now substitute the crystal detector and the phones for the loop of wire (Fig. 13-2). Electrons then tend to flow through the detector and phones in step with the flow of electrons in the tuning circuit.

But hold on! You will remember that the crystal detector acts like an electrical gate, permitting electrons to flow through it only in one direction. Therefore, although the electrons flow back and forth in the tuning circuit, they can flow through the detector and phones only in one direction. This means that because of the crystal detector, the current that flows through the phones is not an alternating current, but a pulsating direct current (see Chapter 9, Fig. 9-10).

The pulses reaching the phones are a series of

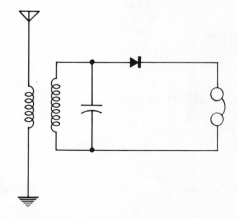

Fig. 13-2. *Diagram showing crystal detector and phones substituted for the loop of wire.*

electron streams, each of very short duration, perhaps one one-millionth of a second or less. Also, the current is direct current—that is, the electrons always move in one direction. You already know that each such electron stream is of too short duration to move the diaphragm of the phones. But when a series or train of such electron streams push together, it can cause the diaphragm to fluctuate, and you can hear a sound. We will investigate how the electrons do this.

Using a Fixed Capacitor across the Phones. Across the phones (in parallel with them), connect a fixed capacitor. As was explained on pages 52-53, the output of the detector is a pulsating direct current with a waveform similar to that shown in Figure 13-3-A below.

As a pulse of current reaches point X (Fig. 13-3-B), it divides, one portion going through the phones and another piling electrons on plate No. 1 of the capacitor. The current flowing through the phones energizes the electromagnet, causing the diaphragm to be drawn in. During the interval between pulses, when no current is flowing, the diaphragm would tend to spring back. During this interval (Fig. 13-3-C), however, the capacitor starts to discharge through the phones from plate No. 1 to plate No. 2,

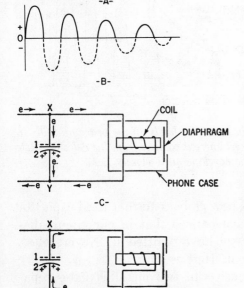

Fig. 13-3. *A—Pulsating direct current output from the detector. The dotted portions of the curve are cut off.*

B—Flow of current through the phones as a pulse comes in.

C—Flow of current through the phones (caused by the discharge of the capacitor) when there is no incoming pulse.

causing current to continue flowing through the phones in the same direction as previously. The effect of the capacitor, then, is to keep direct current flowing continually through the phones, overcoming the tendency of the diaphragm to spring back during the interval of no-current flow from the detector.

You will recall that in Chapter 9, we said that the waveform of the current flowing through the phones can be pictured by drawing a line through the peaks of all the direct-current pulses passing out of the detector; we called this line the *envelope*. Well, strictly speaking, this is not the true picture. Actually, the effect of the capacitor is to level off the peaks of these pulses and fill in the hollows (Fig. 13-4). The curve now presents a continuous line whose fluctuations resemble those of the envelope. Since it is these fluctuations that produce the to-and-fro motion of the diaphragm, the sound coming from the phones is very nearly like the sound first created at the broadcasting station.

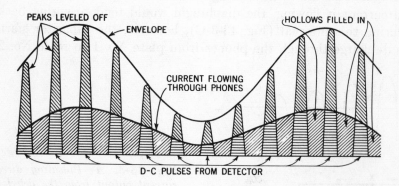

Fig. 13-4. *This graph shows how the capacitor levels off the peaks and fills in the hollows between the pulses of direct current coming from the detector. Note that the resulting curve resembles the envelope quite closely.*

Coils as Capacitors. Let us now go back to that fixed capacitor across the phones. You will have noticed that in our circuit diagrams of the crystal receiver, we have omitted it. Nevertheless, the capacitor was always present. Here is why.

A capacitor, you know, consists of two metallic plates separated by an insulator. In the coil of the phones, we have many turns of copper wire wound next to one another and separated by an insulator. So you see that if we consider two turns of wire next to each other and separated by an insulator, we really have a very small capacitor. Since there are hundreds of such small capacitors in the coil, the total effect is the same as though a large capacitor were connected across the phones. Thus, a coil serves both as an electromagnet and a capacitor at the same time.

In practice, an external capacitor having a capacitance of 0.006 µf is sometimes placed across the phones even though it is not absolutely necessary.

SUMMARY

1. Any electrical device is connected *in parallel* in a circuit when it is one of two or more paths through which some of the current can flow. Devices are said to be *in series* when all of the current must pass through all of the devices one after another.
2. The detector and phones form a parallel path across the tuning circuit.
3. A capacitor across the phones helps to fill in the spaces between the gaps in the pulsating direct current from the detector.
4. In the waveform of current flow from the detector, the *envelope* is a line connecting the peaks of the pulses. The envelope is the waveform of the current that produces the sound in the phones.

GLOSSARY

Parallel Circuit: An electrical circuit in which electrons have two or more paths to follow.
Shunt: One of the paths in a parallel circuit.
Series Circuit: A circuit in which electrons have but one path.

QUESTIONS AND PROBLEMS

1. Draw a dry cell connected to two parallel circuits.
2. Show how electrons behave in a crystal receiver in going through the crystal and phones, the latter being in parallel with the tuning circuit.
3. What is the nature of the current through the phones of a crystal receiver? Indicate it graphically.
4. Describe the action of the fixed capacitor across the phones in the crystal receiver, from an electronic point of view. Why may the capacitor be omitted?
5. What is the rated value of the capacitor placed across the phones?

14

The Vacuum-Tube
Detector—The Diode

PROBLEM 1. *What is meant by the "Edison effect"?*
PROBLEM 2. *What are the principles of a Fleming valve?*
PROBLEM 3. *How may a diode be used as a detector?*

Faults of the Crystal Detector. Having mastered the theory of the crystal receiver, we are now ready to go ahead. If you have constructed the receiver described here and "listened in" on it, you must be aware that the crystal detector has shortcomings. First of all, it is difficult to manipulate. Not every spot will work. You must move the catwhisker about for some time before you touch a spot which enables you to hear radio signals in your phones.

Even after you have found the proper spot, a slight jar may dislodge the fine wire, and the hunt starts over again. Perhaps dirt, grease, or oxidation may spoil the sensitive spot, and you have to start once again.

The Edison Effect. Oddly enough, the first hint as how to improve the detector came in 1883, long before the crystal detector was first used in a radio receiver. In that year, Thomas A. Edison was experimenting with filaments for his new invention, the electric light bulb. He placed a filament in a glass bulb and then exhausted the air, creating a vacuum. By means of an electric current, he heated the filament until it glowed brightly and produced light.

He soon observed an undesirable feature about his bulbs. After a short time, a black substance was deposited on the inside of the glass, interfering with the light given out. In an attempt to eliminate this deposit on the glass, he inserted a metal plate. Now, this plate did not help much, but one day he connected a delicate electric meter between the plate and the positive end of the filament. To his amazement, the meter showed that a small electric current was flowing through the circuit. He did not know why this current should flow, and he merely jotted down this strange fact in his notebook and forgot about it.

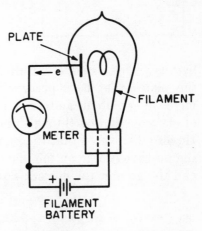

Today, we know why this current flows. When a filament is heated to incandescence (when it becomes hot enough to give off light), it shoots off streams of electrons. This behavior is known as the *Edison effect,* or *thermionic effect,* of a filament heated to incandescence.

These electrons given off by the hot filament collect on the cool plate and, if a path is furnished for them, they will flow

Fig. 14-1. *A diagram of Edison's experiment.*

along this path toward the filament. The meter in that path shows that electrons are flowing.

The Fleming Value. As we stated, this discovery of Edison's was made in 1883. At that time, the electron theory was not known. But in 1904, J. Ambrose Fleming, an Englishman, who understood the flow of the current in terms of electrons, decided to experiment a bit. To depend upon the electrons piling up on the cool plate, thought Fleming, is too slow. Suppose we were to create an actual deficiency of electrons on the plate by placing a positive charge on it, wouldn't that attract still more electrons from the filament? Fleming connected a battery in the circuit from the plate to the filament, in such a way that the positive post of the battery was connected to the plate (Fig. 14-2). He also connected another battery to the filament to heat it to incandescence. Note that this filament battery is not in the plate circuit.

By this arrangement, some of the electrons of the plate were pulled away to satisfy the deficiency at the positive post of the

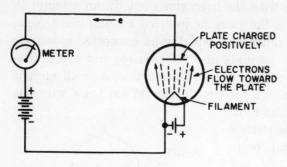

Fig. 14-2. *Fleming's experiment with a positive charge on the plate of the tube. The meter showed that an electric current was flowing through it.*

battery. This removal resulted in a deficiency of electrons on the plate—that is, a positive charge. Fleming now connected a meter in the circuit and, as he had expected, a much greater stream of electrons flowed through than before the battery was attached. He also discovered that the more powerful the battery, the greater the positive charge on the plate, the more electrons were attracted, and the greater the current flow through the meter.

Fig. 14-3. *Fleming's experiment with a negative charge on the plate of the tube. The meter showed that no electric current was flowing through it.*

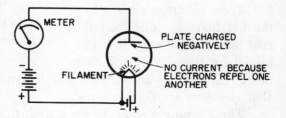

Now Fleming reversed the connection to the battery and observed that the meter showed no current. The explanation is that this time the battery piled electrons onto the plate (gave it a negative charge), and electrons repel one another. Hence the stream of electrons from the filament was repelled from the plate and, therefore, no current flowed through the meter (Fig. 14-3).

Effects of the Fleming Valve on an Alternating Current. By means of an alternating-current generator, Fleming now replaced the direct current of the battery with an alternating current. The symbol for the alternating-current generator is

When the proper instruments were attached and the meter reading taken, Fleming now observed that the current flowing through the meter was direct, not alternating. The explanation (Fig. 14-4) is as follows: During the positive half of the alternating-current cycle, the plate received a positive charge. This charge caused electrons from the heated filament to be attracted to the plate, and a current flowed in the circuit as registered on the meter. During the negative half of the alter-

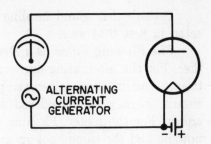

Fig. 14-4. *Fleming's experiment with an alternating-current generator connected to the plate of the tube. Electric current flowed through the meter only during the positive half of the alternating-current cycle.*

nating-current cycle, the plate received a negative charge. This charge repelled the electrons from the filament, and the meter showed that no current was flowing. The effect of this action upon the graph of the waveform is shown in Figure 14-5. Only a pulsating direct current is passing through the meter.

Here, then, is an electrical *gate* or *valve* that will permit current to flow only in one direction. As a matter of fact, the early radio tubes were all called *valves,* and still are in England.

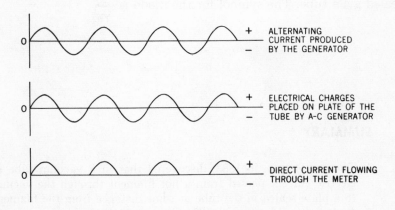

Fig. 14-5. *This graph shows the effect of connecting an alternating-current generator to the plate of Fleming's tube.*

Doesn't this sound familiar? Of course! The crystal detector acted in just that way.

The Fleming Valve as a Detector. Fleming went one step further. For the alternating-current generator, he substituted a radio tuning circuit. Since alternating current flows out of the tuning circuit, it may be considered a sort of alternating-current generator. For the meter, Fleming substituted a pair of phones, and now he had the same hookup as our old receiving set, but, with a new kind of detector (the tube) to replace the crystal (Fig. 14-6).

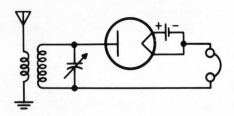

Fig. 14-6. *A radio receiving set that uses a Fleming valve as a detector.*

Why the Fleming Valve Is Called a **Diode.** This type of detector is known as a *Fleming valve*. Because it has two electrodes, the filament and plate, it is also known as a *diode* (*di* means *two;* *-ode* means *pole*). It is easier to operate than a crystal because there is no need to hunt for a sensitive spot. Further, you cannot disturb it by jarring; and no dirt, grease, or air can get inside the sealed glass tube. The symbol for the diode is

SUMMARY

1. Thomas Edison, in 1883, discovered that in a vacuum tube an electric current passed from a hot filament through the vacuum to a plate sealed in the tube at some distance from the filament.
2. J. Ambrose Fleming in 1904 discovered that the current was increased in an Edison tube when the plate was made positive, and ceased when the plate was made negative.

3. The diode or Fleming valve depends upon the principle that alternating currents fed to the plate are changed to direct currents because only during the positive half of an alternating-current cycle are the electrons attracted from the filament to the plate.

GLOSSARY

Diode: A two-electrode tube containing a plate and filament.
Fleming Valve: A tube (valve) used as a detector.
Thermionic Effect: The throwing off of electrons by a body when it is heated to incandescence.
Valve: A tube with a filament and plate which will allow current through it only in one direction.

SYMBOLS

   A-C generator.

   Diode.

QUESTIONS AND PROBLEMS

1. List the defects of a crystal as a detector.
2. Describe Edison's early experiment on vacuum tubes.
3. Why did a current flow from the plate to the filament in Edison's electric light bulb when the two were connected externally? What is the thermionic effect?
4. How did Fleming make use of the Edison effect?
5. What action takes place in the diode tube containing the filament and plate when the plate is made negative?
6. Draw a graph showing the resulting effect when an alternating-current sine voltage is impressed on the plate of Fleming's valve.
7. In what way are the crystal detector and the Fleming valve alike?
8. What is the advantage of the diode over the crystal as a detector?
9. Draw the circuit of a one-tube receiver using the Fleming valve as a detector.

The Vacuum-Tube Detector—The Triode

> **PROBLEM 1.** *What did De Forest contribute to radio?*
>
> **PROBLEM 2.** *By what principles does the grid function?*
>
> **PROBLEM 3.** *How is the grid maintained with the proper negative charge?*
>
> **PROBLEM 4.** *How may we control volume in a one-tube receiver?*

Soon after Fleming's diode tube appeared, in 1907, an American inventor, Lee De Forest, undertook to carry further some ideas suggested by one of Fleming's experiments. De Forest knew that when Fleming placed a positive charge on the plate of his tube by means of a battery connected between the plate and filament (Fig. 14-2), a much greater electric current flowed through the meter than when there was no such charge. Further, the greater the positive charge on the plate, the greater the flow through the meter. (Actually, this did not go on forever. After the positive charge reached a certain value, placing a greater positive charge on the plate had no further effect.)

A *and* B *Batteries.* The circuit traveled by the electrons—starting from the filament of the tube and going across the vacuum in a stream to the plate and back again to the filament by way of the path provided by the meter, battery, and wire—is known as the *plate circuit*. The battery used to place a positive charge on the plate is known as the *plate battery*, or *B battery*. The battery used to heat the filament is known as the *filament battery*, or *A battery* (Fig. 15-1).

Experiments of Lee De Forest. Now, thought De Forest, if we could only use the advantages of the B battery and substitute our phones for the meter, we would get a much louder signal in our phones, because the greater the current flowing through the phones, the greater is the magnetic pull of the coil. Greater magnetic pull means that the diaphragm is bent more, the air is set

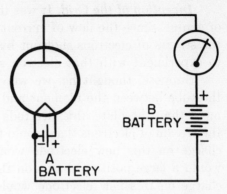

Fig. 15-1. *Diode using a B battery to place a positive charge on the plate of the tube. Current flows through the meter.*

moving more violently, and a louder signal results.

At this point, however, a serious difficulty arose. The large current through the phones must be a direct current that fluctuates in step with the fluctuations of the incoming signal. De Forest quickly discovered that the small charges placed on the plate of the Fleming valve by the alternating current from the tuning circuit were undetectable in the presence of the relatively enormous positive charge placed on the plate by the B battery. Try as he would, De Forest could not utilize the advantages of a B battery in the diode tube (Fig. 15-2).

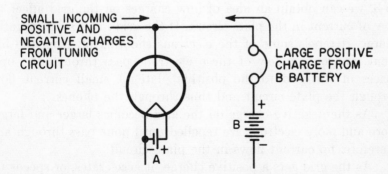

Fig. 15-2. *This diagram shows how the weak positive and negative charges placed on the plate of the diode are overwhelmed by the large positive charge placed on the same plate by the B battery.*

Invention of the Grid. It was then that De Forest had a stroke of genius. Since the flow of current in the plate circuit starts with the stream of electrons shot out by the heated filament, he began to experiment with that electron stream.

Suppose, thought he, we were to place another electrode in the tube between the filament and plate. Being closer to the filament than the plate, this electrode would have a greater effect on the stream of electrons than would the plate. Thus, a small positive charge on this new electrode would pull over electrons just as would a large positive charge on the plate. Also, a small negative charge on this new electrode would repel some of the stream of electrons, and thus a comparatively small number of electrons would reach the plate. When few electrons reach the plate, a very small current flows in the plate circuit. Here, then, thought De Forest, is a method for controlling the flow of current in the plate circuit by means of small charges on the new electrode.

But hold on! Further reasoning and experimenting convinced De Forest that when this new electrode was given a positive charge, it pulled over electrons as expected, but that these electrons went to this new electrode, and none found their way to the plate. After more experiments, De Forest eventually met this difficulty by making the new electrode in the form of a mesh of very fine wire, a *grid*. Since most of the grid consisted of open space, most of the electrons pulled over by a positive charge on the grid now shot through these open spaces and continued right on to the plate. The grid was the solution to his problem.

How the Grid Works. By study of the diagrams in Figure 15-3, we can obtain an idea of how charges on the grid affect the flow of current in the plate circuit. If the grid has a small negative charge, it repels some of the electrons shooting off from the filament, and only a few of these electrons pass through the open spaces of the grid to the positive plate. A small current flows through the plate circuit and thus through the phones.

As the negative charge on the grid becomes larger and larger, more and more electrons are repelled until none pass through and, therefore, no current flows in the plate circuit.

As the grid gets a positive charge, it accelerates, or speeds up, the flow of electrons from the heated filament to the plate. The pull of the grid is now added to the pull of the plate. Most of the electron stream goes through the open work of the grid to the

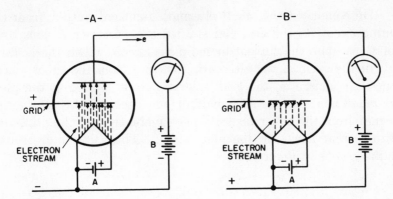

Fig. 15-3. *A—This diagram shows how a positive charge on the grid of De Forest's tube helps pull electrons from the heated filament to the plate. The meter shows that an electron current is flowing through it.*

B—Diagram of the effect of a negative charge on the grid. Since most of the electrons from the heated filament are repelled, few or none reach the plate. The meter shows that only a very small current is flowing through it.

plate. The more positive the grid becomes, the greater the pull it exerts on the electrons; consequently, more electrons reach the plate, and the plate current is greater.

How the Triode Works. Since charges on the grid control the flow of electrons from the filament, we are able to control the flow of the large plate currents by means of a small charge on the grid. And this is just what De Forest set out to do (Fig. 15-4).

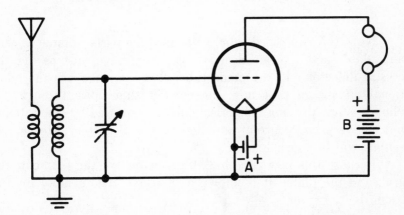

Fig. 15-4. *This diagram shows how alternating current from the tuning circuit places positive and negative charges on the grid of De Forest's tube.*

He connected the small alternating-current output from the tuning circuit to the grid and studied the effects of various combinations upon the current in the plate circuit. When the positive half of the cycle of the alternating current from the tuner placed a positive charge on the grid, a large current flowed in the plate circuit. When the negative half of the cycle of the alternating current from the tuner placed a negative charge on the grid, very little current flowed in the plate circuit. These effects are shown by the graphs in Figure 15-5.

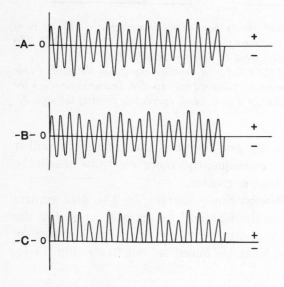

Fig. 15-5. *Graph of the flow of electric current in various parts of the triode circuit.*

A—Alternating current flowing from the tuning circuit.

B—Positive and negative charges placed on the grid of De Forest's tube by the alternating current from the tuner.

C—Fluctuating direct current flowing through the meter.

Now, the remodeled tube, with its three parts—filament, grid, and plate—acts like an electrical gate, or valve, just as did the crystal detector and the diode tube. But this tube has the additional advantage that now the current that flows through the phones is not the small electrical current captured by the antenna but the very large current supplied by the B battery. Hence, our signals will be much louder.

Because this new tube has three elements—the filament, the grid, and the plate—it is known as a *triode*. The symbol for the triode is ⏚ or ⏚

Schematic Diagrams Show Tube Circuits. Look at the diagram in Figure 15-4. You will note a number of paths, or circuits, through which electrons may flow. There is the *antenna-ground system* or *circuit.* There is also the *tuning circuit,* consisting of the secondary of the antenna coupler and the variable capacitor. Then there is the *filament circuit* consisting of the A battery and the filament. There is the *plate circuit* consisting of the filament, the stream of electrons within the tube from the filament to the plate, the plate, the phones, the B battery, and the conductor leading back to the filament.

Finally there is the *grid circuit.* This path consists of the filament, the streams of electrons from the filament to the grid, the grid, the tuning circuit, and the conductor leading back to the filament. Just as current will flow through the plate circuit only when there is a positive charge on the plate, so current will flow through the grid circuit only when there is a positive charge on the grid.

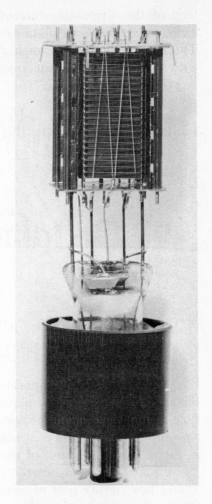

Fig. 15-6. *Cutaway view of the triode.*

Note that all these circuits have a common connection to the ground by means of a wire between the primary and secondary of the antenna coupler. This makes for a more stable receiver without introducing the resistance of the antenna-ground system into the tuning circuit.

Electrons Pass Through a Weak Negative Charge on the Grid. You may have noticed a difficulty by now. In the diode, the bottom loop of the alternating-current cycle was completely cut off because the moment our plate went negative, all plate current ceased. The current flowing through the phones then fluctuated in step with the variations of the envelope, and the signal was faithfully reproduced (Fig. 15-7).

-A- 0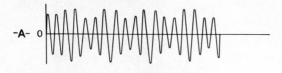

ENVELOPE

-B- 0

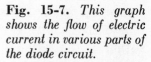

CURRENT FLOWING
IN PHONES

-C- 0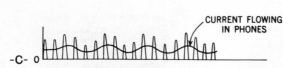

Fig. 15-7. This graph shows the flow of electric current in various parts of the diode circuit.

A—Alternating current flowing from the tuning circuit.

B—Pulsating direct current flowing in the plate circuit.

C—Fluctuating direct current flowing through the phones. Notice how closely these fluctuations follow the fluctuations of the envelope in part B of this figure.

But in the triode, connected as in Figure 15-4, the stream of electrons from the heated filament to the plate would continue to flow, even though the grid were slightly negative. In fact, this flow of electrons would continue until the grid gained a fairly high negative charge, because of the relatively high positive charge on the plate. Thus, plate current, and current through our phones, would flow during part of each negative cycle. In Figure 15-8-C, we see that the graph of the current flowing through the phones does not correspond to the shape of the envelope. The practical effect is that our signal in the phones is distorted.

The Use of a C Battery. Here is how this difficulty was overcome. A small negative charge was placed on the grid by means of a battery. This charge was made too small to cut off all the electrons streaming from the heated filament to the plate. Now the alternating current from the tuner was fed into the grid of the tube (Fig. 15-9).

When the positive half-cycle of the current from the tuner flowed onto the grid, it reduced the negative charge placed there originally. This reduction meant that fewer electrons from the

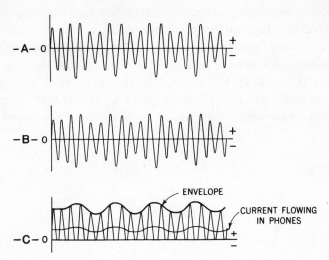

Fig. 15-8. *These graphs show the flow of electric current in various parts of the triode circuit.*

A—Alternating current flowing from the tuning circuit.

B—Positive and negative charges placed on the grid of the triode by that alternating current from the tuner.

C—Fluctuating direct current flowing in the plate circuit. Notice that the current flowing in the phones is very nearly a steady direct current quite different from the fluctuations of the envelope. This current will cause either no sound, or a distortion of the signal will be heard in the phones.

filament were repelled and more of them reached the plate. This greater flow in turn meant a larger plate current.

When, during the negative half-cycle, electrons from the tuner flowed onto the grid, this current, by itself, could not place a negative charge on the grid great enough to cut off completely the flow of electrons to the plate. But if this charge were added to the negative charge we originally placed on the grid by means of the

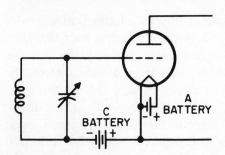

Fig. 15-9. *This diagram shows how a C battery is connected to place a negative charge, or bias, on the grid of the triode. The completed diagram would include earphones and B battery connected as shown in Fig. 15-4.*

battery, then they would be able to stop the flow of electrons, and thus to stop the flow of the plate current.

Now, you can see, practically no current will flow in the plate circuit during the negative half-cycle of the current from the tuner. Just as in the case of the diode, the fluctuations in the current flowing through our phones correspond to the shape of the envelope and, once again, our signal is faithfully reproduced (Fig. 15-10).

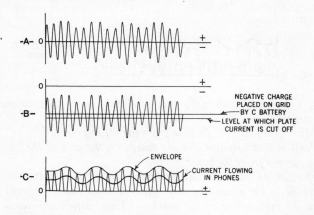

Fig. 15-10. *These graphs show the effects of placing a steady negative charge, or bias, on the grid of the triode.*

A—Alternating current flowing from the tuning circuit.

B—A steady negative charge, or bias, makes the grid negative. The positive half-cycle of the current from the tuner makes the charge on the grid less negative. The negative half-cycle of the current from the tuner makes the charge on the grid more negative, to the point where the flow of current in the plate circuit is cut off.

C—Fluctuating direct current flowing in the plate circuit. Notice that now the current flowing in the phones resembles the envelope.

We place this constant negative charge on the grid by connecting a small battery in the grid circuit in such a way that the negative post of the battery is hooked up to the grid.

This battery is called a *C battery,* or *grid-bias battery.* It must be of such a size that, by itself, it cannot cut off the flow of electrons from the heated filament to the plate, but when added to the negative charge of the current flowing from the tuning circuit, it can do so. The size of this battery differs for different types of tubes. Each tube manufacturer supplies data to show how large this battery should be.

The C Battery May Be Replaced by a Capacitor. While the C battery is effective in placing a negative charge on the grid of the triode, it wears out in time, and we are faced with the nuisance of periodically replacing it. Accordingly, another method was evolved to accomplish the same result without the use of the battery—a small fixed capacitor was placed in the grid circuit as in Figure 15-11.

Here is how it works. When the negative half-cycle of the alternating current from the tuning circuit reaches plate No. 1 of the capacitor, as shown in Figure 15-12-A, it places a negative charge on that plate. This charge drives

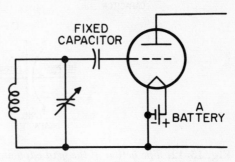

Fig. 15-11. *This diagram shows how a fixed capacitor is connected to place a negative charge, or bias, on the grid of the triode.*

off some of the electrons from plate No. 2 of the capacitor. These electrons seek to get as far away as possible from the negative charge. As a result, they are driven onto the grid of the tube. Here they remain, because the grid is cold and, therefore, cannot shoot off any electrons. Thus, the grid gets a negative charge. But this charge is too small to stop entirely the flow of electrons from the heated filament to the plate.

During the positive half-cycle of the alternating current from the tuner, a positive charge is placed on plate No. 1 of the capacitor (Fig. 15-12-B). The electrons on the grid now are attracted back to plate No. 2. This movement leaves the grid with a positive charge, and most of the electrons shot out by the heated filament of the tube rush to the plate of the tube. It should be noted, however, that some of these electrons strike the positively charged wires of the grid and are pulled over to plate No. 2 of the capacitor.

During the next (negative) half-cycle, electrons are again piled up on plate No. 1 of the capacitor (Fig. 15-12-C). Once again electrons stream away from plate No. 2 to the grid. This time, however, there are more electrons on the grid. The electrons

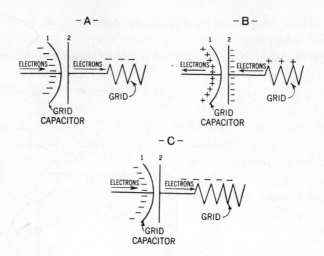

Fig. 15-12. *The action of the grid capacitor.*

A—A negative charge is placed on plate No. 1 of the capacitor by current from the tuning circuit.

B—A positive charge is placed on plate No. 1 of the capacitor by current from the tuning circuit.

C—Another negative charge is placed on plate No. 1 of the capacitor by current from the tuning circuit.

that were collected by the grid from the stream shot out by the filament during the positive half-cycle have been trapped and cannot get away. So this time the grid has a larger negative charge.

As this process goes on, a larger and larger negative charge is collected by the grid. You see, we now have the same effect as when we placed a C battery in the grid circuit.

The Function of the Grid Leak. But this process must not be permitted to go on indefinitely. Soon there will be accumulated upon the grid enough electrons to completely stop any electrons from reaching the plate of the tube. Since the electrons are trapped there, the action of the tube will be completely blocked and no signal can get through.

Fig. 15-13. *Fixed resistor.*

A method had to be worked out, therefore, to permit some of these electrons to flow off. A path was provided across the capacitor, so that when a positive charge was placed on plate No. 1, some of these trapped electrons could flow across to that plate. Provision had to be made so that not all of these trapped electrons could escape, for that would destroy the effectiveness of the capacitor. Only enough of them should be permitted to leak off so that the action of the tube would not be blocked.

To provide this path, a *resistor* is connected across the capacitor. A resistor is a substance that retards the flow of electrons through it. It is usually made of a special type of wire such as nichrome or of certain substances such as carbon. The greater the resistance, the fewer the electrons that can flow through it. The symbol for a resistor is: -⋁⋁⋁-.

In Figure 15-14, you have the diagram of a receiving set using a triode as a detector. The tube used is a type called 1H5-GT.* This tube requires an A or filament battery of 1½ volts. The B or plate battery is 22½ or 45 volts. The capacitor used in the grid circuit is called a *grid capacitor*. This capacitor usually uses mica as a dielectric, and its value is 0.00025 μf.

Across this capacitor is the resistor which furnishes the path by means of which the excess electrons *leak* off the grid. Quite naturally, it is called a *grid leak*. The unit for measuring resistance is the *ohm*. The value of the grid leak is 2,000,000 ohms, or 2 megohms, the prefix *meg* meaning a million.

Fig. 15-14. *Diagram of the complete receiving set, using the triode as a detector. The symbol 2 MEG. over the grid leak stands for 2 megohms. The symbol 30 Ω over the rheostat stands for 30 ohms.*

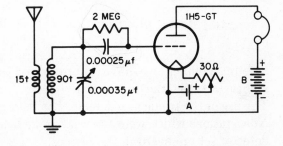

Volume Control. In the filament circuit, between the A battery and one end of the filament, you will notice a device shown by the symbol -⋁⋀- or -⋁⋁⋁- . This is the symbol for a variable resistor, or a *rheostat*, which consists of a length of resistance material, usually wire, over which slides a movable contact. This

* Filament-type triodes are fast becoming obsolete. The type 1H5-GT tube used here actually contains a triode and a diode in the same envelope. (Multiunit tubes are discussed further in Chapter 27.) However, only the triode unit is used here.

rheostat controls the amount of current that can flow from the A battery to the filament. The resistance offered by this rheostat can be made greater or less by increasing or decreasing the length of wire through which the current must pass. This variation in length is produced by a sliding contact or by a switch moving over contact points connected to various points on the wire. Since the more current flowing through the filament, the hotter it gets, this rheostat controls the heat of the filament. The hotter the filament, the more electrons it shoots off. The rheostat, therefore, controls the quantity of electrons shot off by the filament.

Fig. 15-15. *Rheostat.*

The more electrons hitting the plate, the greater the plate current; the greater the plate current, the greater the current through the phones and the louder the volume of the signal. So you see that this rheostat finally controls the volume of the signal. As you have probably guessed, this rheostat is called a *volume control.* Its value is about 30 ohms.

Our receiving set, now, is quite an improvement over the one shown in Figure 8-3. By means of an antenna coupler, we have improved its *selectivity*—that is, the ability to select the radio station desired and to reject all others. The use of the triode as a detector has increased the set's *sensitivity.* Now stations which were too weak to be heard on a crystal or diode detector set are heard in the phones.

SUMMARY

1. Lee De Forest, an American, devised the **triode** tube.
2. The principle of the triode is that a third element, called a **grid,** is placed in the vacuum tube between the filament and plate.

3. The grid, when charged positively, aids electrons to flow through it to the plate, but retards the flow of electrons when it is charged negatively.
4. By means of a C *battery* or by means of a *capacitor* and *grid leak,* the grid may be given a negative charge of the right amount.
5. For a detector, this right amount of negative charge is that charge which will not prevent electrons going from the filament to the plate during the positive half of an alternating-current cycle, but will prevent them during the negative half of the alternating-current cycle.
6. The heat of the filament, and hence the volume of the signal, is controlled by a variable resistor or rheostat.

GLOSSARY

A *Battery:* The battery used to heat the tube's filament; also known as the *filament battery.*
B *Battery:* The battery used to place a positive charge on the plate of the tube. Also known as the *plate battery.*
C *Battery:* The battery used to place a fixed negative charge or bias on the grid of the tube. Also known as the *grid-bias battery.*
Circuit, Filament: The path of electrons from the A battery, through the filament, and back to the A battery.
Circuit, Grid: The path of electrons from the filament to the grid of the tube, through connecting wires and electrical apparatus, and back to the filament.
Circuit, Plate: The path of electrons from the filament to the plate of the tube, through connecting wires and electrical apparatus, and back to the filament.
Grid: An open-mesh metal screen, placed between the plate and the filament of the tube, that controls the stream of electrons going from the filament to the plate.
Grid bias: The fixed negative charge placed on the grid of the tube.
Grid Capacitor: A small fixed capacitor placed in the grid circuit of the tube and used to hand on the electrical energy from the tuning circuit. This capacitor also blocks the flow of electrons, accumulated on the grid, through the grid circuit.
Grid Leak: A resistor placed across the grid capacitor to provide a slight path, or leak, for the electrons accumulated on the grid of the tube.
Meg-: A prefix meaning 1,000,000.
Ohm: The unit in which we measure the resistance to the flow of electrons.
Rheostat: A variable resistor.

Selectivity: The ability of a tuner to select one radio station signal and reject all others.

Sensitivity: The ability of a radio receiver to respond to radio waves of very low strength.

Triode: A three-electrode tube containing a filament, grid, and plate.

Volume Control: A resistance device, usually a rheostat, which controls the volume of the radio signal coming out of the earphones or loudspeaker.

SYMBOLS

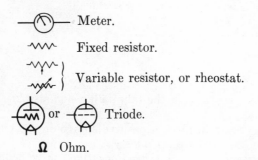

—⊗— Meter.

-\/\/\- Fixed resistor.

Variable resistor, or rheostat.

or Triode.

Ω Ohm.

QUESTIONS AND PROBLEMS

1. Up to a certain saturation point, what is the effect of placing a higher positive voltage on the plate of a diode tube?
2. Why can a B battery not be used with a diode detector receiver?
3. How does the grid control the current flowing from the filament to the plate in a triode tube?
4. Impress an alternating voltage on the grid of a triode tube used as a detector, and make a graph of the current in the plate circuit.
5. Describe the construction of a triode.
6. Why should a triode detector be capable of giving louder signals in a receiver than a diode detector?
7. What effect results when a positive voltage is placed on the grid of a triode detector with C-battery bias?
8. What purpose does the C battery serve? What is the C battery said to give the grid?
9. In what manner does the proper grid bias enable the triode to act as a detector?

10. What is the disadvantage of using a C battery for a grid bias?
11. Explain the operation of a grid leak and grid capacitor in making the triode act as a detector.
12. What is the function of a rheostat in the filament circuit? Explain how it carries out this function.
13. Draw the circuit of a one-tube receiver using a triode as a detector and using a C battery as a grid bias.
14. Repeat the above, using a grid leak and grid capacitor for grid bias.

16

The Regenerative Detector

> PROBLEM 1. *What are the principles of the regenerative system in the detector?*
>
> PROBLEM 2. *How are the faults of this system corrected?*
>
> PROBLEM 3. *How can we build a practical receiving set with a feedback system?*

At this point in the development of the science of radio, there arose a tremendous desire for increased sensitivity in the receiving sets. The thrill of hearing a faraway radio station entranced amateur and professional alike. The hue and cry was for more *DX* (long-distance) reception.

The Feedback Circuit. This demand was satisfied by giving a new twist to the triode detector receiving set. We now call this device the *regenerative,* or *feedback, circuit.* Here is how it works.

When we considered the tuning circuit, you learned that there were two streams of electrons oscillating through that circuit in step with each other. One was the stream set flowing by the discharge of the tuning capacitor. The other was the stream set flowing by mutual induction from the antenna-ground system.

Theoretically, the oscillations of the electrons in the tuning circuit should have continued to build up, or gain, in strength indefinitely. You may see this if you were to consider a man pushing a swing. The first push starts the swing going. Each successive push, though no greater than the first, makes the swing travel further and further, or, we may say, the swinging is *built up.* So the successive pulses from the antenna-ground system should build up the oscillations of the electrons in the tuning circuit.

Actually, however, the resistance in the circuit limited the degree to which these oscillations could be built up. So you see there are two reasons for reducing the resistance against current flow in the tuning circuit. One reason, as you know, is to make our set more selective. The other reason is to build up the oscillations of electrons. With less resistance, a greater current will flow and continue to oscillate in the tuning circuit for a longer time; and, therefore, a weak impulse from a distant station will be built up to the point where we can hear it in our phones.

Try as we may, however, we cannot completely eliminate the resistance from our circuit. A certain minimum will always remain. This minimum can be made small enough so that it does not interfere with the selectivity of the set, but it will always remain large enough to limit the degree to which we can build up the oscillations in the tuning circuit.

An American scientist, Major E. H. Armstrong, conceived the idea of causing a third stream of electrons to flow in the tuning circuit in step with the other two. This third stream supplied the electrical energy to overcome the resistance in the circuit, and now the oscillations could build up to a very high degree.

He accomplished this by causing the plate current to flow through a coil of wire, called a *plate coil* or *tickler* (Fig. 16-1). This plate coil was placed in close proximity to the secondary of the antenna coupler. When the plate current flowed through the plate coil, a magnetic field was created around this coil. This field cut across the turns of the secondary of the antenna coupler and

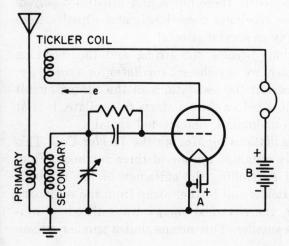

Fig. 16-1. *This diagram shows how plate current is fed back to the tuning circuit by means of the tickler coil.*

set a stream of electrons flowing in the tuning circuit just as did the primary of the antenna coupler.

So you see, energy from the plate circuit has been *fed back* to the tuning circuit. The fluctuating direct current flowing through the tickler coil sets up an alternating voltage that causes current to flow in the secondary of the antenna coupler by transformer action, thereby building up the oscillations (Fig. 10-3-A). Since the variations in the plate current were produced by the variations of current flowing in the tuner, the two currents are in step. This arrangement of the three coils is sometimes called a *three-circuit tuner*. However, the oscillations of electrons in the tuning circuit now are built up so well that another problem presents itself.

The Receiver Becomes a Transmitter. It was stated in Chapter 3 that if electrical pulses are sent through a circuit 10,000 times or oftener per second, a radio wave is created. Here, now, electrical pulses are being sent through the tuning circuit tens of thousands and perhaps millions of times per second. Under normal conditions, the oscillations of electrons in the tuning circuit are too weak to cause any damage. But now, because the resistance of the tuning circuit has been overcome, these oscillations are built up to a point where a strong radio wave is created, and our receiving set becomes a transmitting station.

This radio wave interferes with the incoming signal and causes clicks, whistles, and howls to be heard in our phones. Some of you may remember the early days of the regenerative receiver. You may remember how frequently these howls and whistles occurred. And you may remember receiving these howls and whistles from receiving sets as far away as several streets!

When the oscillations become too strong and the receiving set becomes a transmitter, we say the set *oscillates,* or *spills over.* The trick, then, is to permit the oscillations in the tuning circuit to build up to a point just before the set starts to oscillate. It is at this point that we get our loudest, undistorted signal.

Controlling the Oscillations by Moving the Tickler Coil. This limiting effect is usually obtained by one of three methods. First, there is the method of controlling the efficiency of the feedback action. If we place the tickler coil further away from the secondary of the antenna coupler, the electrical energy transmitted by mutual induction becomes smaller. This means that a smaller stream of electrons is set flowing in the tuning circuit. The trick is to set a stream of electrons flowing which will just fail to overcome the resistance of the tuning circuit. It is this excess resistance that will prevent the oscillations from being built up too much.

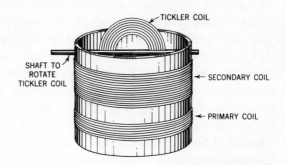

Fig. 16-2. *Three-circuit tuner showing the arrangement to vary the coupling between the secondary coil and the tickler coil.*

The same effect is obtained by changing the angle which the tickler coil makes with the secondary of the antenna coupler. When the two coils are parallel, you get the maximum feedback. When the two coils are at right angles, you get the minimum feedback. By making the angle adjustable, you are able to get the desired amount of feedback. When we use these methods of controlling the

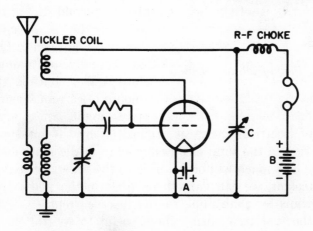

Fig. 16-3. *Three-circuit tuner using the variable capacitor (C) to control the amount of feedback. The inductor marked* R-F Choke *is a small coil of wire used to force some of the plate energy through C.*

feedback we say that we vary the *coupling* between the two coils.

Controlling the Oscillations by Means of a Variable Capacitor.
Another method is to utilize a *variable capacitor* connected as
shown in Figure 16-3. Now some of the electrical energy flowing
in the plate circuit is used up to place a charge on this capacitor.
This means that there is less electrical energy left to be fed back
to the tuning circuit. By varying the size of the capacitor, you can
vary the amount of electrical energy drained away, and thus control the amount of energy to be fed back to the tuning circuit. The
variable capacitor used is usually the same size as the one used in
the tuning circuit. The inductor marked *R-F Choke* (radio-frequency choke coil) is a small coil of wire which hinders, or impedes, the varying flow of electrons to the phones, and thus forces
some of these electrons onto the variable capacitor used to control
the feedback.

Fig. 16-4. *Radio-frequency choke coil.*

**Using a Fixed Capacitor
and a Rheostat to Control the
Feedback.** The third method is
to substitute a *fixed capacitor,*
whose value is usually about
0.00025 μf, for the variable capacitor described above. We now
control the amount of electrical
energy fed back to the tuner by
placing our old friend, the *rheostat,* in the plate circuit, as
shown in Figure 16-5. This rheostat, usually of about 50,000
ohms value, controls the total
amount of current flowing in the
plate circuit. Since a constant

amount of electrical energy is drained off by the fixed capacitor,
the variation in the total electrical energy in the plate circuit will
determine how much will be fed back to the tuner. Since, by means
of the rheostat, we can vary the current in the plate circuit, we
have a means for controlling the feedback current.

Another variation, using the rheostat to control the amount
of feedback, is merely to place a 50,000-ohm rheostat across the
tickler coil as in Figure 16-6. Now the current flowing in the plate
circuit has two paths to follow. Part of the current flows from the

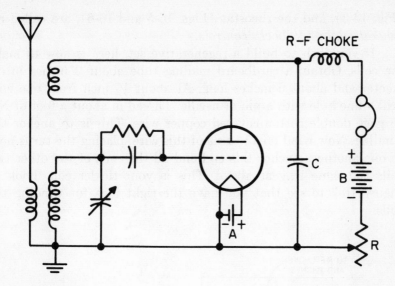

Fig. 16-5. *Three-circuit tuner using a fixed capacitator (C) of about 0.00025 μf and a rheostat (R) of about 50,000 ohms to control the amount of feedback.*

plate, through the rheostat, and into the phones. None of this current is fed back to the tuner. The rest goes through the tickler coil and is fed back to the tuning circuit. The greater the resistance of the rheostat, the less current can flow through it and the more current flows through the tickler coil; and therefore, the more electrical energy is fed back. Thus, by varying the resistance by means of the rheostat, you can vary the amount of feedback.

Building a Regenerative Receiver. These three controls of feedback—the coupling control (Fig. 16-2), the variable capacitor

Fig. 16-6. *Three-circuit tuner using a rheostat (R) of about 50,000 ohms to vary the amount of feedback.*

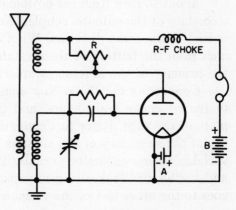

(Fig. 16-3), and the rheostat (Figs. 16-5 and 16-6), are called *regenerative,* or *feedback, controls.*

If you wish to build a regenerative set, here is how to make the coils. Obtain a cardboard mailing tube about 2 inches in diameter and about 6 inches long. At about ½ inch from one end, drill a fine hole with a pin or needle. Thread in about a foot of No. 28 gage double cotton-covered copper wire. This is to anchor the winding. Now wind on 15 turns of this wire, placing the turns next to one another. Anchor this end and all the ends of the other two coils the same way as above. This is your tickler coil. Look at Figure 16-7 to see that you have the right idea for winding the coils.

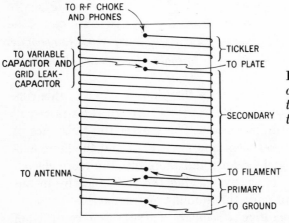

Fig. 16-7. *Diagram of the construction and connections of the three-circuit tuner.*

About ⅛ inch from the bottom of the tickler, start winding the secondary of the antenna coupler. Note that all three coils must be wound in the same direction. Wind on 90 turns of wire. About ⅛ inch from the bottom of the secondary coil, wind on 15 turns for the primary of the antenna coupler.

Connecting the Parts. Now connect the top of the tickler coil to the r-f choke and phones, and the bottom of this coil to the plate of the tube. Refer to Figures 16-3, 16-5, 16-6, and 16-7. The top of the secondary of the antenna coupler goes to one end of the variable tuning capacitor (usually the stationary plate terminal), and to the grid leak and grid capacitor. The bottom of this coil goes to the other end of the variable tuning capacitor (usually the rotary plate terminal) and the filament of the tube. The top of the primary coil of the antenna coupler goes to the antenna; the bottom goes to the ground.

Here is how you operate the regenerative receiver. First tune in your station, just as you would on any other set. Now rotate your regenerative control. The signal will get louder and louder until a point is reached where you will hear clicks, whistles, or howls. Now turn your regenerative control back to just before that point is reached. Your set is now tuned in for most efficient reception. If regeneration does not occur, reverse the connections to the tickler coil. This coil may not have been connected correctly.

We have now traced the development of radio receivers to a point where we have made a set that is both selective and sensitive. The crystal detector has been replaced by the more stable and efficient triode. Reception is not perfect yet, but millions of radio enthusiasts throughout the world, sitting up into the small hours of the night, have listened over such radio receivers to that much desired *DX* station.

SUMMARY

1. The *regenerative principle* was added to radio receiving sets to provide greater sensitivity in radio receivers, and hence the possibility of receiving more distant stations.
2. This regenerative, or *feedback,* principle depends upon a third coil, the *tickler,* connected in the plate circuit, but coupled inductively to the secondary of the tuning circuit.
3. The electron stream in the secondary of the antenna coupler set flowing by the *tickler coil* oscillates in step with the incoming impulses and builds up their strength.
4. The fault of the regenerative system is its tendency to produce whistles in the phones by oscillating like a transmitting station.
5. This tendency to oscillate may be controlled by (a) a movable tickler coil, (b) by connecting the tickler coil in series with a variable capacitor, (c) by using a fixed capacitor in combination with a rheostat, (d) by using a rheostat across the tickler coil.

GLOSSARY

Coupling: The degree to which electrical energy is handed on from one circuit to another.

Grid Coil: The coil which is connected in the grid circuit of the tube. As discussed in this chapter, the grid coil is the secondary of the antenna coupler.

Grid Return: The wire connecting the end of the grid coil with the ground connection of the receiver.

Oscillate: The condition under which the electrons flowing in the tuning circuit of the receiver cause it to become a transmitter of radio waves.

Plate Coil or *Tickler:* The coil which is connected in the plate circuit of the tube.

Radio-Frequency Choke Coil: A small inductor, usually with an air core, placed in a circuit to impede a varying flow of electrons through that circuit. It is called a *radio-frequency* choke coil because its impeding effect, or *impedance,* is greater as the frequency of the current increases. Thus, the impedance is greatest at radio frequencies.

Regeneration: The action whereby electrical energy in the plate circuit is fed back to the grid circuit to be amplified again, and thus produce a louder signal in the earphones or loudspeaker.

Regenerative Control: The device by which the amount of electrical energy fed back to the grid circuit is controlled, thus preventing the receiver from oscillating.

Three-Circuit Tuner: A tuner coupled to the plate circuit as well as to the antenna-ground system.

SYMBOLS

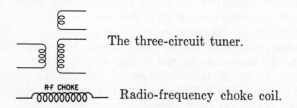

The three-circuit tuner.

Radio-frequency choke coil.

QUESTIONS AND PROBLEMS

1. Explain why oscillations in a tuning circuit usually fail to build up to a point where the receiver becomes a transmitter.
2. Where does the tickler obtain the energy to feed back to the tuned circuit?

3. Explain how direct current flowing in the tickler produces additional energy in the tuning circuit where alternating current is flowing.
4. Under what circumstance will a regenerative detector receiver act as a transmitter?
5. Describe three methods of regeneration control.
6. Draw a diagram of the coil used for a regenerative receiver, indicating the points for connecting of the coils.
7. What is the purpose of a regenerative control?
8. How do you tune a regenerative receiver for a station?

17

The Audio-Frequency Amplifier

PROBLEM 1. *Why is an audio-frequency amplifier needed?*

PROBLEM 2. *How does an audio-frequency amplifier work?*

PROBLEM 3. *What are the practical applications of audio-frequency amplifiers?*

Although our radio set has been developed to the point where it can bring in weak or distant stations and separate out the unwanted ones, it still has a serious drawback. We still have to use earphones. Not only is it a nuisance to wear them but, moreover, only the person who has them on his head can hear the radio program.

The Audio-Frequency (A-F) Amplifier. To meet this objection the audio-frequency amplifier was developed.

You already know how we can attach a large paper cone to the diaphragm of the earphone, and thus get a louder sound. But in order to move this large cone, we must have more electrical power than ordinarily comes out of the detector. It becomes necessary to amplify, or build up, the electrical current flowing out of the detector before it can properly operate the loudspeaker.

The triode furnishes us with the means for this building up. You know that a small current, placing electrical charges on the grid of the tube, will control a much larger plate current. This plate current closely follows the fluctuations and variations of the current being fed into the grid, and thus we get out of the tube a much greater current than was put into it, while all the fluctua-

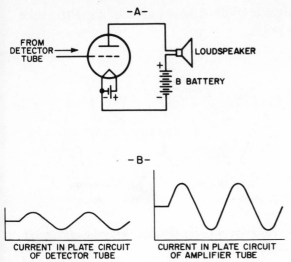

Fig. 17-1. *A—Audio amplifier showing how signal from the detector tube is fed to the grid of the audio-amplifier tube.*

B—Graph showing relationship between current flowing in the plate circuit of the detector tube and current in plate circuit of amplifier tube.

tions are retained in their proper proportions. The signal coming out of the tube will, accordingly, be the same as the signal fed into it except that it will be much stronger. Of course, you know that the B battery supplies the extra power.

All we have to do, therefore, is to feed the plate current from our detector tube into the grid of another tube. The plate current flowing from this second tube will then be our amplified signal (Fig. 17-1).

This second tube is called the *amplifier tube*. Theoretically, all we need is one such amplifier tube to give us the additional power required to operate the loudspeaker. In practice, however, we find that there are certain factors which limit the amplification possible with one tube. We, therefore, usually repeat the whole process, using a second amplifier tube to build the signal up still more to a point where the current will be strong enough to operate the loudspeaker. Each time we amplify the signal by the use of an additional tube, we say that we add one *stage of amplification*. Usually, two stages of amplification are required.

The electrical current flowing in the antenna-ground system and the tuning circuit is radio-frequency current. That is, it alternates millions of times per second. When this current comes out of the detector, it consists of a series of pulses. These pulses, too, occur millions of times per second—that is, at radio frequency. But when you examine Figure 13-4, you see that the current flowing through the phones is fluctuating at a much slower rate. A series, or train, of the fast pulses or fluctuations has combined to make one slow fluctuation, or pulse.

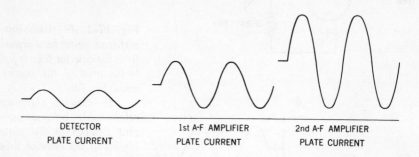

| DETECTOR | 1st A-F AMPLIFIER | 2nd A-F AMPLIFIER |
| PLATE CURRENT | PLATE CURRENT | PLATE CURRENT |

Fig. 17-2. *Graphs showing plate current in the detector, the first audio amplifier, and the second audio amplifier.*

It is this slow fluctuation which moves the diaphragm, and thus produces the sound we hear. We, therefore, say that this slow fluctuation is at *audio frequency*. The range of audio frequency is from about 30 to 15,000 cycles per second. Inasmuch as we are now amplifying our signal after it passes out of our detector (after it is changed from radio frequency to audio frequency), we call the amplifier tubes *audio-frequency amplifiers*. See Figure 17-2.

Coupling the Detector to the Audio-Frequency Amplifier Tube. The next thing to consider is how to feed the current flowing in the plate circuit of the detector tube into the amplifier tube. This is called *coupling*. Look at Figure 17-3 and you will see that

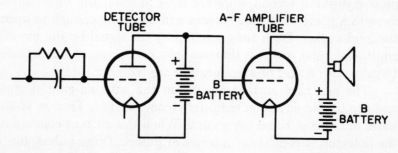

Fig. 17-3. *Diagram showing plate of detector tube connected to the grid of the amplifier tube. The filament circuits are omitted for the sake of simplicity.*

the grid of the amplifier tube is connected to the plate of the detector tube.

A difficulty will immediately be noticed. The large B battery of the detector tube, connected directly to the grid of the amplifier tube, will place a large positive charge on that grid, and thus the fluctuations of plate current will be blanketed out, and no signal will pass. A method must be devised that will pass on the audio-frequency fluctuations of plate current and yet be able to keep out the large positive charge of the B battery.

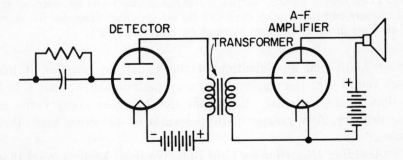

Fig. 17-4. *Diagram showing how the detector is coupled to the a-f amplifier by means of a transformer.*

Here, again, we call upon our old friend, the transformer. We connect the primary in the plate circuit of the detector tube and the secondary in the grid circuit of the amplifier tube (Fig. 17-4). Now the fluctuating plate current in the primary will set up an alternating voltage, or electrical pressure, in the secondary. This voltage will fluctuate in step with the fluctuations of plate current (Fig. 10-3-A).

This fluctuating voltage will place fluctuating positive and negative charges on the grid of the amplifier tube and this, in turn, will control the plate current flowing in the plate circuit of the amplifier. The plate current in the amplifier tube will have the same form as the plate current in the detector tube, but will have a greater amplitude, indicating greater power (Fig. 17-5).

Because these currents are audio-frequency currents, we are able to utilize the greater efficiency of an iron-core transformer. The symbol for such a transformer is: ⦚‖⦚ In addition, we are able to utilize the advantages of a step-up transformer. This gives

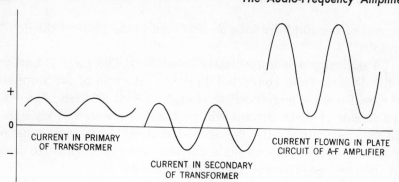

CURRENT IN PRIMARY
OF TRANSFORMER

CURRENT IN SECONDARY
OF TRANSFORMER

CURRENT FLOWING IN PLATE
CIRCUIT OF A-F AMPLIFIER

Fig. 17-5. *Graphs showing current flowing in primary and secondary of the transformer and in the plate circuit of the a-f amplifier. Note that the shape of all three curves is the same although the amplitudes vary.*

us an additional amplification of the signal. In practice, it has been found that the maximum step-up permissible is about 1 to 5 —that is, the secondary has about five times as many turns as the primary. Any greater step-up results in distortion and other losses.

Avoiding Distortion by Grid Bias. We must keep in mind that the amplifier must not only magnify the signal, but must reproduce it in its original form. In other words, there must be a minimum of distortion. One serious objection to our amplifier, as shown in Figure 17-4, is that when the grid of our amplifier tube becomes positively charged by the signal, it will attract some of the electrons streaming from the heated filament, and a current will flow in the grid circuit of the tube. This will produce distortion.

To overcome this defect, a C battery is placed in the grid circuit. This battery places a negative *charge,* or *bias,* on the grid of the amplifier tube, and thus prevents the flow of grid current.

This grid bias keeps the grid negative at all times, and the negative and positive charges placed on the grid by the alternating

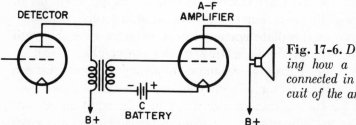

DETECTOR

A–F
AMPLIFIER

C
BATTERY

B+

B+

Fig. 17-6. *Diagram showing how a C battery is connected in the grid circuit of the amplifier tube.*

voltage across the secondary of the coupling transformer make the grid more or less negative (Chaps. 37 and 38).

Another precaution must be taken. In the amplifier tube, unlike the detector tube, the negative charges placed on the grid by the transformer must be prevented from driving the grid so far negative as to cut off the flow of plate current. Such a situation would lop off part of the bottom loop of our curve and distortion would arise (Fig. 17-7-D).

Standard Tubes and Grid Bias. Manufacturers of tubes furnish charts showing the proper value of grid bias to be used with their tubes. Thus, if we use a type 1H5-GT tube as an audio-frequency amplifier with a plate battery of 90 volts, the C battery, or bias, must be 1½ volts negative—that is, a C battery of 1½ volts is

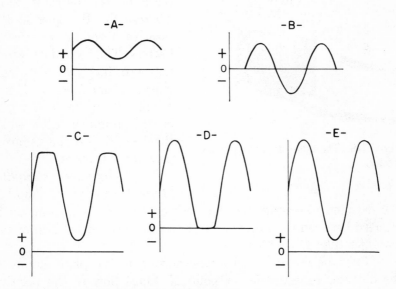

Fig. 17-7. *Graphs showing effects of grid bias.*
A—Graph of current flowing in primary of transformer.
B—Graph of current flowing in secondary of transformer.
C—Graph of current flowing in plate circuit of amplifier tube when grid bias is too low. A large positive signal charge on the grid drives it positive, and it attracts electrons which would normally flow to the plate. A grid current flows, and this causes distortion of the waveform.
D—Graph of plate current when grid bias is too negative. A large negative signal charge drives the grid so far negative that all the electrons are repelled and no plate current flows. This, too, causes distortion of the waveform.
E—Graph of current flowing in the plate circuit of amplifier tube when grid bias is just right. Note that the waveform corresponds to that of graph A.

used with the negative terminal connected to the secondary of the audio-frequency transformer, and the positive terminal going to the filament of the tube (Fig. 17-6).

You may see from the above data that we can use B batteries of much greater voltage than are used in the detector circuit. Thus greater plate current, with enough power to operate the loud-speaker, will be possible.

How to Couple the Audio-Frequency Transformer. This method of coupling one tube to another is called *transformer coupling.* The transformer used is called an *audio-frequency transformer* (Fig. 17-8). The primary winding has two terminals

Fig. 17-8. *The audio-frequency transformer.*

marked P and B+. The P terminal is connected to the plate of the detector tube, whereas the B+ goes to the positive terminal of the B battery. The secondary winding also has two terminals marked G and F—. The G terminal is connected to the grid of the amplifier tube while the F— goes to the negative post of the C battery.

A Different Coupling Method. There is another method used to couple one tube with another. A fixed capacitor is inserted between the plate of the detector tube and the grid of the amplifier tube (Fig. 17-9).

Now, the stream of electrons flowing in the plate circuit of the detector tube divides at point X. Some flow to the positive post of the B battery, while others pile up on plate No. 1 of the capacitor. Thus, a negative charge is placed on this plate. This

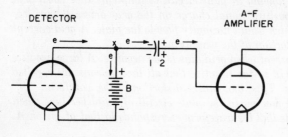

Fig. 17-9. *Diagram showing how a fixed capacitor is used to couple the amplifier tube to the detector.*

negative charge drives electrons away from plate No. 2 of the capacitor, leaving a positive charge there. The electrons thus driven away pile up on the grid of the amplifier tube, making that grid negative. When detector plate current decreases, some electrons leak off plate No. 1 of the capacitor. As a result, electrons from the grid of the amplifier leak back to plate No. 2, and the amplifier grid becomes less negative. Fluctuations in the plate current of the detector tube thus cause a fluctuating charge to be placed upon the grid of the amplifier tube. This, in turn, causes a fluctuating current to flow in the plate circuit of the amplifier tube. This fixed capacitor is called a *coupling capacitor*. Its value is usually about 0.006 μf.

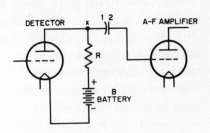

Fig. 17-10. *Diagram showing how plate resistor (R) is placed in the circuit.*

We Need a Resistor in the Detector Plate Circuit. But we have the B battery in the plate circuit of the detector tube to contend with. Because of its large voltage, the positive post has a very large deficiency of electrons. Thus, unless some means is found to prevent it, all the electrons flowing in the plate circuit of the detector tube will be attracted to the positive post, and none will be left to place a negative charge on the capacitor.

To meet this difficulty, a resistor (Fig. 17-10) is placed between the positive post of the B battery and point X. This resistor (R) retards the flow of electrons to the positive post of the B battery, and thus forces some of the electrons flowing in the plate

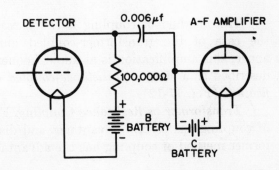

Fig. 17-11. *Diagram showing how the C battery is connected in the grid circuit of the amplifier tube.*

circuit to flow to plate No. 1 of the capacitor. This resistor is called a *plate resistor* and is usually about 100,000 ohms.

As in the case of transformer coupling, a C battery is placed in the grid circuit of the amplifier tube to prevent the flow of grid current which would cause distortion.

A Grid Resistor Is Used in the Audio-Frequency Amplifier. But there is still another difficulty to overcome. We are dealing with strong signals, which means that the stream of electrons may be very large. Thus, it becomes possible that the stream of electrons set flowing from plate No. 2 of the capacitor may become large enough to overcome the voltage of the C battery, and thus push onto the filament. As a consequence, distortion of the signal will result. To meet this difficulty, a resistor is placed in the grid circuit between the C battery and the grid. This resistor impedes the flow of electrons through the C battery, forcing more of them onto the grid of the tube. As a result, the grid of the amplifier tube will receive the full signal variation from the detector and will amplify without distortion. On the other hand, this resistor must not be so large as to prevent excess electrons from leaking off the grid. For this reason, it is called a *grid resistor* or *grid leak*. Its value usually is about 2,000,000 ohms (2 megohms).

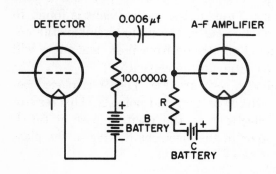

Fig. 17-12. *Diagram showing how grid resistor (R) is placed in the circuit.*

This method of coupling is called *resistance coupling*. As in the case of the transformer-coupled amplifier stage described above, this amplification is at audio frequency and it is, therefore, described as a stage of *resistance-coupled audio-frequency amplification* (Fig. 17-12).

Transformer vs Resistance Coupling. Each of the two methods of coupling has certain advantages and disadvantages. The transformer method of coupling has the advantage that, stage for stage, it will give a greater amplification than does the resistance method of coupling. Two stages of transformer-coupled audio-frequency amplification are about equal to three stages of resistance-coupled audio-frequency amplification. The need of fewer stages with the transformers than with the resistors is due to the amplification resulting from the use of step-up transformers.

Further, we may use a B battery of less voltage with transformer coupling than is needed with resistance coupling to obtain the same plate current. This difference is due to the fact that the large resistor used for a plate resistor in the resistance-coupled audio-frequency amplifier cuts down the amount of positive charge that the B battery can place on the plate of the tube.

Still another advantage is the simplicity of the transformer-coupled stage. Only one part is needed for the coupling, the audio-frequency transformer.

The resistance-coupled amplifier has the advantage that it reproduces the signal more faithfully. The audio-frequency transformer usually introduces a certain amount of distortion. Another advantage is that resistance coupling is cheaper and lighter than the audio-frequency transformer.

The Audio-Frequency Amplifier Unit. In considering the radio receiving set as a whole, the several stages of audio-frequency amplification are usually treated together as a separate unit. In fact, in some receivers, this unit is built separately and apart from the rest of the set. It may consist of several stages of either transformer- or resistance-coupled amplification. Sometimes a stage of resistance-coupled amplification may be followed by a transformer-coupled one.

It is impractical to use more than two stages of transformer-coupled or three stages of resistance-coupled amplification. If we do, we may encounter serious distortion of the signal. Besides, for normal use, more amplification is not necessary.

In Figure 17-13, we have a detector followed by two stages of transformer-coupled amplification. The tubes used are triodes of a type known as 1H5-GT. Instead of using separate A batteries for each tube, the filaments of the tubes are hooked together in parallel and connected to a single battery supplying 1½ volts. The rheostat used as a volume control now limits the amount of current flowing in the filaments of all three tubes. For this purpose, we use a rheostat of 10 ohms.

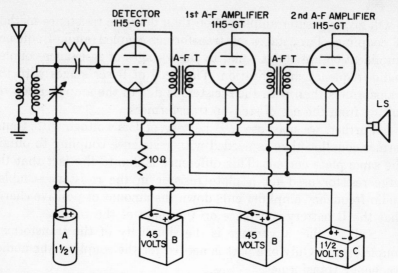

Fig. 17-13. *Diagram showing detector and two stages of transformer-coupled audio-frequency amplification.*

To obtain the B battery of 90 volts, we connect two 45-volt batteries in *series*. That is, we connect the positive terminal of one to the negative terminal of the other. To obtain the 45 volts needed for the detector tube, we make our connections between the negative terminal of the first battery and the positive terminal of this same battery. If, however, we connect between the negative terminal of the first battery and the positive terminal of the second battery, we obtain the 90 volts needed for our amplifier tubes.

The C-battery connections of the two amplifier tubes are likewise connected, and we now can use a single C battery of 1½ volts.

The Public-Address System. We can use the audio-frequency amplifier for other purposes than amplifying a radio signal. Suppose you were to feed an alternating voltage set up by a microphone into the grid of your amplifier tube. You would now have the public address system used by speakers in addressing large audiences.

The microphone is similar to the telephone transmitter of Figure 4-2. Speaking into the microphone varies its resistance, and thus causes the direct current flowing through the primary of the transformer to vary. The direct current varies in step with the variations of the sound waves created by the speaker.

This fluctuating direct current flowing through the primary

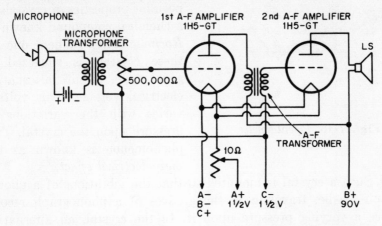

Fig. 17-14. *Diagram showing circuit of the public-address system.*

of the transformer sets up a varying, alternating voltage across the secondary. This alternating voltage places varying charges upon the grid of the amplifier tube, and this variation in turn causes a large, fluctuating direct current to flow in the plate circuit of the tube. After another stage of amplification, the current is strong enough to operate the powerful loudspeaker.

The transformer used in a microphone circuit is similar to the audio-frequency transformer used in the radio receiver. However, in connection with it, note in Figure 17-14 a device that looks like a rheostat across the secondary. This is known as a *potentiometer*. Its use is to divide the voltage output from the secondary of the microphone transformer, and thus control the amount of charge placed on the grid of the tube. This, in turn, controls the volume of the amplifier. Its value in this case is about 500,000 ohms. The symbol for a potentiometer is: ‑⋀⋁⋀‑

Fig. 17-15. *Microphone.*

The Electrical Phonograph. Still another use for the audio-frequency amplifier is the electrical phonograph. Use is made of the

Fig. 17-16. *Potentiometer.*

peculiar properties of crystals of a chemical compound known as *Rochelle salts.* When one of these crystals is squeezed, it generates a minute alternating electrical voltage. This voltage varies with the variations in pressure upon the crystal. This phenomenon is known as the *piezoelectrical effect.*

Such a crystal is mounted so that the vibrations of a phonograph needle, traveling in the grooves of a phonograph record, place a varying pressure upon it. In the crystal, an alternating voltage is generated that varies in step with this pressure. This voltage is fed to the grid of the amplifier tube, placing a varying electrical charge upon it. This charge, in turn, causes a fluctuating direct current to flow in the plate circuit of the tube. After another stage of amplification, the current is strong enough to operate the loudspeaker (Fig. 17-17).

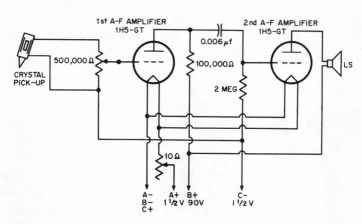

Fig. 17-17. *Diagram showing circuit of the electrical phonograph.*

The crystal and its mounting are known as a *crystal phonograph pickup.* The symbol for such a pickup is: Note that no transformer is necessary here to couple the crystal pickup with the tube. The reason is that the resistance of the pickup is large and it may be applied directly to the grid of the tube. A 500,000-ohm potentiometer acts as a volume control, just as in the case of the public-address system.

This suggests some uses to which the audio-frequency amplifier can be put. It can be used anywhere that a very small electrical voltage is to be amplified. It has been used successfully with

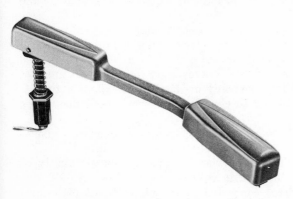

Fig. 17-18. *Phonograph pickup.*

photoelectric cells, as in sound motion pictures, in electrocardiograph machines, and the like. Each day brings forth new uses for this wonderful device.

SUMMARY

1. The purpose of the *audio-frequency amplifier* is to increase the intensity (loudness) of the signals so that a loudspeaker may be used instead of earphones.
2. In the audio-frequency amplifier, an audio-frequency signal is fed to the grid of the tube. The waveform of the plate current of this amplifier will then be an amplified reproduction of the signal fed to its grid.
3. By coupling a second audio-frequency amplifier tube to the plate circuit of the first a-f amplifier tube, a second stage of amplification may be had.
4. Distortion in the amplifying system is prevented by proper values of grid bias.
5. Audio-frequency amplifiers are used for public-address systems, to increase the loudness of phonograph records, for amplifying signals of photoelectric cells, and for many other purposes.

GLOSSARY

Amplifier, Audio-Frequency: A circuit to amplify a-f signals such as those flowing out of the detector, thereby enabling us to use a loudspeaker.

Amplification, Stage of: The tube and its accompanying electrical devices serving as an amplifier.

Audio Frequency (AF): A frequency in the range between 30 and 15,000 cycles per second.

Audio-Frequency Transformer: An iron-core transformer used to transfer electrical energy at audio frequencies from one tube to another.

Coupling Capacitor: A fixed capacitor used in a resistance-coupled amplifier to transfer electrical energy from one tube to another.

Grid Resistor: A resistor connected in the grid circuit of a tube.

Microphone: A device used to change sound waves to a fluctuating electrical current.

Phonograph Pickup: A device used to change variations in a phonograph-record sound-track to a fluctuating electric current.

Piezoelectric Effect: The effect whereby pressure on certain types of crystals produces an electric voltage.

Plate Resistor: A resistor connected in the plate circuit of a tube.

Potentiometer: A resistance device enabling us to tap off portions of the entire voltage placed across it.

Resistance Coupling: Coupling between the plate circuit of one tube and the grid circuit of the next by means of resistors and a coupling capacitor.

Transformer Coupling: Coupling between the plate circuit of one tube and the grid circuit of the next by means of a transformer.

SYMBOLS

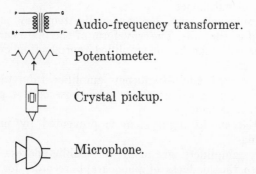

Audio-frequency transformer.

Potentiometer.

Crystal pickup.

Microphone.

QUESTIONS AND PROBLEMS

1. What purpose does an audio-frequency amplifier serve?
2. What is the range of audio frequencies?
3. What is meant by "coupling the energy from the plate circuit of the detector to a stage of audio-frequency amplification"?
4. What are the methods for coupling energy from the detector to an audio-frequency amplifier?
5. What is the maximum voltage step-up tolerated in an audio-frequency transformer?
6. How does the function of a C battery in a stage of audio-frequency amplification differ from the function of that battery in a detector?
7. From what source does an amplifier gain the energy required to operate a loudspeaker that needs a great power input?
8. What advantage does transformer coupling have over resistance coupling?
9. What is the function of a coupling capacitor between two tubes?
10. What is the function of the plate resistor of a tube?
11. What is the ratio of the number of stages of the transformer-coupled audio-frequency amplification to the number of stages of resistance-coupled audio-frequency amplification to obtain the same amplification?
12. What advantages have resistance-coupled audio-frequency stages over transformer-coupled stages?
13. Why can we not use many stages of audio-frequency amplification?
14. How may a few stages of audio-frequency amplification be used as a public-address system?
15. Explain how a few stages of audio-frequency amplification may be used to make a phonograph player.
16. What is the piezoelectrical effect?
17. Draw a circuit containing a regenerative detector and two stages of audio-frequency amplification, having one stage transformer-coupled to the detector and in turn resistance-coupled to another stage of audio-frequency amplification.
18. Identify the numbered parts.

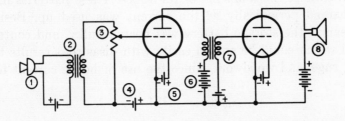

18

Eliminating the
B Battery

Some Faults of Batteries. Having eliminated the nuisance of the headphones, the next problem to be tackled is that of getting rid of the various batteries required. These batteries have several serious drawbacks. They have a limited life, even though the radio receiver be used infrequently. This means periodic replacements which are not only troublesome but costly. Besides, as the batteries start to wear out, the voltage delivered starts to fall off. This deterioration means uneven performance. Furthermore, the batteries are quite bulky, especially those of the high-voltage type used as plate batteries for the amplifier tubes, some of which may require as much as 250 volts.

In the early days of radio, storage batteries were frequently used to heat the filaments of the tubes. These batteries had to be recharged periodically as the current was used up. Besides this nuisance, the storage battery was heavy, bulky, and contained an acid which could be spilled easily with disastrous results to clothing, rugs, and woodwork. Since the use of house current for light-

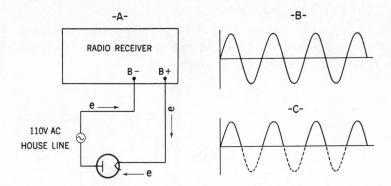

Fig. 18-1. *A—The diode as a rectifier tube.*

> *B—Waveform showing alternating current flowing in house line before rectification.*

> *C—Waveform showing the alternating current after it has been rectified by the rectifier tube. The bottom half of the loop (dotted line) has been cut off, and the current now becomes a pulsating direct current.*

ing purposes is fairly universal, it was only natural to seek a means of using this house current to replace the batteries.

The Diode as a Rectifier. The first battery to be eliminated was the plate or B battery. The house current most widely used in our country is alternating current with a voltage, or electrical pressure, of 110 volts. This alternating current usually has a frequency of 60 cycles per second.

Such an alternating current cannot be applied directly to the plate of the tube, because this plate must always have a steady positive charge. Any fluctuations of the positive charge on the plate due to variations in the plate battery voltage would result in distortion of the signal. It becomes necessary, therefore, to change the alternating current of the house line to a steady direct current before it can be fed to the plate of the tube.

You will recall that the diode tube changes alternating current into pulsating direct current. So we feed the alternating current of the house line into a diode tube as in Figure 18-1.

When the plate of the diode has a positive charge on it, current will flow from the house line to the plate circuits of the radio receiver. When a negative charge is placed on the plate of the diode, no current will flow. A diode used as indicated here is called a *rectifier tube.* Thus, we often say that we have *rectified* the alternating current.

The Filter System. But it is not enough to change the house current from alternating current to *pulsating* direct current. We must change it to a *steady* direct current. To do this, we must pass the pulsating direct current through a *filter*.

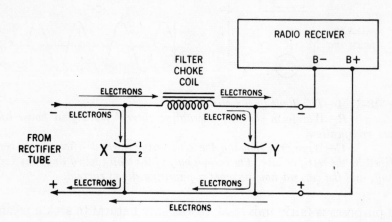

Fig. 18-2. *Hookup showing the filter system.*

In Figure 18-2, you will notice that the pulsating direct current from the rectifier tube is fed into a network consisting of two capacitors (X and Y) and an iron-core inductor. This inductor contains many turns of wire, and is called a *filter choke coil*. An inductor having an inductance of 30 henrys is usually used.

Fig. 18-3. *Filter choke coil.*

As the electrons rush up to the choke coil, they encounter a very great opposition resulting from the inductance of the coil. As a result, they are forced to pile up on plate No. 1 of capacitor X. Here they accumulate until the resulting voltage is equal to the amplitude of the applied pulse. Thus capacitor X acts as a sort of reservoir, or storage tank, for these electrons. Meanwhile, many electrons get through the choke coil. Here they encounter the opposition offered by the receiver and are forced onto the plates of capacitor Y. This capacitor is often known as the *smoothing filter capacitor.*

A result of the action of the choke coil is to level off the peaks of the pulses. Between pulses, when the voltage and current from the rectifier tend to drop, these capacitors discharge towards the receiver, tending to maintain the current and voltage output. The result is a steady direct current and voltage fed to the plates of the receiver tubes. This action is shown in the graph of Figure 18-4.

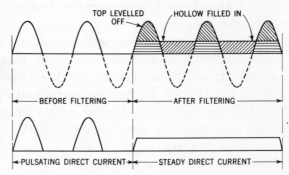

Fig. 18-4. *Waveform showing how the filter system changes pulsating direct current to steady direct current.*

The action of the filter is to hold back the pulsating electron flow until a steady average flow is reached and maintained. When this steady flow results, we say we have *filtered* the current flowing from the rectifier tube.

It makes no difference whether the filter choke coil is placed in the negative or positive side of the filter circuit. The action is the same. In practice it usually appears in the positive side between the two filter capacitors.

The Step-up Power Transformer. The voltage of the current flowing out of the filter is about the same as the voltage of the house current—namely, 110 volts. Since this does not place a very high charge on the plate, someone thought of using a step-up transformer to increase the house-current voltage to about 300 volts. Thus, about 300 volts of steady direct current flow out of the filter, and we are able to place a higher positive charge on the plates of the tubes in the receiver; a greater plate current flows and a louder sound comes out of the loudspeaker.

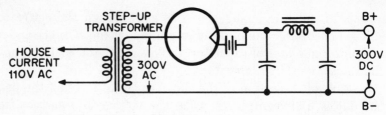

Fig. 18-5. *B-battery eliminator using a step-up transformer.*

In practice, the primary of the step-up transformer is connected to the 110-volt alternating current of the house line. The secondary is connected to the rectifier tube and filter (Fig. 18-5). The step-up transformer used here is called a *power transformer*.

A Step-down Transformer for the Rectifier Filament. To eliminate the necessity for using a filament battery for the rectifier tube, a step-down transformer is used to step down the 110-volt house alternating current to a value that the rectifier tube requires. If we use a type 81 rectifier tube, the transformer steps down the 110-volt alternating current to 7½-volt alternating current. Using alternating current on the filament of the rectifier tube does not cause any interference with the signal.

The primary of the step-down transformer is connected to the 110-volt alternating-current line, and the secondary is connected across the filament of the rectifier tube in place of the filament battery. The step-down transformer used here is called a *filament transformer*. The wiring diagram is shown in Figure 18-6. For convenience, the two secondaries, the step-up to the plate of the rectifier tube, and the step-down to the filament may, by suitable winding, be made to operate from the same primary (Fig. 18-7).

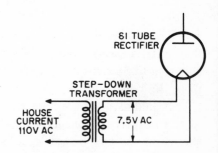

Fig. 18-6. *Step-down transformer used to heat the filament of the rectifier tube.*

Still another improvement was made to utilize the half cycle of alternating current blocked out by the action of the rectifier tube (Fig. 18-1). By connecting up two rectifier tubes as shown in Figure 18-8, this half cycle could be put to use.

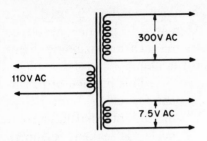

Fig. 18-7. *Transformer with two secondaries to step up the voltage for the plate supply and to step down the voltage for the filament of the rectifier tube.*

Full-Wave Rectification. The high-voltage secondary of the transformer is *center-tapped,* that is, a connection is made to the mid-point of its winding. When point X of this secondary has a positive charge on it (Fig. 18-8-A), point Z has a negative charge. This means that the plate of rectifier tube No. 1 is positive, and the plate of rectifier tube No. 2 is negative. Electrons then stream from the filament of tube No. 1 to the plate and through the secondary to point Y, the electrical mid-point of the secondary. Since Z is negative, it repels these electrons, and they are forced to stream through the wire connecting Y to the filter circuit. Tube No. 2 does not operate. During the next half-cycle (Fig. 18-8-B), the charges on the secondary are reversed. Now, tube No. 1 does not operate while electrons from tube No. 2 stream to point Y and to the filter circuit.

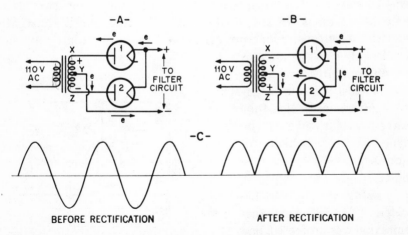

Fig. 18-8. *Full-wave rectification using two rectifier tubes. For the sake of simplicity, the complete filament circuits are omitted.*
A—Electron flow during one half-cycle.
B—Electron flow during the next half-cycle.
C—Waveform showing full-wave rectification.

Since only one half of the secondary winding is used at a time, the turns of the winding are increased to produce a voltage of about 600 volts, or about 300 volts for each half-winding. Thus the output from the filter circuit still is about 300 volts.

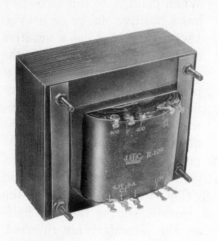

Fig. 18-9. *Power transformer.*

This method of rectification, using both halves of the alternating-current cycle, is called *full-wave rectification*. The method previously described, using only one half of the cycle, is called *half-wave rectification*. The output of the full-wave rectifier is fed to a filter circuit similar to the one previously described. Full-wave rectification is easier to filter because the hollows between the direct-current pulses are smaller (Fig. 18-8-C).

A logical development was to combine the two rectifier tubes into one, using two plates and one filament. In this double tube, the filament is constantly emitting electrons, which are attracted first to one plate and then to the other as the charges on these plates are alternately positive and negative. An example of a full-wave rectifier tube is the type 5Y3-GT which requires five volts for its filament.

Using a Voltage Divider. After full-wave rectification was perfected, one more thing remained to be done. The steady direct current flowing out of the filter circuit is at an electrical

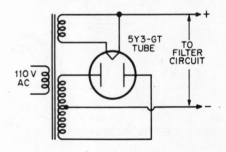

Fig. 18-10. *Type 5Y3-GT rectifier tube with one filament and two plates. This tube is used for full-wave rectification.*

Fig. 18-11. *Cutaway view of full-wave rectifier tube.*

pressure of about 300 volts. This voltage is suitable for the plates of the amplifier tubes, but it is too high for the plate of a detector tube, where a maximum of about 100 volts is needed. A means had to be devised to enable us to tap off a lower voltage for the detector tube. This object was accomplished by connecting a potentiometer across the output terminals of the filter circuit.

Here is how the potentiometer works. Assume that the electrical pressure at the output terminals of the filter circuit is 300 volts. This statement means that the electrons piled up on the negative terminal are seeking to get to the positive terminal with a force which is equal to this electrical pressure of 300 volts. Electricians call this a *drop* of 300 volts. Now we connect a resistor from the negative terminal to the positive terminal. The electrons use up the 300-volt pressure in traveling the entire length of the resistor to the positive terminal. But the drop, or fall in pressure (technically, the drop in potential) is proportional at any point to the fraction of the total resistor which has been traversed by the current.

Suppose we take a point one third of the way down the resistor. At this point, the electrons have used up one third the pressure, and the pressure of the electrons at that point seeking to reach the positive terminal is 200 volts. At a point two thirds of the way down the resistor, two thirds of the original total voltage

Fig. 18-12. *Diagram showing how a potentiometer is hooked up as a voltage divider.*

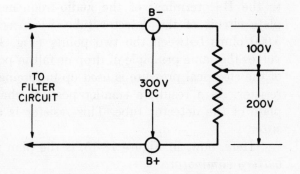

TO FILTER CIRCUIT

B−

300 V DC

100 V

200 V

B+

(or pressure) has been used, and the pressure between that point and the positive terminal is only 100 volts. So by moving the slider of the potentiometer from point to point on the resistor, we can get any desired voltage out of the filter circuit. The potentiometer, hooked up in this circuit, is called a *voltage divider*.

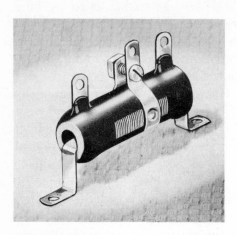

The size of the voltage divider varies with the number of tubes used in the receiver. Generally, the resistance is about 50,000 ohms. The resistance wire must also be heavy enough to stand the current that flows through it without burning out. The amount of current a resistor can safely pass at a given voltage is expressed by its rating in *watts*. A *watt* is a unit of electrical power measured by the product of the current and the voltage

Fig. 18-13. *Variable resistor used as a voltage divider.*

(pressure). Hence, with a given voltage, as the current increases the rated number of watts must increase. It follows that the more current needed for the plate currents in the radio receiver, the heavier this resistor must be. In the present case, with an assumed pressure of 300 volts, the resistor must be rated at about 5 watts.

The Dropping Resistor. There is another way by which we can get the lower voltage needed for the plate of the detector tube. Instead of connecting the positive output terminal directly to the B+ terminal of the audio-frequency transformer in the plate circuit of the detector tube, we insert a resistor of about 5,000 ohms between the two points (Fig. 18-14). This plan involves the same principle of drop or fall in potential, because some of the electrical pressure is used up in forcing current through this resistor. As a result, a smaller positive charge is placed on the plate of the detector tube. This resistor is called a *dropping resistor*.

Here, now, in Figure 18-15, is the plan for our completed *B-battery eliminator*.

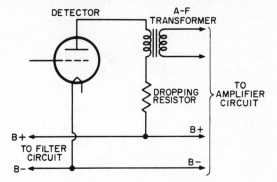

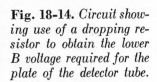

Fig. 18-14. *Circuit showing use of a dropping resistor to obtain the lower B voltage required for the plate of the detector tube.*

How the B Eliminator Works. The primary of the power transformer is connected to the house line which supplies 110-volt alternating current. The step-up secondary increases this voltage to 600 volts. The ends of this secondary are connected to the plates of the full-wave rectifier tube.

The step-down secondary reduces the voltages to 5 volts. The ends of this secondary are connected to the filament of the rectifier tube. The negative line of the B-battery eliminator comes from the mid-point, or *center tap,* of the step-up secondary and is connected to one end of the filter input. The positive line comes from the filament of the rectifier tube and goes to the other end of the filter input. At this point, the current is pulsating direct current

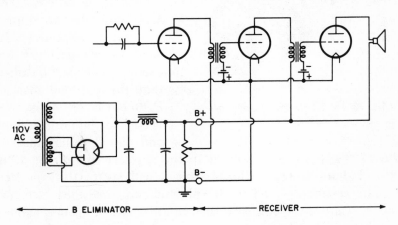

Fig. 18-15. *Completed B eliminator, showing how it is connected to the radio receiver.*

which, after it passes through the filter, comes out as a steady direct current at about 300 volts.

Across the negative and positive terminals of the B-battery eliminator the electrical pressure is 300 volts. The negative terminal is connected to the filaments of the tubes in the radio receiver, just as is the negative post of the B batteries when there is no eliminator. Similarly, the positive terminal of the eliminator is connected to the B+ terminal of the second audio-frequency transformer and the loudspeaker. In most receivers, the B minus terminal is connected to ground, thus furnishing a common point to which the plate, grid, and filament circuits are connected. This ground connection usually is the chassis of the receiver.

Across the terminals of the eliminator, a potentiometer is connected. The sliding tap is adjusted to a point where the electrical pressure, or voltage, is of the desired value, about 100 volts. A connection is made from this sliding tap to the B+ terminal of the first audio-frequency transformer.

Fig. 18-16. *Electrolytic capacitor.*

Electrolytic Capacitors in the Filter Circuit. The capacitors used in the filter circuits are very large, about 8 to 50 μf each. For this purpose, we use *electrolytic capacitors*. These capacitors have plates of aluminum and an aluminum-oxide dielectric. In using these electrolytic capacitors, care must be taken that the terminal marked *POSITIVE* or + is connected to the positive line, and the terminal marked *NEGATIVE* or — is connected to the negative line of the filter circuit. Failure to observe this precaution will destroy the capacitor.

The capacitors used in the filter circuit are called *filter capacitors*. Care must be taken that the dielectric is strong enough to withstand the electrical pressure—in this instance, at least 300 volts. This rating is usually marked on the side of the capacitor.

SUMMARY

1. Batteries became such a nuisance in radio sets that means were sought to eliminate them.
2. The ordinary current delivered to the home is alternating current of 60 cycles at a pressure of 110 volts.
3. By passing an alternating current through a diode tube, the current is rectified to pulsating direct current.
4. By the use of coils having high inductance, called *filter choke coils,* together with filter capacitors, the pulsating current is changed to steady current. This system of chokes and capacitors is called a *filter system.*
5. *Full-wave rectifying tubes* (such as type 5Y3-GT) are made with one filament and two plates. This design makes use of the half-cycle of alternating current that is blocked off during rectification by a single diode.
6. *Voltage dividers* are resistors with sliders, or taps, by the use of which we may obtain any desired voltage through the principle that *drop* in electrical pressure, or voltage, is proportional to resistance through which the current passes.
7. The B-battery eliminator consists of a full-wave rectifier tube with filters and resistors so connected that all the functions of the B battery are performed by energy from house alternating current.

GLOSSARY

B-Battery Eliminator: A device used to eliminate the need for B batteries by supplying plate voltage from the house mains.

Dropping Resistor: A resistor connected in a circuit which uses up a part of the electrical pressure, thus leaving less voltage for the remainder of the circuit.

Electrolytic Capacitor: A fixed capacitor of high capacitance with aluminum plates and a dielectric of aluminum oxide.

Filament Transformer: A step-down transformer used to supply filament current from the house mains.

Filter: An electrical network used to smooth out, or eliminate variations from, a pulsating direct current, thus changing it to a steady direct current.

Filter Capacitor: A fixed capacitor of high capacitance, used in a filter.

Filter Choke Coil: A coil of many turns wound on an iron core, used in a filter circuit.

Full-Wave Rectification: Rectification which uses both halves of the alternating-current cycle.

Half-Wave Rectification: Rectification which uses only one half of the alternating-current cycle.

Power Transformer: A transformer used to step up the 110-volt alternating current from the house mains to a higher voltage. It may have several step-down secondaries, which are used to supply current to heat the filaments of the tubes.

Rectified Current: An alternating current that has been changed to direct current by a rectifier tube or other rectifier device.

Rectifier Tube: A tube whose sole function is that of changing alternating current to direct current.

Voltage Divider: A resistor, placed across the output of the filter system, from which we may obtain various voltages by tapping off at points along its length.

Watt: The unit of electrical power.

SYMBOLS

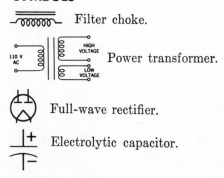

Filter choke.

Power transformer.

Full-wave rectifier.

Electrolytic capacitor.

QUESTIONS AND PROBLEMS

1. Why is it normally desirable to eliminate batteries from a receiver?
2. Why cannot normal alternating current be used directly in the radio receiver plate circuits without the use of a B-battery eliminator?
3. Show how a diode can act as a rectifier. Graph the resulting voltage.
4. By what means is a rectified alternating current changed so that it can be used in our receiver?
5. Explain the operation of an electrical filter system.
6. Explain the operation of a half-wave rectifier.
7. Explain the operation of a full-wave rectifier.
8. Why is it easier to filter the output of a full-wave rectifier than it is that of a half-wave rectifier?
9. How may we secure various voltage levels from our power supply? Explain in detail.

10. What rating of a resistor expresses the amount of current that the resistor can safely pass without burning out?
11. Draw the circuit for a complete full-wave B-battery eliminator or power supply.
12. What care must be taken in using electrolytic capacitors in the filter system of B-battery eliminators?
13. In using capacitors in a B-battery eliminator, what must we consider in addition to the capacitance rating?
14. Identify the numbered parts.

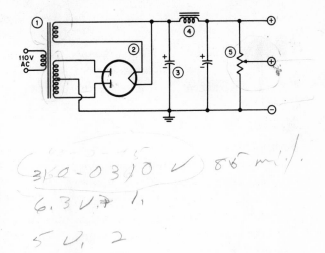

19

Eliminating the A Battery

PROBLEM 1. *What attempts were made to use alternating current directly on the filament?*

PROBLEM 2. *How does the cathode of a tube work?*

Attempts to Use Alternating Current for the Filament. The next battery to be eliminated was the A or filament battery. It is simple enough to use a step-down filament transformer to reduce the voltage from the 110-volt alternating current to 1½-volt alternating current. But alternating current is unsatisfactory for heating the filament of the radio tube even at this reduced voltage.

The reason is that any fluctuations in the stream of electrons shot out by the heated filament cause a hum or distortion of the signal. The plate current is the current produced by the stream of electrons from the filament to the plate. Examine the waveform picture of the alternating current used to heat the filament in Figure 19-1.

When the alternating-current cycle reaches its peak (whether the positive or negative peak makes no difference here), the elec-

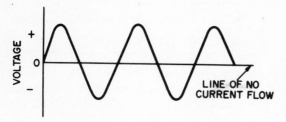

Fig. 19-1. *Waveform of alternating current used to heat the filament of the tube.*

trons are streaming through the filament at their maximum rate, and the filament is being heated to maximum temperature. The electrons being emitted by the heated filament are shooting out at the maximum rate. When the alternating-current cycle reaches the line of no-current flow, however, the filament starts to cool off, and the number of electrons emitted starts to drop off. The result is a fluctuation in the number of the electrons reaching the plate, not caused by variation of the signal charge on the tube grid, with resulting distortion of the signal.

First Experiments with Ribbons. One method that has been used to combat this undesirable condition was to make the mass of the filament greater. Instead of using a thin wire, a ribbon type of filament was used. Because of its greater mass, the temperature in such a filament does not fluctuate as much as in the thinner ones during the changes in the alternating-current cycle.

But the ribbon filament was not wholly successful for two reasons: (1) some fluctuations still remained and (2) to heat this massive filament required great amounts of electric current.

Attempts to Use Rectifiers. Another method used to overcome the difficulty was to convert the 1½-volt alternating current to direct current, using a rectifier consisting of plates of copper and copper oxide. The action of this rectifier is similar to that of the crystal detector.

Still another method of rectifying the alternating current was to use a chemical rectifier. Plates of lead and aluminum were suspended in a solution of borax. This chemical rectifier passes current only in one direction.

The diode tube also was used as a rectifier, following the method described in the previous chapter.

All these methods of rectification were not very practical. They require special apparatus for the rectification and filter systems. The chemical rectifier had the additional drawback of being spilled easily.

Further Attempts to Use Alternating Current for Heating. The use of alternating current directly on the filament of the radio tube was tried in a number of ways, but one difficulty always remained. The grid of the tube, as you know, must be connected to the filament as shown in Figure 19-2. So if alternating current is sent through the filament, then during one half of the cycle, a positive charge is placed on the grid as in Figure 19-2-A. During the next

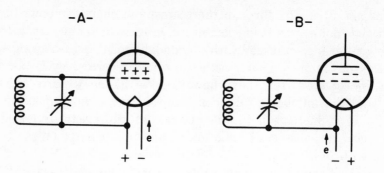

Fig. 19-2. *Circuits showing how alternating current flowing through the filament places an alternating charge on the grid of the tube.*

half of the cycle, a negative charge is placed on the grid (Fig. 19-2-B). Thus, an alternating charge is placed on the grid by the alternating current flowing in the filament. This charge interferes with the flow of electrons to the plate, and distortion results.

To help correct this fault, a resistor of 20 to 40 ohms was connected across the filament. At the electrical center of this resistor, a tap was placed. To this tap was connected the wire going to the grid circuit (Fig. 19-3). It can be seen that whichever side of the filament is positive or negative, the center tap, being halfway between them, is always at the same electrical pressure. Thus, a constant charge is placed on the grid, and there are no unwanted fluctuations in the plate current.

This scheme, together with the use of the heavy ribbon-type filament, gave fairly good results.

The Cathode Sleeve. But a better method, permitting the use of alternating current directly on the

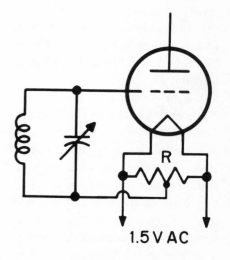

Fig. 19-3. *Circuits showing the use of a 20- to 40-ohm center-tapped resistor (R) to reduce hum.*

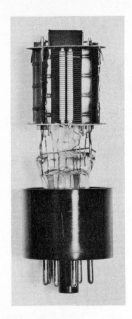

Fig. 19-4. *Cutaway view of tube with a cathode sleeve used as an emitter of electrons.*

filament, was subsequently worked out. Around the filament, but not touching it, was slipped a sleeve of metal. Now the filament was used as a stove to heat this sleeve. As the sleeve became hot, it emitted the stream of electrons which reached the plate (See Fig. 19-4).

This sleeve is now the surface which gives off the electrons and is, therefore, called the *cathode*. Because it is quite massive, the temperature of the cathode does not change with the alternating-current cycle of the current flowing through the filament. Thus the stream of electrons it emits is steady. The symbol for the cathode is: ⌐⌐

The wire going to the grid, which is called the *grid return,* is connected to the cathode instead of to the filament (Fig. 19-5). The filament is thus removed from the circuit bearing the radio signals. Hence, the current used to heat the filament may be either alternating or direct current without causing distortion of signals. The filament in such a tube is now called the *heater*.

In modern tubes, the cathode is usually coated with special chemicals that make it a more efficient emitter of electrons. We shall discuss this matter more fully later.

The Complete A-Battery Eliminator. The use of the cathode simplifies things a great deal. The only extra piece of apparatus for this new type of tube is the step-down filament transformer. An example of a tube using this cathode is the type 6C5.

We have now eliminated the need for the A, or filament, battery. A typical hookup using

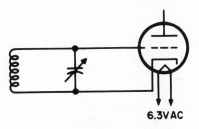

6.3V AC

Fig. 19-5. *Circuit showing how the cathode is connected to the grid return.*

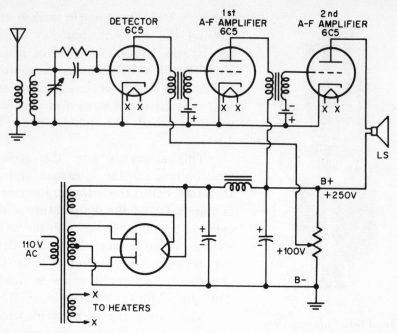

Fig. 19-6. *Radio circuit showing the use of a B-battery eliminator and cathode-type tubes.*

the cathode-type tube is shown in Figure 19-6. In studying this wiring diagram, you should notice that the B minus terminal of the B-battery eliminator is now connected to the cathode instead of the filament. Notice, also, that a third secondary winding has been added to the power transformer. This is a step-down secondary giving the 6.3 volts needed for the filament of the type 6C5 tube.

SUMMARY

1. The alternating current is usually unsatisfactory for heating the filaments of radio tubes directly because of the resulting uneven flow of electrons to the plate.
2. Various means of correcting the faults of the alternating current as a substitute for the A battery were tried before a successful method was found.
3. The device which was most successful is the **cathode sleeve.** The principle in this is that the filament bearing the alternating current does not touch the cathode, but merely heats it because it is close to it. The cathode, therefore, emits the electrons used in the plate circuit to carry the radio signals.

4. The type 6C5 tube has this cathode sleeve and needs to be operated at 6.3 volts alternating current furnished to the heater or filament by a step-down transformer.

GLOSSARY

A-Battery Eliminator: A device used to serve the purpose of the A battery by supplying the current needed to heat the filament of the tube from the house mains.

Cathode: A metal sleeve surrounding the filament in a tube and coated with chemicals that shoot off electrons when heated by the filament.

Heater: The filament of a cathode-type tube.

SYMBOLS

Cathode in a tube.

 or   A triode employing a cathode.

QUESTIONS AND PROBLEMS

1. What undesirable action results when alternating current is fed directly to the filaments of a noncathode-type triode tube?
2. What early attempt was made to overcome the effect of the alternating current in Question 1?
3. List several methods other than that in Question 2 to overcome the effect considered in Question 1.
4. Explain how the use of a center-tapped filament resistor helps to stabilize grid voltage when an alternating current is fed to the filament.
5. What are the advantages of the type 6C5 tube over a tube like the type 1H5-GT?
6. If we are using tubes with cathodes, to what circuit is alternating current delivered?
7. Describe the chief features of the A-battery eliminator. Illustrate by means of a diagram.

20

Eliminating the C Battery

PROBLEM. *How is the grid bias maintained without a C battery?*

Keeping the Grid Negatively Charged. Having succeeded in eliminating the A and B batteries, radio engineers next tried to get rid of the C battery. It proved to be a simple matter to do away with this battery. Let us recall the function of the C battery.

Figure 20-1 shows the C battery connected in the grid circuit of the triode. Since the C battery (or grid-bias battery) is connected with the negative post to the grid return and the positive post to the filament, the grid is more negative than the filament. So all we have to do is to work out a system that makes the grid slightly more negative than the filament, and our C battery is eliminated. One method for doing this is the grid-leak and capacitor method discussed in Chapter 15. There are other methods which are more widely used.

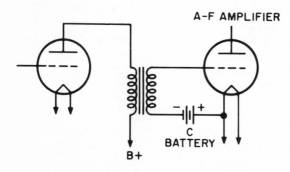

A-F AMPLIFIER

B+

C BATTERY

Fig. 20-1. *Circuit showing a C battery connected in the grid circuit of an amplifying tube.*

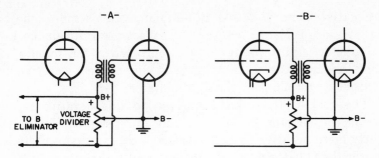

Fig. 20-2. *A—Circuit showing how a filament-type tube is connected to obtain the grid bias from the voltage divider.*

B—Circuit showing how a cathode-type tube is connected to obtain the grid bias from the voltage divider.

Using a Voltage Divider. Turn back to Figure 18-15. The most negative point of the B eliminator is the negative terminal. Note that the filaments of the radio tubes are connected to that point. Now consider a point on the voltage divider a little distance away from the negative terminal and toward the positive terminal. As you now know, this point is a little more positive than the negative terminal.

Now, connect the filament to this new point, which is called B— and is grounded, and connect the grid return to the negative terminal of the eliminator. The grid in this hookup is slightly more negative than the filament, and we have eliminated the necessity for a C battery.

Figure 20-2-B shows how a cathode-type tube is hooked up to eliminate the C battery. This method, as well as the one using the C battery, is called *fixed bias.*

Self Bias. Other methods are used to eliminate the C battery. For example, it has already been stated that the most negative point of the B eliminator is the negative terminal. This means that the greatest excess of electrons has accumulated there. Hence, when the grid return is connected to this terminal, the grid, too, is negative.

The cathode, however, is not connected directly to the negative terminal of the B eliminator, but through a resistor of about 1,000 ohms, as in Figure 20-3. To understand this hookup, compare the pathways of electrons from the B-battery eliminator to the grid and to the cathode, respectively. As the cathode shoots off electrons, other electrons are drawn up from the large supply on the negative terminal of the B eliminator. But some of the electrical pressure is lost in pushing these electrons through the 1,000-ohm resistor, and a voltage drop occurs across the resistor (R). In this hookup, then, the cathode is slightly less negative than the negative terminal of the B eliminator.

The grid of the tube, connected to this negative terminal without the resistor between it and the terminal, is therefore slightly more negative than the cathode. So now again there is no need for the C battery, which created exactly the same effect.

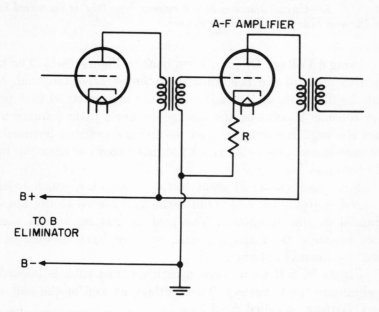

Fig. 20-3. *Circuit showing how a bias resistor (R) is used to obtain grid bias*

This method of grid bias is known as *self bias,* or *cathode bias.* The resistor we connected to the cathode of the tube is called a *bias resistor.* Different types of tubes use different values of bias resistors. The 1,000-ohm resistor mentioned here is suitable for the type 6C5 tube.

Preventing Amplification Loss with a Bypass Capacitor. If you examine Figure 20-4, you will notice that this bias resistor is in the plate circuit. The electrons stream up from the negative terminal of the B eliminator, through the bias resistor to the cathode, across to the plate and through the winding of the loudspeaker, and back to the positive terminal of the B eliminator.

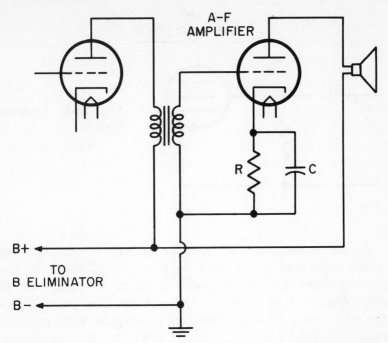

Fig. 20-4. *Circuit showing bias resistor (R) and bypass capacitor (C).*

The incoming signal, you will recall, causes the plate current to fluctuate. Thus the voltage drop across resistor R, the bias voltage for the tube, will also fluctuate. If the signal makes the grid more positive, more plate current will flow. Hence the voltage drop across R becomes greater and the negative charge it places on the grid, too, becomes greater. This, you see, works against the signal which is trying to make the grid more positive.

This condition is not desirable because it reduces the amplification. We should eliminate, somehow, the fluctuations in the voltage drop across R. To do this, a fixed capacitor, called a *cathode bypass capacitor,* is connected across the bias resistor. This capacitor smooths out the fluctuations on the same principle as the filter capacitor in the filter circuit of the B eliminator.*

Contact Bias. There is still another method for obtaining grid bias which frequently is used in the first stage of audio-frequency amplification. This is the *contact-bias* method illustrated in the circuit shown in Figure 20-5.

---

* However, when we discuss *inverse feedback* (page **519**), you will note that under certain circumstances we deliberately omit the cathode bypass capacitor.

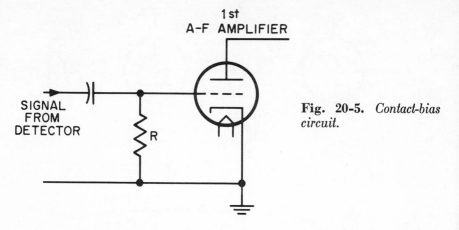

**1st
A-F AMPLIFIER**

SIGNAL
FROM
DETECTOR

R

Fig. 20-5. *Contact-bias
circuit.*

As the electrons stream from the cathode to the plate, some
of them strike and are trapped on the wires of the grid. These
electrons accumulate in sufficient quantity to make the grid
slightly negative with respect to the cathode. This, you will recall,
is the effect created by grid bias and, once again, there is no need
for the C battery.

Although the bias voltage is small (only about a half volt), it
is sufficient for the first stage of audio-frequency amplification.
This bias voltage remains fairly constant. Excess electrons are
permitted to leak off through the resistor R, which generally is
from five to ten megohms. When the bias voltage on the grid
reaches its proper negative value, further electrons are repelled by
the negative charge. When the bias voltage drops, more electrons
are encouraged to strike the wires of the grid, thus raising the
voltage to normal. Note that this method for obtaining a grid
bias is very much like the grid-leak and capacitor method.

The Complete No-Battery Receiver. Having succeeded in eliminating all batteries, we are now ready to present our no-battery
radio receiving set. This is shown in Figure 20-6. In this diagram,
the wires connecting the filaments of the tubes to the step-down
secondary, which gives the 6.3 volts of alternating current needed
to heat these filaments, are omitted for the sake of simplicity. In
wiring this set, however, a certain precaution must be taken. These
wires, carrying alternating current, have a fluctuating magnetic
field around them. If this field cuts across any other conductor
near them, currents will be induced which will interfere with the
reception of the signal.

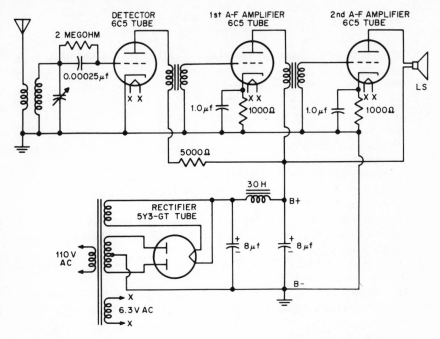

Fig. 20-6. *Diagram showing the circuit of an all-electric receiving set.*

To overcome this unwanted effect, the wires carrying alternating current to the filaments are twisted around one another in such a way that the magnetic fields of these wires neutralize one another.

SUMMARY

1. To have the grid of a tube function properly it must have a small negative charge with respect to the cathode or filament at all times.
2. The C battery which supplies a negative charge to the grid may be eliminated by various circuits.
3. Four methods of connecting the grid so as to obtain the suitable negative charge are: (a) grid-leak and capacitor bias, (b) fixed bias, using a tap on the voltage divider, (c) self bias, using a resistor in parallel with a bypass capacitor on the supply line to the cathode, (d) contact bias.
4. Wires bearing alternating current to the filament should be twisted together to neutralize the magnetic fields produced in single wires by the current.

GLOSSARY

Bypass Capacitor: A fixed capacitor placed across the cathode-bias resistor which serves to smooth out the voltage variations across that resistor and thereby supply the grid with a constant negative charge.

Cathode Bias: Same as self bias.

Cathode-Bias Resistor: A resistor between the B— terminal and the cathode of the tube, which gives the grid a negative bias with respect to the cathode.

C-Battery Eliminator: A device used to eliminate the need for the C battery by obtaining the necessary current from the B-battery eliminator.

Contact Bias: Grid bias obtained by trapping electrons on the grid of the tube and permitting them to leak off slowly through a very large resistance.

Fixed Bias: Grid bias obtained by a C battery or a tap on the power-supply voltage divider.

Grid-Leak and Capacitor Bias: Grid bias obtained by means of a grid-leak resistor and capacitor in the grid circuit.

Self Bias: Grid bias obtained from the voltage drop across a resistor common to the plate and grid circuits.

QUESTIONS AND PROBLEMS

1. What is the purpose of a negative bias on the grid?
2. In what ways can we obtain negative grid bias from the B-battery eliminator?
3. Explain the method of obtaining a negative grid bias by means of a cathode-bias resistor.
4. What is the purpose of the bypass capacitor across the cathode-bias resistor?
5. Why are the wires leading to the heater of a cathode-type tube usually twisted together?
6. Make a diagram of a receiver using an A-, B-, and C-battery eliminator, a detector, and an audio-frequency amplifier coupled by resistance coupling to the detector.

21

The AC-DC Power Supply

| PROBLEM. *How are radio receivers adapted to operate on either alternating- or direct-current power supply?*

The battery eliminators described in the previous chapters all assume the use of 110-volt alternating current. In some localities, however, the house mains supply 110-volt direct current. Since a transformer will not operate on steady direct current, it becomes obvious that the A- and B-battery eliminators previously described will not work in these direct-current localities.

There are other reasons for not using the power transformer, even in alternating-current localities. The innovation of the midget receiving set has placed a premium upon small, light receivers that can be built cheaply. Since the power transformer is bulky, heavy, and expensive, its elimination was desired by the receiving-set manufacturers. Let us see how the problem was solved.

The Transformerless Power Supply. The answer is in our half-wave rectifier system (Fig. 18-5). If we eliminate the step-up transformer and feed the 110-volt alternating current directly to the plate of the rectifier tube and filter system, we can change the house current to a steady direct current. True, we can only get about 110 volts output, but with the invention of the new and more efficient tubes, this voltage suffices for ordinary purposes.

Using this scheme and applying 110-volt direct current so that the positive lead goes to the plate of the rectifier tube, we get the same result as with the alternating current. So here we have a B-battery eliminator that works equally well on alternating or direct current and uses no power transformer.

Using House Current for the Filaments. Now let us plan for the filament current. When the house mains supply 110-volt alternating current, we can get the small voltage required to heat the filaments by one of two methods. We can use a step-down transformer as described in Chapter 19. Or else we can force the 110-volt alternating current to go through a resistor before it goes through the filaments. When current goes through this resistor, its electrical pressure is reduced to (that is, *drops* to) the small amount that is necessary to force the proper current through the filaments (Fig. 21-1).

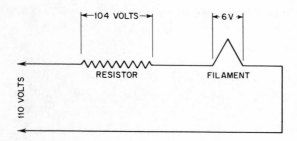

Fig. 21-1. *Diagram showing how a resistor is used to cut down the 110-volt house current to a value suitable for use on the filament of the tube.*

This second method is not as desirable as the step-down transformer method, because it wastes most of the current going through the resistor. But in a direct-current locality, only the resistor method of obtaining the filament current can be used. We, therefore, are compelled to use this method if the receiving set is to be operated in both types of localities.

An increase in efficiency is gained if we connect our filaments in series. Assume that the rectifier tube requires 5 volts to force

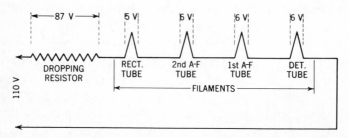

Fig. 21-2. *Diagram showing how the dropping resistor and the filaments of the rectifier, detector, and first and second audio-frequency amplifier tubes are connected in series across the 110-volt house line.*

the current through its filament, and that the detector tube, the first audio-frequency amplifier tube, and the second audio-frequency amplifier tube each require 6 volts.

When any electrical conductors are connected in series (Fig. 21-2), the resistance of the circuit is the sum of the resistances of all the parts. Hence, 23 volts are required for the filaments of the tubes and only 87 volts are wasted in the resistance ($23 + 87 =$ 110 volts).

Modern tubes are being manufactured that require even greater voltage for their filaments, and when they are used there is still smaller waste. As a matter of fact, many modern sets use tubes with such heater voltages that the total heater voltage required for all the tubes connected in series is 110 volts, and no dropping resistor is necessary.

Line-Cord Resistor. The resistor used in these circuits is called a *dropping resistor*. Its value obviously must vary with the type and number of tubes used. One variety of dropping resistor is the *line-cord resistor*. This resembles a common two-wire extension cord attached to a plug of the type used in the ordinary type of electrical outlet. But in addition to the two wires of this electric cord, and attached to one of the terminals of the plug, is a wire resistor of the proper size (Fig. 21-3). Voltage drop in this resistor is enough to give the correct filament voltage to the tubes.

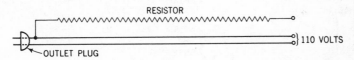

Fig. 21-3. *Diagram showing a line cord with a built-in resistor. The electric cord and resistor are covered with an asbestos and cotton casing, and the assembly looks very much like the electric cord used to connect an electric iron.*

This arrangement furnishes a convenient method for attaching the set to the house current and gives the additional advantage of having the resistor outside the set. Since the dropping resistor heats up somewhat because of the resistance to the current passing through it, it is advantageous to have it outside the set. Needless to say, you must not shorten or cut this cord or else you will reduce the value of the dropping resistor.

Another voltage-dropping device that performs a function similar to that of the dropping resistor or line-cord resistor is the *ballast tube,* which is merely a resistor within a tube envelope. It, too, is connected in series with the tube heaters.

Other Features of AC-DC Sets. Figure 21-4 shows the complete ac-dc power supply. The filaments are connected in series and are supplied by the 110-volt line. Where necessary, a dropping resistor is used. For this circuit, it is immaterial whether alternating or direct current is used.

Note that the 110-volt line feeds the rectifier tube. When direct current is used and the positive $(+)$ side of the line is on the rectifier plate, the rectifier tube passes current at all times, with a resulting B voltage from the power supply. When the plug is so inserted in the outlet that the negative side of the line is on the rectifier plate, current will not pass through the rectifier and there will be no B-voltage output from the power supply. The remedy then would be to reverse the plug in the outlet.

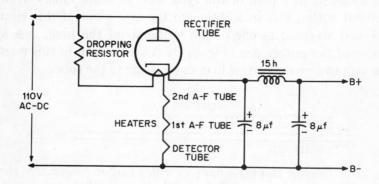

Fig. 21-4. *Diagram showing the circuit of the complete ac-dc power supply. The symbol 15h stands for a filter choke coil of 15 henrys.*

When alternating current is used in the house mains, the rectifier will pass current only when the main line connected to the plate becomes positive. This results in half-wave rectification. Reversing the plug will not affect the power supply.

Practically any radio tube can be used as a rectifier. Some tubes, however, like the type 35Z5, are more efficient for this purpose. Once the B supply is developed, grid bias may be obtained in the usual manner described on pages 155 to 159.

The type 35Z5 tube has a portion of its heater circuit tapped so that there is a voltage drop of 7½ volts between the tap and one end of the heater. (Figure 21-5). We can utilize this voltage drop to supply current to a small 6-volt pilot lamp that indicates when the receiver is turned on.

The Selenium Rectifier. Many ac-dc power supplies use a *dry-disk rectifier* in place of the diode rectifier tube. One form of this dry-disk rectifier consists of several selenium plates connected together. See Figure 21-6. Like the crystal detector discussed in Chapter 8 and like the diode tube, the selenium rectifier passes current primarily in one direction, but blocks it in the

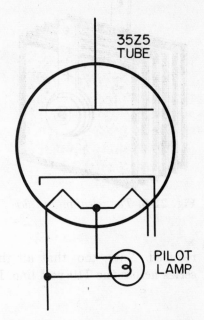

Fig. 21-5. *How the tap on the heater of the type 35Z5 rectifier tube is used to supply current to the pilot lamp.*

other direction. Thus it can act as a rectifier. Unlike the crystal detector, the selenium rectifier is capable of handling the considerable current required of the power supply. The symbol for the dry-disk rectifier is the same as that for the crystal detector, namely,

The bar of the symbol corresponds to the cathode of the rectifier tube and usually is indicated by a plus (+) marked on one terminal of the selenium rectifier. Just as the cathode of the tube, this terminal connects to the B+ line of the power supply.

Other dry-disk rectifiers, such as of germanium and silicon, may be used as well. Dry-disk rectifiers have a number of advantages over the tube type. They are smaller and lighter, and require no filament circuit or power. They are more rugged, have a longer life, and operate at lower temperatures. Also, because they have no filament to heat up, they are instant-starting.

Fig. 21-6. *The selenium rectifier.*

The circuit of a typical power supply of this type is shown in Figure 21-7. Note that the filter choke coil has been replaced by resistor R_2. Modern sets, especially the smaller ones, tend to substitute such a resistor of about 1,000 ohms for the choke coil for filtering. The filter capacitors (C_1 and C_2) then are, generally, of higher value, about 20 to 80 μf each. The filtering action of such an arrangement is sufficient and the cost is greatly reduced. Note, too, that all the tube filaments are connected in series across the 110-volt line. Resistor R_1 is the dropping resistor.

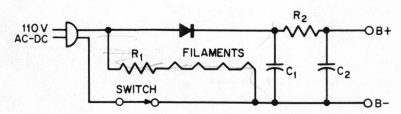

Fig. 21-7. *The ac-dc power supply using a dry-disk rectifier.*

SUMMARY

1. B-battery eliminators made to operate by the use of step-up and step-down transformers cannot be used on direct-current house mains.
2. The principle involved in the modern ac-dc receivers is to connect tube heaters in series across the 110-volt house line, using a dropping resistor where necessary, and to use half-wave rectifiers for the B voltage.
3. Ac-dc sets operate by plugging in to any outlet carrying house current. The extension cord may contain a line-cord resistor to provide the correct voltage for the filaments.
4. On direct-current circuits it is sometimes necessary to turn a plug around in the outlet fixture so that the proper polarity may be obtained.

GLOSSARY

Ac-Dc Power Supply: A battery eliminator that operates without a power transformer from 110-volt alternating or direct current.

Ballast Tube: A resistor within a tube, having the same function as a dropping resistor.

Line-Cord Resistor: A resistor in the power line which uses up most of the 110-volts, leaving a small portion for the filaments.

Rectifier, dry-disk: A rectifier consisting of stacked plates of certain types of metals such as selenium, germanium, and silicon.

SYMBOLS

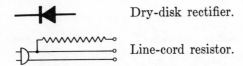

Dry-disk rectifier.

Line-cord resistor.

QUESTIONS AND PROBLEMS

1. Why must we use a special power supply where direct current is furnished?
2. What is the approximate voltage output of an ac-dc power supply into which we feed 110-volt alternating or direct current?
3. How are filament voltages obtained in an ac-dc power supply?
4. What name is given to a resistor in the power cord of an ac-dc receiver?
5. What danger is there in cutting the power cord of an ac-dc receiver to make it shorter and less cumbersome?
6. If a receiver with an ac-dc power supply fails to operate in a direct-current district, after being tested and no faults found, what would you examine in hunting for a possible cause of no operation?
7. Identify the numbered parts.

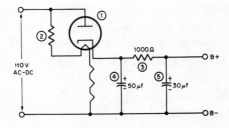

22

The Dynamic Speaker

| PROBLEM 1. *How is the dynamic speaker constructed?*
| PROBLEM 2. *How is the dynamic speaker connected in the receiver?*

Faults of the Paper-Cone Speaker. Turn back to Figure 7-7. Although we have greatly improved our radio receiver since we built the crystal detector set, our loudspeaker has remained a paper cone fastened to the diaphragm of the earphone. Now let us give it some attention.

The loudspeaker, as shown, has one very bad fault. Our amplified signal is carried by a large current. This current from the plate circuit of the last amplifier tube passes through the coil of the speaker. When the resulting strong pull is exerted on the diaphragm, it is bent back until it touches the end of the permanent magnet. The effect is that the speaker rattles on loud signals.

The Electromagnetic Dynamic Speaker. An ingenious device was evolved to overcome this defect. A speaker coil, called a *voice coil,* is wound on a small tube of bakelite. This tube is mounted so that it can slide back and forth over a soft-iron *pole piece.* To this tube, the paper cone is attached. Also attached to this tube, to keep it in place, is a thin springy sheet of bakelite, called a *spider.* (See Figure 22-1.)

An electromagnet of many turns of fine wire is also mounted on the pole piece. This electromagnet, called the *field coil,* is connected to a source of steady direct current. The field coil sets up a strong, steady magnetic field as long as the current flows through it.

The fluctuating current in the final audio-frequency amplifier stage is made to flow through the voice coil. As a result, a fluc-

168

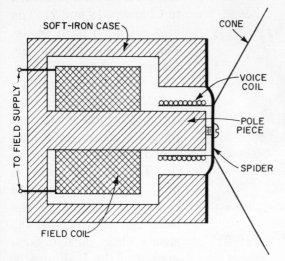

Fig. 22-1. *Diagram of an electromagnetic dynamic speaker.*

tuating magnetic field surrounds this coil. This fluctuating field, reacting with the strong, steady magnetic field of the field coil, causes the voice coil to move back and forth on the pole piece in step with the fluctuations of the plate current.

The thin, springy spider permits the voice coil to move, but forces it to come back once the pull ceases. The paper cone, connected to the voice coil, moves with it. Of necessity, the voice coil, and the tube upon which it is wound, must be very light. The coil consists of a few turns of fine copper wire, and the tube is made of very thin bakelite. Now, large plate currents can move the paper cone quite vigorously without the danger of a diaphragm striking the end of the magnet and thus causing rattling.

This type of speaker is called a *dynamic speaker*. Since it has an electromagnetic field coil, we call it an *electromagnetic dynamic speaker*. The symbol for this type of speaker is

Supplying Current for the Field Coil. Several means exist for obtaining the steady direct current needed for the field coil of this speaker. In the early days of radio a separate storage battery of 6 or 12 volts was used. This method is still used in some portable outdoor loudspeaker systems where very loud sound and, accordingly, a very strong field is needed.

Another method is to rectify and filter the house current,

Fig. 22-2. *Electromagnetic dynamic speaker.*

using the systems described in Chapters 18 and 21. The field coil then must be designed to operate on the higher voltages obtained. This method of obtaining a field-coil current is used for auditoriums or outdoor purposes where very loud sound is desired.

The method that is most commonly used for supplying current to the field coil is to pass the steady direct current flowing out of the B eliminator through the field coil before it passes onto the radio receiver (Figure 22-3). Not only does this system eliminate the need for a separate storage battery or power supply for the speaker, but the field coil acts as a second choke coil, and thus helps further to filter the plate current supplied to the radio receiver. In many receivers, the speaker field coil is the only filter choke coil. In other cases, the speaker field coil may be connected so as to form a portion of the voltage-divider system. In each case, it is energized by relatively smooth direct current.

The Output Transformer. The voice coil cannot be connected directly in the plate circuit of the last amplifier tube. It has been found that the most efficient transfer of power takes place when the resistance of the voice coil equals the resistance of the am-

Fig. 22-3. *Diagram showing how current is obtained from the power supply to operate the field coil of the electromagnetic dynamic speaker.*

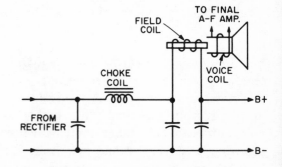

Fig. 22-4. *Diagram show-ing how a step-down trans-former (output transform-er) is used to couple the voice coil of the electro-magnetic dynamic speaker to the plate circuit of the final audio-frequency tube.*

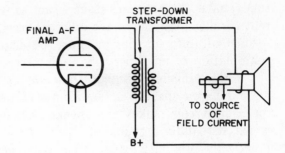

plifier tube (Chap. 38). The tube resistance is quite high, about 10,000 ohms for the type 6C5 tube. But since the voice coil must be kept light, it is wound with a few turns of wire, and its resist-ance usually is from 2 to 30 ohms.

Here our old friend, the step-down transformer, comes to the rescue. The primary, which is connected in the plate circuit, has a great many turns, and its resistance equals the tube resistance, thus insuring the maximum transfer of power. The secondary has few turns, and its resistance is made to equal the resistance of the voice coil, thus again insuring the maximum power transfer. The circuit is shown in Figure 22-4.

The step-down transformer, used in connection with the dy-namic speaker, is called an *output transformer*. Since different

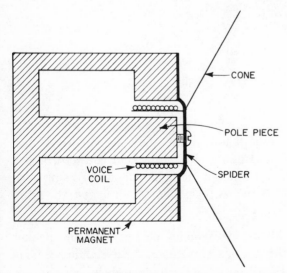

Fig. 22-5. *Diagram of a permanent-magnet dy-namic speaker.*

tubes have different resistances and the voice coils of different speakers, too, may have different resistances, an output transformer of different design must be used to match each new combination of amplifier-tube and voice-coil resistance.

The Permanent-Magnet Dynamic Speaker. The electromagnetic dynamic speaker suffers from a number of defects. The need for a field coil makes the speaker expensive and heavy. Even worse, it requires a source of steady direct current. This makes it practically prohibitive for use in portable receivers that operate from small batteries.

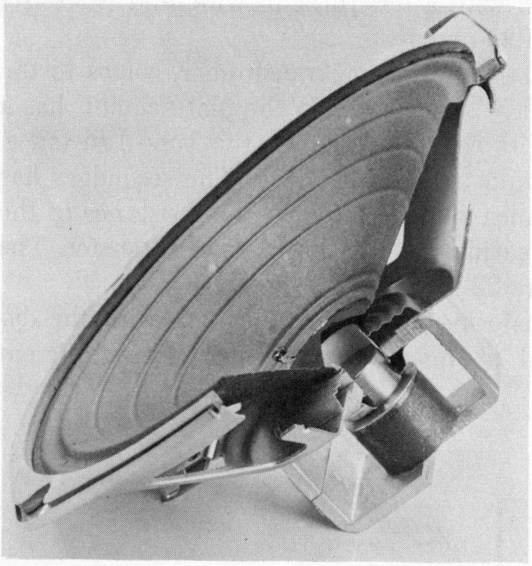

Fig. 22-6. *Permanent-magnet dynamic speaker.*

Accordingly, the field coil has been replaced by a powerful permanent magnet, usually made of an alloy known as Alnico. This magnet is cheaper and lighter than the field coil and, above all, requires no current for its magnetic field. A speaker using such a magnet is known as a *permanent-magnet dynamic speaker* (Figure 22-5). Its symbol is 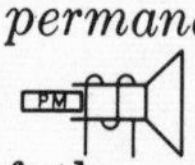

The development of the permanent-magnet type of speaker has largely eliminated the use of electromagnetic dynamic speakers for ordinary home use. Small portable receivers use the permanent-magnet type exclusively. Even for outdoor and auditorium use, this type is widely employed.

SUMMARY

1. In the *permanent-magnet dynamic speaker, a voice coil,* consisting of a small, light coil of a few turns of fine wire, is mounted so that it may slide back and forth on a permanent magnet. This voice coil is connected to the output of the final audio-frequency amplifier tube. The fluctuating plate current flowing through this coil sets up a fluctuating magnetic field around the coil. This fluctuating magnetic field reacts with the constant magnetic field around the permanent magnet and, as a result, the voice coil is forced to move back and forth on the permanent magnet. Attached to the voice coil is a large paper cone and, as it moves with the voice coil, it sets large volumes of air in motion, thus producing loud sounds. A thin, springy bakelite strip, called a *spider,* tends to keep the voice coil in its original position.
2. In the *electromagnetic dynamic speaker,* an electromagnet replaces the permanent magnet for producing the constant magnetic field. Because the electromagnet may have a more powerful field than does the permanent magnet, the interaction with the magnetic field around the voice coil may be greater, and a louder sound may result.
3. An *output transformer* is used to match the voice coil to the final audio-frequency amplifier tube.
4. The electromagnet of the electromagnetic dynamic speaker, often called the *field coil,* may be used as a filter choke coil in the B power supply.

GLOSSARY

Dynamic Speaker: A type of loudspeaker that depends for its operation upon the reaction between a steady magnetic field and the fluctuating magnetic field produced around the voice coil.

Electromagnetic Dynamic Speaker: A dynamic speaker that uses an electromagnet to produce the steady magnetic field.

Field Coil: The electromagnet that furnishes the steady magnetic field for an electromagnetic dynamic speaker.

Output Transformer: A step-down transformer that couples the electrical energy from the plate circuit of the last audio-frequency amplifier tube to the voice coil.

Permanent Magnet: A magnet that retains its magnetism after the magnetizing force which produced it is removed.

Permanent-Magnet Dynamic Speaker: A dynamic speaker that uses a permanent magnet to produce the steady magnetic field.

Spider: A piece of elastic material that constantly tends to return the voice coil to its normal position.

Voice Coil: The small coil of the dynamic speaker through which electrical energy from the plate circuit of the last audio-frequency amplifier tube is fed, setting up a fluctuating magnetic field that reacts with the steady magnetic field to drive a cone, thus producing sound.

SYMBOLS

 Electromagnetic dynamic speaker.

 Permanent-magnet dynamic speaker.

QUESTIONS AND PROBLEMS

1. What was one defect of the diaphragm type of loudspeaker?
2. What current provides the energy for the voice coil of a loudspeaker?
3. What causes the voice coil of a loudspeaker to move?
4. Describe the structure of a permanent-magnet dynamic speaker.
5. Why may the voice coil not be connected directly in the plate circuit of the last amplifier tube?
6. By what means is the voice coil of a loudspeaker coupled to the last amplifier tube?
7. How is the field coil of an electromagnetic dynamic speaker energized (that is, given energy)? Describe two methods.
8. What are some shortcomings of an electromagnetic dynamic speaker?

23

The Radio-Frequency Amplifier

When future historians record the achievements of the first half of the twentieth century, the most outstanding accomplishment, perhaps, will be the conquest of time and space. The invention of the airplane destroyed distance. Oceans were spanned and continents crossed in a matter of a few hours.

But fast though the airplane is, it cannot compare with the speed of radio, which can figuratively flash the spoken word seven times around the world in one second!

More Power Needed. To utilize fully the magical powers of radio, the receiver must be made much more sensitive than the set we have just described. True, the audio amplifier can build up the signal from a whisper in the earphones to a volume loud enough to fill a large auditorium, but in order to function, it has to receive this signal from the detector. The radio-frequency current in the antenna-ground system must be powerful enough to operate the detector.

Now, a very powerful transmitting station, operating a few

175

miles from the receiver, can set currents flowing in the antenna-ground system large enough to give satisfactory results. But weak stations, many miles away, are unable to emit a wave with sufficient energy to build up a signal that can be passed on to the audio amplifier.

The problem, therefore, is to devise a system that will build up the signal before it reaches the detector.

The Radio-Frequency Amplifier. When radio development encountered this problem, the three-element radio tube once again was called on to act as an amplifier. In this case, the current flowing into the amplifier alternates at a frequency of hundreds of thousands or even millions of cycles per second. It alternates, that is, at radio frequency. For this reason, the amplifier is called a *radio-frequency amplifier* to distinguish it from the audio-frequency amplifier in whose circuit the current is alternating at audio frequency—that is, between 30 and 15,000 cycles per second.

The radio-frequency amplifier works in the same way as does the audio-frequency amplifier. A small alternating voltage places an alternating charge upon the grid of the radio tube. This grid charge, in turn, controls the large plate current supplied by the B battery or B power supply (Chap. 17).

The methods for coupling one radio-frequency amplifier tube to another are likewise the same methods used in the audio-frequency amplifier: either transformer or resistance coupling. But resistance coupling in radio-frequency amplifiers is seldom used, and we need not discuss it here.

The method of coupling most commonly used is transformer coupling. The transformer used for radio-frequency amplification differs from the audio transformer in that it is usually an air-core transformer and has fewer turns.*

The Tuned Radio-Frequency Transformer. If you examine Figure 23-1, you will see that the radio-frequency transformer resembles the antenna coupler. The only difference is that the secondary winding of the antenna coupler is in a tuning or "tuned" circuit, whereas the secondary of the radio-frequency transformer is not. However, it was soon discovered that certain advantages could be gained if the secondary of the radio-frequency transformer was made a part of a tuned circuit by connecting it with a

* Many modern radio-frequency transformers are constructed with powdered-iron cores. These differ from the audio-frequency cores which are built up of sheets of iron and cannot be used in radio-frequency coils.

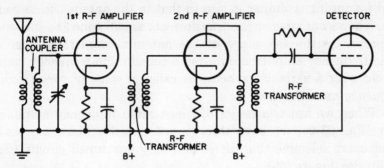

Fig. 23-1. *Diagram showing the circuit of two transformer-coupled radio-frequency amplifier stages.*

variable capacitor similar to the one used to tune the secondary of the antenna coupler.

Advantages of Tuned Radio-Frequency Amplification. You already have learned how the tuning circuit permits the signal from the station of the desired frequency to flow through it and tends to stop all others. However, some unwanted frequencies do manage to get through the tuner. If the signal is forced to pass through a series of such tuning circuits, however, the chances for the unwanted frequencies to leak through become proportionately less. In this way, our set becomes more selective.

A radio-frequency transformer whose secondary is tuned by means of a variable capacitor is called a *tuned radio-frequency transformer*. The tuned radio-frequency transformer is practically the same as the antenna coupler, whereas the variable capacitor

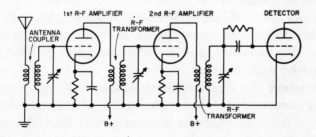

Fig. 23-2. *Diagram showing the circuit of two tuned radio-frequency amplifier stages.*

used for tuning is similar in size to that in the antenna tuning circuit. The secondaries of the transformers are all tuned to the same frequency as the secondary of the antenna coupler. A stage of radio-frequency amplification using a tuned radio-frequency transformer with a variable capacitor is called a stage of *tuned radio-frequency amplification.*

When we use two stages of tuned radio frequency amplification (Fig. 23-2), we have three tuned circuits. Thus, our set is much more selective than if we had only one tuned circuit (Fig. 23-1). See Figure 23-3.

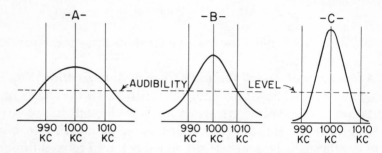

Fig. 23-3. *A—Tuning curve with one tuned circuit. Notice that stations at 990 kc and 1,010 kc are heard when the set is tuned to 1,000 kc.*

B—Tuning curve with two tuned circuits. Note that the two unwanted stations are just at the audibility level.

C—Tuning curve with three tuned circuits. The two unwanted stations cannot be heard.

Tuned radio-frequency amplification has another advantage over an untuned stage. Since the natural frequency of the tuned circuits is the same as the frequency of the incoming signal, the oscillations of the electrons in the tuned circuits are permitted to build up, and this building up results in a louder signal. Of course, one disadvantage of the tuned stage is that it requires an additional variable capacitor, and an additional dial or knob accordingly must be manipulated.

Eliminating the Effect of Stray Magnetic Fields. One of the difficulties encountered in the manufacture of the radio-frequency amplifier is the fact that the magnetic field around one radio-frequency transformer may be large enough to cut across the coils of another such transformer. This action sets an unwanted current flowing in the second transformer, and oscillations and distortion of the signal result. This evil is remedied in several ways.

Of course, we may space these transformers far enough apart to prevent this unwanted effect. But this plan is not practical, especially since we do not want our receiving set to be too large.

Setting the Transformers at Right Angles to Each Other. Another solution is to mount our transformers so that the windings, and hence the magnetic fields, are at right angles to each other (Fig. 23-4-B). In such an arrangement, the transfer of energy from one transformer to another is at a minimum. (See the discussion of coupling in the regenerative receiver in Chapter 16.)

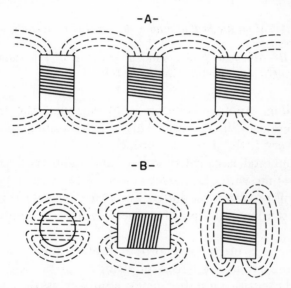

-A-

-B-

Fig. 23-4. *Tuned radio-frequency transformers mounted near one another. The dotted lines around each coil represent its magnetic field.*

A—The radio-frequency transformers are mounted parallel to one another. Note how the magnetic fields couple the coils to one another. The transfer of electrical energy from one coil to the other is fairly large.

B—The radio-frequency transformers are mounted at right angles to one another. Note that the transfer of electrical energy from one coil to the others is at a minimum.

Coils with Smaller Diameters. Another way is to design our transformer so that its magnetic field is kept close to it. A short coil of large diameter has a wider magnetic field around it than a long coil of smaller diameter (Fig. 23-5). We now make our transformers an inch or less in diameter and use more turns of wire.

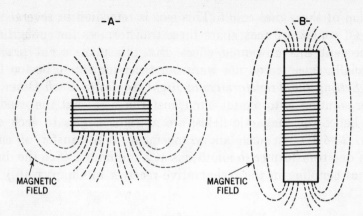

Fig. 23-5. *A—Magnetic field around a short coil of large diameter. Note how the field spreads out.*

  B—Magnetic field around a long coil of small diameter. Note that the magnetic field remains close to the coil.

Shielding. Another solution is to surround the transformer with a metal shield, or case. This shield absorbs the magnetic field and very little of it gets through.

This method is called *shielding,* and radio receivers use this device together with the narrower coil. The symbol signifying a shielded coil consists of a dotted line placed around this coil. The metals most commonly used for shielding are aluminum and copper.

Shielding is often used also to protect the radio-frequency amplifier tube from the effects of stray magnetic fields. Less frequently, the entire radio-frequency amplifier stage, consisting of

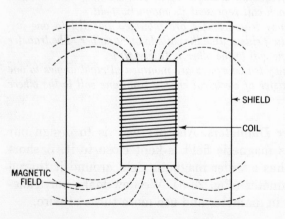

Fig. 23-6. *Coil shielded by a metallic can. Note that very little of the magnetic field penetrates the shield.*

the transformer, the variable capacitor, the radio tube, and the wiring, is enclosed in a shielding case. Such complete shielding is rarely necessary. It is usually enough to shield the radio-frequency transformer and tube. All metal used for shielding must be connected to the ground of the receiver. Thus, any voltages induced in the shield by the magnetic fields are grounded out, and so will not affect any component part within the receiver.

Audio-frequency amplifiers are less subject to the effects of these stray magnetic fields. Nevertheless, the audio transformers are usually shielded and mounted so that the windings of one transformer are at right angles to the windings of the other.

Fig. 23-7. *Radio-frequency transformer and its shield.*

Feedback in a Radio-Frequency Amplifier Tube. In designing radio-frequency amplifiers, means must be taken to avoid feedback. In the regenerative detector circuit, we deliberately caused some of the plate current to be fed back to the grid circuit (pages 108-110). This feedback was carefully controlled and made the set more sensitive.

In the radio-frequency amplifier, however, such feedback is undesirable, because it results in oscillation and other distortions of the signal. Such feedback may come from several sources, and all of it must be eliminated.

The chief source of feedback lies in the tube itself. Any two conductors, separated by a dielectric, will form a capacitor. The electrodes of the tube are such conductors. The dielectric is the vacuum between them.

Capacitance Effects in the Tube. Thus, a capacitance exists between the cathode and the grid, the grid and the plate, and the cathode and the plate (Fig. 23-8). Because of the small area of the conductors, these capacitors have small capacitance. But small though it is, the capacitance provided by the combination of the grid and the plate causes considerable trouble. By means of this small capacitive effect, the output circuit (the plate circuit) and the input circuit (the grid circuit) are linked, and feedback occurs.

Examine the circuit of the stage of radio-frequency amplification shown in Figure 23-9. The B battery places a positive charge on the plate of the tube. Fluctuations of the plate current, resulting from the signal, will cause this positive charge on the plate to fluctuate.

Now, consider the plate and grid as two conductors forming a capacitor. The plate of the tube, being charged positively, causes a certain number of electrons to gather on the grid. The grid, that is, gets a negative charge. The more positively charged the plate, the more electrons are pulled over to the opposite electrode of the capacitor, the grid.

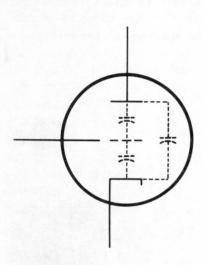

Fig. 23-8. *Diagram showing the capacitive effect existing between the electrodes of the triode. The result is the same as if small capacitors were connected between the electrodes.*

The more highly positive the plate, then, the more electrons flow through the secondary of the radio-frequency transformer to the grid. As the plate loses some of its positive charge, some electrons are forced to flow from the grid back through the secondary of the radio-frequency transformer.

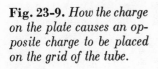

Fig. 23-9. *How the charge on the plate causes an opposite charge to be placed on the grid of the tube.*

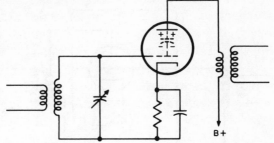

Thus, the fluctuating charge on the plate of the tube sets up a corresponding oscillation of the electrons in the grid circuit. This oscillation causes distortion, and must be eliminated.

Correcting the Influence of the Capacitance Within the Tube. Several methods exist for correcting this tube capacitance. One is to connect a 500 to 1,000-ohm resistor in the grid circuit (Fig. 23-10).

This resistor uses up the electrical pressure of the electrons set oscillating in the grid circuit described above, and the distortion is, therefore, eliminated. This method of eliminating feedback is called the *losser method*. It suffers from the disadvantage that it dissipates not only the unwanted flow of electrons caused by

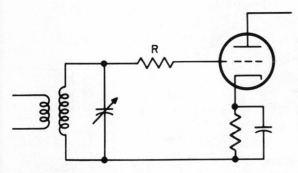

Fig. 23-10. *The losser method of preventing oscillations in the radio-frequency amplifier. The resistor R dissipates the unwanted flow of electrons.*

feedback, but also some of the desired signal voltage. The result is a loss of amplification.

Another method for preventing feedback is the *neutralization method*. A small capacitor, as shown in Figure 23-11, is connected across the grid and plate of the tube in such a way as to neutralize the plate-to-grid capacitance. This eliminates the feed-

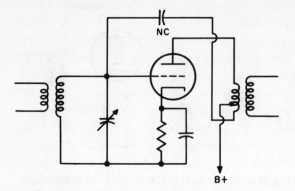

Fig. 23-11. *How a neutralizing capacitor (NC) is employed to eliminate the feedback due to the internal capacitance between the grid and plate of the tube.*

back without a resulting loss of amplification. This small fixed capacitor is called the *neutralizing capacitor*.

One end of the neutralizing capacitor is connected to the grid of the tube, and the other end is connected to the bottom of the primary of the radio-frequency transformer. The B+ is brought to a tap on this primary near the bottom of the coil.

This neutralizing capacitor acts as a storage tank, and electrons which without it would have been sent oscillating in the grid circuit, are instead stored on its negative plate. The action is as though a flow of electrons equal to the feedback, but opposite in direction, were taking place. The opposing streams of electrons cancel out and there is no feedback.

Feedback due to capacitance within the tube is eliminated in modern receiving sets by using tubes of the screen-grid class. We will duscuss this more fully in the chapter dealing with types of tubes.

Decoupling Filters. Undesirable feedback may occur from one stage to another through the power supply, which is common to all. This difficulty is remedied by providing a separate path to ground for

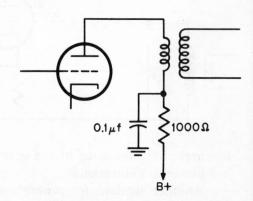

Fig. 23-12. *How a decoupling filter is used to bypass any radio-frequency current leaking across the B supply.*

any radio-frequency current which finds itself headed toward the B+ terminal of the power supply.

A fixed resistor of about 1,000 ohms is connected between the bottom of the primary of the radio-frequency transformer and the B+ line. A fixed capacitor of about 0.1 microfarad is connected between this junction and ground. (See Figure 23-12.)

Then, any radio-frequency current flowing in the plate circuit will pass through the capacitor to the ground (which is an easy path for radio-frequency current), rather than through the resistor to the power supply (which presents a larger opposition to radio-frequency currents) and then to the other tubes. We call such a fixed capacitor and resistor a *decoupling filter.*

(As we shall see later, the screen grid of the pentode also connects to the power supply. Accordingly, similar decoupling filters may be used in the screen-grid circuit to keep out undesirable feedback. On the other hand, some receivers do not employ decoupling filters, relying solely upon good design to keep out the unwanted radio-frequency currents.)

We may use a slightly different device to prevent any radio-frequency current that finds itself in the plate circuit of the detector tube from going into the power supply and the audio-frequency amplifier, where it can cause some distortion.

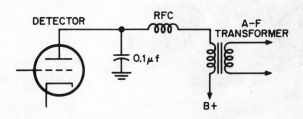

Fig. 23-13. *How a radio-frequency choke coil (RFC) and bypass capacitor are used to keep stray radio-frequency currents from leaking into the audio-frequency amplifier and power supply.*

Between the plate and the primary of the first audio-frequency transformer, we connect a small coil whose inductance is about 2½ millihenrys. We call this coil a *radio-frequency choke coil.* This choke coil offers a high opposition to the radio-frequency current, but not to the fluctuating direct current fed to the audio-frequency transformer. To permit the radio-frequency current to escape, we connect a small fixed capacitor of about 0.1 μf from a point between the plate and the choke coil to the ground.

Bias for the Radio-Frequency Amplifier. As in the case of audio-frequency amplification, a negative bias is placed on the grid of the radio-frequency amplifier tube to prevent distortion. Here, too, care must be taken not to make this negative bias too great, else detection will take place (page 122).

Ganging of the Variable Tuning Capacitors. It is customary to use two stages of tuned radio-frequency amplification before the detector of the receiving set. Using fewer than two stages means not enough amplification, whereas using more makes it extremely difficult to control oscillations. If you examine Figure 23-2, you will see that such a receiver, using two stages of tuned radio-frequency amplification, has three variable capacitors which must be manipulated to bring in the desired station. Since all three tuned circuits are very nearly alike, the variable capacitors, too, will be meshed or unmeshed to about the same degree for receiving any given station.

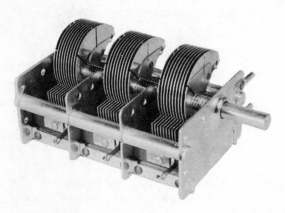

Fig. 23-14. *Three-gang variable capacitor.*

It becomes logical, therefore, to connect all three variable capacitors so that they may be operated simultaneously by turning one dial. This process of connecting the variable capacitors is called *ganging*.

Early methods of ganging the variable capacitors consisted

of hooking them up with gears or a belt. This soon gave way to the simpler method of mounting all three variable capacitors on one shaft. We now speak of a *three-gang variable capacitor*.

Use of Trimmers with Variable Capacitors. It is quite obvious that all three tuning circuits must be identical if the set is to function properly with ganged capacitors. It is impossible, however, to make two coils or two variable capacitors that are absolutely identical. Small variations are bound to creep in.

To overcome these slight discrepancies, a very small capacitor, called a *trimmer,* is connected across each variable capacitor of the tuning circuits. This trimmer usually consists of two metal plates, about ½ inch square, that are separated by a sheet of mica. Turning a screw separates the plates or brings them closer together, thus varying the capacitance of the trimmer. This small capacitor is usually mounted at the side of the variable capacitor.

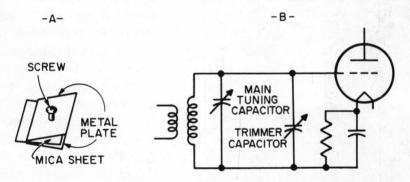

Fig. 23-15. *A—Trimmer capacitor used to align the radio-frequency amplifier stages.*

B—Circuit showing how the trimmer is connected across the main tuning capacitor.

These trimmers are adjusted to compensate for the discrepancies in the various tuning circuits. Their action is to vary slightly the amount of capacitance in the tuning circuit to make the natural frequency of that circuit equal to that of all the other tuning circuits. Once adjusted, the trimmers are left in those positions. This process of matching up the various tuning circuits of a radio receiver is called *aligning the set.*

Use of Trimmers on Antennas. While on the subject of the trimmer capacitor, it should be noted here that one of these trimmers, called the *antenna trimmer,* is sometimes connected in series with the antenna-ground system (Fig. 23-16). The effect of this small capacitor is to lengthen or shorten the antenna electrically.

This change in the antenna is desirable because each set will work most efficiently with an antenna of a certain length. Of course, you may go up on the roof and snip off some of the wire from the antenna, but it is much simpler to adjust the antenna trimmer until the signals are at their loudest. Once set, the trimmer is left alone until a new antenna is put up.

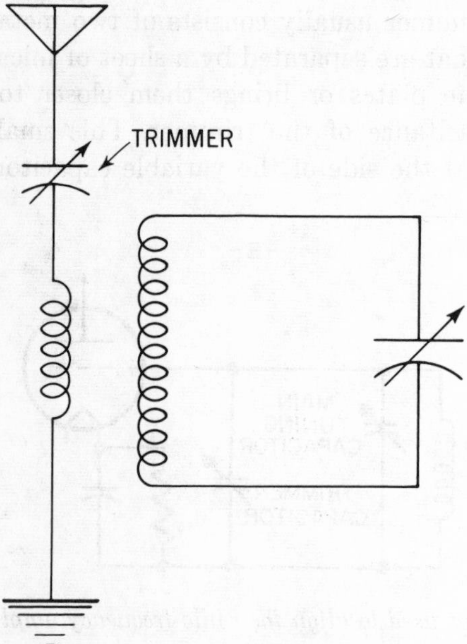

Radio-Frequency Amplification Compared with Audio-Frequency Amplification. In comparing our two types of amplification, we must remember that they complement each other. We cannot use too many stages of either radio-frequency or audio-frequency amplification without running into oscillations, noises, or distortion of signals. Receivers of this type, therefore, usually consist of two stages of radio-frequency amplification, the detector, and two stages of audio-frequency amplification.

Fig. 23-16. *Use of trimmer capacitor to adjust the antenna to the radio receiver.*

A stage of tuned radio-frequency amplification has certain advantages over a stage of audio-frequency amplification. First of all, the sensitivity of the set is increased by radio-frequency amplification. In addition, the selectivity of the receiver is improved. Further, stage for stage, radio-frequency amplification gives greater gain than audio-frequency amplification.

On the other hand, the power output of the audio-frequency amplifier is greater than that of the radio-frequency amplifier. Under normal conditions, the radio-frequency amplifier and detector

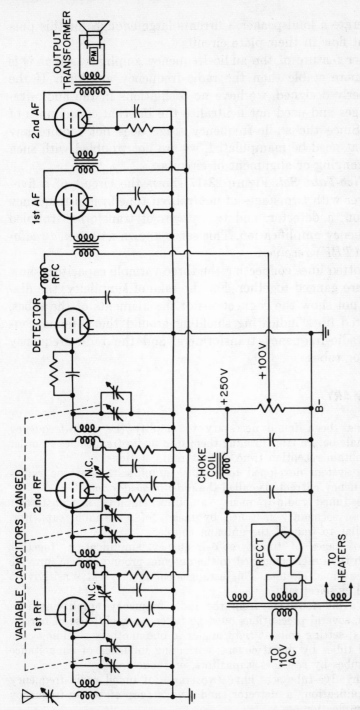

Fig. 23-17. *Circuit for a complete, tuned radio-frequency receiver.*

cannot operate a loudspeaker. Currents large enough for this purpose do not flow in their plate circuits.

Another feature of the audio-frequency amplifier is that it is normally more stable than the radio-frequency amplifier. If the set is properly designed, we have no oscillations in the audio-frequency stages and need not neutralize the internal capacitance of the tube. Since the audio-frequency stage does not require any controls that need be manipulated, we are not troubled with such things as ganging or alignment of circuits.

The Five-Tube Set. Figure 23-17 shows the circuit of a five-tube receiver with two stages of neutralized tuned radio-frequency amplification, a detector, and two stages of transformer-coupled audio-frequency amplification. This set is known as a *tuned radio-frequency (TRF) receiver.*

The dotted lines connecting the three variable capacitors show that they are ganged together. For the sake of simplicity, the diagram does not show the connections of the filaments of the tubes, or the dotted lines indicating shielding around the antenna coupler, the radio-frequency transformers, and the radio-frequency and detector tubes.

SUMMARY

1. It has been found necessary to amplify the radio-frequency signals before transforming them into audio frequencies in order to obtain reception from distant radio stations.
2. The system developed to produce amplification of the radio-frequency currents is called the *radio-frequency amplifier.*
3. The tuned radio-frequency amplifier employs a transformer whose secondary is tuned by means of a variable capacitor, similar to that of the antenna coupler.
4. Two stages of tuned radio-frequency amplification, together with the tuner connected to the antenna-ground system, provide three tuned circuits. This arrangement gives great sensitiviy as well as selectivity.
5. To avoid feedback from the radio-frequency amplifying system, several precautions must be taken—namely: use of narrow coils; setting coils at right angles to one another; shielding coils and tubes by metal covers; correcting influence of capacitance in tubes by resistors, capacitors, or choke coils.
6. Many five-tube sets have two stages of tuned radio-frequency amplification, a detector, and two stages of audio-frequency amplification.

GLOSSARY

Antenna Trimmer: A small variable capacitor in the antenna circuit used to adjust the length of the antenna electrically.

Alignment: The process of adjusting the tuned circuits of a TRF receiver so that all of them have the same natural frequency.

Bypass Capacitor: A fixed capacitor that shunts to the ground any unwanted radio-frequency currents.

Feedback: The transfer of electrical energy from the plate circuit of a tube to a preceding grid circuit. This is usually undesirable, and produces distortion of the signal. (But see *Regeneration,* page 108.)

Ganged Capacitors: Variable capacitors, so hooked up that they turn simultaneously from a common shaft.

Neutralization: The elimination of the feedback due to the interelectrode capacitance between the plate and grid of the tube.

Neutralizing Capacitor: A small capacitor connected in such a way as to neutralize the capacitance between the plate and grid of a tube.

Radio Frequency: The frequency of the radio wave. Those in the broadcast band range between 535 and 1,605 kc per second.

Radio-Frequency Amplifier: An amplifier that amplifies the radio-frequency current from the tuning circuit before feeding it into the detector.

Radio-Frequency Choke Coil (RFC): A coil of many turns offering a high resistance to radio-frequency currents, but not to low-frequency currents.

Radio-Frequency Transformer: A transformer, usually wound with an air core, used to couple radio-frequency electrical energy from one circuit to another.

Shielding: The act of surrounding a current-carrying device by a metal container to keep magnetic fields in or out.

Trimmer: A small variable capacitor connected across the large tuning capacitor used to adjust the latter (see *Alignment,* above).

Tuned Radio-Frequency (TRF) Receiver: A receiver using one or more tuned radio-frequency amplifier stages, a detector, and one or more audio-frequency amplifier stages.

Tuned Radio-Frequency Transformer: A radio-frequency transformer whose secondary is tuned by a variable capacitor.

SYMBOLS

Radio-frequency transformer.

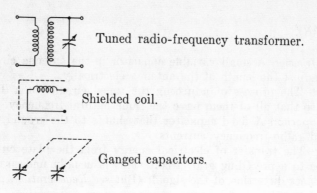

Tuned radio-frequency transformer.

Shielded coil.

Ganged capacitors.

QUESTIONS AND PROBLEMS

1. What is the chief fault of a receiver using a regenerative detector and two stages of audio amplification?
2. How may we overcome the weakness discussed in Question 1?
3. What is meant by a radio-frequency amplifier?
4. How do we usually couple radio-frequency amplifiers to each other and to the detector?
5. In what way does a radio-frequency transformer differ from an audio-frequency transformer?
6. Why do we gain more selectivity by using several stages of tuned radio-frequency amplification?
7. Draw a sketch of a circuit from the antenna and ground system to the detector, using two stages of tuned radio-frequency amplification.
8. List several advantages of tuned radio-frequency stages over untuned radio-frequency amplifier stages.
9. How do we prevent the stray magnetic fields developed by our radio-frequency transformers from producing unwanted voltages in other parts of our receivers? Mention three devices used.
10. How is a shield usually connected?
11. What is the source of feedback or regeneration in a radio-frequency amplifier stage, and what does such feedback cause?
12. Explain the capacitor action or capacitance effect between the plate and grid of the triode radio-frequency amplifier stage.
13. Explain the losser method of oscillation control of a radio-frequency triode amplifier.
14. Explain the neutralization method of oscillation control in a radio-frequency triode amplifier.
15. What is the most modern method of oscillation control in radio-frequency amplifiers?

16. How do we prevent unwanted radio-frequency currents from getting into the B battery or B eliminator?
17. Describe the behavior of a RFC (radio-frequency choke coil).
18. What is the purpose of ganging capacitors?
19. Why do variable capacitors in tuned radio-frequency amplifiers have trimmers on them?
20. What is meant by "aligning the receiver"?
21. What is the purpose of an antenna trimmer?
22. Compare radio-frequency amplification with audio-frequency amplification.
23. Draw a schematic diagram of a TRF (tuned radio-frequency) receiver.

24

Volume Control

PROBLEM 1. *How is volume controlled in battery sets?*

PROBLEM 2. *What problems arise in controlling the volume in line-powered sets?*

PROBLEM 3. *What devices are used to control the volume automatically?*

PROBLEM 4. *How are modern sets wired for automatic volume control?*

Every radio receiving set must have some method for controlling volume, or loudness, of the sounds from the speaker. Otherwise, nearby powerful stations would blast through the loudspeaker with uncomfortable loudness and less powerful stations would be heard very faintly.

Volume Control in Battery Sets. Volume control for battery-operated sets is a relatively simple matter. A simple device is a rheostat of from 10 to 30 ohms connected in series with the A battery and the filament of the radio tube, as in Figure 24-1.

This rheostat controls the temperature of the filament, and in this way, controls the quantity of electrons emitted by the filament and, therefore, the plate current flowing in the plate circuit. This current, in turn, controls the loudness of the signal coming out of the loudspeaker.

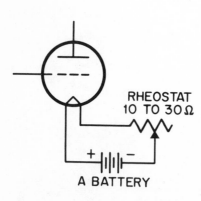

Fig. 24-1. *Rheostat in the filament circuit used to control volume.*

Another method that is less frequently used is to connect a rheostat of about 250,000 ohms in the plate circuit of the tube (Fig. 24-2). This rheostat controls the positive charge placed on the plate by the B battery, and in this way, controls the plate current, and thus the loudness of the sound.

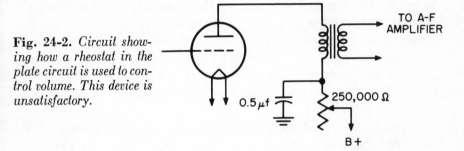

Fig. 24-2. *Circuit showing how a rheostat in the plate circuit is used to control volume. This device is unsatisfactory.*

This rheostat must be bypassed by a fixed capacitor of about 0.5 μf to filter off any radio-frequency currents that may leak through. This method is rarely used, since it has a tendency to upset the tuning of the set unless the value of the rheostat is kept very high, and then it does not permit a large positive charge to be placed on the plate.

Volume Control on House-Current Sets. In the nonbattery set, it is desirable to keep the filament current constant. This rules out

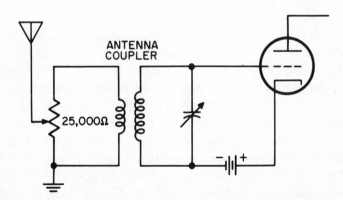

Fig. 24-3. *Circuit showing how a potentiometer across the primary of the antenna coupler is used as a volume control.*

the rheostat in the filament circuit. Other methods of volume control were developed.

One method is to connect a 25,000-ohm potentiometer across the primary of the antenna coupler and to connect the antenna to the sliding arm, as in Figure 24-3.

This hookup controls the amount of current fed into the tuner, and thus controls the sound ultimately coming from the loudspeaker. This method suffers from the disadvantage that although it cuts down the amount of electrical energy picked up by the antenna and, therefore, the amount of outside static or outside electrical interference, it does not reduce the amount of electrical interference created inside the set itself. These latter interferences come through and are amplified within the set. The result is that the set is quite noisy.

Another method, shown in Figure 24-4, is to connect a 5,000-ohm rheostat across the primary of the transformer in the plate circuit of the second radio-frequency tube.

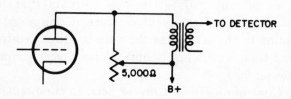

Fig. 24-4. *Circuit showing how a rheostat connected across the primary of the last radio-frequency transformer is used as a volume control.*

This method has the advantage of cutting down the electrical interference in the radio-frequency stages within the set simultaneously with cutting down the signal strength by dissipating a part of the plate current of the second radio-frequency stage.

Still another method of volume control, shown in Figure 24-5, is to connect a 500,000-ohm potentiometer across the secondary of the first audio-frequency transformer. The grid of the first audio-frequency tube is connected to the sliding arm. The potentiometer then controls the charge placed on the grid of the tube.

Sometimes the method shown in Figure 24-5 is combined with that shown in Figure 24-4. The 500,000-ohm potentiometer and 5,000-ohm rheostat are mounted on the same shaft, so that,

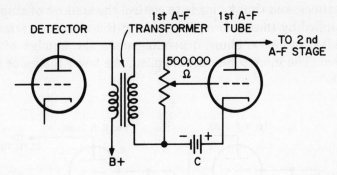

Fig. 24-5. *Circuit showing how a potentiometer is connected across the secondary of the first audio-frequency transformer to act as a volume control.*

although they are insulated from each other, they are rotated together by the same control knob.

Control of Volume when a Cathode-Type Tube Is Used. The use of a cathode and a grid bias resistor furnishes us with a simple and effective means of controlling the volume. Hooked up in series with the bias resistor is a rheostat, as in Figure 24-6.

By varying the rheostat, the resistance used to place a negative charge on the grid of the amplifier tube is made larger or smaller. (This resistance now consists of the bias resistor plus the resistance of the rheostat.) This variation in turn makes the grid more negative or less negative. The more negative the grid, the smaller the number of electrons flowing to the plate and the less the amplification.

This rheostat may be connected to the bias resistors of one

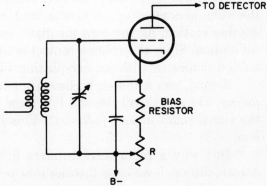

Fig. 24-6. *Circuit showing how a rheostat (R) is placed in series with the bias resistor to act as a volume control.*

or more tubes, and thus be made to control the amount of amplification supplied by these tubes. The value of this rheostat varies from about 5,000 to 50,000 ohms, depending upon the number of tubes controlled. The more tubes so controlled, the lower the value of the rheostat.

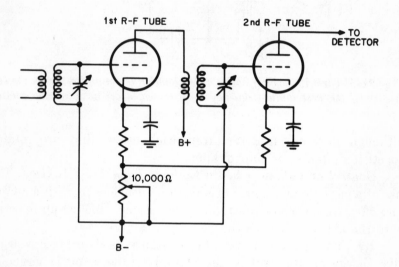

Fig. 24-7. *Circuit showing how the rheostat used as a volume control varies the grid bias of both radio-frequency tubes.*

The Need for Automatic Volume Control. While on the subject of the volume of the sound coming out of the radio receiver, let us consider two problems which must be solved for the greater enjoyment of radio reception.

First, having tuned in a fairly weak station, you have turned the volume control up to give a loud sound. Now, you tune in another station. As you turn the dial, you happen to pass a powerful station. Since the volume control is turned up to *loud,* the new station comes in with an earsplitting blast.

Second, you will soon become acquainted with the nuisance of *fading.* The signal will rise and fall, grow louder and softer. We say the signal *fades in* and *fades out.* This is the more serious problem.

Just why a radio wave behaves in this manner is not fully known, although we have theories that tend to explain it. We think it is due to the shifting of a layer of electrified air particles, called the *Heaviside layer,* far above the surface of the earth. It is not our purpose at this point to discuss this phenomenon, except to recognize that it exists and that it tends to spoil our enjoyment of the radio program (Chap. 35).

If we had a method of automatically turning our volume control to *loud* when the signal became weaker, and to *soft* when the signal became stronger, both of these problems would be solved. This task is accomplished by the *automatic volume control* (abbreviated AVC).

Automatic Volume Control by Varying the Grid Bias. How automatic volume control operates is fairly easy to understand. What is required of AVC is a negative grid bias on the grids of the radio-frequency amplifier tubes which will vary with the strength of the signal at the antenna. That is, if the signal is strong, we wish to have a greater negative bias to reduce the amplification. If the signal is weak, we wish to have a smaller negative bias to increase the amplification.

To obtain this bias, we tap off a portion of the signal current (before detection), rectify and filter it, and apply it to the grids of the radio-frequency amplifier tubes, where it increases the negative bias normally present on these grids. The greater the signal strength, the greater the increase in negative bias, and the lower the amplification. The smaller the signal, the less the increase in negative bias, and the greater the amplification.

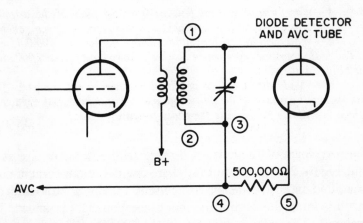

Fig. 24-8. *Circuit showing how the diode acts as a detector and automatic-volume-control tube.*

The net effect is that the greater the signal strength, the less the tubes will amplify it; and the less the signal strength, the more the tubes will amplify it. This arrangement tends to keep the volume of sound coming out of the loudspeaker at a constant level and helps to eliminate blasting and fading.

Details of the AVC System. Modern receivers generally employ a diode detector to produce the necessary AVC voltage. Examine the diode detector circuit of Figure 24-8.

As in the case of the ordinary diode detector (Chap. 14), the signal is impressed on the plate of the diode. When the plate is negative, no electrons are attracted from the cathode. When the plate is positive, electrons are attracted and are set flowing around the plate circuit from the plate to points 1, 2, 3, 4, 5, and back to the cathode. The more positive the plate, the greater the plate current.

As the current flows through the 500,000-ohm resistor, a voltage drop occurs across it, making point 4 negative with respect to point 5. The greater this current flow, the more negative point 4 becomes—that is, the stronger the signal on the detector plate, the more negative is point 4.

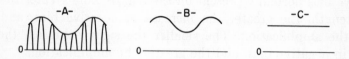

Fig. 24-9. *A—Waveform of current flowing from the plate of the detector. This current contains direct, audio-frequency, and radio-frequency components.*

    B—Waveform of current and voltage across the 500,000-ohm resistor. The radio-frequency component has been filtered out by the 0.00025-μf capacitor (Fig. 24-10).

    C—Steady direct voltage produced by filtering out the audio-frequency component by means of the 2-megohm resistor and the 0.1-μf capacitor. This voltage is suitable for biasing the radio-frequency tubes.

The waveform of the current flowing in the detector circuit is shown in Figure 24-9-A. Note that there are two main components —the rectified radio-frequency component (really a pulsating direct current) and the audio-frequency component (as shown by the envelope). The voltage drop across the 500,000-ohm resistor has the same waveform as the current and, therefore, is not suitable as bias for the grids of the radio-frequency tubes, where a steady bias is required. Therefore, we must filter out the radio- and audio-frequency components, leaving a steady direct voltage which may be applied to the grids.

We eliminate the radio-frequency component by offering it an easy path to ground through a small capacitor connected to point 4, as indicated in Figure 24-10. This is usually a 0.00025-µf capacitor which offers little opposition to the radio-frequency currents, but blocks the passage of the direct and audio-frequency currents. If the audio-frequency current could flow through this capacitor, it would escape to the ground, and there would be no signal left to pass on to the audio-frequency amplifiers. The waveform of the remaining current appears as in Figure 24-9-B. This is a direct current whose strength varies at the audio frequency, and is the audio signal.

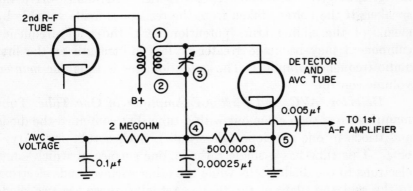

Fig. 24-10. *The complete AVC circuit.*

This audio-frequency current produces a voltage drop across the 500,000-ohm resistor which still is unsuitable for biasing the tubes. The next step is to eliminate the audio component. To do this, we use a filter somewhat similar to that used in the power supply, consisting of the 2-megohm resistor and the 0.1-µf capacitor. This filter smooths out the audio variations, producing a steady direct voltage (shown in Fig. 24-9-C) which is suitable for the AVC biasing.

Another point should be noted. Since the voltage across the 500,000-ohm resistor varies at audio frequency, it may be coupled through the 0.005-µf capacitor to the first audio-frequency ampli-

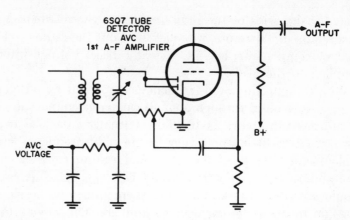

Fig. 24-11. *Circuit showing how the type 6SQ7 tube is used as a detector, automatic volume control, and first audio-frequency amplifier.*

fier grid to give the audio response which will finally drive the speaker. If the voltage taken from the resistor is made variable by means of the sliding arm (potentiometer), the audio-frequency component may be made greater or less in strength at the first audio-frequency amplifier. The potentiometer is thus our *manual* volume control.

Detector, AVC, and First A-F Amplifier in One Tube. Tube manufacturers soon came out with a tube that combined the diode and triode in one envelope (glass bulb). Such a tube is the type 6SQ7. This tube has a single cathode, one surface of which emits electrons to the diode plate, while the other surface sends electrons to the grid and plate of the triode. Actually, there are two diode plates in this tube, but for our purpose, we connect them together and treat them as one plate. The advantage of such a tube is that in one envelope we have the diode detector, the automatic-volume-control tube, and the first audio-frequency amplifying tube. Figure 24-11 shows how it is connected.

Other automatic-volume-control circuits have been developed, but the principle upon which they work is the same as that described here.

SUMMARY

1. The loudness of the signals coming from the speaker is known as **volume.**
2. In battery sets, volume is easily controlled by a rheostat that

regulates the current in the filament and hence the temperature and the number of electrons emitted.

3. Control of volume by a potentiometer across the primary of the antenna coupler is less satisfactory than the use of a rheostat across the primary of the transformer in the plate circuit of the second radio-frequency amplifier.

4. Another method, sometimes combined with the last method mentioned in (3), is to use a high resistance (500,000-ohm) potentiometer across the secondary of the first audio transformer.

5. A cathode-type tube with a grid-bias resistor and a rheostat is a good practical method for manual volume control.

6. *Automatic volume control* is achieved by devices which give a greater negative grid bias when greater signals come through, and conversely. This negative bias in turn controls directly the amplification in the radio-frequency amplifiers.

GLOSSARY

Automatic Volume Control (AVC): An automatic control of volume in the radio receiver which operates by making the receiver more sensitive to weak radio signals and less sensitive to powerful radio signals.

Fading: An undesired weakening of the radio signal.

Heaviside Layer: A layer of electrified air, consisting of charged particles called *ions,* from 60 to 200 miles above the surface of the earth, which acts as a reflector for radio waves. Changes in this layer are believed to be the chief cause of fading. The layer is also known as the Kennelly-Heaviside layer, or ionosphere.

Manual Volume Control: A control of volume, usually a variable resistor or potentiometer, which can be manipulated by the person operating the radio receiver.

QUESTIONS AND PROBLEMS

1. How is the volume of a battery receiver usually controlled?
2. What are the methods of manual volume control used in modern ac or ac-dc power-supply receivers?
3. Why is it desirable to have automatic volume control in a receiver?
4. What is one possible cause of fading?
5. How is automatic volume control accomplished in a receiver?
6. Draw the diagram of a diode detector with automatic volume control.

25

Tone Control

PROBLEM 1.	*How is the tone of sound waves related to the frequency?*
PROBLEM 2.	*What factors in radio receiving sets affect tone?*
PROBLEM 3.	*How do methods of tone control separate high-pitched tones from low-pitched tones?*

What Is Meant by Tone? In the last chapter, you learned how the volume of sound coming out of the loudspeaker may be controlled. In this chapter, you will learn how we control the tone of the radio receiving set.

As you know, sound is caused by air waves that strike our eardrums and produce the sensation we call *hearing*. To describe a sound, we say not merely that it is loud or soft, but we also describe its tone. The tone depends upon the frequency of the sound wave. The human ear can detect frequencies from about 30 to 15,000 cycles per second.

Those sound waves whose frequencies are low are described as *deep, bass,* or *low-pitched* sounds. Those whose frequencies approach 15,000 cycles per second are called *shrill, treble,* or *high-pitched* sounds. Those whose frequencies fall in between are called *middle-register* sounds.

Music and speech, generally, are not composed of sounds having only one frequency. High- and low-frequency sound waves usually are merged to produce a distinctive combination. If the result of mixing these sound waves of different frequencies is a sound whose predominant tone is that of the middle register, we say the sound has a *normal* tone.

If the sound has a preponderance of high-frequency sound waves, we say the tone is *high-pitched*. Women's voices generally fall into this category. If the sound has a preponderance of low-frequency sound waves, we say the tone is *low-pitched*. Men's voices generally fall into this category.

The tone of the sound coming out of the loudspeaker of the radio receiver, then, may be normal, high-pitched, or low-pitched, depending upon the combination of high- and low-frequency sound waves present.

What Determines the Tone of a Radio Receiver? Since tone is an audio-frequency phenomenon, we must look for the answer in the audio-frequency part of the set—that is, in the events after the electron impulses have reached the plate of the detector tube. Investigation shows that the audio-frequency amplifier usually does not amplify all the frequencies to the same extent. Thus, the high frequencies may be amplified more than the low frequencies, or vice versa. Or some intermediate frequencies may be amplified more or less than those at either end of the audio scale.

Furthermore, the loudspeaker does not respond to all frequencies in like degree. The early speakers of the metallic-horn type failed to bring out the deep notes. The result was an unpleasant tinny sound.

Good practice in designing a radio set is to match the loudspeaker to the audio-frequency amplifier so that one compensates for the variations of the other. The result is a fairly uniform reproduction of sound at all frequencies.

The Problem of Tone Control. It also is desirable to be able to control the tone of a radio set. Speech is clearer when it is somewhat higher pitched. On the other hand, many people prefer their music somewhat lower pitched. Some people do not enjoy listening to a soprano voice because of the preponderance of high-frequency tones.

The ideal method for controlling the tone of a radio receiver would be by means of controls which would regulate the amplification of the high- and low-frequency notes separately. Such a method does exist, but it is quite complicated. It is used almost exclusively for high-fidelity systems and studio purposes. The ordinary radio receiver uses a much simpler method, which closely approximates the ideal method in results.

There is a peculiarity about human hearing. Take a sound of

normal tone. The high and low frequencies are present in certain proportions. If, now, we amplify the low frequencies, we get a bass, low-pitched sound which has the same normal amount of the high frequencies, but more of the low frequencies.

Take the same sound of normal tone described above. Now, remove some of the high frequencies. Although we have not added any new low frequencies, nevertheless we get the effect of a bass, low-pitched sound. This is called *false bass*.

Similarly, if we remove some of the low frequencies from the normal tone, we get the effect of a high-pitched, treble tone. This is a *false treble*.

How to Separate High Pitch from Low Pitch. Our next problem is to devise a method of removing some of either the high or low frequencies. The electric currents flowing in the audio-frequency amplifier fluctuate within the audio range—that is, between 30 and 15,000 cycles per second. These currents cause the diaphragm or cone of the loudspeaker to vibrate in step with them. Thus, a current fluctuating at about 100 cycles per second will cause a deep note to come forth from the loudspeaker, but a current fluctuating at about 10,000 cycles per second will produce a high-pitched note. Remember that when we speak here of high frequency, we mean high audio frequency, not radio frequency.

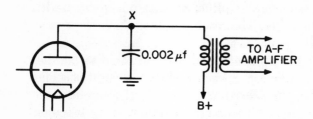

Fig. 25-1. *Circuit showing how a capacitor is used to filter out some of the high-frequency current.*

To remove some of the high-frequency current, we place a fixed capacitor across the path of the audio-frequency current. It may be shown that a capacitor of proper capacitance furnishes a path of lower impedance than that of the plate circuit to currents of high frequencies, but not to currents of low frequencies. Hence, the fluctuating current flowing in the plate circuit of the detector tube divides at point X (Fig. 25-1). Some of the high-frequency current passes through the 0.002-μf capacitor and goes on to ground. The main part of the plate current, however, containing all the low frequencies, passes through the primary of the first audio-frequency transformer and is amplified. Since some of the high frequencies are missing from the sound emitted by the loud-speaker, our radio set now has a bass tone.

We can vary the amount of high-frequency current bypassed by the capacitor by connecting a 500,000-ohm rheostat in series with it, as in Figure 25-2. The more the resistance in that circuit, the less the amount of high-frequency current that will be by-passed and, therefore, the more treble the tone.

The combination of fixed capacitor and rheostat is called a *tone control*. It may be placed anywhere in the audio circuit, across the primary of the audio transformer (as shown) or across the secondary. It may be applied to any of the audio-frequency stages.

Fig. 25-2. *Circuit show-ing how a rheostat is con-nected in series with the capacitor to control the amount of high-frequency current filtered out.*

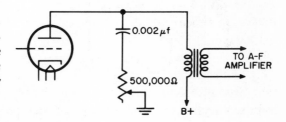

Treble-Bass Tone Control. Another type of tone control is shown in Figure 25-3. This tone control consists of two arms. In one arm, A, is a 0.1 μf capacitor. In the other, B, a 0.1-μf capacitor is connected in series with a choke coil of about 85 millihenrys. One end of each arm is connected to the plate of the final audio-frequency tube. Across the other ends, a 100,000-ohm potenti-ometer is connected with the sliding arm going to the ground.

The action of the choke coil is opposite to that of the capaci-tor. It offers a higher impedance to currents of higher frequencies. Hence, it conducts more readily the parts of the current with low frequencies.

First, consider the circuit with the sliding arm of the poten-tiometer all the way to the left. None of the resistance is in arm A: it is all in arm B. Current flowing in the plate circuit of the audio-frequency tube divides at point X as described in Figure 25-1. Some of the high-frequency current is lost through the capacitor. The main part of the current passes through the output transformer and our set now has a bass tone.

When the slider arm is all the way over to the right, the entire 100,000 ohms is in arm A. This prevents the loss of the high-frequency currents. As a result, the diverted current flowing from point X must now pass through arm B. Since the choke coil offers a high impedance to the high-frequency current, it is only low-frequency currents that pass through and go on to the ground. Since we have lost some of the low frequencies, our tone now is

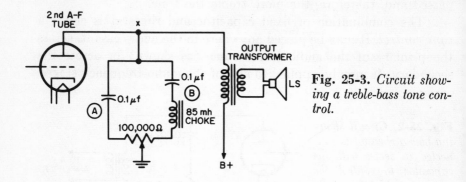

Fig. 25-3. *Circuit showing a treble-bass tone control.*

treble. Varying the sliding arm of the potentiometer varies the amount of high or low frequencies lost, and thus the tone of the set is controlled.

Tone May Be Controlled by Using Two Speakers. There is still another method of tone control that is sometimes used. Some sets have two speakers. One is a speaker which reproduces the low frequencies better than the high frequencies. The other reproduces the high frequencies better. Both of these speakers are connected

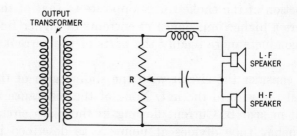

Fig. 25-4. *Circuit showing how tone control may be obtained through the use of high-frequency and low-frequency loudspeakers. The potentiometer (R) determines which speaker shall obtain the greater current.*

to the output transformer by a potentiometer which controls the amount of current flowing through each (Fig. 25-4).

In addition, a choke coil in the circuit of the low-frequency speaker permits low-frequency audio currents to flow through the speaker, but impedes the flow of high-frequency audio currents. These currents, however, find an easier path through the capacitor in the high-frequency speaker circuit, and hence through that speaker. Thus, if the potentiometer is adjusted so that more current flows through the high-frequency speaker and less through the low-frequency speaker, the high frequencies are louder, and the tone is treble. If the conditions are reversed, the tone is bass. The potentiometer, then, acts as a tone control.

Different manufacturers of radio sets may use different types of devices for tone control, but upon analysis of the circuits, you will see that they usually are variations of the ones described here.

SUMMARY

1. Sounds having regular frequencies are called musical *tones.*
2. The frequency of a tone is related to its *pitch:* low pitch means low frequency, and high pitch means high frequency.
3. The tones coming from a speaker are influenced both by the components of the audio-frequency system and also by the kind of loudspeaker.
4. The principles of *tone control* that are made use of within the receiver are: (1) capacitors offer a path of less impedance to high-frequency currents than to low-frequency currents and (2) choke coils offer more impedance to high-frequency currents and less impedance to low-frequency currents.
5. An effective tone control makes use of a divided circuit leading to the ground, in one arm of which is a capacitor, and in the other arm, a choke coil. A slide arm on the potentiometer controls the tone by permitting more or less high-frequency current to pass through.
6. Two speakers having different qualities—one good for high pitch, the other for low pitch—may be hooked to one receiver. The tone can be controlled by varying the amounts of current in the two speakers.

GLOSSARY

Tone: The sound resulting from the mixture of air waves of different frequencies.

Bass Tone: The tone resulting when low frequencies are predominant. Also called *low-pitched tone.*

Middle-Register Tone: The tone resulting when high and low frequencies are present in about equal proportions. Also called *normal tone.*

Treble Tone: The tone resulting when high frequencies are predominant. Also known as *high-pitched* or *soprano tone.*

Tone Control: An electrical circuit used to emphasize high- or low-frequency notes in a combination of sound frequencies.

QUESTIONS AND PROBLEMS

1. Upon what factors does the tone of a sound depend?
2. What is the frequency range of human hearing?
3. What is meant by a bass tone? A middle-register tone?
4. What conditions in a receiver cause distortion or inaccurate reproduction of tone?
5. What should be the pitch of the tone of speech over the radio amplifier to make it clearer?
6. What must be the function of a tone control?
7. What peculiarities of hearing enables us to use a practical tone control?
8. What is a false bass?
9. What is a false treble?
10. Draw a sketch of a practical tone-control circuit.
11. In what part of a receiver circuit do we usually place a tone control?
12. What is the purpose of using two speakers in a receiver? How do they function?

26

The Superheterodyne Receiver

PROBLEM 1. *What are the shortcomings of the tuned radio-frequency amplifier receiver?*

PROBLEM 2. *What is the principle of beats?*

PROBLEM 3. *How is the principle of beat currents applied to obtain sharp tuning over a wide range of frequencies?*

PROBLEM 4. *What are the essential principles of the superheterodyne receiver?*

It is interesting to note how one great invention or discovery leads to other inventions or discoveries. Many examples of this are found in the history of radio. After the invention of the system of tuned radio-frequency amplification, radio engineers began looking for means to correct the flaws and drawbacks of this circuit. This search led to the next improvement.

Shortcomings of Tuned Radio-Frequency Receivers. The drawbacks of the circuit were found to lie in the inability to have a wide range of reception and at the same time sharp tuning. To obtain maximum sensitivity and selectivity, the tuning circuit should have a natural frequency exactly equal to the frequency of the broadcasting station. But our tuning circuit is made so that we may tune in all frequencies lying in the broadcasting range—that is, from 535 to 1,605 kc. To obtain this broad coverage, a compromise is made in the design of our tuned radio-frequency transformer, and some of the selectivity and sensitivity is sacrificed.

The ideal way would be to have a separate set of tuned radio-frequency transformers for each frequency received. This, of course, is impractical for home receivers.

The General Principle of a Superheterodyne Receiver. The invention of the superheterodyne receiver resulted from the experiments seeking to approach this ideal condition. In the system to which the name superheterodyne is given, we have, instead of a separate set of tuned radio-frequency transformers for each frequency received, one set of tuned radio-frequency transformers that are tuned to one predetermined frequency. After selecting the radio station we desire, we change the frequency of the currents flowing in our receiver to that certain predetermined frequency and then feed it into our tuned radio-frequency amplifier.

In this manner, we have the advantage of using tuned radio-frequency transformers that operate at only one frequency without the drawback of needing a separate set for each frequency. Our set is more selective and sensitive than the tuned radio-frequency set described in Chapter 23.

What Is Meant by Beats? In order to understand how the frequency of the incoming signal is changed to that for which the radio-frequency transformers are tuned, you must first learn about the phenomenon of *beats*.

Strike middle C on the piano. The sound you hear has a frequency of 256 cycles per second. Now strike the note before it, B. This note has a frequency of 240 cycles per second. Now strike both keys together. The sound you hear is neither B nor C, but a mixture of the two. If you listen closely, you will notice that this new sound rises and falls in loudness, or intensity. If you time this rise and fall of sound, you will notice that it occurs 16 times per second, the exact difference between the frequencies of B and C.

We call this rise and fall the *beat note*. Its frequency (that is, the number of beats) is equal to the difference between the frequencies of the notes producing it.

The production of beat notes occurs not only in the case of sound waves, but whenever any kind of waves of different frequencies clash or beat against one another. Under certain conditions, light waves may produce beats. Also, radio waves of different frequencies may be mixed, resulting in beats whose frequency equals the difference between those of the two original waves.

Now we can explain how we are able to change the frequency

of the incoming signal to that for which the radio-frequency trans-formers are tuned. The problem is to mix with the incoming signal another radio-frequency current whose frequency is such that the difference between the two is equal to the predetermined and de-sired frequency.

Forming Beat Frequencies in the Receiver. Assume we have set our radio-frequency transformers so that their natural fre-quency is 175 kc. Let us suppose that we are receiving the signal from a station whose frequency is 1,000 kc. All we need do is to generate a radio-frequency current whose frequency is 1,175 kc. We mix this radio-frequency current with the incoming signal (1,000 kc) and a *beat current* results whose frequency is 175 kc (1,175 − 1,000 = 175 kc). This 175-kc beat current is fed into the radio-frequency transformers, and amplification occurs at maxi-mum efficiency. The idea is shown in diagram form in Figure 26-1.

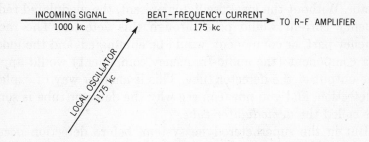

Fig. 26-1. *Diagram showing how the incoming signal mixes with the current produced by the local oscillator to produce the beat-frequency current.*

The device used to generate the radio-frequency current which beats against the incoming signal is called the *local oscillator*. To make this process clearer, let us consider another example, using the same tuning system having a natural frequency of 175 kc. Assume the incoming signal has a frequency of 800 kc. The local oscillator must now produce a radio-frequency current whose fre-quency is 975 kc. The beat-current frequency, again, is 175 kc, the frequency at which the radio-frequency transformers are set.

To produce a beat-frequency current of 175 kc, the local oscillator produces a radio-frequency current whose frequency is 175 kc above that of the incoming signal. Since frequencies in the broadcast band lie between 535 and 1,605 kc, the local oscillator for our set must be capable of producing radio-frequency currents whose frequencies are between 710 kc (535 + 175), and 1,780 kc (1,605 + 175). Further, we must connect together the control that selects the incoming signal with the control that regulates the frequency of the local oscillator in such a way that the difference in frequency is always 175 kc.

Heterodyning is another name for the production of beats. It is from this word that we get the name of our new-type radio set, the *superheterodyne receiver.*

Beat Production Occurs in the First Detector. As in the case of the tuned radio-frequency receiver, the incoming signal is selected by the tuning circuit consisting of the antenna coupler with a variable capacitor across the secondary. The radio wave, a modulated carrier wave, causes a correspondingly modulated radio-frequency current to flow in the tuning circuit. This radio-frequency current is fed into the grid of an ordinary grid-leak-capacitor detector. Without the local oscillator present, the modulated radio-frequency current would pass through this detector. The radio-frequency part, or component, would be eliminated, and the modulating component (the audio-frequency component) would appear at the output of the detector tube. This is another way of explaining detection, and you now can see why the detector tube is sometimes called the *demodulator tube.*

But in the superheterodyne system, before detection occurs, the steady or unmodulated radio-frequency current from the local oscillator is mixed with the incoming signal. As a result, coming out of the plate of the detector tube is a new radio-frequency current whose frequency is the beat frequency and whose amplitudes are modulated with the same waveform as was the incoming signal. This new radio-frequency current is then fed into the radio-frequency amplifiers that are tuned to the same frequency as that of the beat frequency.

Since the mixing of the two radio-frequency currents takes place in the detector tube, this tube is also called the *mixer tube.* It is called the *first detector tube* to distinguish it from the *second detector tube,* which follows the radio-frequency amplifier tubes and is a standard detector.

The Principle of the Local Oscillator. For the local oscillator we have to go back to the regenerative receiver (Chap. 16). Turn back to Figure 16-1. Current flowing in the plate circuit of the

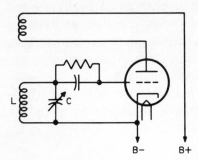

Fig. 26-2. *Circuit of the local oscillator. Note how it resembles the regenerative detector.*

triode is fed back to the tuned circuit by means of a plate coil. This feed-back overcomes the resistance of the tuned circuit, and the radio-frequency current flowing in that circuit (the oscillations of the electrons) is built up (Fig. 26-2).

The frequency of this radio-frequency current is determined by the electrical values of the inductor and variable capacitor in the tuned circuit ($L \times C$). Changing the setting of the variable capacitor will change the frequency of the current produced.

Here, then, is our local oscillator. By connecting the variable capacitor of this oscillator with the variable capacitor of the first detector circuit so that they turn together, and selecting the proper component parts (L and C), we are able to produce a radio-frequency current which at all times will be 175 kc over the frequency of the incoming signal (Fig. 26-3).

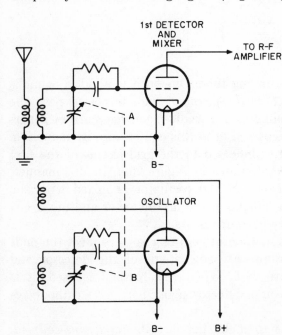

Fig. 26-3. *Capacitors A and B are connected and turn together. (This ganging is shown by the dotted lines running from one variable capacitor to the other.) Thus, the natural frequencies of both tuned circuits are always a certain number of kilocycles apart (the beat frequency).*

Note that 175 kc is taken only as an example. Actually, we can make this difference any frequency we wish, provided we have set our radio-frequency transformers to tune to that frequency. Also, as we shall see later (Chapter 39), there are other oscillator circuits that may be employed for our local oscillator.

Coupling the Oscillator to the First Detector. Several methods are used in feeding the radio-frequency current generated by the

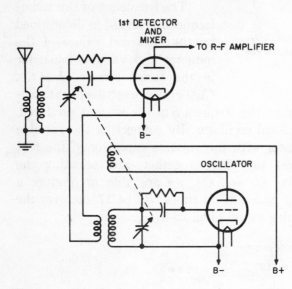

Fig. 26-4. *Circuit showing how current from the local oscillator is inductively coupled to the first detector and mixer circuit.*

local oscillator into the mixing tube. One such method is to make the circuits *inductive-coupled*. A coil of wire is placed near the tuned circuit of the oscillator. The radio-frequency current generated by the oscillator is passed onto this coil of wire by induction. The ends of the coil are connected in the grid circuit of the first detector and mixer tube as shown in Figure 26-4. In this manner, the radio-frequency current of the oscillator is mixed with the radio-frequency current flowing in the first detector and mixer circuit. The beat-frequency current results.

A variation of this method of coupling is to connect the ends of the coupling coil in the cathode circuit of the detector and mixer tube as in Figure 26-5. When this method is used, it is customary to have the first detector hooked up as a cathode resistor-biased detector.

Another method is to make the circuits *capacitive-coupled*.

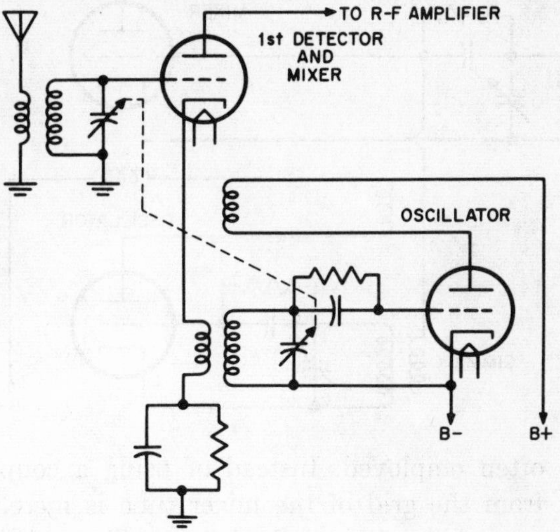

TO R-F AMPLIFIER

1st DETECTOR
AND
MIXER

OSCILLATOR

Fig. 26-5. *Circuit showing how current from the local oscillator is inductively coupled to the cathode of the first detector and mixer tube.*

B−   B+

Here a small fixed capacitor transfers the radio-frequency current from the oscillator to the grid of the first detector and mixer tube as shown in Figure 26-6. The radio-frequency choke in the plate circuit of the oscillator tube forces the radio-frequency current through the coupling capacitor to the grid of the first detector tube.

There is a variation of this capacitive-coupling method that is

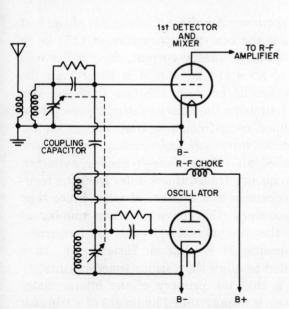

1st DETECTOR
AND
MIXER

TO R-F
AMPLIFIER

COUPLING
CAPACITOR

B−

R-F CHOKE

OSCILLATOR

B−   B+

Fig. 26-6. *Circuit showing how a small fixed capacitor is used to couple the current from the local oscillator to the grid of the first detector and mixer tube.*

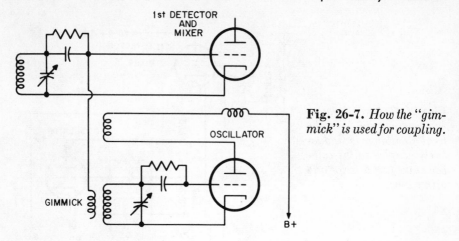

Fig. 26-7. *How the "gimmick" is used for coupling.*

often employed. Instead of using a coupling capacitor, the wire from the grid of the mixer tube is merely wound a turn or two around the main coil of the oscillator (Fig. 26-7). The few turns of wire, called a *gimmick,* forms a small capacitor with the windings of the oscillator coil and in this way we get our coupling.

With the invention of new types of tubes, a third method of coupling was developed. In this method, the two circuits are coupled through the electrodes within the tube itself. We shall discuss this electron coupling further in the chapter dealing with types of tubes (page 244).

The Intermediate-Frequency Amplifier. Coming out of the first detector and mixer tube is the beat-frequency current (175 kc in our example). This is a radio-frequency current, since it lies well above the audio range of about 15 kc. But it is lower than the broadcast frequencies which lie between 535 and 1,605 kc. We, therefore, call this beat frequency the *intermediate frequency* (abbreviated to *if*). The tuned radio-frequency transformers set for this beat frequency are called *intermediate-frequency transformers,* and the amplifier is called an *intermediate-frequency amplifier.*

The intermediate-frequency transformers differ from the regular radio-frequency transformers in a number of ways. Since they are tuned to a lower frequency, they have a greater number of turns of wire. Also, since they are to respond to only one frequency, the regular variable capacitor is eliminated. Instead, we use a trimmer capacitor adjusted to align the various tuned circuits.

Another difference is that the primary of the intermediate-frequency transformer, too, is usually tuned by means of a trimmer

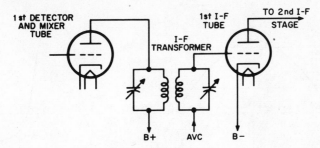

Fig. 26-8. *Circuit of the intermediate-frequency transformer.*

capacitor. This arrangement increases the selectivity of the set. Although it is quite possible to tune the primary of the ordinary radio-frequency transformer, the difficulty of ganging the extra variable capacitors needed presents quite a problem and, therefore, this primary is not tuned. A diagram of the intermediate-frequency transformer used for an amplifier is shown in Figure 26-8.

As previously stated, the use of an intermediate-frequency transformer tuned to a fixed frequency means much greater sensitivity and selectivity. So sensitive is the superheterodyne set that it is quite possible to use a small loop antenna built inside the cabinet of the set itself, instead of a long wire up on the roof.

The increase in selectivity may be shown by tuning curves in Figure 26-10. In Figure 26-10-A, the curve indicates that when

Fig. 26-9. *The intermediate-frequency transformer.*

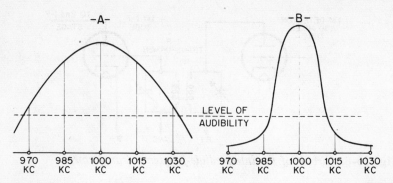

Fig. 26-10. *A-Tuning curve for the tuned radio-frequency receiver tuned to 1,000 kc. Note that stations whose frequencies are 970 kc and 1,030 kc lie above the level of audibility. This condition means that they may be heard faintly in the background of the desired station.*

B-Tuning curve for the superheterodyne receiver tuned to 1,000 kc. Note that the unwanted stations fall below the level of audibility.

you tune in the 1,000-kc station, the two stations whose frequencies lie 30 kc on either side can be heard slightly. This tuning curve is typical for the tuned radio-frequency receiver.

Figure 26-10-B represents the tuning curve of the superheterodyne receiver. Here you will notice that stations 30 kc away from the desired station (1,000 kc) lie well below the level of audibility.

Can a Receiver Be Too Selective? So selective is the superheterodyne receiver that another problem may be presented. The set may be too selective! Here is what happens.

At the radio station, audio-frequency currents whose frequencies run up to 15 kc are mixed with the steady radio-frequency carrier current generated by the transmitting set to produce the modulated radio-frequency current. Assume that our broadcasting station has a carrier wave whose frequency is 1,000 kc. The resulting beat current then would be 1,000 minus 15, or 985 kc.

In discussing the production of beats, we omitted to mention that when waves of two frequencies are mixed, not only is the beat frequency the *difference* between these two frequencies, but a beat frequency is also produced which is the *sum* of these two frequencies.

When we considered the beat-frequency current produced by mixing the incoming signal with the radio-frequency current generated by the local oscillator, we omitted the beat produced by adding the two frequencies because this beat lay well outside the range of our receiver. You will recall that we assumed an incoming signal whose frequency was 1,000 kc. One beat frequency produced was 175 kc. The other beat frequency which we did not consider was 1,000 plus 1,175, or 2,175 kc. Since our intermediate-frequency transformers were tuned to 175 kc, the second beat could not be amplified.

But at the transmitting station, the mixing of the 15-kc audio current with the 1,000-kc carrier current produces beat currents that have two different frequencies, one of 985, and the other of 1,015 kc. The radio station, therefore, broadcasts a wave whose frequencies lie between 985 and 1,015 kc. The difference between the two frequencies (30 kc) is called the *band width*.

Now, if you will refer to Figure 26-10-B, you will notice from the tuning curve for the superheterodyne receiver that when it is tuned to 1,000 kc, the extremes of the 30-kc band width lie below the level of audibility. This means that some of the high notes will not be heard. We call this *cutting the side bands.*

In other words, so great is the selectivity and so narrow is the tuning curve that the beat frequencies of 985 and 1,015 kc lie below the level of audibility. Thus, the tone of the set will be too bass. To remedy this defect, we are compelled to reduce the selectivity of the set. The ideal condition would be to have the 985 and 1,015 kc on the tuning curve a little above the level of audibility, as shown in Figure 26-11.

This broadening is accomplished by adjusting the trimmer capacitors so that the set is slightly out of alignment. This adjustment broadens the tuning curve so as not to cut the side bands.

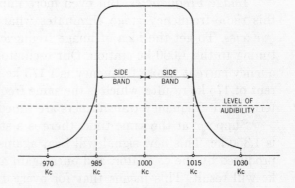

Fig. 26-11. *Ideal tuning curve for the superheterodyne receiver. Note that the side bands are fully received, but the unwanted stations are well below the level of audibility.*

Although it is possible to judge this condition by ear, best results are accomplished by the use of special electrical instruments. Except for the differences already noted, the intermediate-frequency amplifier is similar to the radio-frequency amplifier discussed in Chapter 23.

The Second Detector and Audio-Frequency Amplifier. The second detector following the intermediate-frequency amplifier is similar to the one used in the tuned radio-frequency set. A diode detector is customarily used, since the amount of amplification of the intermediate-frequency amplifier is great enough to overcome the lack of amplification that results from using a diode instead of a triode detector.

The automatic-volume-control system, the manual volume control, the tone control, and the audio amplifier are the same as those used in the tuned radio-frequency receiver.

Using a Radio-Frequency Stage Before the First Detector. Sometimes a stage of ordinary radio-frequency amplification is placed in front of the first detector. Although it is not necessary to increase the sensitivity or selectivity of the superheterodyne receiver (which is sensitive and selective enough without it), this radio-frequency stage serves two useful functions.

First, it serves to reduce the volume of any unwanted signals from powerful radio stations that may be in the vicinity of the receiver. If this stage were not present, this unwanted powerful signal would be impressed on the first detector and might cause some interference. Although the radio-frequency stage may not completely eliminate this interfering station, it can reduce its signal strength to the point where the tuned circuit of the first detector can eliminate it completely.

Image Frequencies. But even more important is the fact that this radio-frequency stage eliminates what are called *image frequencies.* To get the idea of image frequency, assume that we are tuning to the 1,000-kc station. Our oscillator produces a radio-frequency current whose frequency is 1,175 kc. A beat-frequency current of 175 kc results, which is the same frequency to which our intermediate-frequency transformers are tuned.

Suppose, at the same time, there is a station whose frequency is 1,350 kc. This new signal will beat against the 1,175-kc current produced by the oscillator, and once again a beat frequency of 175 kc will result. This means that for every frequency produced by

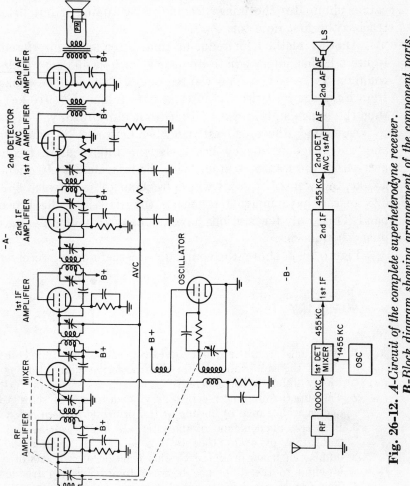

Fig. 26-12. *A-Circuit of the complete superheterodyne receiver.*
B-Block diagram showing arrangement of the component parts.

the oscillator, there are *two* frequencies that will produce the desired beat frequency, one 175 kc *above* the oscillator frequency and one 175 kc *below* the oscillator frequency. Thus, two stations may be passed on to the intermediate-frequency amplifier at the same time. This second and unwanted frequency (1,350 kc) is called the *image frequency*. The stage of radio-frequency amplification eliminates the image frequency by tuning it out before it reaches the first detector.

Another method for reducing image-frequency interference is to use a higher intermediate frequency, such as 455 kc, which is in common usage today. The wanted signal then will be separated from its image by twice the intermediate frequency (910 kc), and thus the image station can be tuned out quite readily.

Also, since the broadcast band lies between 535 and 1605 kc and the image frequency lies twice the intermediate frequency away from the wanted station, with the intermediate frequency at 455 kc, few wanted stations whose frequencies lie between 535 and 695 kc can have image frequencies that fall into the broadcast band. Thus, only few stations have the possibility of suffering from image frequencies.

Figure 26-12 shows the complete superheterodyne receiver.

SUMMARY

1. The tuned radio-frequency receiver cannot be tuned sharply and at the same time remain able to receive many stations with widely different frequencies.
2. The superheterodyne receiver provides a means of sharp tuning over a wide range by means of the principle of **beat notes.**
3. Beat is a phenomenon of the alternate reinforcement and neutralization of each other by waves of two frequencies. The number of beats produced by this reaction of two sets of waves is equal to the difference between their vibration frequencies.
4. The **first detector** in a superheterodyne receiver is a tube in which the radio currents from the antenna are mixed with the currents from a local oscillator.
5. The local oscillator is tuned so that the beat note produced by its current mixed with an incoming radio current will always be at the fixed natural frequency of the intermediate-frequency amplifier.
6. The current from the first detector tube is a beat-frequency

current that is of radio frequency, but lower than the broadcast frequencies.

7. The radio-frequency amplifiers are set for this beat frequency, and such an amplifying system is called an *intermediate-frequency amplifier.*
8. The superheterodyne receiver is very sensitive and tunes so sharply that trimmer capacitors sometimes are adjusted to keep the set a trifle *out of alignment* in order to make it include the *side bands.*

GLOSSARY

Band Width: The range of frequencies of the radio wave sent out by a transmitting station.

Beats: The result of combining two waves of similar nature but of different frequencies. Thus, we can combine two sound waves or two alternating currents of different frequencies. The result, in the case of the sound waves, will be a new sound wave whose amplitudes vary at a frequency equal to either the difference between the two frequencies or the sum of the two frequencies. In the case of the alternating currents, the amplitudes of the resulting current will vary in the same manner.

Capacitive Coupling: A method of coupling electrical energy from one circuit to another through a capacitor.

Heterodyning: The production of beat notes or currents by mixing two waves or two alternating currents of different frequencies.

Image Frequency: A frequency that is as much above the oscillator frequency as the desired station frequency is below that of the oscillator. Thus, the signals from two different stations may be fed into the intermediate-frequency amplifier at the same time.

Inductive Coupling: A method of coupling electrical energy from one circuit to another by mutual induction.

Intermediate Frequency: The frequency that lies between the radio frequency of the received signal and audio frequency. It results from heterodyning two different radio frequencies.

Intermediate-Frequency (I-F) Transformer: A transformer tuned so that its natural frequency falls within the intermediate-frequency range.

Local Oscillator: A generator of radio-frequency currents in a super-heterodyne receiver.

Mixer Tube: A tube in the superheterodyne receiver in which the incoming signal current is mixed with the radio-frequency current from the local oscillator to produce the intermediate-frequency current.

Side Band: The band of frequencies on either side of the fundamental carrier frequency, simultaneously transmitted with it by
the broadcast station.

Superheterodyne Receiver: A radio receiver using the heterodyne
principle.

SYMBOLS

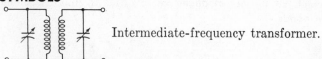

Intermediate-frequency transformer.

QUESTIONS AND PROBLEMS

1. List some of the weaknesses of a tuned radio-frequency receiver.
2. What is meant by a beat note?
3. What is the function of the local oscillator in the superheterodyne receiver?
4. Describe what occurs in the first detector of a superheterodyne
   receiver.
5. Describe the operation of the local oscillator.
6. How is the local oscillator coupled to the first detector mixer
   tube?
7. What advantage lies in the use of intermediate-frequency
   transformers in the superheterodyne receiver?
8. What is meant by intermediate-frequency?
9. What are the advantages of a superheterodyne receiver over
   other types of receivers studied?
10. What happens to the beat frequency, which is the sum of the
    two mixed frequencies, in a superheterodyne receiver?
11. What is meant by band width?
12. What is meant by "cutting the side bands"?
13. How is the cutting of side bands in the superheterodyne elimi-
    nated?
14. What type of second detector is commonly used in a super-
    heterodyne receiver?
15. Why is a radio-frequency amplifier stage placed in front of
    the mixer in a superheterodyne receiver?
16. What is image frequency?
17. Draw a complete superheterodyne receiver, with automatic
    volume control.
18. Why will a higher intermediate frequency reduce the image-
    frequency interference to a greater extent than a lower one?

27

Radio Tubes and Transistors

PROBLEM 1. *How are tubes with different numbers of electrodes or elements designed for different functions in a receiver?*

PROBLEM 2. *How may the functions of several tubes be combined in one tube?*

PROBLEM 3. *How do tube envelopes and bases vary?*

PROBLEM 4. *How may a transistor act like a radio tube?*

As you have learned, it is possible to have radio without radio tubes. Nevertheless, the radio tube has changed what was a scientific toy into one of the world's greatest industries. It has greatly influenced our present civilization.

General Principles of Radio Tubes. The basic principles of the radio tube are, nevertheless, extremely simple. Let us study this tube more attentively. The heated filament or cathode emits a stream of electrons which form a one-way path to a positively charged plate, or anode. The more the cathode is heated, the more electrons it sends out. The more positive the charge on the plate, the more of these electrons it attracts. It should be remembered that these two statements hold true between certain limits. If you heat the filament too much, it will burn up. After a certain limit is reached, placing a higher positive charge on the plate will attract no more electrons (Chap. 37).

In some tubes, the cathode is the filament itself. This filament may be a thin wire, as in type 1H5-GT tubes. Or else it may be a heavy metal ribbon coated with certain chemicals to permit it to shoot off more electrons, as in the type 45 tubes.

In tubes of other types, the filament is merely an electric stove, or heater, heating up the relatively heavy metal tube, or sleeve, that fits over it. This tube, or sleeve, is the cathode, which when heated sufficiently emits the electrons that find their way to the plate. The type 6C5 tube is an example of this class.

Tubes having thin filaments usually are heated by direct current. Alternating current is generally used to heat the heavy ribbon filaments. The separate-heater types of tubes may be heated either by direct or alternating current.

Filament or Heater Voltages. In practice, the tube manufacturers design the filaments and heaters of their tubes to operate at certain voltages. Thus, the 1H5-GT tube has a filament which operates from the 1½ volts furnished by a single dry cell.

Other types of tubes require different voltages. The type 45 uses 2½ volts on its filament. The heater of the 117Z3 tubes uses 117 volts. There are many other types of tubes using other voltages. But the voltage at which the filament or heater of the tube operates does not determine the character or nature of the tube.

The Diode. Simplest of all radio tubes is the two-element tube, or *diode*. These two elements consist of an emitter of electrons (either a filament or separately heated cathode), and a plate. These two elements are sealed inside a glass bulb from which all air has been evacuated.

As described in Chapter 14, the diode makes for an excellent detector. It is also used as a rectifier, changing alternating current into direct current to be used by the B eliminator (Chap. 18) and by the automatic-volume-control circuit (Chap. 24).

The 1V2 and 1B3-GT types of tubes are typical diodes. Sometimes two diodes are sealed into one envelope to make a *full-wave rectifier,* as in 5Y3-GT, 5U4-G, 35Z5, and 6H6 tubes.

The Triode. When Dr. DeForest placed a third element, the grid, between the cathode and plate of the diode, he introduced the magical word—*amplification*. As already explained in Chapter 15, a small voltage placed upon the grid of the tube controls the large stream of electrons rushing from the cathode to the plate. Since this large plate current varies in step with the small voltage placed upon the grid, amplification results.

The amplifying quality of a tube is called the *amplification factor,* which appears in electrical formulas as the Greek letter *mu* (μ). Here is what it means.

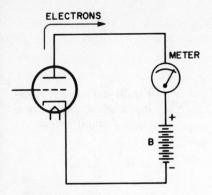

ELECTRONS

METER

B

Fig. 27-1. Meter connected in the plate circuit of the triode to show the flow of electrons.

In Figure 27-1, we have a triode with a meter in the plate circuit. Electrons flowing from the filament are attracted to the positively charged plate and flow on through the meter, which registers their flow. Assume that you now increase the B battery by 35 volts. The greater positive charge on the plate attracts more electrons, and the meter now shows that more are flowing through it.

At this point, a negative charge is placed on the grid. This will cut down the flow of electrons to the plate, and fewer electrons will flow through the meter. Assume that when you have placed a negative charge of 5 volts on the grid, the meter will show the same current flowing through it as before the plate charge was raised by 35 volts. This means that 5 volts applied to the grid will have the same effect as 35 volts (of opposite charge) applied to the plate of the tube. The amplification factor or *mu* (μ) of this tube is, therefore, 35 divided by 5, or 7.

What Determines the Amplification Factor of a Triode? The amplification factor of a triode is determined by the mechanical construction of the tube. The nearer the grid is to the cathode, the greater is its effect on the stream of electrons flowing to the plate, and the greater is the *mu*, or amplification factor of the tube. Also, the finer the mesh of the grid, the greater the effect of a charge upon the grid, and again the greater the *mu*. If the open spaces in the grid are wide, the electrons are able to rush to the plate without being very much affected by the grid charge. This condition, accordingly, makes for a smaller amplification factor.

In the triode, we are unable to use a grid of very fine mesh because the consequently larger area of the grid would greatly increase the internal grid-to-plate capacitance. This would increase the feedback and cause the receiver to oscillate, resulting in distortion, as was shown on pages 182-183. It is partly because of this fact that triodes have a relatively small amplification factor. The type 6C5 tube has a *mu* of 20.

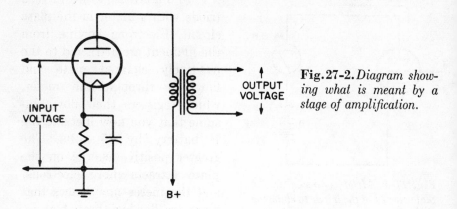

Fig. 27-2. *Diagram show-*
ing what is meant by a
stage of amplification.

Another factor limits the *mu* of the triode. The electrons shot off by the cathode have a negative charge. Thus, they tend to repel one another, and many more are shot out than actually reach the plate. Of these electrons that do not reach the plate, a large number accumulate and fill the space around the cathode inside the envelope of the tube. This accumulation charges the space around the cathode, and is, therefore, called the *space charge*.

Any new electrons shot off by the cathode must fight their way through this space charge to reach the plate. It is estimated that about 85 per cent of the positive charge on the plate of the tube is used to overcome the repelling effect of the space charge, leaving about 15 per cent for amplification purposes. The space charge, surrounding the grid, also interferes with its action and thus further reduces the *mu* of the tube.

The Gain of a Stage. In addition to the amplification furnished by the tube, there may be the amplification due to the step-up action of the transformer. Figure 27-2 shows what is meant by a *stage of amplification*. We may calculate the amplification, or gain, of this stage by dividing the output voltage by the input voltage. Thus, if the output voltage is 50 volts and the input voltage is 5 volts, the amplification furnished by this stage is 50 divided by 5, or 10.

The Power Tube. We must remember that the radio tube is a voltage-operated device—that is, the varying voltage which is fed into the grid controls the current flowing in the plate circuit of the tube. It becomes the function, then, of each stage of amplification to amplify the variations of voltage fed into the grid. Each stage has this function, except the final audio-frequency stage, whose function it is to supply the fluctuating current or power that operates the loudspeaker.

Electrons, shot out by the cathode of such a tube and attracted to the plate, travel through the loudspeaker. In the case of a dynamic loudspeaker, the current goes through a transformer primary which couples the output power to a speaker voice coil (pages 170-172). The frequency of sound coming from the speaker depends upon the frequency of variations in the electron stream. The volume, or loudness, of this sound depends upon the amplitude of these variations. Thus, to operate our speaker at a loud level, we need a dense stream of electrons flowing in the plate circuit. Therefore, the cathode must be capable of emitting a large quantity of electrons, and the tube must be able to pass them on to the plate in order to furnish enough power to operate the loudspeaker.

It is for this reason that the last stage of audio-frequency amplification is called the *power stage,* and the tube that operates in this stage is called the *power tube.* If the power tube is of the filament type, this filament is usually made quite heavy and rugged, and is coated with chemicals that increase the electronic emission. A power tube may also contain a number of filaments connected together to give the same effect as one heavy filament. Tubes such as the type 45 and the type 2A3 are examples. Where the tubes have separately heated cathodes, these cathodes are large and are able to emit a large number of electrons. The 6AC5-GT is such a tube.

When the electrons strike the plate, they are traveling with considerable speed, and the force of the impact heats up the plate. For this reason, the plate of the power tube must be larger and more rugged than for the other types of tubes. It is usually coated with graphite to give it a black surface, so that it may radiate away its heat more effectively.

Power Tubes Have a Small Amplification Factor. Although the grid of the power tube must control the flow of electrons from the cathode to the plate, it must not block off too many of these electrons that are needed so badly in the plate circuit. For this reason, the grid of the power tube has an open mesh and is not placed so close to the cathode, as in the case of other types of amplifier tubes.

This construction, in turn, reduces the amplification factor of the power tube. Thus, the *mu* of the type 2A3 tube is only 4.2 and that of the type 45 tube 3.5. Power tubes of the triode class generally have a low amplification factor.

Since the grid of the power tube is of open mesh and relatively far from the cathode, changes in the grid voltage do not affect the flow of electrons in the plate circuit as much as if the grid were of finer mesh and closer to the cathode. In order to create a certain variation in the plate current, therefore, any change in the charge on the grid of the power tube needs to be greater than the change needed by another type of amplifier tube. We say that power tubes of the triode class have low *power sensitivity.*

Because this greater *grid-voltage variation,* or *swing,* is necessary to operate the power tube, it is important that most of the voltage amplification of the signal should occur before the current is fed into the power tube. For this reason, it is customary to have at least one stage of audio-frequency amplification between the detector and power stage.

Two Power Tubes in Parallel. Sometimes the power required for the loudspeaker is too great for a single tube to handle. In such cases, we can connect two identical power tubes in *parallel.* The grid of one tube is connected to the grid of the other, the plate to the other plate, and the cathode to the other cathode (Fig. 27-3).

The voltage placed upon the grids of two tubes in parallel is the same as that on the grid of one tube. But because two cathodes

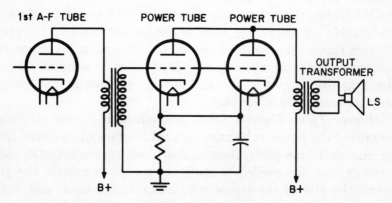

Fig. 27-3. *Circuit showing how two power tubes are connected in parallel to handle greater power.*

are emitting electrons, the current set flowing in the plate circuit of the tubes is twice as large. Thus, from two tubes we can get nearly twice the power output that a single tube can deliver to operate the loudspeaker. It is quite obvious that three or more tubes may be connected in parallel. It is not practical, however, to use more than two tubes for ordinary purposes.

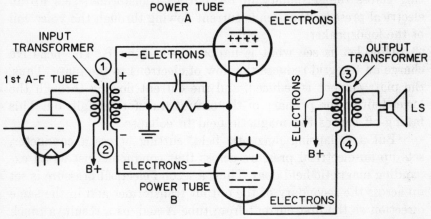

Fig. 27-4. *Circuit showing how two power tubes are connected in push-pull.*

The Push-pull System for Power Tubes. Another method of multiplying the output of the power tube is to connect two of them in *push-pull*. Figure 27-4 shows this circuit.

You will notice that the secondary winding of the input transformer is center-tapped. Each end of this winding goes to the grid of one of the power tubes. The center tap is connected to the grid-bias resistor, which, in turn, is connected to both cathodes. Thus, a negative bias is placed on the grids of the tubes (pages 155-156).

The primary of the output transformer also is center-tapped. Each end of that winding goes to one of the plates, and the B+ terminal is connected to the center tap. Here is how this hookup works.

The fluctuating current in the plate circuit of the first audio-frequency tube sets up an alternating voltage across the secondary of the input transformer. Assume an instant when point No. 1 of the secondary is positive; point No. 2 then is negative. In this situation, a positive charge is placed upon the grid of tube A and a negative charge upon the grid of tube B.

In tube A, the electrons shot out by the cathode are sped on to the plate and flow to point No. 3 of the primary of the output transformer. They then flow through the coils of the primary, to the center tap, and out to the positive post of the B supply.

As the current flows through the upper half of the primary of the output transformer, a magnetic field is built up. This field, cutting across the secondary of the output transformer, sets up an electrical pressure that sends current flowing through the voice coil of the loudspeaker.

Now let us see what is happening in tube B. The negative charge on the grid reduces the flow of electrons to the plate. Thus, the plate current is reduced, and the current flowing through the lower half of the primary of the output transformer falls off. This falling-off causes the magnetic field to collapse.

But a collapsing magnetic field, cutting across a conductor, sets up an electrical pressure across that conductor just as an expanding magnetic field does. Thus, a second electical pressure is set up across the secondary of the output transformer and in the same direction as the first current from tube A and, as a result, a much greater current flows through the voice coil of the loudspeaker.

Note that while the current flowing in one tube is increasing, the current in the other tube is diminishing. Also notice that we need twice the grid voltage that is needed to operate a single tube in order to operate a pair of tubes in push-pull, since each tube must get the same voltage on its grid as that necessary for a single tube. Power tubes connected in push-pull produce very little distortion of the signal.

The Phase Inverter. The push-pull power stage may be coupled to the first audio stage by resistance coupling as well as by the transformer-coupling method just described. Let us see what the push-pull stage requires.

First of all, as the grid of one of the push-pull tubes becomes more negative, the other grid must become less negative. Second, the grid-voltage variations, or swings, of both tubes must be equal —that is, one grid going as much more negative as the other goes less negative.

In the transformer-coupling method just described, the first requirement is met by connecting the grids to opposite ends of the secondary of the input transformer. The second requirement of equal grid swing is met by connecting both cathodes of the push-

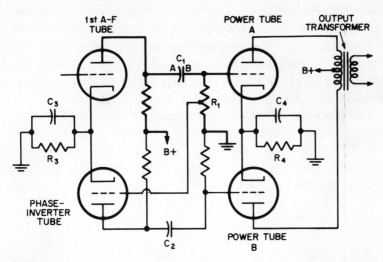

Fig. 27-5. *The phase-inverter circuit.*

pull tubes to the center tap of this secondary through the cathode-bias resistor.

If resistance coupling is desired, it is usual to employ another tube, called a *phase inverter,* in a circuit such as that shown in Figure 27-5. Note that the top half of this diagram (shown in heavy lines) is an ordinary example of resistance coupling similar to that shown in Figure 17-12.

If we assume that the grid of the first audio-frequency amplifier tube receives a positive signal, the plate current of that tube will increase, piling electrons onto plate A of coupling capacitor C_1. This drives electrons off plate B of the capacitor onto the grid of power tube A, making that grid more negative.

Part of this negative signal voltage is tapped off through the grid-leak resistor R_1 and is fed to the grid of the phase-inverter tube. If you look carefully, you will notice that the bottom half of the diagram (shown in lighter lines) is really another example of resistance coupling between the phase-inverter tube and power tube B.

When the negative voltage is applied to the grid of the phase-inverter tube, its plate current decreases, resulting in a less negative voltage on the grid of power tube B, as explained on pages 124-125. Thus, the first requirement is met—namely, that the grid of power tube A becomes more negative as the grid of power tube

B becomes less negative. The second requirement of equal grid swings is met by choosing the proper tap point on grid resistor R_1.

Note that the first audio-frequency amplifier tube and the phase-inverter tube have a common self-bias circuit consisting of resistor R_3 and capacitor C_3. Similarly, the two power tubes have a common self-bias circuit made up of resistor R_4 and capacitor C_4.

The Tetrode. It was stated, earlier in this chapter, that the triode has a low amplification factor because:

1. We cannot use a fine-mesh grid, since this causes too great a grid-to-plate capacitance, and thus too much feedback, especially at higher frequencies.

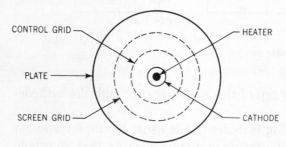

Fig. 27-6. *Looking down on the top of a screen-grid tube showing the arrangement of the electrodes.*

2. The space charge within the tube wastes about 85 per cent of the positive charge on the plate.

To overcome these difficulties, in some tubes a second grid is placed between the original grid, now called the *control grid,* and the plate. This new grid is called the *screen grid.*

The screen grid is connected to the B+ terminal, but usually a dropping resistor reduces the positive charge on it to a value less than that on the plate. Thus, if a positive charge of 250 volts is placed on the plate, 100 volts usually is placed on the screen grid.

Action of the Screen Grid in the Tetrode. This new grid acts as a screen between the plates of the capacitor formed inside the tube by the control grid and plate. When a grounded screen is placed between the plates of a capacitor, it acts to reduce the total capacitance. Similarly, if a grounded screen is placed between the plate and the control grid of a tube, the internal capacitance between these two electrodes is greatly reduced.

The screen grid of a tetrode is such a grounded screen. This may not be evident from Figure 27-7, since the screen grid is

Fig. 27-7. *The screen-grid tube circuit.*

+100V +250V

connected to the +100-volt terminal of the power supply. The positive voltage on the screen grid is necessary for the proper functioning of the tube. However, note that the screen grid is connected to ground through capacitor C, known as the *screen bypass capacitor*. Thus, while the screen grid is at +100 volts as far as direct-current components are concerned (since these currents cannot pass through the capacitor), it is grounded as far as the alternating-current components of the signal are concerned (since the capacitor is of such value as to offer very little opposition to them). Thus, it acts as a grounded screen as far as the signal is concerned, and the internal capacitance between the control grid and plate is reduced. For example, whereas the triode 6C5 tube has a grid-to-plate capacitance of two $\mu\mu$f, the tetrode 24A tube has a control grid-to-plate capacitance of approximately 0.007 $\mu\mu$f. Thus, the amount of feedback is cut down to almost zero and the evil of oscillation is eliminated. As a result, we can now use a closely meshed control grid, and this structure gives us a much greater amplification factor.

Another result of introducing the positively charged screen grid is the dissipation of the space charge. The electron cloud which otherwise fills the inside of the tube is attracted to the screen grid. Some of the electrons hit the wires of this grid and go off to the positive post of the B supply. But most of them go through the openings and travel on to the plate, which has a higher positive charge. This electron stream gives a greater plate current and a much greater amplification factor for the tube, because now any new electrons emitted by the cathode need not dissipate themselves battling the repellent effect of the space charge.

We can fully appreciate the effect of the screen grid when we compare the amplification factor of 20 for a triode such as the type 6C5 with that of 400 for the type 24A screen-grid tube. Although losses in the circuit may cut the real *mu* down to 40 or 50, nevertheless, you can readily see the advantage of the screen-grid tube.

Since the screen grid forms the fourth electrode in the tube, we call this new type of tube a *tetrode,* meaning *four electrodes.* Because of the low grid-to-plate capacitance of the tetrode, there is no danger of oscillations being set up as the result of feedback. This condition makes it unnecessary to neutralize the radio-frequency and intermediate-frequency stages of amplification. Figure 27-8 shows the circuit of a typical radio-frequency stage using the tetrode. Note that the screen grid is bypassed to ground by a 0.001-µf capacitor.

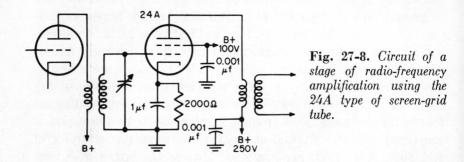

Fig. 27-8. *Circuit of a stage of radio-frequency amplification using the 24A type of screen-grid tube.*

The tetrode may also be used as a detector and as an audio-frequency amplifier. However, since the pentode is superior to the tetrode, the latter type is not employed today.

Variable-Mu *Tubes.* As a result of the fine-meshed control grid the electrons that stream through the spaces between the wires are forced to pass quite close to those wires. A very small charge upon the wires of the grid, then, has a great effect on the electron stream flowing to the plate of the tube. The screen-grid tube is ideal for the purpose of delivering a large voltage from a small one.

The very construction that makes this tube so suitable for handling small voltages prevents it from handling high voltages. It does not require a great negative charge on the control grid to stop entirely the flow of electrons to the plate. Thus, if a large alternating voltage should be fed into the grid, the positive half of the cycle would go through well enough, but most of the negative half-cycle would be blocked out, and detection or rectification would result.

If the screen-grid tube is used as a radio-frequency amplifier in a set which is located near a powerful station, the strong signal from that station will cause the automatic-volume-control system to send a large negative bias to the control grid of the tetrode. This bias plus the negative half-cycle of the incoming signal will cut off the flow of electrons to the plate, and the radio-frequency tube will act as a grid-bias detector (pages 98-101). This phenomenon causes a form of distortion called *cross modulation*.

This interference does not occur if the wires of the control grid are widely spaced. Charges on the grid have little effect on the electrons as they stream through the wide open spaces. But, of course, the amplification factor of the tube is much less.

The ideal condition, then, would be to hook up one tube with a close-meshed control grid and one with an open-meshed control grid in such a way that weak signals would travel through the close-meshed tube, where they would be greatly amplified, and the strong signals, that did not need so much amplification, would travel through the open-meshed tube, where they could not cause distortion. This ideal was achieved in one tube by constructing a control grid that is close-meshed at the ends and open-meshed in the center (Fig. 27-9).

When a weak signal comes in, the automatic volume-control sends little negative bias to the control grid of the radio-frequency tube, and this tube then acts as a conventional screen-grid amplifier. When a strong signal comes in, the negative bias of the tube is increased. This increased bias means that the electrons cannot get through the fine mesh at both ends of the control grid. But in the center, where the mesh is open, the electrons can get through, and the tube now acts as a low-*mu* amplifier.

Such a tube is called a *variable-mu tube* or *super-*

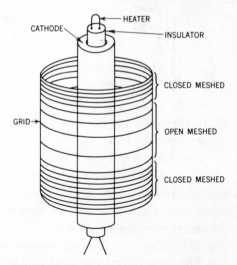

Fig. 27-9. *Diagram showing the construction of the control grid of a variable-mu tube.*

control radio-frequency amplifier. One example of such a tube is the type 6SK7.

The Radio-Frequency Pentode. Although the screen-grid tube makes an excellent radio-frequency amplifier, it suffers from one defect. Because the space charge has been overcome, and also because of the added pull of the positive charge on the screen grid, electrons leaving the cathode attain a speed as great as 20,000 miles per second and strike the plate with great force.

The force of impact is great enough to knock some electrons off the plate. This phenomenon is called *secondary emission.* These electrons fly about in space and either are pulled back by the positive charge of the plate or else are attracted to the positively charged screen grid nearby. The electrons lost to the screen grid reduce the supply left for the plate circuit of the tube, and amplification falls off.

To remedy this defect, a third grid is placed between the screen grid and the plate. This new grid is connected to the filament or cathode of the tube. Since it is connected to the cathode, this new grid has the same charge on it and, therefore, has little effect upon electrons passing through it. But as compared to the positive charge on the plate, this new grid is negative. Therefore, any electrons knocked off the plate by secondary emission will be turned back by this grid to the plate

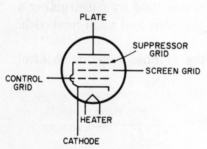

Fig. 27-10. *Arrangement of electrodes in the pentode tube.*

where they belong. Because of this fact, the new grid is called the *suppressor grid* (Fig. 27-10).

Because they have five electrodes (cathode, three grids, and a plate), tubes of this type are called *pentodes.* They make excellent radio-frequency and intermediate-frequency amplifiers because they have the sensitivity and high amplification factor of the screen-grid tubes plus the ability to suppress secondary emission. They are also known as *radio-frequency pentodes.*

The type 1T4 tube is of this category. The suppressor grid is connected internally to one end of the filament. Sometimes, the suppressor grid is led out to one of the base connections. We then must connect it to the cathode externally. The type 6SK7 tube is an example.

The Power Pentode. Like the screen-grid tube, the radio-frequency pentode is not suited for use as a power tube. Let us see if we can design a good power tube.

First of all, it must be capable of handling a good deal of power. Hence, the cathode must be a very strong emitter of electrons. These electrons must find their way to the plate quite readily. Hence, we must have an open-meshed grid. The plate must be large and rugged to withstand the bombardment of electrons.

So far we have described our old friend, the triode power tube. Now, let us see if we can step up its amplification factor. We cannot make the grid more fine-meshed because doing so would cut

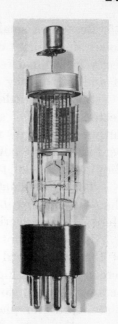

Fig. 27-11. *Cutaway view of a radio-frequency pentode.*

down the flow of needed electrons, and thus reduce our power. But we can eliminate the space charge that uses up about 85 per cent of the positive charge on the plate. So between the control grid and the plate, we place a positively charged screen grid, and the amplification factor shoots up.

But not so fast. We are dealing here with heavy streams of electrons. Without the restraining effect of the space charge, the electrons hit the plate with tremendous impact, knocking off clouds of electrons. A large number of these electrons are attracted to the positively charged screen grid, and down goes our amplification factor.

Well, let us put in a suppressor grid between the screen grid and the plate. Connect this suppressor grid to the cathode, and the electrons knocked off by the impact are forced back to the plate, and up goes the amplification factor.

This tube is called a *power pentode,* and one example is the type 6K6-GT. Compare its amplification factor of more than 100 with that of the triode type 45, whose amplification factor is

3.5. Because a small grid voltage can control a large amount of power in its plate circuit, the power pentode may even work directly from the detector without any need for an intervening stage of audio-frequency amplification.

Like the triode power tube, the power pentode can be connected in parallel and in push-pull circuits to get greater power output. Although they are both pentodes, the radio-frequency pentode and the power pentode are not interchangeable. In reality, they are tubes of two different types.

The Beam Power Tube. Although it has only four electrodes, the *beam power tube* is in reality a variation of the power pentode. Here is how it works.

Electrons, shot off from the cathode, pass between the wires of the control grid and the positively charged screen grid. This screen grid has a higher positive charge than the plate. This charge acts as a brake, slowing down the electrons in their flight to the plate. Deflector plates, connected to the cathode and, therefore, having the same charge, concentrate these electrons into a cloud or beam, moving slowly towards the plate. Any electrons knocked off by secondary emission are repelled back to the plate by this beam of electrons. Thus, the space charge created by the beam of electrons acts just as the suppressor grid to overcome the effects of secondary emissions. Examine the diagram in Figure 27-12.

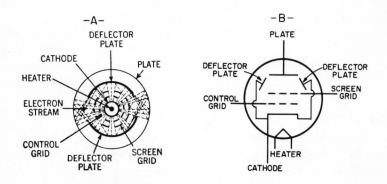

Fig. 27-12. *A-Looking down on beam power tube, showing electron streams threading their ways through the grids.*
        B-Symbol of the beam power tube.

Fig. 27-13. *A-Arrangement of control grid and screen grid in most tubes. Note that comparatively few electrons get through to the plate.*

  B-Arrangement of control grid and screen grid in beam power tube. More electrons get through to the plate.

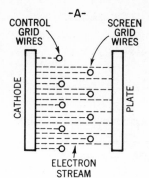
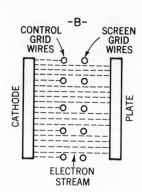

Another innovation of the beam power tube is the special construction of the grids. In other types of tubes, the control grid and screen grid appear as shown in Figure 27-13-A.

Note that a considerable portion of the electrons hit the screen grid, and thus are lost to the plate. If a meter were connected in the screen-grid circuit, it would show a considerable flow of electrons from the screen grid to the B+ terminal.

Figure 27-13-B shows the grid construction of the beam power tube. Note that the wires of the control grid shade the wires of the screen grid in such a way that very few of the electrons hit the screen grid. A meter connected in the screen-grid circuit of a beam power tube, accordingly, would show a very small flow of current.

More electrons, therefore, strike the plate of a beam power tube, and the efficiency of the tube is raised. Figure 27-14 shows how the 6L6 tube, a typical beam power tube, is connected in a circuit. Note that the positive charge on the plate is less than that upon the screen grid, since some of the electrical pressure is

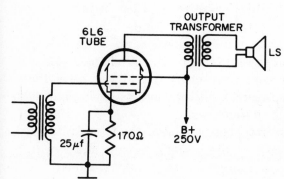

Fig. 27-14. *Circuit of beam power tube used as a power tube.*

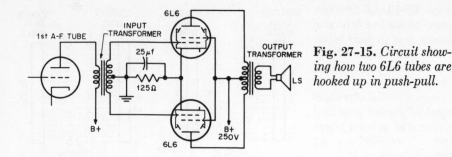

Fig. 27-15. *Circuit showing how two 6L6 tubes are hooked up in push-pull.*

lost while forcing its way through the primary of the output transformer.

Some idea of the efficiency of such a beam power tube as the 6L6 can be gained by comparing it with a triode such as the type 45. With a signal of 50 volts applied to the grid, the type 45 tube delivers 1.6 watts of electrical power to the loudspeaker. The 6L6 tube delivers 6.5 watts of electrical power, and needs only 14 volts on the grid. As in the case of other power tubes, the beam power tube can be connected in parallel and in push-pull to deliver greater power. See Figure 27-15.

Multielectrode Tubes. Tubes containing more electrodes than a triode are generally called *multielectrode tubes.* We have already discussed tetrodes and pentodes. There are others with even more electrodes. Although they may appear quite complicated at first glance, their operation is quite simple if we keep in mind the basic principle of the radio tube—that is, that electrons are shot out by the heated cathode and find their way to the positively charged plate.

In their travels, the electrons pass between the wires, or meshes, of a number of grids. These grids either attract or repel the electrons, either speed them up or retard them. The effects that these grids exert upon the traveling electrons depend upon the charges placed upon the grids. A positively charged grid will attract the electrons, a negatively charged grid will repel them. A varying charge upon the grid will produce a varying effect on the electrons. And that is all there is to it.

The Pentagrid Converter. Let us look at the type 6BE6 tube, which has a cathode (and separate heater), a plate, and five grids as shown in Figure 27-16. The grids are numbered from 1 to 5, counting from the cathode toward the plate.

This tube is often used as both the mixer (first detector) tube and oscillator tube in a superheterodyne receiver (Chap. 26). When used·for this purpose, it is called a *pentagrid* (five grids) *converter.* Here is how it works.

Let us consider the cathode, grid No. 1, and grid No. 2. If we place a positive charge on grid No. 2 and consider it as a "plate" (although an open-mesh one), you can see that we have here a "triode." This "triode" is employed by the local-oscillator circuit just as is the triode in Chapter 26. The oscillator signal is fed to grid No. 1 and, as a result, the stream of electrons flowing from the cathode is made to fluctuate at the oscillator frequency (1,175 kc, in our example).

Of course, most of these electrons flow through the mesh of our "triode plate" toward the real plate of the tube. Hence we may consider the cathode, grid No. 1, and grid No. 2 as a sort of composite "cathode." Only in this case, instead of emitting a steady stream of electrons, it emits a stream of electrons that is fluctuating at the oscillator frequency.

Under these circumstances we may consider the entire tube as a "pentode." The cathode, grid No. 1, and grid No. 2 form the composite "cathode"; grid No. 3 is the control grid; grid No. 4 (which is connected to grid No. 2 and, therefore, has a positive charge) is the screen grid; grid No. 5 is the suppressor grid; and finally there is the plate.

The incoming signal (1,000 kc in our example) is fed to the control grid No. 3. The charge on this grid will vary at that frequency. Through this grid flows electrons, already fluctuating at the rate of 1,175 kc. Beats result, and through grid No. 3 comes a stream of electrons that fluctuate at the rate of 1,175 kc minus 1,000 kc, or 175 kc—the exact frequency to which the intermediate-frequency transformers are tuned. A typical pentagrid-converter circuit is shown in Figure 27-17.

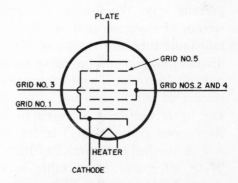

Fig. 27-16. *Diagram showing the arrangement of electrodes in the pentagrid converter tube.*

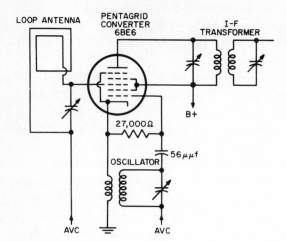

Fig. 27-17. *Typical pentagrid-converter circuit.*

You will recall that when we discussed coupling the oscillator to the mixing circuit on pages 216-218, we said that in addition to the inductive and capacitive methods, there was a third method whereby the two circuits were coupled through the electrodes within the tube. This third method, used in the converter just described, is sometimes called *electronic coupling* for obvious reasons.

Multiunit Tubes. It is quite possible to place two or more complete tubes in one envelope. Such tubes are called *multiunit tubes*. All the tubes in the envelope may even share the same cathode, but they differ from the multielectrode tube in one important way. Whereas in the multielectrode tube there is one stream of electrons that is acted on by all the electrodes, in the multiunit tube the stream of electrons flowing from the cathode divides into two or more parts, and each part flows through its own unit of electrodes. These tubes are constructed so that the electron stream of one unit is not affected by the electrodes making up any other unit, but proceeds to flow from the cathode through its various grids (if any) to its own plate.

A number of typical multiunit tubes are illustrated in Figure 27-18. Of course, many other combinations can and will be designed.* But regardless of how complex they seem to be, the basic principle is a simple one: a heated cathode emits a stream of elec-

* The manuals of the various tube manufacturers may be studied for the types of tubes they illustrate.

trons which threads its way through intervening grids to a positively charged plate.

Tube Envelopes. Radio tubes first were made with bulbs, or envelopes, of glass in which were sealed the various electrodes. These glass envelopes are usually either pear-shaped or tubular and range in size from about ¾ to 2½ inches in diameter and from about 1½ to 5½ inches in height. The connections to the electrodes are made through the base, but in some instances, one of the electrodes (usually the control grid) is connected to a cap sealed into the top of the envelope. See Figure 27-19.

Later, tubes were made with metal envelopes. A metal shell is welded to a glass base, and the air is pumped out of the envelope. Electrode connections are made through the glass base and, in some instances, one connection is made to a cap on the top of the metal shell. Metal tubes usually are tubular in shape, about one inch in diameter, and range from about 1¼ to 3¾ inches in height. The chief advantage of the metal envelope is its shielding effect. The envelope usually is connected to a pin in the base which, in turn, is connected to ground.

Another type in common use is the glass miniature tube.

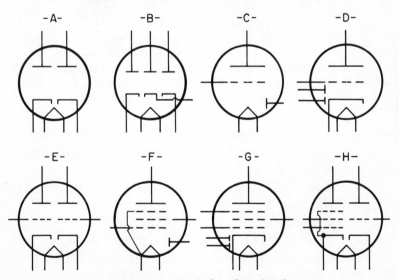

Fig. 27-18. *Typical multiunit tubes*

A—*2 diodes (type 6ALS).* *E*—*2 triodes (type 6SN7-GTB).*
B—*3 diodes (type 6BC7).* *F*—*1 pentode, 1 diode (type 1U5).*
C—*1 triode, 1 diode (type 1H5-GT).* *G*—*1 pentode, 2 diodes (type 12F8).*
D—*1 triode, 2 diodes (type 6SQ7).* *H*—*1 pentode, 1 triode (type 6AN8).*

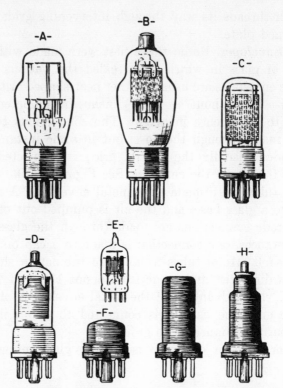

Fig. 27-19. *Types of tube envelopes.*

A—Glass, pear-shaped, no grid cap.   *E—Glass, miniature.*
B—Glass, pear-shaped, grid cap.   *F—Metal, type 6H6 tube.*
C—Glass, tubular, no grid cap.   *G—Metal, no grid cap.*
D—Glass, tubular, grid cap.   *H—Metal, grid cap.*

These tubes have diameters of ¾ inch, for the 7-pin variety, and ⅞ inch, for the 9-pin types. Their heights range from about 1¾ to 2⅝ inches over all.

Tube Bases. The electrodes usually are connected to pins or prongs set in a base of bakelite, ceramic, or other insulating material. These prongs fit into a socket designed to receive them. Permanent connections are made to the terminals on the socket, and thus a tube may be replaced merely by removing it from its socket and inserting another one in its stead.

In some receiving-type tubes, the base is cemented to the bottom of the glass envelope. Such a base usually is about 1½ inches in diameter and may contain from four to seven prongs. See Figure 27-20-A.

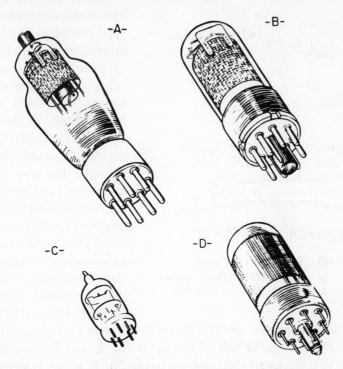

Fig. 27-20. *Types of tube bases.*
A—Early type base. These may have 4, 5, 6, or 7 prongs.
B—Octal base.   C—Miniature button base.
D—Lock-in Loktal base.

The *octal* base is used with virtually all metal tubes as well as with a large number of glass tubes. In this base, usually about 1¼ inches in diameter, eight pins are arranged in a circle around a central centering pin. In the glass tube, this base is cemented to the envelope; in the metal tube, it is crimped to the shell. If eight pins are not needed for all the electrodes, one or more gaps are left in the circle of pins. See Figure 27-20-B.

Another type of base is the *lock-in* or *loktal* type, which resembles the octal type except that the pins are welded directly into the glass that forms the bottom of the envelope and the central centering pin has a lock-in feature that anchors the tube to its socket. See Figure 27-20-D.

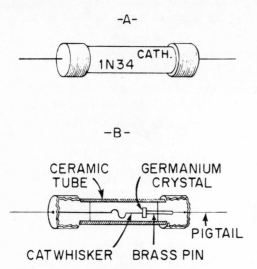

-A-

-B-

CERAMIC   GERMANIUM
TUBE   CRYSTAL

PIGTAIL

CATWHISKER   BRASS PIN

Fig. 27-21. *A—The crystal diode.*
B—Cross-section view,
showing how the diode is constructed.

Still another type of base is the *minature button* type, employed with the minature tubes that are but ¾ inch in diameter. Such tubes have seven or nine prongs embedded in the glass bottom of the envelope. (Fig. 27-20-C). The bottom is made thick for strength, but care must be taken not to twist the tube when it is being inserted or removed from its socket.

In both the octal- and lock-in-type bases, the same pin-numbering system is followed. If the tube is held horizontally with the pins toward you and the lip on the central centering pin facing down, the pin to the left of the lip is No. 1, and the numbers increase in a clockwise direction up to pin No. 8, which is at the right of the lip. Gaps left for pins that are not needed should be included in the count.

In the miniature-type tube, you will note an extra-wide gap between two of the pins of the base. If the tube is held so that the pins face you and the extra-wide gap is down, the pin to the left of this extra-wide gap is No. 1, and the count proceeds in a clockwise direction.

The Crystal Diode. Before ending this chapter on radio tubes, we should discuss, briefly, two devices which, though not tubes, act like them and are replacing them in many applications. One of these devices, the *crystal diode,* is our old friend the crystal detector in modern dress and without some of the defects that plagued the early experimenters. Look at Figure 27-21.

A thin wire catwhisker touches a small crystal of germanium. The catwhisker and its connecting wire (*pigtail*) is called the *anode.* The germanium crystal, the brass pin upon which it rests, and its connecting wire form the *cathode.* The whole unit is enclosed in a protective ceramic tube to keep out air and corrosion.

Because the catwhisker is fixed in its position, there is no need to hunt for a sensitive spot.

As you learned when we discussed the crystal detector (Chapter 8), these crystals offer a low resistance to current flowing from the cathode to the anode (called the *forward* direction), but a high resistance to current flowing in the opposite, or *reverse,* direction. Thus, you see, these crystals can act just like diodes to rectify alternating current.

In Figure 27-22-A, the crystal is connected in the circuit so that the anode is positive and the cathode is negative. As a result, current will flow through the crystal in the forward direction, as indicated by the arrows. In Figure 27-22-B, you see an analogous circuit using a diode tube. The more positive we make the anode (with respect to the cathode), the more current will flow through the crystal. If we place a varying positive charge on the anode, the current flowing through the crystal will vary in like manner.

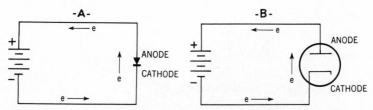

Fig. 27-22. *A—Current flow through crystal in the forward direction.*
B—Analogy showing current flow through the diode tube in the forward direction.

The Transistor. The transistor resembles the crystal diode, except that *two* catwhiskers, spaced a few thousandths of an inch apart, touch the surface of the crystal. See Figure 27-24-A. One of these catwhiskers is called the *emitter* and the other the *collector.* Electrical contact to the bottom of the germanium crystal is made through the metallic *base* upon which it rests. The symbol for the transistor is shown in Figure 27-24-B.

The basic transistor circuit is shown in Figure 27-25. You will note that there are two circuits, one involving the emitter and the crystal (base) and the other involving the collector and the crystal. Note, too, that battery A in the emitter-base circuit makes the emitter positive with respect to the base. Thus current flows in the forward direction and the resistance offered by the crystal is low.

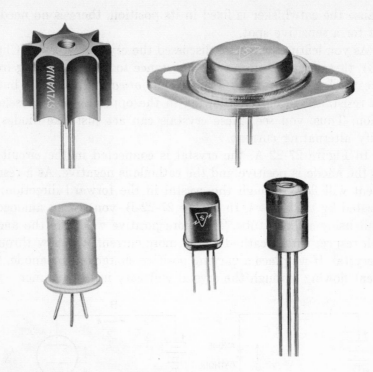

Fig. 27-23. *Several types of transistors.*

Note, however, that battery B in the collector-base circuit makes the collector negative with respect to the base. This is the reverse direction and the crystal offers a very high resistance to the flow of current. However, since the two catwhiskers are so close to each other, the two circuits interact. The flow of current in the emitter-base circuit acts to cause current to flow in the collector-base circuit. And the greater the current flow in the emitter-base circuit, the greater will be the current flow in the collector-base circuit.

A typical transistor circuit is shown in Figure 27-26. The input signal, as represented by the a-c generator, varies the current flowing in the emitter-base (input) circuit. This current flow, in turn, causes a current with similar variations to flow in the collector-base (output) circuit.

As this varying current flows through the resistor (R) in the input circuit, a relatively large voltage drop appears between the ends of this resistor. Since this voltage (which is the output

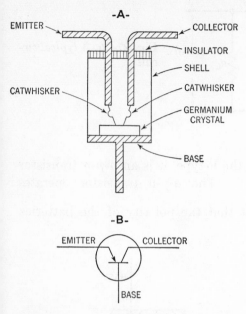

Fig. 27-24. *A—Cross-section of the transistor.*

B—The symbol for the transistor.

signal) varies in step with the variations of the smaller input signal, we thus obtain amplification of the signal.*

The transistor we have described is known as the *point-contact* type. There is another type of transistor known as the *junction* type. Although its action is somewhat similar to the point-contact type, the junction transistor is constructed differently. It consists of three thin slabs of germanium crystals placed face to face. Its action depends upon the fact that there are two types of germanium crystals. These types are determined by the kind of impurities the crystals contain in microscopic amounts. One type of germanium crystal is known as the n-type. The other is the p-type.

In the junction transistor, one type of germanium crystal is sandwiched between two of the other type. See Figure 27-27. The middle layer of the sandwich is the base. The two outside ones become the emitter and collector. If the two outer layers are of the p-type germanium, the transistor is called a *p-n-p* type and its symbol appears as .

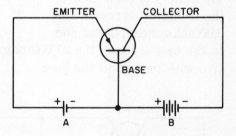

Fig. 27-25. *The basic circuit of the transistor.*

* The student must be warned that this explanation has been greatly over-simplified. However, there is no room here for a fuller explanation.

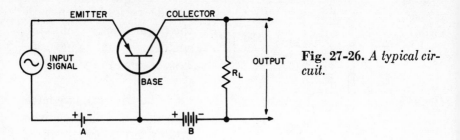

Fig. **27-26.** *A typical circuit.*

If the two outer layers are of the n-type, it is an *n-p-n* transistor whose symbol is ⊕ . The n-p-n transistor operates just as the p-n-p type, except that the polarity of the batteries must be reversed. Thus the typical n-p-n transistor circuit is as indicated in Figure 27-28.

In Figure 27-29 you see a typical stage of audiofrequency amplification using a p-n-p transistor. The output is designed to operate a pair of 2,000-ohm headphones. Note that the emitter is positive with respect to the base. Also, since the negative post of the battery is connected to the collector through the 2,000-ohm headphones and

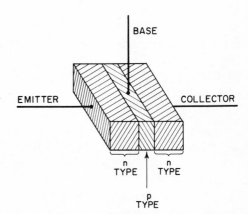

Fig. **27-27.** *The p-n-p junction transistor.*

to the base through the 27,000-ohm resistor, the collector is negative with respect to the base.

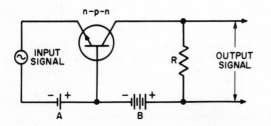

Fig. **27-28.** *A typical n-p-n transistor circuit.*

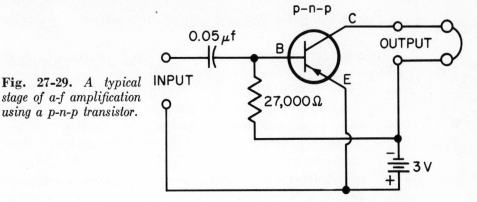

Fig. 27-29. *A typical stage of a-f amplification using a p-n-p transistor.*

The transistor may also be employed as an oscillator, a typical circuit of which is illustrated in Figure 27-30. Inductor L, and capacitor C form the oscillatory circuit. Feedback to compensate for losses and thus keep the oscillations going comes from the collector circuit through L_2 which is inductively coupled to L_1. The r-f output from the oscillator is obtained through L_3 which is inductively coupled to L_1. With a transistor such as Raytheon type CK762 this circuit can produce oscillations whose frequencies may be as high as about 25 megacycles.

The transistor presents a number of advantages over the ordinary triode. It is smaller, more rugged, and requires no vacuum. Because it has no filament or heater, it requires no heater current, nor is there a warming-up period. Its life is much greater

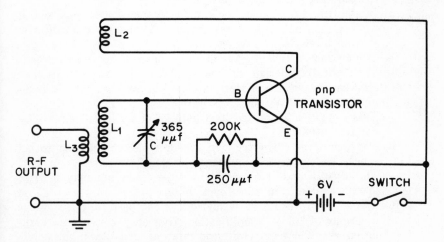

Fig. 27-30. *Typical transistor r-f oscillator circuit.*

than that of the radio tube and as a result it requires very little power.

Present-day transistors, on the other hand, cannot handle as much power as can some tubes. Nor can the transistor operate at frequencies as high as those at which some high-frequency tubes can function. However, these deficiencies are being overcome rapidly as research continues. Meanwhile, the transistor is replacing the tube wherever its small size and low-power characteristics are particularly useful. Such applications include portable and automobile receivers, hearing aids, electronic computers, proximity fuses, and similar devices.

SUMMARY

1. The fundamental principle operating in all radio tubes is that electrons emitted by a filament or cathode are drawn to a positively charged plate.

2. Tubes with only an electron emitter and a plate are diodes; tubes with an electron emitter, grid, and plate are called triodes.

3. Tubes having more electrodes than a triode, called *multielectrode tubes,* are made by adding additional grids with various charges and mesh design (for example, the tetrode, pentode, etc.)

4. When two or more complete tubes are enclosed in one envelope, the tube is called a *multiunit tube.*

5. In multielectrode tubes, only one stream of electrons passes, whereas in multiunit tubes, there may be several different streams of electrons, each one on its way to its own plate.

6. The characteristics of a tube depend upon its structural design. Thus, we may design voltage amplifiers or power tubes with different amplification factors; or, a variable-mu tube, a high-mu tube, or a low-mu tube.

7. Tubes may be connected in a parallel or push-pull circuit for greater output.

8. The pentagrid converter is a tube for electron mixing to get a beat intermediate frequency.

9. The crystal diode behaves like a tube diode and may be used in many circuits in place of a tube.

10. The transistor is a crystal device that can perform many of the functions of tubes—amplification, frequency conversion, oscillation, etc. There are two basic types of transistors: the point-contact type and the junction type.

GLOSSARY

Amplification Factor (Mu): The ratio between a change in the grid voltage and a corresponding change in plate voltage needed to bring the plate current back to its original value.

Beam Power Tube: A pentode-type tube wherein the suppressor grid is replaced by a slow-moving beam of electrons.

Control Grid: The grid of a tube upon which the signal voltage is impressed.

Cross Modulation: A condition in which a strong local signal comes in with sufficient strength to force the first radio-frequency tube to act as a detector, thus producing distortion.

Crystal Diode: A crystal, generally of germanium or silicon, and a point contact (catwhisker) that functions as a diode tube.

Electronic Coupling: A method of coupling electrical energy from one circuit to another through the stream of electrons in a tube.

Grid Swing: The amount of grid-voltage variation produced by the incoming signal.

Multielectrode Tube: A tube with many electrodes, mainly grids, each of which acts on the single stream of electrons flowing from the cathode to the plate.

Multiunit Tube: A tube combining several independently acting tubes in one envelope. The electron stream divides into several parts, each part being acted upon by one set of electrodes.

Pentagrid Converter: A tube containing five grids in addition to the plate and cathode. This tube is used in the superheterodyne receiver to perform the functions of first detector, local oscillator, and mixer tubes at one and the same time.

Pentode: A five-element tube containing a cathode, plate, control grid, screen grid, and suppressor grid.

Power Sensitivity: A measure of the extent to which small changes in grid voltage control large changes of power in the plate circuit of a tube.

Power Tube: A tube designed to handle more current than the ordinary amplifying tube. This tube is used in the last stage of the audio-frequency amplifier to furnish power to some device such as a loudspeaker.

Push-Pull: A method of connecting two tubes to supply great power to a loudspeaker with little distortion.

Screen Grid: A grid of a tube placed between the control grid and the plate to reduce the space charge and plate-to-grid capacitance.

Secondary Emission: The cloud of electrons knocked out of the plate by the impact of the electron stream sent out by the cathode.

Space Charge: A cloud of electrons filling the space between the cathode and plate of a tube.

Supercontrol Radio-Frequency Amplifier Tube: A variable-*mu* tube.

Suppressor Grid: A grid placed in a tube between the screen grid and the plate to reduce the effect of secondary emission.

Tetrode: A four-element tube containing an electron emitter (cathode), plate, control grid, and screen grid.

Transistor, Junction: A sandwich made of a thin slice of either n-type or p-type germanium crystal between two thin slices of either p-type or n-type, respectively.

Transistor, Point-Contact: A small piece of germanium crystal, generally n-type, with two catwhiskers set very close together, touching its surface and forming a p-n-p transistor.

Variable-Mu Tube: A tube with a specially wound grid producing a change in the amplification factor with signals of different strength.

SYMBOLS

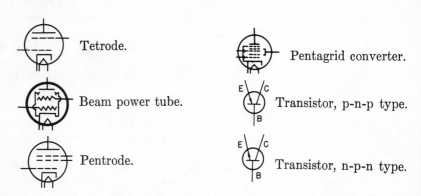

Tetrode.

Pentagrid converter.

Beam power tube.

Transistor, p-n-p type.

Pentrode.

Transistor, n-p-n type.

QUESTIONS AND PROBLEMS

1. Explain two types of electron emitters used in radio tubes.
2. Name the different electrodes in a diode, triode, tetrode, pentode, and beam power tube. Explain the function of each electrode.
3. How did the introduction of a control grid make amplification by a tube possible?
4. Why do triodes have relatively low amplification factors?
5. How does a power triode, like the 2A3 tube, differ structurally from a high-mu triode voltage amplifier?
6. Why is it advisable to have an audio-frequency voltage amplifier between the detector and power tube of a receiver?
7. Draw the circuit of two power tubes in parallel.
8. Explain the operation of a push-pull power stage using transformer coupling.
9. Explain how a screen grid acts as a grounded grid for a signal, yet has a high B+ voltage on it.

10. Explain the action of a phase inverter in a push-pull power stage.
11. What factors give a pentode a higher mu than a triode?
12. What is the cause of cross-modulation? How is it eliminated?
13. How are the effects of secondary emission reduced in a tube?
14. Explain the operation of a beam power tube.
15. Explain how the pentagrid converter produces the intermediate-frequency signal in a superheterodyne receiver.
16. How does a multiunit tube differ from a multielectrode type?
17. How does a p-n-p junction transistor differ from an n-p-n type?
18. How does a point-contact transistor differ from a junction transistor?
19. Draw the circuit of a typical transistor amplifier, using an n-p-n junction transistor.
20. What are the advantages of transistors over tubes?

28

Modern Radio Receivers

| **PROBLEM 1.** *What are the circuits for typical modern radio receivers using multielectrode and multiunit tubes?*
| **PROBLEM 2.** *What is the circuit for a typical transistor radio receiver?*

Up to this point, we have considered receivers using only triode tubes. This was deliberate, since we did not desire to complicate the discussion of the various circuits by introducing multiunit and multielectrode tubes. However, such tubes are used in modern receivers, and we may now examine the circuits of such receivers to see how they are modified to employ the more complex types of tubes.

A-C Superheterodyne Receiver. The circuits presented here are typical, though each manufacturer may provide his own variations. The circuit illustrated in Figure 28-1 is that of an a-c superheterodyne receiver employing a power transformer. Miniature tubes are used throughout, except for the 5Y3-GT rectifier tube.

Because of the high sensitivity of the receiver, a loop antenna, that is contained in the set's cabinet, is employed. This loop is tuned to the incoming signal, just as any other coil, by capacitor C_1, which is part of a three-gang variable capacitor (C_1, C_5, and C_8). Capacitors C_2, C_6, and C_9 are small trimmer capacitors used to vary slightly the capacitances of C_1, C_5, and C_8 respectively, and thus help align the various tuning circuits. Alignment of the oscillator circuit is further aided by the *padding capacitor* (C_7).

After amplification in the r-f amplifier stage, the signal is passed on to grid No. 3 of the converter tube. The local oscillator (transformer T_2 and its associated components) feeds its output to grid No. 1 of the same tube. As a result, the output of the converter tube is at the intermediate frequency (455 kc in this example) and contains the modulations present in the original signal picked up by the loop antenna.

The i-f signal next is amplified by the i-f amplifier stage. Note that the primaries and secondaries of the i-f transformers (T_3 and T_4) are tuned by variable capacitors (C_{11}, C_{12}, C_{14}, and C_{15}). These capacitors are of the trimmer type and are to be found within the cans that shield the transformers.

The signal next is fed to the diode section of the 6AV6 detector tube where it is detected. The output of the detector stage appears as a voltage across resistor R_7 and potentiometer R_8. Part of this output is filtered by R_6 and C_{13} and R_4 and C_3, and becomes the AVC voltage which is fed to the r-f amplifier, converter, and i-f amplifier stages. The balance of the output is taken from across potentiometer R_8 (which is the manual volume control) and fed to the grid of the triode section of the same tube (which forms the a-f amplifier stage).

Note the filter network consisting of C_{16}, C_{17}, and R_7. This network filters out any of the i-f signal remaining in the output of the detector stage.

The output of the a-f amplifier stage divides into two parts. One is fed directly to the grid of one of the two 6AQ5 power amplifiers that are connected in push-pull. The other part is tapped off from the junction of resistors R_{14} and R_{15} and is fed to the grid of the phase-inverter tube. The output of this tube is equal in amplitude and opposite in polarity to the signal at the grid of the first power amplifier tube. This is fed to the grid of the second power amplifier tube, thus meeting the requirements of the push-pull stage. The output of this stage is coupled to the voice coil of the permanent-magnet dynamic speaker by the output transformer (T_6). The network consisting of C_{26} and R_{18} across the primary of the output transformer acts to filter out some of the higher audio-frequency currents to give the receiver a more pleasing tone.

Bias for the r-f and i-f amplifier stages comes partially from cathode resistors (R_1 and R_5 respectively) and partially from the AVC voltage. Bias for the converter stage comes solely from the AVC voltage. Bias for the a-f amplifier and phase-inverter stages is developed by the contact-bias method (See Chapter 20).

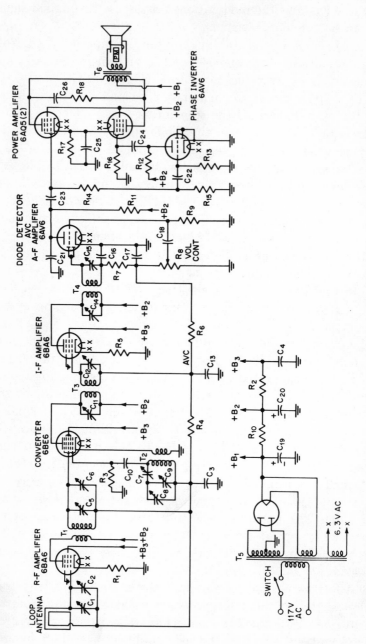

Fig. 28-1. A-C superheterodyne receiver. (Courtesy of Radio Corporation of America)

List of Values for Receiver in Figure 28-1.

C_1, C_5, C_8	Ganged tuning capacitors, 10-365 $\mu\mu$f
C_2, C_6, C_9	Trimmer capacitors, 4-30 $\mu\mu$f
C_3, C_{13}	0.05 μf, paper, 50 v.
C_4	0.05 μf, paper, 400 v.
C_7	Oscillator padding capacitor—follow coil manufacturer's recommendation.
C_{10}	56 $\mu\mu$f, mica
C_{11}, C_{12}, C_{14}, C_{15}	Trimmer capacitors for i-f transformers
C_{16}, C_{17}	180 $\mu\mu$f, mica
C_{18}, C_{22}	0.01 μf, paper, 400 v.
C_{19}, C_{20}	20 μf, electrolytic, 450 v.
C_{21}	120 $\mu\mu$f, mica
C_{23}, C_{24}	0.02 μf, paper, 400 v.
C_{25}	20 μf, electrolytic, 50 v.
C_{26}	0.05 μf, paper, 600 v.
R_1, R_5	180 ohms, $\frac{1}{2}$ watt
R_2	12,000 ohms, 2 watts
R_3	22,000 ohms, $\frac{1}{2}$ watt
R_4, R_6	2.2 megohms, $\frac{1}{2}$ watt
R_7	100,000 ohms, $\frac{1}{2}$ watt
R_8	1 megohm potentiometer (volume control)
R_9, R_{13}	10 megohms, $\frac{1}{2}$ watt
R_{10}	1800 ohms, 2 watts
R_{11}, R_{12}	220,000 ohms, $\frac{1}{2}$ watt
R_{14}, R_{16}	470,000 ohms, $\frac{1}{2}$ watt
R_{15}	8200 ohms, $\frac{1}{2}$ watt
R_{17}	270 ohms, 5 watts
R_{18}	15,000 ohms, 1 watt
T_1	R-F transformer, 540-1600 kc
T_2	Oscillator coil for use with 10-365 $\mu\mu$f var. cap. and 455 kc i-f transformer.
T_3, T_4	I-F transformers, 455 kc
T_5	Power transformer, 250-0-250 v. at 120 ma for plates of rectifier tube; 5 v. at 2 amp. for filament of rectifier tube; 6.3 v. at 3 amp. for filaments of other tubes.
T_6	Output transformer for matching impedance of voice coil to 10,000-ohm plate-to-plate tube load.
Loop Antenna	For tuning to 540-1600 kc with 10-365 $\mu\mu$f var. cap.
Switch	Single-pole, single-throw, mounted on back of volume-control potentiometer (R_8).

The bias for the power amplifier stage is developed by the cathode resistor (R_{17}).

Note that the filter section of the full-wave rectifier circuit is of the *RC* type (resistors R_{10} and R_2 and capacitors C_{19}, and C_{20}). With resistors R_2 and R_{10} also acting as a voltage divider, we have three values of B+ voltage. The largest voltage ($+B_1$)

is applied to the plates of the power amplifier tubes. The next largest ($+B_2$) is applied to the plates of the other tubes and to the screen grids of the power amplifier tubes. The smallest ($+B_3$), about 100 volts, is applied to the screen grids of the r-f amplifier, converter, and i-f amplifier tubes. You can see that there appear to be no screen-grid bypass capacitors. However, this function is performed by C_4 which bypasses the $+B_3$ line. The switch that turns the set on and off is mounted on the back of the volume-control potentiometer (R_8) and is controlled by its shaft.

AC-DC Superheterodyne Receiver. Most radio receivers manufactured today are of the small AC-DC table model that does not use a power transformer. A typical circuit is the one employed in the General Electric Model 412 receiver that is illustrated in Figure 28-2. This is a superheterodyne circuit using five miniature tubes.

Receivers of this type generally do not have an r-f stage of amplification. The incoming signal received by the loop antenna is fed directly into the converter tube. So is the signal from the local oscillator (transformer T_1 and its associated components). Capacitors C_1 and C_3 are ganged so that the loop and oscillator circuits are tuned together. Capacitors C_2 and C_4 are trimmers that help to align their respective tuning circuits.

The output of the converter stage (at the intermediate frequency of 455 kc) is fed to the i-f amplifier. Note the symbol above and below the primaries and secondaries of the i-f transformers T_2 and T_3. This symbol stands for a movable powdered-iron core that slides in and out of each winding and thus varies its inductance. You may recall that when we discussed the tuning circuit (Chapter 6) we stated that we can vary its natural frequency by varying the values of its inductance, its capacitance, or both. Here, we adjust the natural frequency of the i-f transformers to 455 kc by varying the inductances of their windings, keeping the capacitances fixed. The fixed capacitors are contained within the cans used to shield the transformers.

From the i-f amplifier stage the signal is fed to the diode section of the 12AV6 tube. A portion of the detected signal is filtered and forms the AVC bias that is fed to the converter and i-f amplifier stages. The rest of the signal is passed through the 0.5-megohm manual volume control and on to the triode section of the tube which acts as an a-f amplifier. From there it is am-

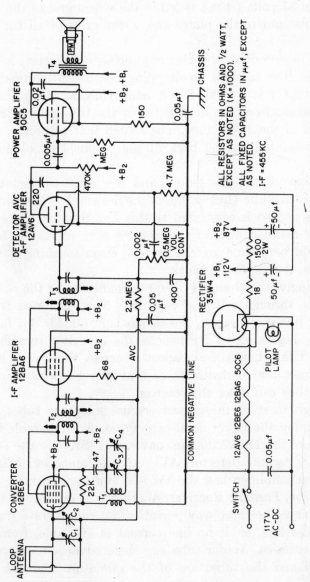

Fig. 28-2. *AC-DC superheterodyne receiver. (Courtesy of General Electric Company)*

plified by the power amplifier and is fed to the permanent-magnet dynamic speaker.

The power supply is the typical ac-dc power supply discussed in Chapter 21. The 35W4 tube is a half-wave rectifier and an *RC* filter circuit is used. Two positive B voltages are obtained. One of 112 volts ($+B_1$) is fed to the plate of the power amplifier tube. The other of 87 volts ($+B_2$) is fed to the screen grid of the power amplifier tube and to the plates and screen grids of all the other tubes.

Since the sum of all the filament voltages (in series) is about equal to the line voltage, no dropping resistor is required. The pilot light (P.L.) is a small 6-volt lamp (Mazda #47) that obtains its voltage from the drop between the tap and one end of the filament of the 35W4 tube. The switch that turns the set on and off is mounted on the back of the volume-control potentiometer.

Note that all the grid-return and B— leads connect to the common negative line (heavy line in the drawing). Note, too, that the power line also is connected to this line through the switch. If, now, the metal chassis of the receiver were connected to this line, it would be at line voltage and a person touching it would be in danger of receiving a shock.

Accordingly, the chassis (⌁) is connected to the common negative line through a 0.05-µf capacitor. Now, as far as the 60-cycle power line is concerned, the chassis is insulated. But for currents at the higher signal frequencies the capacitor furnishes an easy path. The other 0.05-µf capacitor across the power line is used to bypass any r-f disturbances that may be present in that line before they can enter the receiver.

Although most of these receivers use minature tubes, some of them employ the larger octal-base types. A comparable set of such tubes are the 12SA7 for the converter, 12SK7 for the i-f amplifier, 12SQ7 for the detector, AVC, and a-f amplifier, 50L6-GT for the power amplifier, and the 35Z5-GT for the rectifier.

Three-Way Portable Receiver. Another type of receiver that is quite popular is the three-way portable that can operate from an a-c line, a d-c line, or, if no line current is available, from self-contained batteries. A four-tube superheterodyne circuit usually is employed and the tubes are of the miniature filament type. Most commonly, a type 1R5 tube is used as the converter, a type

1U4 tube as the i-f amplifier, a type 1U5 as the diode detector, AVC, and a-f amplifier tube, and a type 3V4 as the power tube. The filaments of these tubes operate at 1½ volts each, except the 3V4 tube whose filament requires three volts.

A typical power supply for such a receiver is that used in the Philco Model E-670 receiver and illustrated in Figure 28-3. Where line current is not available, the receiver operates on a B

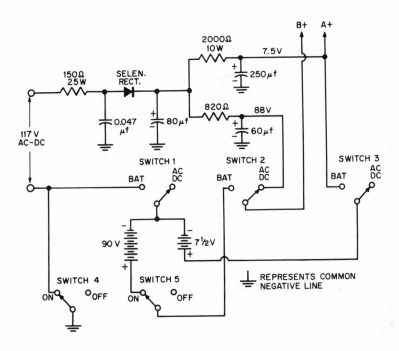

Fig. 28-3. *Power-supply and switching circuit of the three-way portable receiver. (Courtesy of Philco Corporation)*

battery of 90 volts and an A battery of 7½ volts. Where house current is available (either ac or dc) a half-wave selenium rectifier is employed to furnish a B voltage of 88 volts and an A voltage of 7½ volts. To obtain this A voltage, a portion of the B voltage is dropped to the necessary value by means of a 2,000-ohm resistor. *RC* filters are used for both the A and B voltages.

Switching from line to battery operation is performed by switches Nos. 1, 2, and 3 that are ganged and operated in unison.

The set is turned on and off by switches Nos. 4 and 5 that also are ganged and operated together.

When the receiver is to be operated from the house line, the line plug is inserted into an outlet. Switches Nos. 4 and 5 are set to their ON positions, connecting one end of the line to the common negative and thus completing the power-supply circuit. Switches Nos. 1, 2, and 3 are set to their AC-DC positions. The

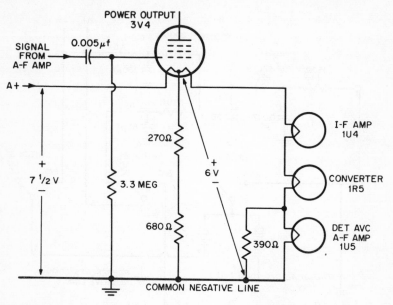

Fig. 28-4. *Filament and bias circuit of the three-way portable receiver.*

B+ voltage is applied to the receiver through switch No. 2. The A+ voltage from the power supply is permanently connected to the positive side of the filaments of the tubes.

When the receiver is to be operated by its batteries, the line plug is removed from its outlet and switches Nos. 1, 2, and 3 are set to their BAT. positions. Switch No. 1 connects the A— and B— to the common negative. Switch No. 2 connects the plus (+) terminal of the B battery to the receiver and switch No. 3 connects the plus (+) terminal of the A battery to the filaments of the tube.

By connecting all the tube filaments in series (as illustrated in Figure 28-4) they may be operated from the 7½ volts supplied by the power supply or the A battery. The bias required for the 3V4 tube is 6 volts. This is obtained by utilizing the voltage drops across the filaments of the three 1½-volt tubes and half the filament of the 3-volt 3V4 filament, all connected in series. By connecting the control grid of the power output tube to the common negative line through the 3.3-megohm grid resistor, this grid acquires a negative bias of 6 volts with respect to the center tap of its filament.

The filaments of the tubes operate at a current of 50 milliamperes. The resistances of the filaments are such that when they are connected in series across a 7½-volt source, exactly 50 milliamperes will flow through them. However, to this must be added the plate current flowing through the 3V4 tube, thus creating a serious overload upon the filaments. To avoid this overload, a resistance of 950 ohms (270 ohms and 680 ohms in series) is connected across the filaments, thus providing a parallel path for the excess current.

Similarly, the plate currents flowing through the 1U4, 1R5, and 1U5 tubes overload the filaments of these tubes. Since these plate currents are small, they may be neglected. However, the 1U5 filament is at the end of the string and receives the cumulative effect of the three plate currents. Accordingly, a 390-ohm resistor is connected across this filament to take care of the overload.

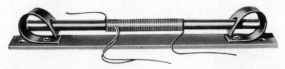

Fig. 28-5. *Ferrite loop or loopstick.*

To save the space occupied by the loop antenna, some receivers are supplied instead with a coil of wire wound upon a special powdered-iron core. This is called a *ferrite loop* or *loopstick*. See Figure 28-5. The efficiency of this small device is very high and it can function as well as the ordinary loop antenna.

Portable Transistor Receiver. The newest, and smallest, member of the family of radio receivers is the portable transistor receiver. This self-contained portable is small enough to fit into

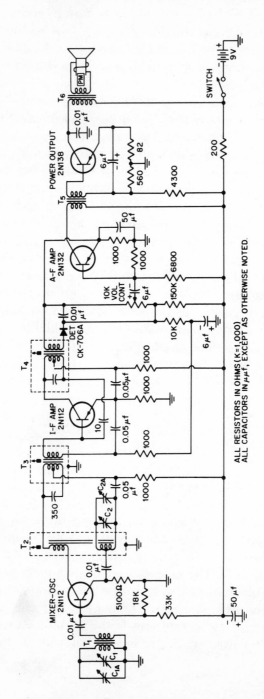

Fig. 28-6. *Portable Transistor Receiver.* (*Courtesy of Raytheon Manufacturing Company*)

the pocket. A typical circuit is that of the Raytheon Model T-100-5 receiver illustrated in Figure 28-6. Note that the transistors are shown here as a converter, as well as i-f, a-f, and power output amplifiers.

The antenna is a ferrite loop (T_1) that is tuned by capacitor C_1 which is ganged to capacitor C_2 (which tunes the local-oscillator circuit). Capacitors C_{1A} and C_{2A} are trimmers used with their respective variable capacitors.

The signal is fed to the mixer-oscillator transistor. Note that the signal is fed to the base of this transistor, the emitter being grounded through the 5,100-ohm resistor. A transistor may be operated with any one of its electrodes grounded provided, of course, that the correct polarity is maintained between these electrodes. Thus you may see circuits where the signal is fed to the base (as in this illustration), to the emitter, or to the collector.

Note, too, that all the transistors employed in this receiver are of the p-n-p type. This type, you will recall, requires that the base be negative with respect to the emitter, and positive with respect to the collector. Of course, n-p-n type transistors might be used as well, only in that case the polarities must be reversed. Some receivers use p-n-p and n-p-n transistors in combination.

The output from the local oscillator (T_2 and its associated components) is mixed with the incoming signal and the resulting intermediate-frequency signal is fed to the i-f amplifier transistor through the i-f transformer T_3. Note the 10-$\mu\mu$f capacitor between the base of this transistor and the second i-f transformer (T_4). This is a neutralizing capacitor performing the same function for the transistor that it does for the triode tube in an r-f stage of amplification. (See page 183).

From the i-f amplifier stage the signal is passed to the crystal-diode detector, through the 10,000-ohm volume-control potentiometer, and on to the a-f amplifier stage. This latter stage is transformer-coupled to the power output stage. An output transformer (T_6) couples the output of this stage to the permanent-magnet dynamic speaker.

The entire power for this receiver comes from a small 9-volt battery. Note that the positive terminal of this battery is grounded. The switch that turns the set on and off is mounted on the back of the volume-control potentiometer and is operated by its shaft.

Fig. 28-7. *Portable transistor radio. (Courtesy of I.D.E.A. Inc.)*

Because transistors and their associated components are so small, many transistor portable receivers are wired by means of *printed circuits.* Instead of using soldered wires to connect the components, connections are printed with metallic ink on an insulating sheet of plastic or ceramic. At the proper points, the various components are soldered to the printed wires. Resistors may be printed with special inks and small capacitors can be made by printing plates on opposite sides of the insulating sheet which acts as the dielectric. The result, when used with miniature components, is a very compact receiver.

There are a number of variations of the printed-circuit technique. For example, a copper plate can be deposited upon an insulator sheet. Then the circuit is printed upon the copper plate with a protective ink. Where the copper is exposed, it is etched away with chemicals, leaving the connecting copper strips beneath the ink.

Designed primarily for military use, as, for example, in the proximity fuse, the printed-circuit technique is ideal for receivers using transistors. However, it has also found its way into receivers using the larger tubes. Some receivers may be wired partially by means of printed-circuits and partially by means of the older method of using soldered wires.

SUMMARY

1. The modern AC superheterodyne receiver uses multielectrode and multiunit tubes in the signal circuits. The power supply utilizes a power transformer, rectifier, and filter circuit.
2. The signal circuit of the AC-DC superheterodyne receiver is similar to that of the AC superheterodyne receiver. The power supply utilizes a rectifier and filter circuit.
3. The three-way portable receiver is a superheterodyne receiver using tubes with filaments as electron emitters. The power supply is designed to select, by switching, either battery or line power. In line-power operation, there usually is a selenium rectifier and an A and a B filter circuit. Grid bias for the power tube is obtained from the voltage drop across the tube filaments. Often, a ferrite loop antenna is used for signal pickup.
4. The transistor receiver is basically a superheterodyne with transistors and a diode crystal instead of tubes. Power is obtained from a small battery.

GLOSSARY

Ferrite Loop: An antenna, consisting of a small coil of wire wound on a powdered-iron core. It serves the same function as the loop antenna and is similarly tuned. It sometimes is called a loopstick.
Loop Antenna: An antenna, usually contained within the radio cabinet, made up of a number of loops of wire. Together with a tuning capacitor, usually one section of the ganged capacitors, it forms a tuning circuit for the reception of signals.

SYMBOLS

 Loop antenna.

 Ferrite loop antenna.

QUESTIONS AND PROBLEMS

1. Explain the purpose of a padder capacitor.
2. How does an AC-DC superheterodyne receiver differ from an AC superheterodyne receiver?

3. How can you design an AC-DC receiver so that possible shock hazard from touching the chassis is removed?
4. Draw a typical power supply for a three-way portable receiver.
5. How is grid bias obtained for the output tube of a three-way portable receiver?
6. How is overloading of filaments prevented in the three-way portable receiver?
7. What is a ferrite loop antenna?
8. How does the transistor superheterodyne receiver differ from the AC-DC superheterodyne receiver?
9. What is a printed circuit?

Part II

Introduction to Part II

TO THE STUDENT

You may have noticed that the theory of the radio receiver has been presented in Part I of this book without the use of mathematical formulas. However, mathematics is a tool to be used when the underlying principles are pretty well understood, when measurement is needed, or when a student proposes to enter the technical radio field as a profession.

Therefore, in the second part of this book, frequent use is made of this tool. However, the mathematics consists of simple algebra, with a few principles of trigonometry. Where we need mathematical explanations, we will try to explain fully and to present as far as possible all mathematical steps.

We will try to explain further the nature of electricity and the radio wave. On this higher plane, we will meet our old friends *capacitance, inductance,* and *resonance.* We will explore more fully the operation of the antenna and the characteristics of radio tubes. We shall try to learn something about the radio telegraph and telephone transmitter. And, finally, we shall investigate the cathode-ray tube, a device that holds out to us a promise of wonderful things to come.

29

Direct Current and the Nature of Electricity

PROBLEM 1. *What is the modern explanation of the electric current?*

PROBLEM 2. *What is Ohm's law and how is it used to measure the properties of an electric current?*

PROBLEM 3. *What are the principles of joining resistors and of measuring their combined resistance?*

PROBLEM 4. *How are electric currents produced by chemical action?*

Origin of the Word **Electricity.** Man discovered electricity many centuries ago. The ancient Greeks knew that when a piece of amber was rubbed on some fur or cloth, it acquired the property of attracting to it small pieces of paper, dust particles, and other light substances. Indeed, it is from the Greek word *elektron,* meaning amber, that we obtain the word electricity.

Charging Glass and Rubber. In 1600 A.D., William Gilbert, an English scientist, discovered that many other substances, when rubbed together, possessed the same mysterious property of attracting light pieces of paper and dust particles. These substances, after being rubbed together, are said to be *electrified,* or to have been given a charge of electricity.

Let us experiment a bit. Rub a small glass rod with a piece of silk cloth. Suspend the rod from a silk thread so that it may swing freely. Now rub another such glass rod with another piece of silk. Suspend this rod too. Bring the two suspended rods near each other. They will repel each other.

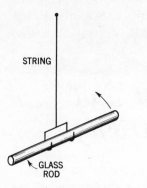

STRING

GLASS
ROD

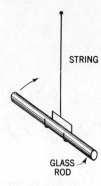

STRING

GLASS
ROD

Fig. 29-1. *How two glass rods that have been rubbed with a silk cloth repel each other.*

Now rub a hard rubber rod on a piece of flannel, suspend it, and bring it near one of the glass rods. The hard rubber rod and the glass rod will attract each other.

Benjamin Franklin explained this phenomenon as follows: When the glass rod was rubbed by the silk, it received an electric charge which Franklin designated as *positive.* When the hard rubber rod was rubbed by the flannel, it received a *negative* charge. Experiments showed that *like charges repel and unlike charges attract.* That is why the positively charged glass rod repelled the other positively charged glass rod, but attracted the negatively charged rubber rod.

The Electroscope. So far, we have dealt with stationary, or *static*, electricity. The electric charge put upon the glass or rubber rods remained where placed —that is, it was *static:* it *stayed.*

William Gilbert also invented the device known as the *electroscope.* This instrument consists of a metal rod mounted upright

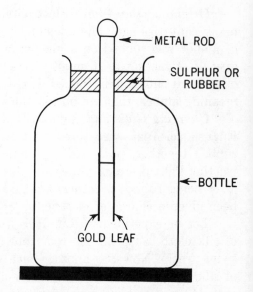

METAL ROD

SULPHUR OR
RUBBER

BOTTLE

GOLD LEAF

Fig. 29-2. *The gold-leaf electroscope.*

in a block of sulphur, rubber, or similar nonmetallic material. At the bottom of the metal rod are attached two strips of gold leaf (Fig. 29-2). The metal rod and its mounting are placed in a glass bottle, with the upper end of the rod protruding.

Now rub the glass rod on the silk. Touch the charged glass rod to the metal rod of the electroscope. The two strips of gold leaf move apart, and when the glass rod is removed from contact with the metal, the gold leaves stay apart. When the metal rod is touched with your finger the leaves fall together again. More-over, if the experiment is repeated, but this time using a charged rubber rod, the behavior of the gold leaves is the same as with the charged glass rod.

Franklin made the following explanation of these happenings: The electric charges brought to the metal rod flowed down this rod to the gold leaf. Since both pieces of gold leaf had similar charges, they re-pelled each other and swung apart. When the fin-ger was touched to the metal rod, the charges on the electroscope flowed up the rod, into the finger. The leaves, chargeless, fell to-gether because of their weight.

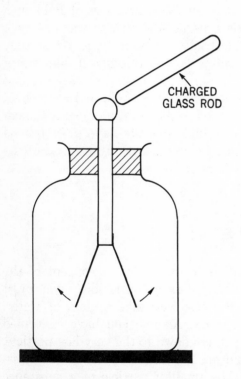

CHARGED GLASS ROD

Fig. 29-3. *The effect of a charged rod on the gold-leaf electroscope.*

Conductors and Insu-lators. Some new terms now have to be learned. First of all, we have discovered that certain substances permit an electric charge to flow through them. We call such substances *conductors*. Metals are the most common examples of such conductors.

There are other substances, such as glass, hard rubber, and sulphur, that do not permit an electric charge to flow through them. An electric charge, placed upon any of their surfaces, stays put. We call such substances *insulators,* or *nonconductors.*

Static and Current Electricity. The concepts (ideas) of stationary and moving charges also have been given names. We call the stationary electric charge *static electricity,* and electricity in motion is called *current electricity* or an *electric current.*

Electricity First Thought to Be a Fluid. Early scientists observed that if a negatively charged body was connected to a positively charged body by means of a metallic wire, an electric current flowed through the wire. They made an attempt at explaining this phenomenon by declaring that electricity was a sort of fluid such as water. To the early scientists, positive electricity was one type of such fluid, and negative electricity, another type. When they had access to a wire, both fluids flowed through it like water through a pipe.

Benjamin Franklin suggested that there was only one fluid which flowed from the positive (+) to the negative (−). Although both the two-fluid and the one-fluid concepts have been proved wrong, electricians of today continue to speak of an electric current as flowing from positive to negative.

THE ELECTRON THEORY

Molecules. Modern scientists have a different concept of the phenomenon of electricity. To understand this idea, you must think about small particles. Suppose you take a glass of water. Pour off half of it. Divide it again. Assume you have continued this process of division until you are down to the very last particle. This particle is still water and has all the properties of the glassful with which you started. The smallest particle of a substance having all the properties of the substance is called a *molecule.*

Atoms. Further experiments show that this molecule of water consists of a number of smaller particles. It has been found that the molecule of water can be decomposed by the electric current and that each molecule consists of two particles of the gas *hydrogen* and one particle of the gas *oxygen.* Chemists call a substance that can be decomposed into two or more simple substances a *compound;* water is such a compound. A substance which cannot be decomposed into more simple substances is called an *element;* oxygen and hydrogen are elements. The smallest particle of an element is called an *atom.*

Atoms are the building blocks of all matter. The atoms of any one element are alike, but they differ from the atoms of other elements. There are ninety-two* natural elements, and the atoms of each element are of a distinct and different kind. Just as bricks may be combined to form a great many different types of buildings, so these relatively few types of atoms, when combined in different arrangements, constitute the multitude of different substances known to man.

Electrons and Protons. For a great many years, the atom was considered to be the very smallest particle of matter. But later investigation has shown us that every atom consists of even still smaller particles. This knowledge leads to the *electron theory.*

According to this theory,** all atoms (and, therefore, all matter) are composed of three principal types of particles. One is a particle with a *positive electrical charge,* called a *proton.* The second is a particle with a *negative electrical charge,* called an *electron.* The third is a particle without a charge (acting somewhat as a combined proton and electron) and is called a *neutron.* The atom is pictured as having a *nucleus* (that is, a core or central part) consisting of a number of protons and neutrons packed together.*** Revolving around this nucleus are the electrons. See Fig. 29-4.

Different kinds of atoms have different combinations of protons and electrons. The protons are always to be found in the nucleus. The electrons are pictured as revolving around the nucleus in orbits or paths in a manner resembling the movement of the planets around the sun.

How Atoms Become Charged. In the uncharged or *neutral*

---

* Recently, as a result of research in nuclear energy, several new elements have been created artificially.

** The electron theory is presented here in simplified form. The present-day theory is a good deal more complicated. However, for our purposes, this simplified version will do.

*** Scientists have detected a number of other particles such as *mesons* and *neutrinos,* coming out of the nucleus. However, such particles exist in their free states for extremely short periods of time and, for the purposes of our discussion, will be disregarded.

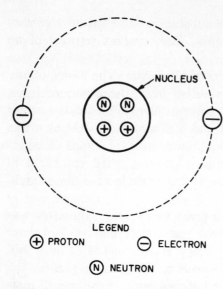

Fig. 29-4. *The helium atom, showing two electrons revolving around the nucleus. The nucleus contains two protons and two neutrons. The positive charge of the nucleus is just balanced by the two electrons. Hence, the atom has a neutral charge.*

LEGEND

⊕ PROTON   ⊖ ELECTRON

Ⓝ NEUTRON

atom, the total number of protons in the nucleus equals the number of electrons revolving about the nucleus. But if we should remove one or more electrons from the outer orbit, the number of protons would be greater than the number of electrons, and the atom then would have a *positive* electrical charge. Conversely, should we add one or more electrons to the outer part of the atom, the number of electrons would exceed the number of protons, and the atom then would have a *negative* electrical charge.

Scientists are not agreed about the nature of the nucleus, and hold a great variety of opinions about the electron theory. But we need not go into this disagreement. The idea of an electron as a minute negatively charged particle is very generally accepted. This idea suffices to explain the phenomena of electricity for our purposes.

The Charge on a Glass Rod. We can now understand what happened when we rubbed the glass rod with the silk cloth. The act of rubbing tore away a number of electrons from the atoms that went to make up the glass rod. Thus, the glass rod became positively charged.

Where did these electrons go? They went onto the silk and we should expect, therefore, that the silk cloth would have a negative charge. Our expectation is correct.

A Charged Rubber Rod Has an Excess of Electrons. When we rubbed the flannel cloth over the hard rubber rod, however, electrons were torn away from the cloth by the rubber. The rubber rod, therefore, having an excess of electrons, became negatively charged, and the flannel cloth, with a deficiency of electrons, became positively charged.

Differences in Atomic Structure. What determines whether a substance may lose electrons (as in the case of the glass rod) or acquire new electrons (as in the case of the hard rubber rod)? We believe that the difference appears to depend upon the arrangement of protons and electrons in the substance.

Since the protons of the nucleus are in the center of the atom and are closely bound together, it is an extremely difficult matter to get at them. But a number of electrons revolve around the nucleus. These electrons are more easily disturbed, and some of these are assumed to have been pulled away.

The electrons that revolve around the nucleus are called *planetary electrons.* They are believed to be arranged in a definite pattern of concentric circles or ellipses. You may visualize these concentric shells or orbits if you think of the layers of an onion. See Fig. 29-5.

The first shell of electrons, next to the nucleus, is able to contain two such planetary electrons, and no more than two. Where more than two such electrons are present in the atom, they form more rings outside of the first one. The second ring may contain

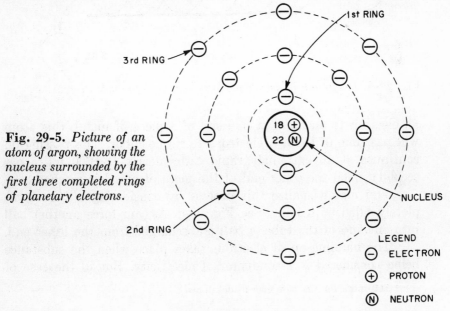

Fig. 29-5. *Picture of an atom of argon, showing the nucleus surrounded by the first three completed rings of planetary electrons.*

any number of electrons up to eight. The third also may contain
no more than eight. The fourth and fifth may hold up to eighteen;
the sixth, thirty-two; and so on until a total of ninety-two electrons are arranged outside of the nucleus.*

Conductors and Insulators. The electrons in the outer orbit
of an atom are more easily removed than those of the inner orbits.
Such electrons that are removed are called *free* electrons and may
travel from atom to atom. The electrons of certain substances are
more easily freed than those of other substances.

Substances whose electrons may be freed easily are called
conductors. Metals generally fall into this class. Substances whose
electrons are relatively difficult to free are called *insulators.* In
this class, we generally find nonmetallic substances such as glass
and rubber.

Explaining the Electric Current. Now we shall be able to delve
a little deeper into the subject of the electric current. The electrons in the outermost ring of the atom of a metal are loosely
held. Using this theory, one of the explanations of the electric
current being conducted through a metal is as follows: If we add

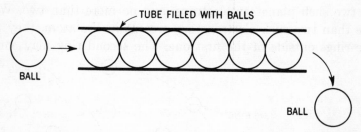

Fig. 29-6. *Diagram to illustrate motion of electrons through a conductor.*

an electron to an atom at one end of a piece of metal, this atom
will pass one of its own electrons to its neighbor. The passing-on
continues at an extremely rapid rate (nearly 186,000 miles per
second), until the other end of the piece of metal is reached.

You may visualize this process by considering a tube completely filled with balls. See Fig. 29-6. As you force another ball
into one end of the tube, a ball is discharged from the other end.

The handing-on of electrons takes place when the substance
being considered is a conductor of electricity. But in the case of

* And more for the new man-made atoms.

an insulator, adding an electron to one end will not start a flow of electrons. The additional electron will remain where it is placed. This is one explanation of why conductors carry electric currents and why insulators do not pass an electric current. It is believed that insulators merely retain the electrical charge on their surfaces. This explanation of conductors and insulators should be looked upon as a workable theory but not as a complete explanation.

THE THREE FACTORS OF AN ELECTRIC CURRENT

Electromotive Force. We have stated that if an electron were placed at one end of a conductor, it would cause ι flow of electric current to the other end. This statement is not strictly true because an electrical pressure is needed to move the electric current from one end of the conductor to the other.

To get an idea of *pressure,* let us consider a simple analogy. Assume we have a U-shaped tube with a valve or stopcock at the center (Fig. 29-7). Assume that the valve is closed. We now pour water into arm A to a height represented by X. Pour water into arm B to a height represented by Y. If the valve is now opened, the water will flow from arm A to arm B until X and Y are equal.

What caused the water to flow? It was not *pressure* in arm A, because when X and Y are of equal length, no water flows even though the water in arm A still exerts a pressure.

It was the *difference of pressure* between the two arms that

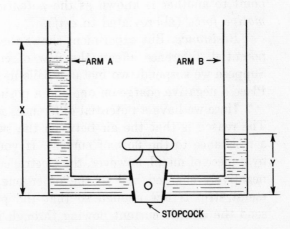

Fig. 29-7. *Diagram illustrating the fact that it is the* difference of pressure *which causes a fluid to flow through a tube.*

ARM A   ARM B

X

Y

STOPCOCK

caused the water to flow. This flow continued until the pressures in both arms were equal.

So it is with electrons. If at one end of a conductor, electrons are piled up, and at the other end, electrons are few in number or are being taken away, the excess electrons will flow toward the point of deficiency.

In Figure 29-7, the water in arm A can do no work until the valve is opened. Nevertheless, it represents a *potential* source of energy—that is, energy due to position. But the actual work is not done by the potential energy of the water in arm A, but by the *difference of potential energy* between the water in A and B.

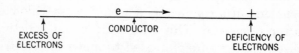

Fig. 29-8. *Diagram illustrating that it is the* difference of electrical pressure *which causes electrons to move through a conductor.*

Similarly, in Fig. 29-8, it is not simply the potential energy caused by piling up electrons at one end of the conductor that causes the electric current to flow. It is the *difference* between the amounts of potential energy at the two ends of the conductor that does the work. We say that an electric current flows through a conductor because of the difference of potential energy between the ends of the conductor. The force that moves the electrons from one point to another is known as the *potential difference,* or *electromotive force* (abbreviated to *emf*).

Resistance. But experiment shows that another factor besides potential difference affects the flow of current. Let us see how. Suppose we suspend two metallic balls in air several inches apart. Place a negative charge on one and a positive charge on the other.

Here we have a potential difference, and yet no current flows. The reason is that the air between the two balls offers too great a resistance to the flow of current. If you connect the two balls by a piece of metal, however, the electric current will flow from the negatively charged ball to the other one. The resistance of the metal strip is low enough so that the potential difference may send the electric current flowing through it.

But it is not necessary to connect the two balls with a metal strip to cause the electrons to flow from one to the other. All we need do is to increase the charges. When the potential difference is great enough, the electrons will jump across through the air in the form of an electric spark. We conclude then, that, *for electric current to flow, the potential difference must be great enough to overcome the resistance of the path.*

Different substances offer different resistances to the flow of electric current. Metals, generally, offer little resistance and are good *conductors.* Silver is the best conductor known, and copper is almost as good. Other substances such as glass, rubber, sulphur, and the like, offer a very high resistance and are known as *insulators.* But all substances will permit the passage of some electric current, provided the potential difference is high enough.

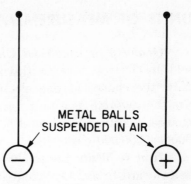

METAL BALLS
SUSPENDED IN AIR

Fig. 29-9. *Figure showing two oppositely charged balls suspended far apart in air. Although there is a potential difference between them, no current flows because the resistance of the path between them is too great.*

Current Depends on Both Electromotive Force and Resistance.
Refer to Figure 29-7. We measure the flow of water from one arm to the other in terms of quantity per unit of time. We say so many gallons flow past a certain point in a minute. Similarly, we measure the flow of electricity by the number of electrons that flow past a point on a conductor in one second.

What determines the amount of water per unit of time that flows through the valve in Figure 29-7? Obviously, it is the difference between the amounts of potential energy in the water in the two arms of the tube and the size of the opening in the valve (that is, the resistance the valve offers to the flow of water).

In the case of the electric current, the quantity of electricity per second (the number of electrons per second) which flows in a conductor depends upon the potential difference and the resistance of the conductor. *The greater the potential difference, the larger the quantity of electricity that will flow in a second; the greater the resistance, the smaller the quantity of electricity per second.*

UNITS OF MEASUREMENT

Quantity of Electrical Charge. We have seen that when we add an electron to a neutral atom, we give it a negative charge. Now the charge of one electron is small indeed. We, therefore, use the *coulomb* as a unit for measuring the quantity of electrical charge. A coulomb is equal to the combined charge of 6,280,000,-000,000,000,000 electrons.

How to Write Large Numbers. The number mentioned above is awkward to handle. Scientists use a sort of shorthand to express such large numbers. For example, multiply 10 by 10. You get 100. Since 100 is formed by *two* tens multiplied together, the scientists express 100 as 10^2. Similarly, 1,000 is formed by *three* tens multiplied together. It may, therefore, be expressed as 10^3. Thus, a coulomb is equal to the combined electrical charge of 6.28 times 10^{18} electrons; that is, 6.28 multiplied by 18 tens which have been multiplied together. The symbol $\times$ means *multiplied by*. The coulomb, therefore, is equal to 6.28×10^{18} electrons.

In the number 10^{18}, the small figure 18 is called the *exponent*. If we wish to express the number 1,000 by means of the exponent system, we write 10^3. If we wish to indicate 1/1000, we may write $1/10^3$. Another method is to write 10^{-3}. The figure -3 is called the *negative exponent*. Thus, 10 may be expressed 10^1, and 1/10 as 10^{-1}. Similarly, 100 may be expressed 10^2 and 1/100 as 10^{-2}.

Electric Current ($\mathbf{I}$). When we talk of electric current, we mean electrons in motion. When the electrons flow in one direction only, the current is called a direct current (dc). In the discussion in this chapter, we are speaking only of direct currents. It is important to know the number of electrons that flow past a given point on a conductor in a certain length of time. If a coulomb (6.28×10^{18} electrons) flows past a given point in one second, we call this amount one *ampere* of electrical current. Hence, the unit of electric current is the ampere.

Measuring Current by Its Chemical Effects. Aside from the fact that the electrons are too small to be seen, we would find it impossible to count them as they flowed by. Accordingly, we have devised another method to measure the current. It has been found that when an electric current passes through a solution of a silver salt from one electrode to another, silver is deposited out of the solution and upon the electrode which has an excess of electrons (the negative electrode). The amount of silver so deposited is in proportion to the strength of the electrical current. The more current, the more silver is deposited. Careful measurements show that *one ampere of current will cause 0.001118 gram of silver to be deposited in one second.*

In an electrical formula, the capital letter *I* stands for the current.

Factors Causing Resistance (R). The resistance which a substance offers to the flow of electric current depends upon a number of factors. First of all, there is the nature of the substance itself. We have seen that different substances offer different amounts of resistance to the flow of current.

Resistance is also affected by the length of the substance. The longer an object is, the greater its resistance. Another factor is the cross-sectional area of the substance, which is the area of the end exposed if we slice through the substance at right angles to its length. The greater this cross-sectional area, the less the resistance to current flow. In other words, for a given kind of material, the resistance varies directly as its length and inversely as its cross-sectional area.

Resistance is also affected by the temperature of the substance. Metals, generally, offer higher resistance at higher temperatures. Certain nonmetallic substances, on the other hand, offer lower resistance at higher temperatures.

The Ohm Is the Unit of Resistance. The unit of resistance is the *ohm. It is the resistance to the flow of electric current offered by a uniform column of mercury, 106.3 cm long, having a cross-sectional area of one square millimeter at 0° C.*

The symbol for the ohm is the Greek letter *omega* (Ω). In an electrical formula, the capital letter *R* stands for resistance.

The Volt Is the Unit of Electromotive Force (EMF). Another unit of measurement is the unit of electrical pressure (that is, *electromotive force* or *potential difference*). This unit is called the *volt.* The volt is defined as *that electromotive force that is necessary to cause one ampere of current to flow through a resistance of one ohm.* In an electrical formula, the capital letter *E* or the initials emf may stand for electromotive force.

The Watt Is the Unit of Electrical Power (P). Power is the rate at which energy is expended. Thus, the electrical pressure (expressed in volts) times the number of electrons flowing per second (expressed in amperes) equals the electrical power. The unit of electrical power which is designated by the capital letter P, is the *watt*. Thus:

$$watts = \text{volts} \times \text{amperes} \qquad \text{or} \qquad P = E \times I$$

Here is an example of how this formula is used. Assume that an electric-light bulb used on the 110-volt house line is found to pass 0.9 ampere of current. How much power is it consuming? Substituting the given values in our formula, we get

$$P = 110 \times 0.9 = 99 \text{ watts}.$$

We say that this bulb is a 100-watt (actually 99-watt) bulb.

OHM'S LAW

The relationship between the electromotive force, current, and resistance was discovered by a German scientist, Georg Simon Ohm, at the beginning of the nineteenth century. The unit of resistance was named in his honor.

This relationship can be expressed by means of the following formula:

$$\text{Current} = \frac{\text{emf}}{\text{resistance}} \qquad \text{or} \qquad I = \frac{E}{R}$$

This statement means that the greater the emf, the greater the current and the greater the resistance, the smaller the current.*

Practice in Using Ohm's Law. Let us see how we use this formula.

EXAMPLE 1. Suppose that we are attempting to light the filament of a type 5Y3-GT tube from the 110-volt house line. Since the filament of this tube requires about five volts, we are forced to get rid of the excess pressure of 105 volts by means of a dropping resistor. The tube manufacturer tells us that the type 5Y3-GT tube requires a current of two amperes to heat the filament. The problem is to determine the proper resistance of the dropping resistor so that 105 volts will be used up in passing through it.

Since two amperes of current must flow through the tube filament, it must also flow through the dropping resistor. We, there-

---

* Mathematically stated, the current varies directly as the electromotive force and inversely as the resistance.

fore, know that the electromotive force (or *drop in potential*) across the resistor is 105 volts and the current is two amperes. Substituting these values in our formula, we get

$$2 \text{ amperes} = \frac{105 \text{ volts}}{\text{resistance (ohms)}}. \tag{1}$$

Multiplying both sides of this equation by the resistance, we get

$$2 \text{ amperes} \times \text{resistance} = 105 \text{ volts}. \tag{2}$$

Dividing both sides of Equation (2) by 2, we get

$$\text{resistance} = \frac{105 \text{ volts}}{2 \text{ amperes}} = 52.5 \text{ ohms.} \tag{3}$$

EXAMPLE 2. Consider another example. Look at Figure 20-6. The bias resistor used in the cathode of the last type 6C5 tube is 1,000 ohms. The tube manufacturer tells us that when 250 volts are used on the plate of the tube, a current of 0.008 ampere flows from the cathode to the plate. What is the voltage across the bias resistor which is used to place a negative charge on the grid of the tube?

Our formula is originally

$$I = \frac{E}{R} \tag{1}$$

But we may convert this so as to express E in terms of I and R. Multiplying both sides by R, we get

$$I \times R = \frac{E \times R}{R} \tag{2}$$

Or canceling the R's in the fraction, we get

$$I \times R = E$$

Substituting our known values for current in the resistor and resistance of the resistor we get

$$E = 0.008 \text{ ampere} \times 1,000 \text{ ohms} = 8 \text{ volts.} \tag{3}$$

Since the bottom of the resistor which goes to the grid return is more negative than the top, a bias of −8 volts is thus placed upon the grid of the tube.

Transposing a Formula. By means of Ohm's law, we have been able to express current in terms of electromotive force and resistance ($I = E/R$), and emf in terms of current and resistance ($E =$

$I \times R$). We can also express resistance in terms of electromotive force and current. Take the formula $E = I \times R$. Dividing both sides by I, we get $R = E/I$.

HEATING EFFECT OF THE ELECTRIC CURRENT

As the electromotive force or potential difference forces current to flow through a conductor, the resistance encountered causes the conductor to become heated. In every conductor, some of the energy desired for useful work is lost by being transformed into heat. It is the electrical power (watts) that determines the heating effect, or we might more correctly say, the electrical energy is being transformed into heat energy. The formula for determining the electric power in terms of electromotive force and current, we have just learned, is

$$P = E \times I \qquad (1)$$

P represents power in watts. To express the heating effect in terms of the resistance of the conductor, we substitute for E in Equation (1) its equivalent $E = I \times R$. We now get

$$P = (I \times R) \times I = I^2 \times R \qquad (2)$$

Thus, if we know I and R, we are able to determine the power P. Let us try an example. In example 1, page 290, we know that I equals 2 amperes and R equals 52.5 ohms. Substituting in our formula, we get

$$P = (2 \text{ amperes})^2 \times 52.5 \text{ ohms} = 4 \times 52.5 = 210 \text{ watts}.$$

Moreover, we can check this answer by our original formula for power,

$$P = E \times I$$

Since the voltage drop was 105 and the amperes 2, then 105 volts $\times$ 2 amperes = 210 watts.

In practice, it is usual to have a safety margin of about 100 per cent, else our resistor may burn up. We, therefore, specify that the dropping resistor have a resistance of 52.5 ohms and be capable of passing 400 watts of electrical power.

We have expressed our power formula in terms of emf (voltage) and current ($P = E \times I$), and in terms of current and resistance $(P = I^2 \times R)$. We may also express it in terms of voltage and resistance. In our original power formula, $P = E \times I$, substitute the equivalent for I (that is, E/R). Thus, we get

$$P = E \times \frac{E}{R} = \frac{E^2}{R}$$

We make use of the heating effect of the electric current in tube filaments, electric heaters, toasters, and other appliances. Another use of this heat effect of an electric current is in fuses.

Fuses. When we connect delicate instruments in an electrical circuit, danger exists that too much current may pass through

Fig. 29-10. *Diagram showing how a fuse is used to protect electrical instruments or appliances.*

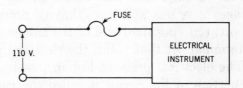

them and burn them up. We, therefore, connect in series with them a link of metal which has the property of melting when too much current flows through it. Thus, the link (or *fuse,* as it is called) melts before the instruments are damaged. This melting breaks the circuit, and the flow of current ceases.

Fuses are rated by the number of amperes of current that may flow through them before they will melt. Thus, we have 10-ampere fuses, 30-ampere fuses, and so on. Care should be taken that the fuses used in any circuit be rated low enough to melt or *blow* before the electrical instruments are damaged. Thus, in a house wired to stand a maximum current of 15 amperes, it would be best to use 10-ampere fuses so that a 15-ampere current could never pass.

Electrical Circuits. An electrical circuit may be described as the path or paths followed by electrons from the source of *high potential* (negative post) to the source of *low potential* (positive post). There are several types of circuits.

Series Circuits. In the *series circuit,* the electrons can follow only one path, from the negative to positive (Fig. 29-11). The electromotive force (110 volts) forces the electrons through this circuit. Since there is only one path, the number of electrons per

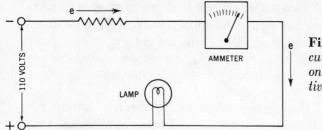

Fig. 29-11. *The series circuit. Electrons can follow only one path from negative to positive.*

second (which determine the number of amperes) in each part of the circuit is the same.

But some of the electrical pressure is used up in pushing the electrons through each part of the circuit. The electrical pressure (voltage) gets less and less (that is, drops) as we approach the low-potential (positive) end of the circuit until we reach the positive terminal. At that point, the electrical pressure is zero.

The electrical pressure lost in pushing the electrons through each portion of the circuit is called the *voltage drop* in that portion. The sum of all the voltage drops in a series circuit is equal to the original electromotive force (110 volts, in this instance). Thus, we may have, for example, a voltage drop of 20 volts across the resistor, 2 volts across the ammeter, and 88 volts across the lamp. As you can see, the total is 110 volts.

RULE: *The resistance of a series circuit is the sum of all of the resistances in the circuit.*

Thus, the resistor may have a resistance of 10 ohms; the ammeter, one ohm; and the lamp, 44 ohms. The total is 55 ohms. Applying Ohm's law to get the current:

$$I = \frac{E}{R} = \frac{110 \text{ volts}}{55 \text{ ohms}} = 2 \text{ amperes.}$$

Thus, we have 2 amperes of current flowing through all parts of the circuit.

Parallel Circuits. In a *parallel circuit,* the electrons can follow two or more paths simultaneously. In the circuit of Figure 29-12 the electron stream divides at X. Part flows through the resistor and back to the positive terminal. Another part flows through the lamp, joins the main electron stream at Y, and flows to the positive terminal.

It is evident that the electromotive force (110 volts) across the resistor is the same as that across the lamp (disregarding the slight resistance of the wires connecting the resistor to the lamp). Thus, the voltage drop across the resistor and the lamp are equal.

But the currents flowing through both parts of the circuit are not necessarily equal. If the electron stream encounters more resistance in the lamp, fewer electrons will flow through that path than through the resistor.

Resistors in parallel do not add their resistances to obtain the total. Instead, the total resistance for several resistors in parallel is determined by the following formula:

$$\frac{1}{\text{Total resistance}} = \frac{1}{R_1} + \frac{1}{R_2} + \frac{1}{R_3} +, \text{ and so forth.}$$

Another way of stating this formula is

$$\text{Total resistance} = \frac{1}{\dfrac{1}{R_1} + \dfrac{1}{R_2} + \dfrac{1}{R_3} +, \text{ and so forth.}}$$

In Figure 29-12, R_1 would be the resistance of the resistor and R_2

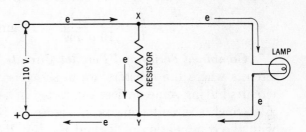

Fig. 29-12. *The parallel circuit. Here the electrons have more than one path to follow.*

that of the lamp. If we assume the resistance of the resistor to be 10 ohms and that of the lamp to be 20 ohms, substituting these values in our formula, we get

$$\frac{1}{\text{Total resistance}} = \frac{1}{10} + \frac{1}{20}. \qquad (1)$$

This reduces to

$$\frac{1}{\text{Total resistance}} = \frac{2}{20} + \frac{1}{20} = \frac{3}{20}. \qquad (2)$$

Cross multiplying, we get

$$1 \times 20 = 3 \times \text{total resistance}. \qquad (3)$$

This, in turn, gives us

$$\text{Total resistance} = \frac{20}{3} = 6.66 \text{ ohms.} \tag{4}$$

By Ohm's law, we may find the total current I:

$$I = \frac{E}{R} = \frac{110 \text{ volts}}{6.66 \text{ ohms}} = 16.5 \text{ amperes.}$$

This 16.5 amperes is the total current flowing in the circuit. But since the resistance of the lamp is twice that of the resistor, only half as much current flows through the lamp as through the resistor. This fact is based on the principle that the current varies inversely as the resistance. Thus, 11 amperes flow through the resistor and 5.5 amperes flow through the lamp. To verify these figures, we may use Ohm's law to find the current in each branch of the circuit separately. In the lamp where $R = 20$ ohms, the formula reads

$$I = \frac{E}{R} = \frac{100 \text{ volts}}{20 \text{ ohms}} = 5.5 \text{ amperes.}$$

In the resistor where $R = 10$ ohms, we have

$$I = \frac{E}{R} = \frac{110 \text{ volts}}{10 \text{ ohms}} = 11 \text{ amperes.}$$

Combined Series and Parallel Circuits. In addition to having circuits where the resistors are in series *or* parallel, we may have circuits having some devices connected in series and others in parallel. Such a circuit appears in Figure 29-13. Here R_1 is in series with the combination of R_2 and R_3. But R_2 and R_3 are connected parallel with each other. To find the total resistance, first find the total resistance of R_2 and R_3 by use of the formula

$$\frac{1}{\text{Total R}} = \frac{1}{R_2} + \frac{1}{R_3}$$

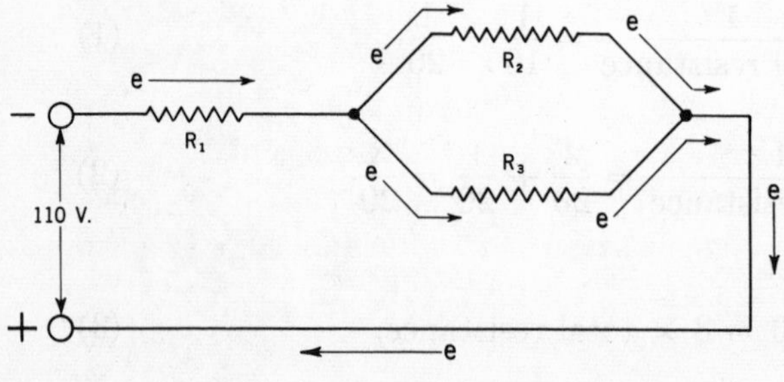

Fig. 29-13. *The series-parallel circuit.*

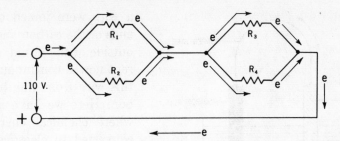

Fig. 29-14. *Another arrangement of the series-parallel circuit.*

Then the complete circuit is treated as a series circuit where R_1 is in series with the computed resistance of R_2 and R_3 in parallel.

Another arrangement is one where two sets of resistors in parallel are in series with each other (Fig. 29-14). Here we first find the equivalent resistance of R_1 and R_2 in parallel. We then find the equivalent resistance of R_3 and R_4 in parallel. We then treat these two equivalent resistances as though they were in series with each other, and by adding them together, we get the total resistance of the circuit.

THE BATTERY

Primary Cells. We have seen that when electrons are piled up, an electrical pressure or potential is created. These electrons will tend to flow to a point of lower electrical pressure, or potential, provided a path be furnished them. What causes these electrons to pile up?

You already know that stroking a hard rubber rod with a piece of flannel tears some electrons off the cloth and deposits them upon the rod. But this method is not a convenient means of piling up electrons. Besides, once the excess electrons have flowed off, we must rub the rod once again with the flannel. A more efficient method is needed for piling up excess electrons and for continuously adding electrons to replace those which flow away.

Early in the nineteenth century, an Italian scientist, Alessandro Volta, discovered that if two dissimilar substances, such as zinc and carbon, were placed in an acid solution, the chemical action would pile electrons on the zinc rod, making it negative with respect to the carbon, which does not react with the acid. If

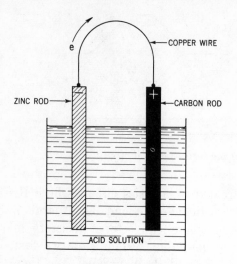

Fig. 29-15. *The voltaic cell.*

a wire were joined to the ends of the carbon and zinc outside of the liquid, a current flowed continuously in this wire from zinc to carbon. Here we have a case where chemical energy is converted to electrical energy. Such a device is called a *voltaic cell* in honor of its inventor.

As long as the rods are in the acid solution (this solution is called the *electrolyte*), the electrons continue to be accumulated on the zinc rod. Thus, we have a continuous source of electrical potential. In time, the acid will completely dissolve the zinc rod, which then must be replaced.

The potential difference (electromotive force) between the carbon and zinc rods remains the same regardless of the size of these rods. The material, not the size, of these rods determines the potential difference. Of course, a cell made with a larger zinc rod will last longer; and the larger the area of the rods, the more cur-

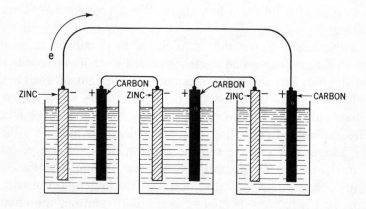

Fig. 29-16. *Three voltaic cells in series. Note that in series connections the + pole of one cell is always joined to the − pole of the next cell.*

rent may be obtained from the cell. However, the electromotive force of such a cell is always 1.5 volts.

Other materials may be used for the two rods (we call these the *electrodes*), and different electrolytes may be employed. In each case, electromotive force depends upon the materials used.

Batteries of Cells. If two or more such cells are connected together, we call them a *battery*. If several similar cells are connected in *series*—that is, with the zinc of one connected to the carbon of another (Fig. 29-16), the electromotive force of each one is added to the others, and the total electromotive force is the sum of all of them. Thus, the total electromotive force which will cause electrons to flow through the wire in the diagram shown in Figure 29-16 is 1.5 volts × 3 = 4.5 volts.

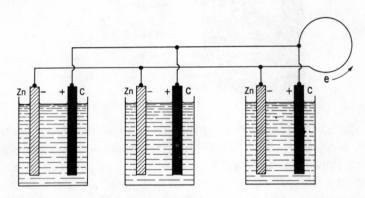

Fig. 29-17. *Three voltaic cells in parallel.*

If three cells such as those above are connected in *parallel*—that is, with all the zincs connected together and all the carbons joined (Fig. 29-17), the battery acts as one cell, with electrodes having three times the area of a single cell. The electromotive force of this battery is that of a single cell (1.5 volts). The current which can be obtained is nearly three times as great as that which we can get from the single cell.

The Dry Cell. Because of the nuisance of spilling the electrolyte, the *dry cell* was developed. The positive electrode is a carbon rod; the negative electrode is a cylindrical zinc shell or can closed at the bottom. The electrolyte is a paste made of ammonium chloride mixed with other chemicals (Fig. 29-18). This cell is *dry* only in the sense that the liquids are prevented from spilling out.

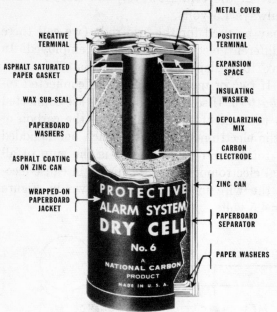

NEGATIVE TERMINAL

ASPHALT SATURATED PAPER GASKET

WAX SUB-SEAL

PAPERBOARD WASHERS

ASPHALT COATING ON ZINC CAN

WRAPPED-ON PAPERBOARD JACKET

METAL COVER

POSITIVE TERMINAL

EXPANSION SPACE

INSULATING WASHER

DEPOLARIZING MIX

CARBON ELECTRODE

ZINC CAN

PAPERBOARD SEPARATOR

PAPER WASHERS

PROTECTIVE ALARM SYSTEM DRY CELL No. 6 A NATIONAL CARBON PRODUCT MADE IN U.S.A.

Fig. 29-18. *Cross-sectional view of the dry cell. (Courtesy of National Carbon Co., Inc.)*

The electrolyte is poured into the zinc shell, in the center of which is set the carbon rod. Sealing wax is poured over the electrolyte to prevent it from spilling. The whole is enclosed in a cardboard case for protection, and binding posts are fastened to the carbon and zinc to provide for connections. The dry cell will continue to furnish current until either the electrolyte or the zinc is consumed, although at decreasing efficiency.

B Batteries. For radio use, a number of dry cells may be connected in series, and the whole sealed into a single block by means of wax or pitch. These blocks are known as B batteries. The most commonly used types are blocks of 15 cells (22.5 volts) and 30 cells (45 volts). Should we wish to obtain a higher electromotive force, we may connect several such B batteries in series (Fig. 29-19).

In the cells described above, current may be furnished until one of the electrodes is eaten away by the chemical action. We call such cells *primary cells.*

Storage Cells. In another kind of cell, the chemical action does not destroy any of the electrodes, but electrons are released by certain chemical changes. If two lead plates are immersed in sul-

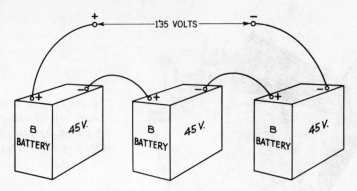

Fig. 29-19. *Circuit showing three B batteries in series.*

phuric acid and a direct current is sent into them, the plate connected to the positive source of current will turn to brown lead peroxide, and the plate attached to the negative source will remain lead.

Now remove the source of current, and connect between the two plates an ordinary electric bell. The bell rings, showing there is a current. In fact, electrons are flowing through the bell from the lead plate to the plate of lead peroxide (Fig. 29-20).

As the current continues to flow, the two plates are changed gradually to lead sulphate, and when this happens, the current ceases to flow. If current is again fed into the cell, the plates will turn back to lead peroxide and spongy lead, and the whole process may be repeated.

This device is called a *storage cell.* The electrical energy fed into the storage cell is changed into chemical energy which is stored in the cell. When the cell is called upon to deliver current, the chemical energy is changed back to electrical energy.

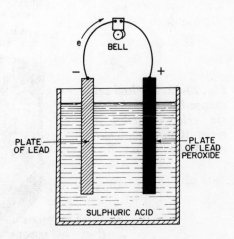

Fig. 29-20. *The lead-acid storage cell.*

Fig. 29-21. *The lead-acid storage cell showing how the plates are hooked up. (Courtesy of General Motors Corp.)*

A storage cell of this kind has an electromotive force of about two volts. Here, too, the voltage does not depend upon the size of the plates. But the amount of electrical energy which can be stored (and the amount which may be delivered) does depend upon the area of the plates. The greater the area, the greater the amount of electrical energy which may be stored.

In practice, a cell may consist of a number of plates (elec-

Fig. 29-22. *The lead-acid storage battery containing six cells connected in series (Courtesy of General Motors Corp.)*

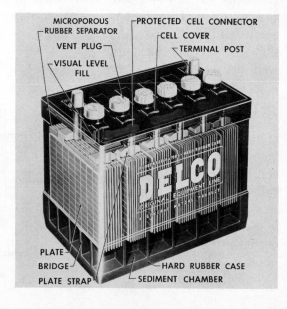

MICROPOROUS RUBBER SEPARATOR
PROTECTED CELL CONNECTOR
CELL COVER
VENT PLUG
TERMINAL POST
VISUAL LEVEL FILL
DELCO
PLATE
BRIDGE
PLATE STRAP
HARD RUBBER CASE
SEDIMENT CHAMBER

trodes) which are sandwiched together with insulators of wood or other material (called separators) separating the positive and negative plates. All the negative plates are connected together, and the same is true for the positive plates (Fig. 29-21).

The whole combination of plates and separators is submerged in the sulphuric-acid electrolyte. In the chemical action involved, the electrolyte changes in density—that is, in weight per unit volume. As the cell has electrical energy fed into it, the density of the sulphuric acid increases, and as electrical energy is taken from the cell, the density decreases. By means of a *hydrometer,* an instrument used to measure the density of a liquid, we can tell how much electrical energy is left in the cell.

When electrical energy is being stored in the cell, we say we are *charging* the cell. When we draw electrical energy from the cell, we say we are *discharging* the cell.

Three such cells are usually connected in series to form a battery whose electromotive force is around six volts. The whole battery is encased in a hard rubber or similar case and is known as a *lead-acid storage battery* (Fig. 29-22).

The storage battery is used where a great deal of current is desired. Primary cells would quickly wear out and would have to be discarded, but the storage battery may be recharged and used over and over. Early radio sets used storage batteries, called A batteries, to supply the current needed to heat the filaments.

The Edison Storage Battery. Another type of storage cell is the *Edison cell.* In this type, electrodes of iron oxide and nickel hydrate are used. The electrolyte is a caustic potash (potassium hydroxide) solution. This cell is more rugged than the lead-acid storage cell, but its relatively high cost prevented it from being used by the average radio enthusiast.

SUMMARY

1. Chemists tell us that all matter is made up of many different kinds of building blocks called **atoms.** When two or more of the atoms unite, they form what is called a **molecule.**
2. According to the electron theory, all atoms are composed mainly of a combination of three types of electrical particles— the positively charged **proton,** the noncharged **neutron,** and the negatively charged **electron.** The atom is like a miniature solar

system, with neutrons and protons at the center, and electrons whirling around the central nucleus like miniature planets.

3. Similarly charged electrical particles repel one another; oppositely charged electrical particles attract one another.

4. In electrical *conductors,* the planet-like electrons are easily dislodged, and move about freely. In electrical *insulators,* there are relatively few free electrons. An electric current is the continuous movement of free electrons through a conductor when an electromotive force is applied.

5. An electric current flows through a conductor from the negative to the positive pole because of the potential difference between the ends of the conductor. This potential difference is the electromotive force. The unit of electromotive force is the *volt.*

6. All electrical currents encounter more or less resistance in flowing through a conductor. The unit of electrical resistance is the *ohm.*

7. Electrical current is measured by the number of *amperes* flowing. By *Ohm's law,* the amount of current flowing in a circuit increases as the electromotive force increases, and decreases as the resistance increases. Expressed in an equation, $I = E/R$.

8. Electrical power is the rate at which electrical energy is expended. The unit of electrical power is the *watt.* The number of watts expended is found by multiplying the amount of current (amperes) by the electromotive force (volts) of a circuit.

9. The heat produced by an electrical current in a circuit is in direct proportion to the watts dissipated: the greater the number of watts, the greater the heat. *Fuses* are used to protect circuits from overheating. Fuses are rated in maximum amperes of current which they will permit to flow through them before they melt.

10. In a *series circuit,* the electrons have only one path to follow through the circuit. In such a circuit, the total resistance is the sum of the component resistances, the current is the same throughout the circuit, and the sum of all the voltage drops across the components is equal to the applied electromotive force.

11. In a *parallel circuit,* the electrons have two or more paths to follow. In such a circuit, the electromotive force across each parallel path is the same, and the currents flowing through each parallel path will be different if the resistance of each path is different. The total resistance of such a circuit is:

$$\text{Total resistance} = \frac{1}{\dfrac{1}{R_1} + \dfrac{1}{R_2} + \dfrac{1}{R_3} + \cdots}$$

12. A *cell* is a device which converts chemical energy into electromotive force. A *primary cell* is one that is eventually consumed by use, like a dry cell. A *storage cell* is one, like the lead storage cell, which may be recharged for use. Both are sources of direct current.
13. Cells may be connected together in groups to form a *battery*. When connected in series (+ pole to − pole), the total voltage is the sum of the voltages of each cell. When connected in parallel (+ pole to + pole, − pole to − pole), the total voltage is that of one cell alone, but the battery is capable of delivering more current.

GLOSSARY

Ampere: The unit of electrical current, represented by the passage of one coulomb of electron charge past a point in the circuit in one second.

Atom: The smallest particle of an element, from which all matter is built.

Battery: A connected group of cells.

Conductor: A material which permits a fairly easy flow of electrons through itself.

Coulomb: The amount of negative charge possessed by 6.28×10^{18} electrons.

Current Electricity: Electrons moving through a conductor.

Electrified: Given a charge of electricity.

Electrolyte: The acid, salt, or base solution used in a cell.

Electron: A negative electrical particle.

Electron Theory: The explanation of all matter from the point of view of what is considered fundamental electrical particles.

Electroscope: A device to test for the presence of a charged body.

Fuse: A wire of fairly high resistance and low melting point used to protect a circuit from too great a current flow.

Hydrometer: A device to test the state of charge or discharge of a lead-acid storage cell.

Insulator: A material which does not permit a fairly easy flow of electrons through itself.

Molecule: The smallest particle of a chemical compound which has all the properties of the substance.

Ohm: The unit of resistance, standardized as the resistance of a uniform column of mercury, 106.3 cm long with cross-sectional area of one square millimeter at 0° C.

Parallel Circuit: An electrical circuit with two or more paths from − to +.

Primary Cell: An electrical cell which may not be recharged.

Proton: A positive electrical particle.

Series Circuit: An electrical circuit with a single path from − to +.

Static Electricity: A stationary electrical charge.
Storage Cell: A cell which may be recharged.
Volt: The unit of potential difference, standardized as that electromotive force necessary to cause one ampere to flow through a resistance of one ohm.
Voltaic Cell: A device to change chemical energy into electrical energy over an extended period of time.
Watt: The unit of electrical power or rate of expending electrical energy.

QUESTIONS AND PROBLEMS

1. How may an insulator be electrified? Explain how this electrification occurs.
2. Distinguish between an insulator and a conductor.
3. Explain the flow of an electric current as an electronic phenomenon.
4. Briefly explain the electron theory of matter.
5. Explain the electrical state of affairs in a neutral atom; in a negatively charged atom; in a positively charged atom.
6. Explain how an electroscope may show the presence of a charged body.
7. What factors determine the current flow through any particular electrical circuit? Explain each.
8. Express Ohm's law in words. Express the same law mathematically.
9. Express the following as simple numbers or fractions: 8×10^4, $8/10^4$, 2×10^{-5}, 2.8×10^3.
10. Explain what is meant by a coulomb; by an ampere. Give another definition of the ampere.
11. Upon what factors does the resistance of any conductor depend?
12. What is the unit of resistance? How is it defined?
13. What is the unit of electrical pressure? How is it defined?
14. In what units is electrical power measured? What is its significance? How is it calculated?
15. In purchasing a resistor, how should its precise description be given?
16. In what manner is electrical energy dissipated in a resistor?
17. How may a circuit be insured against too great a current flow through it? How does the result come about?
18. Differentiate between a series and a parallel circuit as to current and voltage drop.
19. Explain what is meant by voltage drop. How is voltage drop calculated?
20. How may the total resistance of a series circuit containing several resistances be calculated?

21. How may the total resistance of a parallel circuit of several resistors be calculated?
22. How do we consider series-parallel circuits in calculating the total resistance?
23. Describe the operation of a voltaic cell.
24. Upon what factors does the voltage of a cell depend?
25. How may a greater voltage than that of a single cell be obtained from a group of cells? A greater current?
26. What is a B battery?
27. Explain the charging and discharging of a lead-acid storage cell. How can the state of charge or discharge be determined?

30

Magnetism, Motors,
and Measuring Instruments

PROBLEM 1. *What is the theory of magnetism?*
PROBLEM 2. *How is magnetism related to electricity?*
PROBLEM 3. *How is magnetism used in an electric motor?*
PROBLEM 4. *What are the principles of the voltmeter, ammeter, ohmmeter, and wattmeter?*

A Bit of History. The story of magnetism is fascinating. About 100 B.C., a poet named Nicander wrote a poem about a shepherd who, one day while he was tending his flock, was startled to find the iron nails of his shoes attracted to a mysterious rock upon which he stood. The name of this shepherd was Magnes, and it is from that name that we get the word *magnetism.*

The mysterious stone, called the *lodestone,* which has the property of attracting to it pieces of iron, intrigued the minds of men. Perhaps the best-known legend is that of the "History of the Third Calender" as related in the *Arabian Nights.* According to this tale, when a ship passed near a certain mysterious mountain, all the nails and other fittings made of iron were forcibly pulled out and attracted to the mountain.

Early scientists believed that the electrical charge created by rubbing amber on cloth was the same as the magnetism by which the lodestone attracted iron. Today we know that these two forms of electricity are not identical.

The Gravitational Field and the Dielectric Field. The earth moves around the sun. Why does not the earth move away from the sun and follow an independent path?

The reason, we say, is that the pull of gravity exists between the earth and the sun and that this pull holds them together. This pull or force acts between the two bodies even though there is no material bond (such as a chain or cable) connecting them. The force acts through space. We say that there is a gravitational *field of force* attracting the earth to the sun.

You will recall that a hard rubber rod takes a negative charge, that a glass rod takes a positive charge, and that when these two rods were charged and suspended near each other, they attracted each other. We say that between the two oppositely charged bodies a *dielectric field of force* exists which pulls them together. This field of force is also known as the *electrostatic field* and as the *electric field*.

Lines of Force. We visualize this field around an electric charge by a number of lines radiating out from the charge in all directions. We call these *lines of force*. In one sense, they are imaginary lines; but see pages 314-315, where we deal with somewhat similar lines of force.

In discussion or in drawings, the number of such lines of force indicates the intensity of the field. We also use arrowheads to show the *direction* of the field. The direction of the force is the one in which a charged particle moves or tends to move when acted on by the force, just as a cork floating in a stream shows which way the stream is flowing.

In testing the direction of a dielectric field, our scientists have agreed to use a small positive charge as a test. You can see, there-

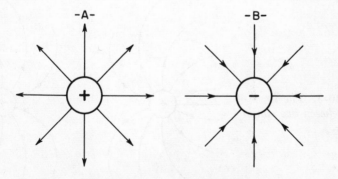

Fig. 30-1. *A—Lines of force around a positive charge.*
B—Lines of force around a negative charge.

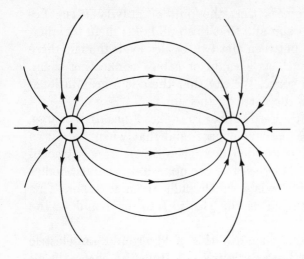

Fig. 30-2. *The lines of force between two opposite charges.*

fore, that this test charge will be repelled from another positive charge and attracted to a negative charge. The arrowheads on the lines of force thus point away from a positive charge and in toward a negative charge.

If two opposite charges act upon each other, the dielectric field may be represented by lines of force connecting these charges, with the arrowheads pointing from the positive toward the negative charge, as in Figure 30-2. Figure 30-3 shows the field between two like charges.

Magnetic Fields and Magnetic Substances. Now let us turn back to our lodestone. Since it can attract a piece of iron through space, there must be a field of force between it and the iron. We

Fig. **30-3.** *The lines of force between two similar charges.*

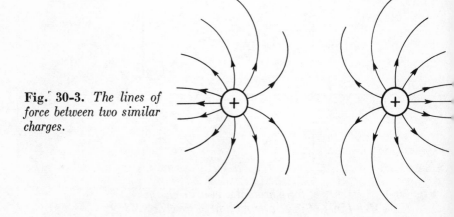

call this the *magnetic field of force,* or simply the *magnetic field.* Where did the magnetic field come from?

Since an electron has an electrical charge, there is a dielectric field around it. Scientists believe that if we can move this dielectric field or if the electron can move this dielectric field or if the electron moves through this field, a new field of force is created. This is the magnetic field.

Now, since electrons in all materials are in constant motion revolving around the nuclei, there must be magnetic forces present inside the atoms of all substances. Why, then, do not all substances attract one another? Why does the lodestone attract only a few substances like iron and nickel?

The reason is that, in most substances, the magnetic field established by one electron revolving in one direction is canceled by the magnetic field set up by another electron revolving in another direction. Thus, no *external* magnetic field exists. We say that such substances are *nonmagnetic.*

However, there are a few substances the majority of whose electrons revolve in one direction. Since there is no cancellation of the magnetic fields set up by some of these electrons, these substances have an external magnetic field and can be attracted to

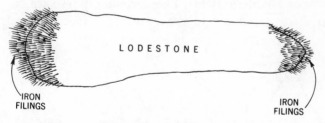

Fig. 30-4. *Iron filings attracted to the poles of a magnet.*

the lodestone. Such substances are iron, nickel, and a few others. We say that they are *magnetic* substances. The lodestone is an iron compound. Substances that are able to attract pieces of iron or nickel are called *magnets.*

The Poles of a Magnet. If we sprinkle iron filings over a magnet, the filings adhere to it, but the greatest number of filings is found clustered at two opposite points of the magnet. It seems as though all the magnetism is concentrated at these points. We call these points the *poles* of the magnet. See Fig. 30-4.

It has been found that the earth is a huge magnet. The magnetic poles of the earth are found to be located very close to its geographic poles. If we suspend a magnet so that it can swing freely, it will always assume a position so that one of its poles points to the North Pole of the earth and the other to the earth's South Pole.

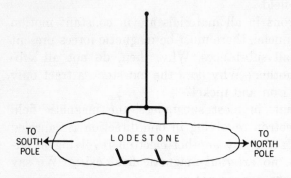

TO SOUTH POLE ◄——— LODESTONE ———► TO NORTH POLE

Fig. 30-5. *Figure showing how a freely swinging magnet turns so that its poles face North and South Poles.*

The pole of the magnet which points to the North Pole is called the *north-seeking pole,* or simply the *north pole.* The opposite pole of the magnet is called the *south-seeking* pole, or the *south pole.*

Law of Magnetic Poles. The ancient Chinese are credited with first utilizing as an aid to navigation the fact that a freely sus-

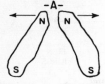
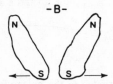
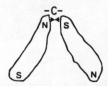

-A-   N   N

-B-   N   N   S   S

-C-   N   S   S   N

Fig. 30-6. *A—Two north poles repel each other.*
    B—Two south poles repel each other.
    C—A north and south pole attract each other.

pended magnet will always assume this north-south position. Such a suspended magnet is called a *magnetic compass.*

Experimenters soon discovered a number of interesting facts about magnets. It was found that if the north pole of one magnet is brought near the north pole of another, the poles repel each other. This also occurs if two south poles are brought near each

Fig. 30-7. *A—Poles on a magnet.*
      B—Arrangement of poles on a magnet broken in half. Note that each piece has two poles.

other. On the other hand, if the north pole of one magnet is placed near the south pole of another, the poles are attracted. Thus, *like magnetic poles repel each other* and *unlike magnetic poles attract each other.*

Another fact of interest was the discovery that a north or south magnetic pole could not exist by itself. For every magnetic pole, there is an opposite pole that has equal strength. If a magnet is broken in half, we get two magnets, each with its own north and south poles.

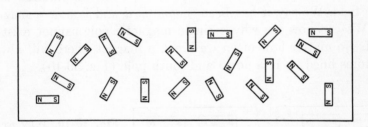

Fig. 30-8. *Helter-skelter arrangements of particles of a piece of unmagnetized iron.*

Magnetizing a Piece of Iron. It was also found that if a magnetic substance like iron, which is unmagnetized originally, is stroked with a magnet (such as lodestone), the iron becomes a magnet, too, with a north and south magnetic pole.

Let us see how scientists explain these facts. The electrons of an atom, you will recall, move through the dielectric field within the atom and set up a magnetic field. Thus, each atom becomes a small magnet. In an ordinary substance, these small magnets are arranged helter-skelter, and the magnetic fields neutralize one another, with the result that there is no external magnetic field (Fig. 30-8).

But if the south pole of a lodestone, for example, is moved across a magnetic substance such as iron, say, in a left-to-right direction, all the north poles of the little magnets in the iron are attracted to the south pole of the lodestone and are left all facing to the right after the lodestone has passed (Fig. 30-9).

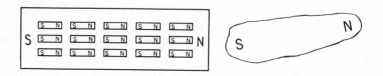

Fig. 30-9. *Orderly arrangement of particles of a piece of magnetized iron.*

Thus, the left end of the iron has all south poles and acts like a large south pole. The right end becomes a large north pole. The magnetic fields about the atoms of the iron no longer neutralize but aid one another. The iron now has an external magnetic field. We say it has been *magnetized* and is now a magnet.

We can now see why a single magnetic pole cannot exist by itself. No matter how often we break a magnet, there will always be atoms lined up in a north and south pole (Fig. 30-10).

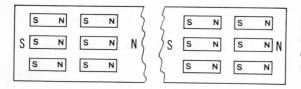

Fig. 30-10. *Why we get two magnets, each with a complete set of poles, when we break a magnet in half.*

The Pattern of a Magnetic Field. It was also found that the magnetic force can act through any substance that is not magnetic. Thus, a magnet may attract iron filings through a piece of paper.

Place a magnet on a wooden table and cover it with a piece of cardboard. Sprinkle on iron filings and tap the cardboard gently. The iron filings will arrange in the pattern shown in Figure 30-11.

The iron filings follow the magnetic lines of force, and thus we get a picture of what we call the *magnetic field* around a magnet. These lines of force pass through the inside of the magnet from

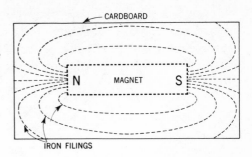

Fig. 30-11. *How to get a pattern of the lines of force around a magnet by the use of iron filings.*

atom to atom and through the space around the magnet in ever-widening loops. The lines of force outside the magnet can attract magnetic substances such as iron filings, but those lines flowing through the magnet have no external effects. Thus, the space directly above the magnet is clear of iron filings.

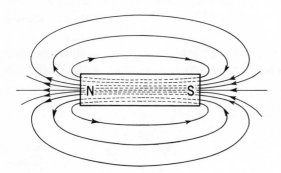

Fig. 30-12. *Pattern of lines of force around a magnet, showing the direction of the field.*

The *direction* of the external magnetic field is conventionally said to be from the north to the south pole. The field around a magnet is then represented by Figure 30-12, the arrowheads indicating the direction of the field. Note that the lines of force are more numerous around the poles of the magnet.

We are now able to see why like magnetic poles repel, and unlike poles attract, one another. When two like poles are brought near each other, the magnetic field about them is as shown in Figure 30-13. The two magnetic fields oppose each other, and the poles are pushed apart. If, however, two unlike poles are brought near each other, the magnetic fields about them are as shown in Figure 30-14. The two magnetic fields aid each other and the poles are attracted.

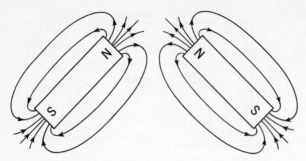

Fig. 30-13. *Why two like poles repel each other. Notice that the lines of force are in opposition.*

Permanent and Temporary Magnets. Some substances, like steel, retain their magnetism after the magnetic field used to magnetize them has been removed. We call such magnets *permanent magnets*.

Other substances, like soft iron, remain magnets only when they are in the field of another magnet. After these fields are removed, the atoms go back to their helter-skelter positions, and the soft iron loses its magnetism. We call such magnets *temporary magnets*.

Since it is the orderly arrangement of the atoms that makes a permanent magnet, we must expect the magnetism to be destroyed

Fig. 30-14. *Why two unlike poles attract each other. The fields aid each other. Some lines of force go from one magnet to the other.*

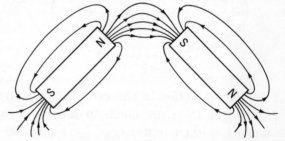

if this order were upset. Jarring or heating a permanent magnet disarranges the atoms, and the magnetism is lost.

Units of Measurement of Magnetism. We have seen that the *magnetic line of force* is a closed loop, or path, running from the north to the south pole, and completed through the magnet itself. The space through which these lines of force act is called the *magnetic field*.

The *magnetic flux* (ϕ) is equal to the sum total of the magnetic lines existing in the magnetic circuit and corresponds to current in the electric circuit. The unit of flux is one line of force, and is called the *maxwell*.

The *magnetomotive force* (mmf) tends to drive the flux through the magnetic circuit and corresponds to the electromotive force of the electric circuit. The unit of magnetomotive force is the *gilbert*.

Reluctance ($\mathcal{R}$) is the resistance a substance offers to the passage of magnetic flux and corresponds to resistance in the electric circuit.

We can state an analogy of Ohm's law for magnetic circuits as

$$\text{Flux} = \frac{\text{magnetomotive force}}{\text{reluctance}}.$$

Permeance ($\mathcal{P}$) is the opposite of reluctance. It may be defined as the property of a substance which permits the passage of the magnetic flux. Substituting permeance as the reciprocal of reluctance in the above formula, we now get

$$\text{Flux} = \text{magnetomotive force} \times \text{permeance}.$$

Permeability (μ) is the ratio of the flux existing in a certain material to the flux which would exist if that material were replaced by a vacuum, the magnetomotive force acting upon this portion of the magnetic circuit remaining unchanged. The permeability of a vacuum is taken as unity (that is, 1), and all other substances except iron, steel, nickel, and a few others may be considered as having a permeability of unity. Iron and steel may have a permeability of from about 50 to more than 5,000. Some substances, as bismuth, have a permeability of less than 1.

Electromagnetism. In 1819, Hans Christian Oersted, a Danish physicist, brought a small compass near a wire that was carrying an electric current. This compass consisted of a small, magnetized needle pivoted at the center so that it was free to rotate. As he brought the compass near the wire, Oersted noticed that the needle was deflected. This discovery started a chain of events that has helped shape our industrial civilization.

Let us see what caused the compass needle to be deflected. As was previously stated, scientists believe that when an electron moves through a dielectric field of force, it sets up a magnetic field. Since a current flowing through a wire consists of a great many electrons in motion, we may expect to find a magnetic field around

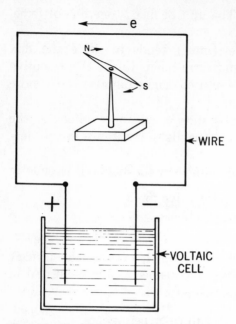

Fig. 30-15. *Showing how the magnetic field around a conductor carrying an electric current deflects the compass needle.*

the wire. It is this magnetic field, reacting with the magnetic field of the compass needle, which causes the needle to deflect.

Thus, we see that the wire carrying the electric current acted like a temporary magnet. The magnetic lines of force, in the form of concentric circles around the wire, lie in planes perpendicular to the wire. The magnetic field exists only so long as the current flows. When the current is started through the wire, we may think of the magnetic field as coming into being and sweeping outward from the wire. When the flow of current ceases, the field collapses toward the wire and disappears. It was soon discovered that if the wire is formed into a coil, each turn adds its magnetic field to the other turns' fields, and the result is a stronger magnet. We call such a magnet an *electromagnet.*

Strength of an Electromagnet. Scientists evolved a formula to show the relationship between the magnetomotive force, the electric current flowing through the coil, and the number of turns or loops in the coil. It is

$$\text{mmf} = 1.257 \times I \times N$$

where mmf is the magnetomotive force expressed in gilberts, I is the electric current in amperes, and N is the number of turns in the coil.

From this formula, we may see that the strength of an electromagnet depends upon the $I \times N$ or *ampere-turns*. Thus, an electromagnet of 100 turns with one ampere of current flowing through it is as strong as an electromagnet of 10 turns with 10 amperes of current flowing through it. The number of ampere-turns is the same in each case—namely, 100.

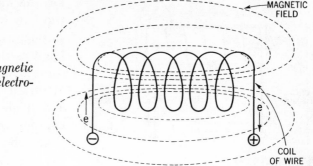

Fig. 30-16. *The magnetic field around an electromagnet.*

Which End of an Electromagnet Is North? Of course, we can determine which end of a coil is a north and which end is a south pole by bringing the north pole of a compass needle near each end of the coil. The north pole of the electromagnet repels the north pole of the compass needle, whereas the south pole of the electromagnet attracts the north pole of the needle.

The Left-Hand Rule. We have another method for determining the polarity of the electromagnet. If the coil is grasped in the left hand so that the fingers follow around the coil in the direction in which the electrons are flowing, the thumb will point toward the north pole (Fig. 30-17).

Practical Electromagnets. In the construction of an electromagnet, it is customary to wind the coil upon a soft iron core. Since the permeability of the iron is greater than that of air, this tends to concentrate the lines of force in the core. Thus, there is a greater concentration of these lines at the poles of the electromagnet, and this is accompanied by an increased amount of attracting power.

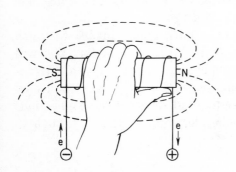

Fig. 30-17. *Method for determining the polarity of an electromagnet.*

The electromagnet is one of our most important tools. Samuel Morse used it when he invented the telegraph. Using a switch, or

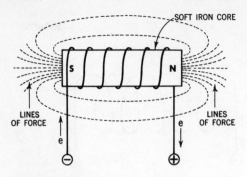

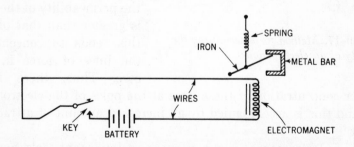

Fig. 30-18. *Diagram showing, by use of a soft-iron core, how lines of force of an electromagnet are concentrated at the poles.*

key, he was able to control the flow of electric current through the coil. When the key was closed, the coil became an electromagnet that attracted a piece of iron and made it click against another piece of metal. When the key was opened, the coil lost its magnetism, and a spring pulled the piece of iron back. By means of a code of long and short intervals between clicks (dashes and dots), Morse was able to communicate with points many miles away over wires. (See appendix.)

In our earphones, we use the electromagnet to move the diaphragm to set up sound waves. In the electromagnetic dynamic speaker, we employ an electromagnet with thousands of turns to give us the powerful field we need.

In industry, tremendous electromagnets are built with a great many turns and carrying many amperes of current. These magnets are capable of lifting tons of iron at a time.

The Electric Motor. Perhaps the most important use to which the electromagnet has been put is in the electric motor. You will recall that when Oersted brought a compass needle near a current-carrying wire, the needle was deflected. The wire was connected across a voltaic cell. Now, if Oersted had reversed the connections of the cell to the wire so that the electrons streamed through in

Fig. 30-19. *How the electromagnet is used in the telegraph.*

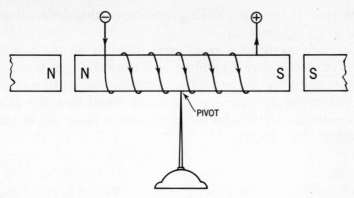

Fig. 30-20. *The electromagnet pivoted so that it may rotate between two fixed poles.*

the opposite direction, the direction of the magnetic field would have been reversed, and the needle deflected in the opposite direction.

Now, suppose that you pivot an electromagnet so that it can rotate freely. Opposite one end of the electromagnet rigidly fix the north pole of a permanent magnet, and opposite the other end, fix the south pole of another permanent magnet (Fig. 30-20).

Now, pass an electric current through the coil of the electromagnet in such a way that the pole of the electromagnet facing the north pole of the permanent magnet becomes a north pole, and the pole facing the south pole of the permanent magnet becomes

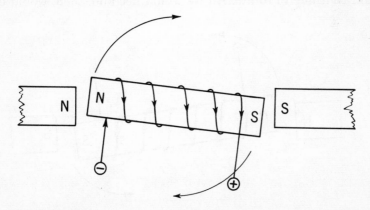

Fig. 30-21. *Looking down on the top of an electromagnet. Since like poles repel, the electromagnet is rotated in a clockwise direction.*

a south pole. If you were looking down upon this device, it would appear as in Figure 30-21.

The two north poles repel each other, as do the two south poles. The electromagnet revolves in a clockwise direction around its pivot, aided by the attraction between the north and south poles. When the electromagnet has made a half turn, it will come to rest with the north poles facing the south poles and attracting each other (Fig. 30-22).

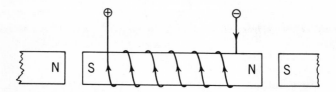

Fig. 30-22. *The electromagnet, having rotated a half turn, now comes to rest with unlike poles facing each other.*

Suppose that just as the inertia carries the magnet beyond this resting position, you reverse the direction of the flow of current through the electromagnet (Fig. 30-23). Its poles will become reversed, and once more it will be spun around in a clockwise direction. If this process could be continued, the electromagnet would continue to rotate. All we would need do, then, would be to

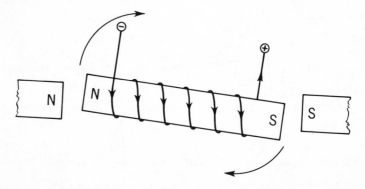

Fig. 30-23. *Now the direction of current flowing into the electromagnet is reversed. This reverses the poles of the electromagnet and, since now like poles are facing each other, the electromagnet is again rotated in a clockwise direction.*

attach a pulley to the electromagnet, and we would have an electric motor. The electromagnet and its soft iron core are called the *armature*. The permanent magnets are called the *field magnets*.

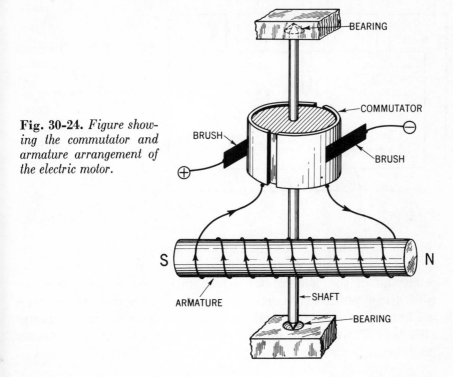

Fig. 30-24. *Figure showing the commutator and armature arrangement of the electric motor.*

An ingenious device is used to reverse the direction of current through the coil of the armature at the proper time. Attached to the armature is a shaft. On this shaft and insulated from it is a metal band that had been split and slightly separated in the middle. To each half of the metal band, or ring, one end of the wire of the electromagnet is attached. Pressing against each half of the ring is a springy strip of metal or a piece of carbon, called a *brush*. These brushes are attached to a source of electric current, and it is their function to transmit this current to the split ring, and thus to the armature. The split-ring device is called the *commutator* (Fig. 30-24).

This commutator rotates with the armature. When it is in one position, the electrons flow in through the negative brush to one half of the commutator, through the coil of the electromagnet,

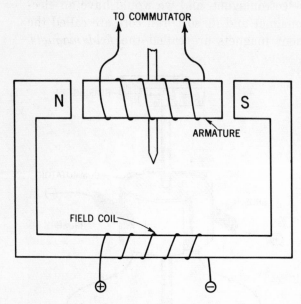

Fig. 30-25. *Diagram showing how an electromagnet is used to supply the field of a motor.*

to the other half of the commutator, and out by means of the positive brush. But as the armature makes a half turn, so does each half of the commutator, which thereupon comes in contact with the opposite brush. The electrons now flow into the opposite half of the commutator, and thus through the coil in the opposite direction. This reverses the poles of the armature, and it continues to rotate.

Fig. 30-26. *Hookup of a parallel or shunt motor.*

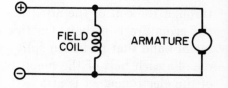

We can improve our motor by substituting another electromagnet for the field magnets (Fig. 30-25). This new electromagnet is called the *field coil*. We may use either the same or another source of electric current to operate this field coil.

In our diagrams, we usually represent the field electromagnet as ─⌒⌒⌒⌒⌒─ and the armature and commutator assembly as ⎍ .

Shunt-Wound Motors. Of course, we may use the same source of current to operate both the armature and the field. We then have a choice of connections. We may connect the field and armature in parallel as in Figure 30-26. Such a motor is called a *paral-*

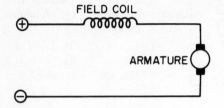

FIELD COIL

ARMATURE

Fig. 30-27. *Hookup of a series motor.*

lel, or *shunt,* motor. Shunt motors have difficulty in starting if they are attached to a heavy load, but once started, they run at a fairly constant speed regardless of load variations.

Series-Wound Motors. Another method of connecting our motor is to have the field and armature in series. Such a motor is called a *series* motor (Fig. 30-27). A series motor can start with a large load, but its speed falls off rapidly as the load is increased.

So far we have considered motors whose armatures had but two poles. We may build motors with more than one armature

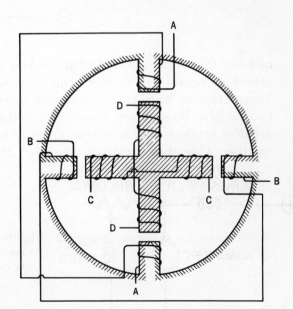

Fig. 30-28. *A four-pole motor with two sets of field and armature windings.*

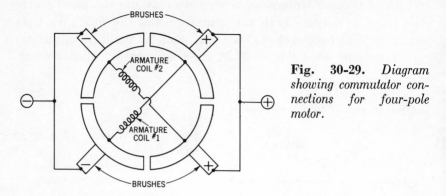

Fig. 30-29. *Diagram showing commutator connections for four-pole motor.*

winding. These motors have four, six, eight, or more poles, and have two poles for each additional armature winding.

Four-Pole Motors. Figure 30-28 shows the diagram of a four-pole motor. The armature has two windings. The commutator

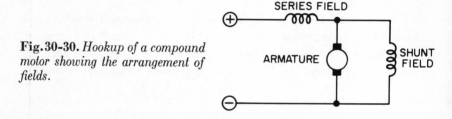

Fig. 30-30. *Hookup of a compound motor showing the arrangement of fields.*

now has four segments, and each winding of the armature is connected to opposite segments. The field, too, has two windings. There are four brushes, one for each commutator segment. The two positive brushes are connected together, and so are the two negative brushes. You see that you really have two motors wound together. This gives greater power. With this motor, you are able

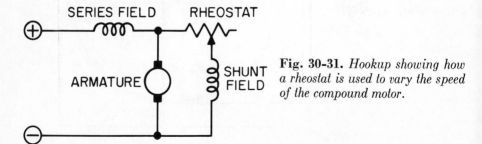

Fig. 30-31. *Hookup showing how a rheostat is used to vary the speed of the compound motor.*

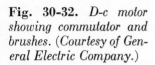

Fig. 30-32. *D-c motor showing commutator and brushes. (Courtesy of General Electric Company.)*

to connect one field in shunt with the armature and the other in series. Such a motor is called a *compound* motor and has some of the best features of the series and shunt motors (Fig. 30-30).

The speed of the motor may be controlled by changing the current supplied to the field or armature coils. This changes the magnetic flux produced by these coils. This change is made by connecting a rheostat in series with one of these coils.

ELECTRICAL MEASURING INSTRUMENTS

The Galvanometer. We could not get very far in our study of electricity if we did not have instruments capable of measuring the electric current, the electromotive force, resistance, and so on, of our electrical circuits. One of the simplest and most widely used of such instruments is the *moving-coil galvanometer.*

Turn back to Figure 30-20, which is a diagram of a simple electric motor. Rotation of the armature is obtained by sending a current through the coil. The armature makes a half turn and stops with the north and south poles facing and attracting each other.

The strength of the field of the armature depends upon the number of its ampere-turns (see page 318). Since the number of turns is constant, the greater the current (that is, the more amperes), the stronger the field of the armature.

Suppose we have a spring pulling the armature back to its original position—that is, with the like poles facing each other.

The pull of such spring opposes the repelling effect of the similar poles. The greater the repelling effect, the more the armature turns; the smaller the repelling effect, the less the armature turns.

This repelling effect depends upon the interaction between the field of the permanent magnets and the field of the armature. Since the field of the permanent magnets is of constant strength, the stronger the field of the armature, the greater the repelling effect; and the weaker the field of the armature, the less the repelling effect.

But we have seen that the strength of the armature field depends upon the amount of current flowing through it. Therefore, the greater the flow of current through the armature coil, the greater the repelling effect and the more the armature will turn.

Here, then, is a device for measuring the flow of current. If a current of one ampere will cause the armature to make a quarter-turn, a current of two amperes will cause the armature to make a half-turn. All we need do is to fasten a pointer on the armature and by means of a scale, we may determine the degree of rotation of the armature, and thus the strength of the current.

The Moving-Coil Type of Galvanometer. Figure 30-33 shows such an instrument, which is called a *D'Arsonval galvanometer* after its inventor. The armature core is a soft-iron ball upon which is wound the armature coil, consisting of a number of turns of very fine wire. The complete armature is delicately pivoted upon

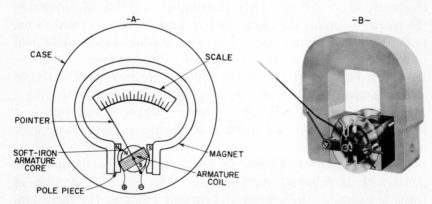

Fig. 30-33. *A—Diagram of the moving-coil or D'Arsonval galvanometer.*
B—"Phantom" view of a commercial permanent-magnet moving-coil instrument. (Courtesy of Weston Electric Instrument Corp.)

jewel bearings, and its rotation is retarded by a small spiral spring (not shown in this diagram). A light aluminum pointer is fastened to the core and moves with it.

Instead of two separate magnets, a horseshoe-shaped permanent magnet supplies the field. Attached to the poles of this magnet are two soft iron pole pieces which concentrate the magnetic field. Wires are brought from the armature coil to two binding posts, and the whole instrument is enclosed in a glass-faced case to protect it from dust and air currents.

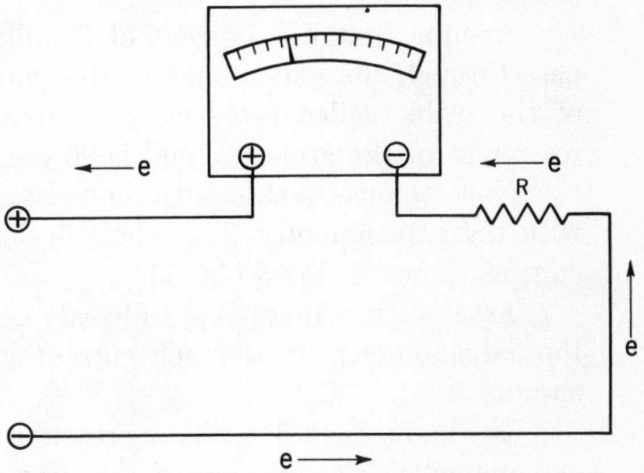

Fig. 30-34. *Circuit showing how the galvanometer is used to measure the electric current flowing through a resistor* (R).

The maximum rotation of the armature is about a quarter turn in a clockwise direction. Care should be taken to send the current into it so that it does rotate in this clockwise direction, else the pointer may be twisted. For this reason, the binding posts are marked plus (+) and minus (−), respectively. The plus binding post must be connected to the positive side of the electrical circuit, and the minus binding post to the negative side.

Since the armature coil consists of very fine wire, care must be taken not to send too much current through it, or it will burn up. The amount of current the usual type of galvanometer can safely stand is no more than a few milliamperes (a milliampere being one one-thousandth of an ampere). The symbol for the galvanometer is —(G)— .

The Ammeter. Of course, there are many occasions when we desire to measure currents greater than the few milliamperes the galvanometer will safely carry. Under these conditions, we connect a heavy metal bar, called a *shunt,* in parallel with the galvanometer.

From our study of parallel circuits, we know that the electric current will divide when it reaches the junction of the galvanometer and the shunt. Part of the current will flow through the galvanometer and part will flow through the shunt. We also know that the greater portion of the current will flow through the path that offers lower resistance. If, then, the resistance of the galvanometer is 99 times as great as that of the shunt, 99/100 of the current will flow through the shunt, and 1/100 will flow through the galvanometer.

Assume that if a current of 5 milliamperes (5 ma) were to pass through the galvanometer, the pointer would reach the end of the scale (called *full-scale deflection*). Also, assume that the resistance of the armature coil is 99 ohms.

Now, connect a shunt whose resistance is one ohm in parallel with the galvanometer. The whole is then connected into the circuit, as shown in Figure 30-35.

Assume that there is a full-scale deflection of the pointer of the galvanometer. How much current is flowing in the electrical circuit?

We know that 5 milliamperes must be flowing through the galvanometer because that is the amount of current which will give us a full-scale deflection. But we also know that 99 times as much current must be flowing through the shunt because the resistance of the galvanometer is 99 times as great as is the re-

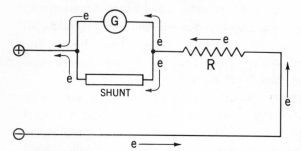

Fig. 30-35. *Circuit showing how an ammeter (galvanometer plus shunt) is used to measure the current flowing through the resistor (R).*

sistance of the shunt. Therefore, 99 times 5 milliamperes must be flowing through the shunt. This gives us 495 milliamperes, which when added to the 5 milliamperes in the galvanometer, gives us 500 milliamperes of current flowing in the complete circuit. The galvanometer scale is calibrated to read up to 500 milliamperes.

The galvanometer together with its shunt is called an *ammeter*. The symbol for an ammeter is ──(A)── . Since we use it to measure the current which flows through a circuit, we must connect our ammeter in *series* in the circuit.

The shunt, as you can see, must be carefully calibrated (prepared as to electrical size and marked accordingly) to match the galvanometer, because unless the ratio between the resistance of the galvanometer and the resistance of the shunt have a precise ratio to each other, the readings on the galvanometer scale will be meaningless.

Types of Ammeters. Some ammeters are built with shunts that are permanently connected inside the case of the instrument: we call these *internal-shunt ammeters*. Others have the shunt attached on the outside: these are *external-shunt ammeters*.

Ammeters are manufactured with a number of different ranges. The greater the current to be measured, the greater must be the ratio between the resistance of the galvanometer and the resistance of the shunt. Since the resistance of the galvanometer is fixed, the greater the current to be measured, the lower must be the resistance of the shunt.

Care must be taken not to use a low-range ammeter to measure high currents. The amount of current passing through the coil of the galvanometer may be great enough to burn it out. An ammeter must be used whose range is greater than the largest current we may encounter in the circuit to be tested.

The Voltmeter. When we seek to measure the electromotive force of a circuit, we wish to know the entire fall in potential between two points. Hence, we must connect our galvanometer from the high-potential (negative) side of the circuit to the low-potential (positive) side. The instrument is, therefore, always connected in *parallel* with the circuit to be measured.

In this position, there is danger that too much current may flow through the fine wire of the armature coil and burn it up. Of course, we may put a shunt across the galvanometer, but since the resistance of the shunt is very low, the bulk of the current in the electrical circuit would flow through the shunt, leaving very little current to flow through the galvanometer and the rest of the circuit.

The difficulty is solved by placing a large resistor in series with the galvanometer (Fig. 30-36). This resistor limits the

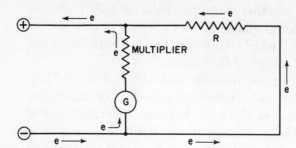

Fig. 30-36. *Circuit showing how a voltmeter (galvanometer plus multiplier) is used to measure the voltage of the line.*

amount of current that can flow through the galvanometer, and thus serves to protect the coil from burning out and to force almost all the current to flow through the rest of the circuit. A certain amount of current is side-tracked through the galvanometer, but if the resistor in series with it is large enough, this amount is negligible.

We call a galvanometer with its *limiting resistor* (also called *multiplier*) a *voltmeter*. Although current is flowing through our voltmeter, the amount of current will depend upon the electromotive force in the circuit and will be in proportion to it. Our scale is now calibrated to read in volts. The symbol for the voltmeter is ──Ⓥ──

Here, too, we must take certain precautions. We must be sure that the current flows through the voltmeter in the correct direction. Thus, the binding post marked minus (−) must go to the high-potential (negative) side of the circuit, and the post marked plus (+) to the low-potential side.

Practical Uses of Voltmeters. Voltmeters are manufactured with differ-

Fig. 30-37. *Commercial multirange d-c voltmeter. (Courtesy of Weston Electrical Instrument Corp.)*

ent ranges, each designed to measure a certain maximum electromotive force. The higher the voltage to be measured, the greater
must be the resistance of the limiting resistor. If we connect a voltmeter with a low range across a high-potential circuit, too much
current may be forced through the armature coil, and it will be
destroyed.

We may use the voltmeter to measure the difference of potential across a part of a circuit—that is, between any two points
in a circuit. In Figure 30-38, it is desired to measure the potential

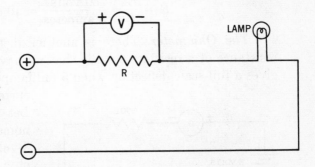

Fig. 30-38. *Circuit show-*
ing how the voltmeter is
used to measure the poten-
tial drop across the resistor
(R)

difference between the two ends of resistor R. This difference is
called the *potential drop* across the resistor. There is a difference
of potential because some of the electrical pressure is used up in
forcing electrons through the resistor.

We connect the voltmeter so that the binding post marked
minus goes to the high-potential (−) side of the resistor. The
other post goes to the low-potential (+) side. The reading of the
voltmeter in volts is the fall of potential, or potential drop, across
the resistor.

How to Measure Resistance. We have a number of methods

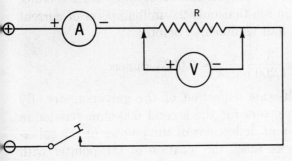

Fig. 30-39. *The voltmeter-*
ammeter method of finding
the resistance of (R).

for finding the resistance of a resistor or other electrical devices. Connect an ammeter in series with the resistor to find how much current is flowing through it, and connect a voltmeter across the resistor to find its voltage drop. Connect a battery or other source of electricity together with a pushbutton in the circuit. Press the button and take a simultaneous reading of the ammeter and the voltmeter.

Assume that the ammeter reads 5 amperes and that the voltmeter reads 50 volts. From Ohm's law, we get

$$R = \frac{E}{I} = \frac{50 \text{ volts}}{5 \text{ amperes}} = 10 \text{ ohms.}$$

The Ohmmeter. There is another method used to find the resistance of a resistor. Assume that we have a galvanometer that gives a full-scale deflection when 5 milliamperes (0.005 ampere) of current passes through it. Let us connect the galvanometer in series with a 3-volt battery and a 600-ohm resistor (Fig. 30-40).

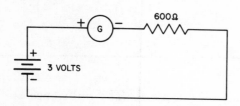

Fig. 30-40. *Circuit showing a 600-ohm resistor connected in series with a 3-volt battery and a galvanometer.*

By means of Ohm's law, we can determine the amount of current flowing in this circuit. (We are ignoring the resistance of the galvanometer.) Thus,

$$I = \frac{E}{R} = \frac{3 \text{ volts}}{600 \text{ ohms}} = 0.005 \text{ ampere.}$$

In this case, we get a full-scale deflection of the galvanometer.

Now, assume that we place another 600-ohm resistor in series with the first (Fig. 30-41). Then the total resistance is 1,200 ohms. From Ohm's law you can see that only 2.5 milliamperes of current will flow in the circuit, half as much as before:

$$I = \frac{E}{R} = \frac{3 \text{ volts}}{1,200 \text{ ohms}} = 0.0025 \text{ ampere.}$$

We now get a half-scale deflection of the galvanometer. By substituting different resistors for the second 600-ohm resistor in this circuit, we get different deflections of the pointer of the galvanometer. On the scale, we mark the location of the pointer with a series of known resistances.

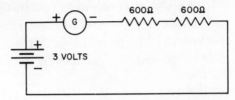

We now have a device for finding the value of an unknown resistor. Figure 30-42 shows this circuit. To determine the resistance of any device, all we need do is connect our unknown resistor to the two binding posts marked X. The pointer will be deflected according to the value of the unknown resistor. If the scale of the galvanometer is suitably calibrated, we can tell the resistance of the unknown resistor by reading the deflection on the scale.

Fig. 30-41. *Circuit showing two 600-ohm resistors connected in series with a 3-volt battery and a galvanometer.*

Such an instrument is called an *ohmmeter*.

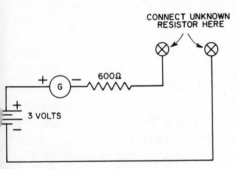

Fig. 30-42. *Circuit of the ohmmeter.*

The Wattmeter. There are several methods by which we may determine the electrical power (watts) consumed by an electrical circuit. Since we know that Watts = volts × amperes, we may connect a voltmeter in parallel with the circuit and an ammeter in series with it. Take the readings in volts and amperes. If we multiply the number of volts by the number of amperes, we get the number of watts (Fig. 30-43).

There is another method for measuring the watts. In the galvanometer (Fig. 30-33), we have the field of the armature reacting against the field of the permanent magnet to give us the deflection of the pointer. You will recall that the field of the permanent magnet is constant, and the variations of the armature field give the variations of deflection.

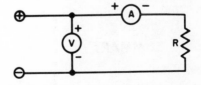

Fig. 30-43. *Circuit for calculating the power (watts) consumed by the resistor.*

Suppose that we were to substitute an electromagnet for the permanent magnet and connect this electromagnet in series with the circuit. The amount of current flowing in the circuit would then determine the strength of the field of this electromagnet.

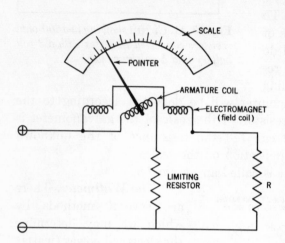

Fig. 30-44. *Circuit of wattmeter connected to measure power consumed by resistor (R).*

Now, connect the coil of the armature (through a limiting resistor) in parallel with the circuit just as we connect a voltmeter. The electromotive force of the circuit will then determine the strength of the field of the armature (Fig. 30-44).

Since the deflection is the result of the two magnetic fields acting on each other, the movement of the pointer will measure the product of the current flowing in the circuit and its electromotive force. But the product of the current and electromotive force is equal to the number of watts of electrical power. Hence, by proper calibration of the scale, the deflection of the pointer can be made to indicate the number of watts consumed by the electrical circuit.

SUMMARY

1. The **magnetic field** about a magnet consists of lines of magnetic force that run from the north to the south pole.
2. The pole of a freely suspended magnet that points to the north pole of the earth is called the north pole of the magnet. Such a freely suspended magnet is a **compass**.

3. A modern explanation of magnetism is: (a) an electron is surrounded by a dielectric field of force and (b) when this field is moved relative to the electron, a new field, called the *magnetic field of force,* is created.

4. A law of magnets is that *unlike poles attract,* and *like poles repel* each other.

5. *Electromagnets* are produced when an electric current is passed through a coil. The strength of the electromagnet is increased by a soft-iron core.

6. The *direction* of the north pole of an electromagnet is the direction of the thumb of the left hand when the fingers of the hand grasp the coil in the direction of electron flow.

7. An electric motor consists of a movable electromagnet, called an *armature,* suspended between the poles of another magnet, called the *field.* Motion is produced by the attraction and repulsion of the poles of the armature by the poles of the field. In order to keep the armature from coming to a stop, a device called a *commutator* causes the direction of the current in each coil of the armature to change automatically. The result is that as a pole of the armature approaches a field pole, it is attracted, but the same armature pole is repelled at the instant it passes the field pole.

8. A *galvanometer,* a *voltmeter,* and an *ammeter* each consist of a movable coil of wire suspended by a spring in a permanent magnetic field. The turning of the coil is caused by the reaction of the magnetic field produced around it with the magnetic field of the permanent magnet. The amount of reaction and turning is proportional to the current in the coil.

9. *Voltmeters* must be connected *parallel* to the circuit to be measured, and *ammeters* must be connected in *series* with the circuit to be measured.

GLOSSARY

Ammeter: A galvanometer with a very low resistance across the coil designed to measure current in amperes.

Dielectric Field of Force: The energy field surrounding a charged particle (also known as *electrostatic* or *electric* field).

Electromagnet: A magnet created by passing a current through a coil.

Galvanometer: A device acting in a manner similar to that of the motor, designed to measure very small currents or voltages.

Gilbert: The unit of magnetomotive force.

Left-Hand Rule: The rule for determining the polarity of an electromagnet.

Lodestone: A natural magnet.

Magnetic Field of Force: The energy field surrounding a magnet.

Magnetic Flux: The sum total of the magnetic lines of force.

Magnetic Lines of Force: The imaginary lines in the field of force along which the force makes itself felt.

Magnetic Poles: Points of concentration of the magnetic strength of a magnet.

Magnetomotive Force: The force creating magnetic flux.

Maxwell: The unit of magnetic flux.

Motor: A magnetic device that changes electrical energy into the energy of rotary motion.

Multiplier: A limiting resistor in series with a galvanometer coil, used to convert the latter into a voltmeter.

N-Seeking Pole: The pole of a freely swinging magnet pointing toward the earth's north magnetic pole.

Ohmmeter: A galvanometer adapted to give direct readings of resistance.

Permanent Magnet: A magnet retaining most of its magnetism after any magnetizing force is removed.

Permeability: The ratio of the flux existing in a certain material to the flux which would exist if that material were replaced by a vacuum, the magnetomotive force acting upon this portion of the magnetic circuit remaining unchanged.

Permeance: The reciprocal of magnetic reluctance.

Reluctance: The resistance to passage of magnetic flux.

S-Seeking Pole: The pole of a freely swinging magnet which points towards the earth's magnetic south pole.

Shunt: A low-value resistor hooked up in parallel with a galvanometer when it is to be used as an ammeter.

Temporary Magnet: A magnet that loses most of its magnetism after any magnetizing force is removed.

Voltmeter: A galvanometer with a high series resistor used to measure voltage.

Wattmeter: A modified galvanometer used to measure directly the power consumed in a circuit.

QUESTIONS AND PROBLEMS

1. How does an electron make its influence felt on another electron?
2. How does a magnet make its influence felt on another nearby magnet?
3. What is one theory for the making of a magnet?
4. How would a freely swinging horizontal magnet align itself? Why?
5. Explain the interaction between like magnetic poles; between unlike magnetic poles.

6. How is the magnetizing of a piece of steel by rubbing it with a lodestone explained?

7. Draw a sketch of the lines of force inside and outside a bar magnet.

8. What is the conventional direction of the lines of force outside a bar magnet? Inside the bar magnet?

9. What is a temporary magnet? A permanent magnet?

10. What is meant by magnetic flux and how is it measured?

11. What is meant by magnetomotive force and in what unit is it measured?

12. What is meant by magnetic reluctance?

13. State the analogy of Ohm's law for magnetic flux.

14. What contribution did Oersted make to the study of electromagnetism?

15. What effect occurs when a current is impressed through an electrical conductor? What occurs when the current is cut off?

16. What is the mathematical formula for computing the magnetomotive force?

17. State the rule for determining the polarity of an electromagnet.

18. How may the strength of an electromagnet made of wire wound on a cardboard form be increased? Explain why.

19. Where and in what manner are electromagnets used practically?

20. Draw a diagram of a motor and explain its operation, indicating all functional parts.

21. Compare the characteristics of a series-wound motor, a shunt-wound motor, and a compound-wound motor.

22. Explain the construction and operation of a moving-coil galvanometer.

23. Explain how a shunt in an ammeter enables us to place the instrument in a circuit of high current.

24. How is an ammeter connected in a circuit to measure the current flowing?

25. When measuring difference of potential across an electrical device, how is the galvanometer connected and how is it protected from burning out?

26. Explain the purpose and operation of an ohmmeter.

27. Explain the principles involved in the operation of a wattmeter.

31

Alternating Currents—
Theory and Measurement

PROBLEM 1. *How are induced voltages set up in a conductor?*

PROBLEM 2. *What is Lenz's law for induced currents?*

PROBLEM 3. *How are alternating currents generated?*

PROBLEM 4. *How are alternating currents represented by graphs?*

PROBLEM 5. *How do we measure the electromotive force, the current, and the impedance of alternating currents?*

PROBLEM 6. *What are the principles of operation of alternating-current meters?*

Induced Electromotive Force. You will recall that Oersted discovered that when an electric current passes through a conductor, a magnetic field is created around that conductor. In 1831, Michael Faraday, an English scientist, discovered that when a magnetic field cuts across a conductor, an electromotive force is set up in that conductor.

It appears not only that a moving dielectric field of force produces a magnetic field, but also that a moving magnetic field of force produces a dielectric field. This dielectric field of force causes the electrons of the conductor to flow in a stream through a complete circuit, which is another way of saying that an electric current is set flowing through that conductor. It is not enough for the conductor to be *in* the magnetic field. In order that an electric

340

current be set flowing, the conductor must be moving *through* that magnetic field.

Experiments with Induced Currents. Obtain a sensitive galvanometer whose zero point appears in the center of the scale. When current flows through the instrument in one direction, the pointer is deflected one way; when the current is flowing through in the opposite direction, the pointer is deflected the other way.

Connect the ends of the galvanometer to a coil of about 50 turns of wire wound in the shape of a cylinder about two inches in diameter. Now plunge

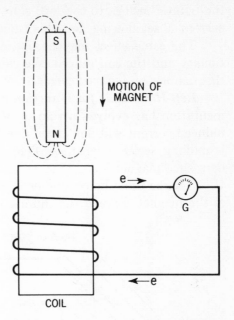

Fig. 31-1. *The magnet is plunged into the coil of wire. An electric current is induced in the coil.*

the north end of a permanent magnet into the center of the coil (Fig. 31-1). Observe that the pointer is deflected to the right, showing that an electric current was set flowing for a moment in the coil and galvanometer.

When the magnet comes to rest inside the coil, the pointer swings back to zero, showing that the current has ceased flowing. Now remove the magnet from the coil (Fig. 31-2). As you do so,

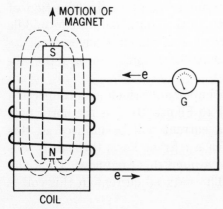

Fig. 31-2. *The magnet is pulled out of the coil. Once again an electric current is induced in the coil.*

the pointer swings to the left, showing that once more an electric current is set flowing, but this time in the opposite direction.

The same effect may be obtained if the magnet is held stationary and the coil moved. We call an electric current created in this manner an *induced current*.

Left-Hand Rule for Direction of the Induced Current. Experimentation has evolved a rule to determine in which direction an induced current will flow. Examine Figure 31-3, where a conductor is moving across a magnetic field set up between two poles of a horseshoe magnet.

Assume that the conductor is moving down between the poles of the magnet. Extend the thumb, forefinger, and middle finger of

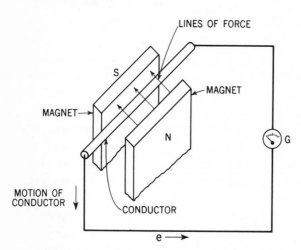

Fig. 31-3. *Diagram of a conductor cutting across lines of force between poles of a magnet.*

the left hand so that they are at right angles to one another. Let the thumb point in the direction in which the conductor is moving (down). Now let the forefinger point in the direction of the lines of force (from the north to the south pole). The middle finger will then indicate the direction in which electrons will be set flowing by the induced electromotive force (toward the observer).

Lenz's Law. There is another important principle in connection with induced currents. Turn back to Figure 31-1. As the north pole of the magnet enters the coil, a current will be induced in this coil. You know already that when a current flows through a conductor, it sets up a magnetic field around this conductor. Thus, the coil becomes an electromagnet. The induced current in this coil is set flowing in such a direction that the end of the coil facing the north pole of the magnet becomes a north pole, too. Since like poles repel, this arrangement of magnets tends to prevent the insertion of the north pole of the magnet into the coil. Work must be done to overcome the force of repulsion.

When you try to remove the magnet from the coil, the induced current is reversed. The top of the coil becomes a south pole and, by attraction to the north pole of the magnet, tends to prevent you from removing it. Thus, once again, work must be done—this time to overcome the force of attraction. You see, you must perform work to create the induced electric current. Of course, the same holds true if the magnet is stationary and the coil is moved.

These results may be summarized in a statement known as Lenz's law: *An induced current set up by the relative motion of a conductor and a magnetic field always flows in such a direction that it forms a magnetic field that opposes the motion.*

Strength of the Induced Electromotive Force. We have seen that the induced electromotive force is set up only when lines of force are cut. From this it follows that the faster the lines of force are cut, the greater the induced electromotive force. Moreover, the stronger the magnetic field, the more lines of force there are. Hence, both the strength of the magnetic field and the rate of relative motion of conductor and magnetic field affect the electromotive force.

If we have two conductors cutting the lines of force, twice as many of the lines will be cut as if there had been only one conductor. Thus, by increasing the number of turns of the coil cutting across the magnetic field, we increase the electromotive force induced in the coil.

We may summarize by stating that *the strength of the induced electromotive force depends upon the number of lines of force cut per second.* Experimentation has shown that 100,000,000 (10^8) lines of force must be cut per second to produce an induced electromotive force of one volt. Hence, we see that the induced electromotive force may be increased by (1) increasing the number of turns of wire, (2) increasing the speed of the relative motion, and (3) increasing the strength of the magnetic field.

Generating Alternating Electromotive Force. In discussing the electromotive force generated by the chemical energy of the voltaic cell, we dealt with a continuous-current phenomenon; the voltaic current was always uniform and in the same direction. We referred to current of this nature as *direct current* (dc).

But in the case of induced electromotive force generated as shown in Figures 31-1 and 31-2, the current starts from zero (magnet outside the coil and at rest) and builds up in one direction (as the magnet enters the coil). The electromotive force dies down to zero again (magnet at rest inside the coil), then builds up in the opposite direction (as the magnet is being removed from the coil), and dies down to zero again (magnet at rest outside the coil).

We call this type of current *alternating current* (ac). Alternating current may be defined as *current which continually changes in magnitude and periodically reverses in direction.*

The Generator. It is not practical to generate an alternating electromotive force by moving a magnet in and out of a coil of wire. The same result may be accomplished more easily by rotating a coil of wire between the poles of a powerful magnet. Such a device is called a *generator.*

Mount a single loop of wire so that it may be mechanically rotated on a shaft between the north and south poles of a powerful magnet (Fig. 31-4). The two ends of the loop are connected, respectively, to two brass or copper rings, A and B, called *slip,* or *collector, rings,* which are insulated from each other and from the shaft on which they are fastened. Thus, these collector rings rotate with the loop of wire. Two stationary brushes (A₁ and B₁) make a wiping contact with these rotating collector rings and lead the current that has been generated to the external circuit. These brushes

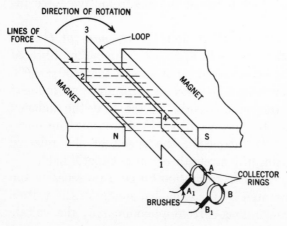

Fig. 31-4. *A simple alternating-current generator. It consists of a single loop of wire rotating in the magnetic field between two poles of a magnet.*

are usually made of copper or carbon. This arrangement of loop, magnetic field, collector rings, and brushes constitutes a simple generator.

How the Current Changes in One Complete Revolution. Let us assume that the loop starts from the vertical position as shown in Figure 31-4 and rotates at a uniform speed in a clockwise direction. At this initial position, no lines of force are being cut because the conductors 1-2 and 3-4 are moving parallel

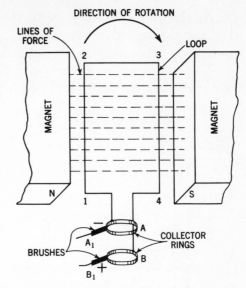

Fig. 31-5. *The loop after a quarter turn.*

to the lines of force, not across them.

As the loop moves away from the vertical position, the conductors begin to cut across the lines of force at an increasing rate and, therefore, the induced electromotive force becomes larger.

At the horizontal position (Fig. 31-5), the loop has the maximum electromotive force induced in it, because a small rotation from this position causes the conductors 1-2 and 3-4 to cut across the maximum number of lines of force per second, since the conductors are moving at right angles to the field.

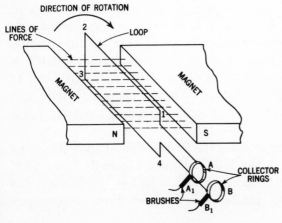

Fig. 31-6. *The loop after a half turn.*

As the loop continues on to the vertical position of Figure 31-6, the electromotive force is still in the same direction, but diminishes in value until at the vertical position it is again zero.

The loop now has made one half turn, during which the induced electromotive force increased to a maximum and then gradually fell off to zero. Since now the conductors 1-2 and 3-4 are in reversed position, the induced electromotive force changes in direction in both conductors. The electromotive force, however, again increases in strength and becomes maximum when the loop is horizontal (Fig. 31-7).

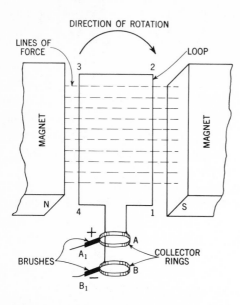

Finally, the last quarter of rotation brings the loop back to its original position (Fig. 31-4), during which movement the electromotive force decreases to zero again. As the rotation is continued, the cycle of events is repeated over and over.

Fig. 31-7. *The loop after a three-quarter turn.*

The Alternating-Current Cycle. The term *cycle* really means circle—a circle or series of events which recur in the same order. A complete turn of the loop is a cycle. So also is the series of changes of the current. As the loop of the alternating-current generator makes one complete revolution, every point in the conductors describes a circle. Since a circle has 360 degrees (360°), a quarter turn would be equal to 90 degrees (90°); a half turn, to 180 degrees (180°); a three-quarter turn, 270 degrees (270°); and a full turn, 360°. The number of degrees measured from the starting point is called the *angle of rotation.*

Thus, Figure 31-4 represents the 0° position; Figure 31-5, the 90° position; Figure 31-6, the 180° position; Figure 31-7, the 270° position; and Figure 31-4 again (after a complete revolution), the 360° position. Of course, positions in between these points may

Fig. 31-8. *Figure showing degrees of a circle. If the complete circle is taken to stand for one revolution, then a quarter turn would amount to 90°, a half turn 180°, a three-quarter turn 270°, and a full turn or revolution 360°.*

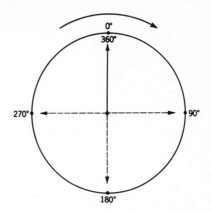

be designated by the corresponding degrees. However, it is customary to use the *quadrants* (that is, the four quarters of a circle) as the angles of rotation for reference.

Let us assume that the maximum electromotive force generated by this machine is 10 volts. We designate the direction in which the current flows by a plus (+) and minus (−). Now we are able to make a table, as in Figure 31-9, showing the electromotive force being generated during each angle of rotation.

Angle of rotation	0°	90°	180°	270°	360°
Induced emf (volts)	0	+10	0	−10	0·
Time in seconds	0	¼	½	¾	1

Fig. 31-9. *Table showing relationship between the degree of rotation of the loop, the induced voltage, and the time (assuming the loop makes one revolution in a second).*

You will note that in one complete revolution of the loop there are two positions (Figure 31-4 and 31-6) at which there is no induced voltage and, therefore, no current in the external circuit. There are also two positions (Figs. 31-5 and 31-7) at which the voltage is at maximum value, although in opposite directions. At intermediate positions, the voltage has intermediate values.

Assuming that the loop of our generator makes one complete revolution (360°) in one second, then at ¼ of the second, the loop would be at the 90° position, at ½ of the second the loop would be

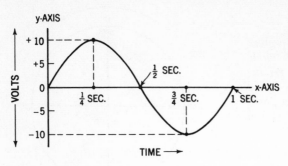

Fig. 31-10. *Curve showing relationship between time and the induced voltage.*

at the 180° position, and so on. Let us now look at the graph (Fig. 31-10) which shows the induced electromotive force at various intervals in the one second required for the loop to make a complete revolution. The graph was made from the data in Figure 31-9. The time is plotted on the horizontal axis (*x*), and the electromotive force, on the vertical axis (*y*).

Now you must not get the impression that the electric current is flowing in this scenic-railway type of path. Actually, the current is flowing back and forth through the external circuit. What this curve does show, however, is the strength of the induced electromotive force and its direction (+ or −) at any instant during one revolution. So at the ¼-second mark, the electromotive force is 10 volts and is acting in the direction indicated by plus (+). At the ¾-second mark, the electromotive force again is 10 volts, but this time it is acting in the opposite direction as indicated by minus (−). In the interval between the ¼-second mark and the ¾-second mark, the electromotive force changes from +10 volts to −10 volts, dropping to zero at the ½-second mark, at which instant the electromotive force changes its direction.

We call an electromotive force, whose strength and direction varies as indicated by the curve of Figure 31-10, an *alternating electromotive force.*

THE SINE CURVE

What Is a Sine? We can represent the generation of an alternating electromotive force by means of a *sine curve.* As many of you know, the term *sine* has importance in mathematics. The sine of an angle is one of its trigonometric functions and can be repre-

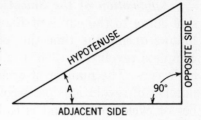

Fig. 31-11. *Diagram illustrating what we mean by the sine of an angle. The sine of angle A is equal to the value of the opposite side divided by the hypotenuse.*

sented very simply in terms of the sides of a right triangle. In Figure 31-11, the sine of angle A is equal to the opposite side of the triangle divided by the hypotenuse. We can make a table to show the value of the sine for any angle. Figure 31-12 gives the sines of angles from 0° to 360° in 30° steps.

Angle	0°	30°	60°	90°	120°	150°	180°	210°	240°	270°	300°	330°	360°
Sine	0	0.50	0.866	1.00	0.866	0.50	0	−0.50	−0.866	−1.00	−0.866	−0.50	0

Fig. 31-12. *Table showing relationship between angles (in 30° steps) and their respective sines.*

If we were to make a graph of the sine of an angle plotted against degrees, we would get the sine curve (Fig. 31-13).

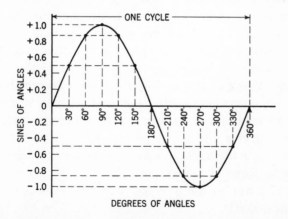

Fig. 31-13. *Curve showing relationship between angles (in 30° steps) and their respective sines. Note that this is merely another way of presenting the table in Figure 31-12.*

Application of the Sine Curve. Note the resemblance of the sine curve to the curve of Figure 31-10. The path the sine curve follows during the time the loop of the generator is making one complete revolution (360°) is called a *cycle.* The symbol for the cycle is ~. The number of cycles per second will depend upon the number of revolutions per second of the generator loop. The number of cycles per second is called the *frequency.* The symbol for frequency is *f*.

Since the loop of our generator makes one revolution per second, the induced electromotive force goes through one cycle per second, and the frequency of the electromotive force is one cycle per second. The electric current set flowing through the loop by the induced electromotive force will have a frequency of one cycle per second also.

But if the loop were rotated 60 times per second, the induced electromotive force would go through one cycle in 1/60 second. The frequency would then be 60 cycles per second, which is the usual frequency of commercial alternating current. Radio-frequency currents have frequencies that may run into millions or even billions of cycles per second. No generator can be rotated at any such tremendous number of revolutions per second. But we have several other means of producing high-frequency currents, as we shall see later.

Peak Value of a Sine Curve. Alternating electromotive force and current are continually changing in magnitude. That is, the instantaneous values are changing. From the sine curve, you can see that there are two *maximum* or *instantaneous peak values* for each cycle—a positive maximum and a negative maximum. These maximum values are known as the *amplitude* of the curve.

Average Value of a Sine Curve. If you observe the sine curve of alternating electromotive force or current, you will see that the true average value for a full cycle is zero, because there is just as much of the curve above the zero line (+) as there is below it (−). But when we use the *average values* in connection with alternating electromotive force or current, we do not refer to the average of the full cycle, but to the average of a half-cycle (or *alternation,* as it is also called).

To get the average, it is merely necessary to add the instantaneous values of one alternation as plotted on a curve and divide by the number taken. It can be proved by higher mathematics that the average value of a half-cycle of a sine curve is equal to 0.636 times the maximum or peak voltage.

Thus,

$$\text{Average current} = 0.636 \times \text{maximum current}$$

and

$$\text{Average emf} = 0.636 \times \text{maximum emf.}$$

Effective, or Root Mean Square, Value. In practice, we use neither the instantaneous nor average values of the electromotive force or current. To make alternating current compare as nearly to direct current as possible, it is necessary to use an *effective value.* In other words, we must find the value for the sine curve of alternating electromotive force or current which would have the same effect in producing *power* as a corresponding direct-current value. You will recall that the direct-current formulas for power are

$$P = I^2 R \qquad \text{and} \qquad P = \frac{E^2}{R}$$

From this relation, you can see that the power is proportional to the square of the current ($I \times I$) or to the square of the electromotive force ($E \times E$). Thus, we must get the average (or *mean*) of the instantaneous values squared (instantaneous value $\times$ instantaneous value), and then calculate the square root of this average. To extract the square root of a number means obtaining another number which when multiplied by itself (squared) will give us the original number. Thus, the square root of 100 is 10; for 10×10 equals 100.

Because of the method used to determine the effective value, it is known as the *root mean square* (abbreviated to *rms*) *value.* By means of mathematics, it can be proved that the effective value is equal to 0.707 times the maximum or peak value and that the peak value is equal to 1.41 times the effective value.

Method of Plotting a Curve. Before going further, let us be sure we understand the making of a graph. In Chapter 9, we explained graphs only to the extent necessary at that point. Now we need to be able to make graphs and to read them intelligently. When we make a graph, we usually say that we *plot a curve.* We usually plot two sets of values *against* each other. Thus, in the graph of Figure 31-13, we plotted degrees against the sines of angles.

In addition to the curve, the graph has two lines at right angles to each other. The vertical line is called the *Y axis* and the horizontal line the *X axis.* Along one of these axes we lay out, from the point of intersection of the two axes, one set of values, and along the other, we lay out the other set of values. We usually call all points *above* the *X* axis *positive* (+) values and all points *below* the *X* axis *negative* (−) values.

Thus (Fig. 31-13) along the *X* axis we lay off the degrees and along the *Y* axis we lay off the sines of the angles. If we wish to find the point on the curve corresponding to the sine of 90°, we draw a line *upward,* perpendicular to the *X* axis, from the point on that axis marked *90°.* We draw this line upward because the sine of *90°* is a positive value.

Then, from the point on the *Y* axis which corresponds to the sine of 90° (1.0), we draw a line perpendicular to the *Y* axis (and parallel to the *X* axis). Where these two lines meet (that is, at their intersection) is the desired point on the sine curve.

Similarly, we plot a number of such points, and then by connecting all these points with a continuous line, we obtain the sine curve. Sometimes, instead of referring to the *X* and *Y* axes, we designate the axes by the values plotted along them, in this case as the *degree axis* and the *sine of angles axis.*

Plotting Curves of Current and EMF Together. Now let us see how the use of graphs helps us to understand electric currents. The electromotive force causes the current to flow. Thus, we should expect that when the alternating electromotive force reaches its maximum in one direction, the alternating current also will reach its maximum in that direction. When the electromotive force drops to zero, the current, too, will drop to zero. We may show this relationship graphically by plotting the alternating electromotive force against degrees of rotation and, on the same two axes, plotting the alternating current against degrees of rotation (Fig. 31-14).

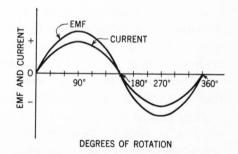

Fig. 31-14. *Curves showing the relationship between emf and current and the degree of rotation (in phase).*

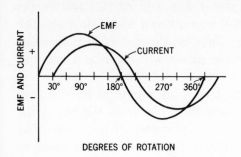

EMF AND CURRENT

DEGREES OF ROTATION

Fig. 31-15. *Emf and current curves showing the current lagging 30° behind the emf.*

What Is Meant by Phase? You will notice in Figure 31-14 that in both curves the electromotive force and current reach their maximum in the same direction at the same time and are likewise at zero at the same time. When the electromotive force and current have this relationship to each other, we say that they are *in phase*.

But in practical circuits, for reasons we will discuss later, the electromotive force and current may not be in step with each other. The current may either lag behind or lead the electromotive force. We then say that the electromotive force and the current are *out of phase* with each other. Figure 31-15 shows such a condition.

Note that the electromotive-force curve reaches its peak 30° (30 degrees) before the current curve and that it crosses the zero line 30° ahead of the current. We say the electromotive force is *leading* the current by 30° or that the current is *lagging* 30° behind the electromotive force. Another way of describing this condition is to say that the *phase angle* (the difference between the electromotive force and the current) is 30°. The symbol for phase angle is the Greek letter *theta* (θ).

Vectors. Mathematicians have given us another way of looking at the relationship between an alternating current and its electromotive force. In studying this principle we shall get a clearer understanding of the sine curve.

Let us represent the induced electromotive force by an arrow (OA in Fig.

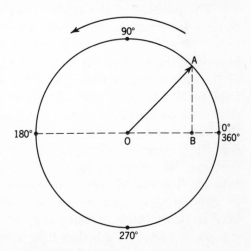

Fig. 31-16. *Diagram showing what is meant by a vector.*

31-16) of unit length, fixed at one end to a point (O) and free to revolve at a uniform rate about this point as a center, in step with the revolution of the generator. Thus, as the generator makes one complete revolution, the tip of the arrow will describe a circle or 360°.

The instantaneous electromotive force produced by the generator may be represented by dropping a line from the tip of the arrow perpendicular to the horizontal diameter of the circle. The length of this line (AB) will indicate the instantaneous value of the electromotive force. By plotting these instantaneous values against degree of rotation, as in Figure 31-17, we once more obtain our sine curve.

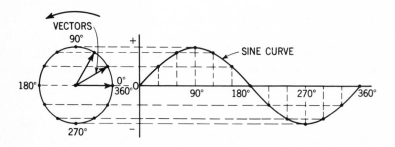

Fig. 31-17. *Diagram showing the relationship between the vector and sine-curve methods of representing alternating currents and voltages.*

The position of the arrow (depending upon the degree of rotation), its direction (as shown by the arrow head), and its magnitude (as indicated by the length of the line from its tip to the horizontal diameter of the circle) at any instant is called the *vector* of the electromotive force. A vector is the representation of any force or motion by a line. The *direction* of the force or motion is shown by an arrow, and the *magnitude* is shown by the length of the line drawn to some defined scale. Every vector must have definite length and direction. A *vector quantity* is any quantity that can be expressed by a line, such as force, acceleration, or velocity. The magnitude of the electromotive force can be pictured by choosing any convenient scale. Thus, a vector one inch long may be taken to represent, say, 10 volts. Under these circumstances, a vector two inches long would then represent 20 volts; three inches would stand for 30 volts; and so on.

Of course, we may have a vector picture for the current as

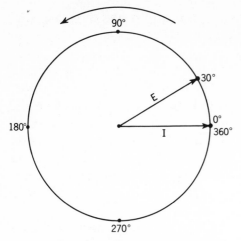

Fig. 31-18. *Vector diagram showing the current (I) lagging 30° behind the emf (E). Compare this diagram with the curve in Figure 31-15.*

well as for the electromotive force.

Vector Diagrams May Show Phase Relationship. We can show the phase relationship between electromotive force and current by means of these vector diagrams. We do so by picturing both vectors as connected to the same center. Thus, if we wish to show the current as lagging 30° behind the electromotive force, we picture this relationship as in Figure 31-18.

The angle between the electromotive force (E) vector and the current (I) vector is the phase angle. The lengths of the vectors are independent of each other and depend upon the scales selected for each. In practice, when we draw our vector diagrams, we omit the circle around them and indicate the phase angle numerically (Fig. 31-19).

Addition of Alternating Electromotive Forces or Currents by Vectors. When we wish to add the electromotive forces from two batteries, the process is a simple problem in addition. The electromotive force from a battery always flows in one direction and is constant in value.

But when we wish to add together two alternating electromotive forces, we have a different problem. In an alternating electromotive force, not only is the direction periodically changed, but the value is likewise constantly changing. Moreover, the two alternating electromotive forces may not be in phase.

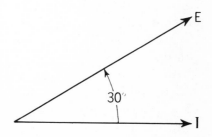

Fi.g 31-19. *In practice, the circle is omitted from the vector diagram. This is analogous to Figure 31-18.*

Since the vector represents the magnitude and direction of an alternating electromotive force at a certain instant, we may use vectors to solve our problem.

Assume that the vector for one electromotive force is represented by line OA in Figure 31-20. Assume that you wish to add another electromotive force that is twice as great as the first at a particular instant, and the vector of this second is represented by line OB. Join the two vectors at point O, making the angle between them equal to the angular difference in phase (obviously, E_1 leads E_2).

Now, from point A draw a line parallel to OB, and from point B, draw a line parallel to OA. These two lines intersect at point C, thus completing a parallelogram. Draw line OC with an arrowhead toward point C. This line is the vector of the electromotive force resulting from the addition of the other two electromotive forces.

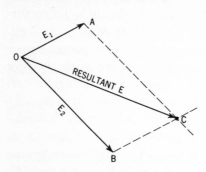

Fig. 31-20. *Vector diagram showing how two voltages (E_1 and E_2) are added together to give the resultant voltage (Resultant E).*

In summary, to find the resultant of two electromotive forces at a particular instant, we draw vectors to represent the magnitudes and directions (angular difference) of the two electromotive forces. On these lines, we construct a parallelogram. The resultant electromotive force is the diagonal of the parallelogram from the point of origin of the two vectors to be added. We follow the same procedure in adding together two alternating currents.

Impedance. The rules and formulas that we use in connection with direct-current circuits must be modified in order to apply to alternating-current circuits. These formulas are applicable only to voltages and currents that are in phase. If we are to use effective values of electromotive force and current, we must take into consideration certain factors not present in direct-current problems. For example, if a steady direct current is flowing through a coil, the only resistance encountered by the current is the resistance of the coil itself. But if an alternating current is set flowing through the coil, not only is its flow opposed by the resistance of the coil, but the magnetic field set up around the coil, unlike the field set up by the direct current, is constantly expanding and collapsing. Thus, the magnetic field is continually cutting across the coil itself, setting up a counter-electromotive force, the effect of which is to further oppose the flow of current.

The total opposition to the flow of alternating current in a circuit is called the *impedance*. Since it is an opposition to the flow of current, it has the same unit of measurement as resistance—that is, the *ohm*. The symbol used to represent impedance is Z.

Under special conditions where the voltage (electromotive force) and current are in phase, the impedance and the resistance of the circuit are identical. But where the voltage and current are out of phase, the impedance is always *greater* than the resistance. The method for finding how much greater the impedance is for any value of phase angle will be taken up later.

Ohm's Law for Alternating Currents. If we replace R in the direct-current Ohm's law by Z, it will apply to alternating-current circuits. Thus, Ohm's law for alternating current can be written as follows:

$$I = \frac{E}{Z} \quad \text{or} \quad E = I \times Z \quad \text{or} \quad Z = \frac{E}{I}$$

Power Factor. We have seen that in direct-current circuits, the electrical power may be calculated by means of the following formula:

$$P = E \times I$$

This holds true for alternating-current circuits as well *if* we merely consider *instantaneous* values. Then,

$$P_{instantaneous} = E_{instantaneous} \times I_{instantaneous}$$

Of greater importance to us are the effective values. Thus,

$$P_{effective} = E_{effective} \times I_{effective}$$

The formula for the effective or apparent power holds true only as long as the voltage and current are in phase—that is, as long as they reach their respective peaks at the same instant and reach zero together. When they are out of phase (Fig. 31-15), there are times during the cycle when the voltage is negative while the current is positive, and vice versa. During those intervals when the voltage and current have opposite signs, current is being fed back into the source. This means that there is *less* power consumed in the external circuit than is indicated by the apparent power. Under such conditions, the *true power* is always less than the *apparent power.*

The ratio of the true power to the apparent power is called the *power factor.* Thus,

$$\text{Power factor} = \frac{\text{true power}}{\text{apparent power}}.$$

This ratio may be expressed either as a fraction or as a percentage. We may say that the power factor is, for example, ½ or 50 per cent. Where the current and voltage are in phase, the apparent power is equal to the true power. The power factor in this case is unity—that is, 1, or 100 per cent. The power factor can never be greater than unity or 100 per cent (pages 398-399). Another way of stating the above formula is

True power = apparent power × power factor.

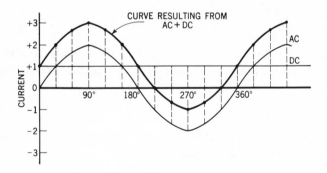

Fig. 31-21. *Curve showing the result of adding alternating and direct currents.*

Adding Alternating and Direct Current. Alternating and direct currents may be added together. Assume that we have a battery and a generator connected in series, both supplying electric current to an external circuit. We can show the result graphically, as in Figure 31-21.

The direct current from the battery, having a constant value, may be pictured as a horizontal, straight line above and parallel to the X axis. We assume its value to be one ampere. Let us further assume that the alternating current from the generator has a peak value of two amperes. Plot the sine curve showing this alternating current on the same axis with the direct-current line.

Now, let us suppose that the battery and the generator start furnishing current in the same direction at the same instant. The direct current from the battery rises instantaneously to its maximum value (+1 ampere) and maintains a steady flow at that level as long as the circuit is completed.

Now consider the alternating current during its first half cycle. The current gradually rises until the peak value of +2 amperes is reached at the 90° position. Then the current gradually falls off until it reaches zero at the 180° point. During this time the alternating current and direct current are flowing in the same direction and, therefore, the currents are added to each other. Thus, at the 90° position, the peak of the combined alternating and direct currents reaches +3 amperes.

But when the alternating current reaches zero (at 180°), the direct current is still +1 ampere. Thus, the curve showing the combined alternating and direct current has a value at this point of the sum of 0 ampere (from the generator) and +1 ampere (from the battery), giving a total of +1 ampere. In fact, it is not until the alternating current starts flowing in the opposite direction and reaches a value of −1 ampere that it is able to neutralize the +1 ampere of direct current. At that point, the total current flow is zero.

As the alternating current increases in its negative value, the

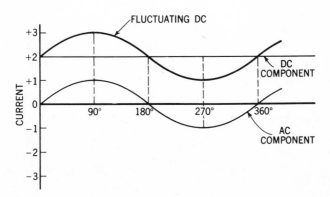

Fig. 31-22. *Curves showing how a fluctuating direct current may be broken down to its steady d-c component and its a-c component.*

combined current becomes more and more negative. At the 270° point, the alternating current reaches its negative peak of −2 amperes. If we add to this the +1 ampere from the battery, we get a total of −1 ampere, which is the current flowing in the circuit at this point (270°). As the alternating-current cycle approaches the 360° mark, the negative current decreases, and the curve of the combined alternating and direct currents approaches the zero line. When the negative current from the generator drops to −1 ampere, the zero line is reached. From that point on, the total current increases until, at the 360° mark (the alternating current being zero and the direct current +1 ampere), the total current flowing is +1 ampere. Then the cycle repeats itself.

The curve of the combined alternating and direct currents will resemble the one shown in Figure 31-21 if the peak of the alternating-current curve exceeds the direct-current value. Where the direct current is greater than the peak of the alternating current, the combined curve takes on the form shown in Figure 31-22. The form of this combined curve will resemble a sine wave, but since the direct current is always greater than the alternating current, at no time will the curve go below the *X* axis. The result, then, is a *fluctuating direct current*.

Applications of Combined Currents in Radio. This curve should be familiar to you. In it you will recognize our friend, the fluctuating direct current, that we find flowing in the plate circuit of the radio tube. A fluctuating direct current really, then, consists of (at least) two parts, or *components*. One component is the steady direct current, and the other component is an alternating current.

We can, therefore, break up the fluctuating direct current flowing in the plate circuits of the tubes into the steady direct-current component supplied by the B battery and the alternating-current component supplied by the signal. This alternating current in an audio-frequency amplifier has a frequency that lies in the audio range—that is, from 30 to 15,000 cycles per second.

You can now see what we meant when, in discussing the tone control of the radio set (Chap. 25), we said some of the high-frequency current was bypassed by the capacitor connected across the primary of the audio-frequency transformer (Fig. 25-1). Obviously, since the direct current has no frequency, it was the alternating-current component about which we were talking.

We may also see why a pulsating direct current, if fed into the primary of a transformer, will produce alternating current in the secondary, just the same as alternating current fed into the primary (Fig. 10-3). The alternating-current component of the pulsating direct current does the job.

Alternating-Current Meters. If we were to connect the moving-coil galvanometer used for measurement in direct-current circuits into an alternating-current circuit, the pointer would merely vibrate back and forth. Here is the reason.

The movement of the pointer depends, you will recall, upon the interaction between the magnetic field of the permanent magnet and that of the armature coil. If alternating current is passed through the armature coil, the field around this coil is expanded and collapsed very rapidly (depending upon the frequency of the current). Before the pointer is able to give us the deflection, the magnetic field begins to collapse, and the spring pulls the pointer back. Thus we get a to-and-fro vibration of the pointer.

Of course, we may rectify our alternating current, and thus change it to a pulsating direct current (Chap. 18). To do this would necessitate the changing of our scale to take into account the average current.

The Iron-Vane Type of Meter. Another method is to construct a meter as shown in Figure 31-23. Two soft-iron pieces, or vanes, are placed inside of a coil of wire. One of these vanes is fixed, and the other is free to move. Attached to the movable vane is a shaft carrying a pointer. As current passes through the coil, the vanes become magnetized. Since they are magnetized in the same way (north pole to north pole and south pole to south pole), even though the direction of the current is

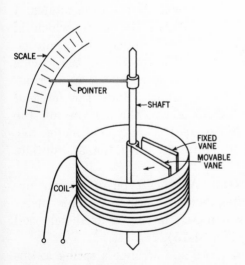

Fig. 31-23. *Diagram of a moving-vane a-c meter.*

changing rapidly, the two vanes repel each other. The movable vane swings away, turning the shaft and the pointer. The force of repulsion is proportional to the current flowing through the coil. A spring (not shown here) pulls the movable vane back.

This meter is called the *moving-vane* or *iron-vane* type of alternating-current meter. A shunt may be connected across the coil, and the instrument may be used as an alternating-current ammeter, or a multiplier may be connected in series with the coil, and the instrument becomes an alternating-current voltmeter.

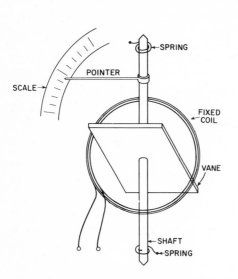

The Inclined-Coil Meter. Another type of alternating-current meter is the *inclined-coil* meter (Fig. 31-24). Here, a fixed coil is set at an angle to a shaft upon which is mounted a soft-iron vane set at right angles to the coil. As current flows through the coil, the vane attempts to turn to a position where it will line up with the magnetic lines of force around the coil. As the vane rotates, it turns the shaft, which in turn moves the pointer. The rotation of the vane is opposed by the two springs shown. Since the force of rotation is proportional to the current flowing through the coil, the pointer indicates the force of that current. This type of meter, too, can be used as an ammeter or voltmeter with the appropriate shunts or multipliers.

Fig. 31-24. *Diagram of the inclined-coil a-c meter.*

Dynamometer Type of Meter. Another type of alternating-current meter employs the *dynamometer principle.* This meter resembles the direct-current wattmeter, having a fixed field coil and a movable armature coil (Fig. 31-25).

If we connect both coils in series and arrange a spring to oppose the tendency of the movable coil to turn, then the pointer attached to the movable coil is deflected in proportion to the cur-

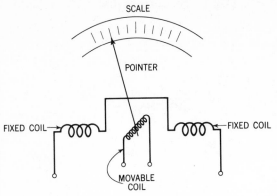

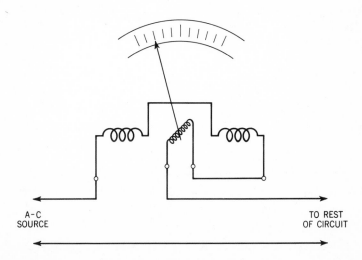

Fig. 31-25. *Diagram of the dynamometer principle.*

rent (Fig. 31-26). Note that it makes no difference which way the current is flowing, because the magnetic fields of *both* coils will change together in step with the current. We can use this meter to measure the current.

If we now connect the fixed coil in series with the line and connect the movable coil in parallel with the line through a multiplier (a resistance in series) as in Figure 31-27, then, if the line current is kept at a constant average value, the current flowing through the movable coil (and the resulting deflection of the pointer) will be proportional to the electromotive force.

The Hot-Wire Ammeter. Still another type of instrument is

Fig. 31-26. *Diagram showing how the dynamometer type of meter is hooked into the circuit to read alternating current.*

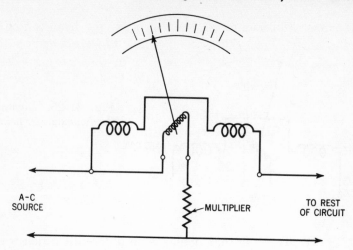

Fig. 31-27. *Diagram showing how the dynamometer type of meter is hooked into the circuit to read alternating voltage. (The effective current must be kept constant.)*

used as an alternating-current ammeter. It is called the *hot-wire ammeter* (Fig. 31-28). Current passes through a fine wire tightly stretched horizontally. From the center of this wire is attached another wire ABC which is secured at point C and exerts a constant pull on the fine wire. A fine thread DB, attached to the spring, exerts a sidewise pull on this second wire. This thread passes over a small roller to which the pointer is attached. Any slight movement of the thread deflects the pointer.

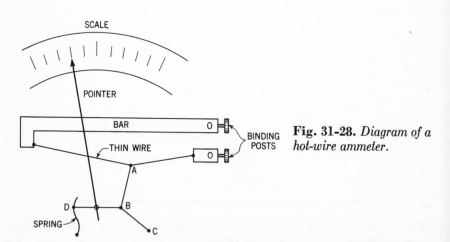

Fig. 31-28. *Diagram of a hot-wire ammeter.*

As current flows through the fine wire, the heat causes it to expand slightly. This expansion permits the spring to pull the thread, and the pointer is deflected. Since the heating effect on the wire (and, therefore, the amount of expansion) depends upon the current passing through it, the deflection of the pointer shows the value of the current.

The hot-wire ammeter is quite commonly employed to measure the small alternating currents of high frequency used in radio.

The Thermocouple Meter. Still another instrument used for radio-frequency work is the *thermocouple meter*. Here is how it works.

When two wires of dissimilar metals are connected together at one end and the junction is heated, it will be found that a direct-current electromotive force (voltage) is developed between the open ends of the wire. The voltage will be directly proportional to the difference in temperature between the connected (hot) ends and the unconnected (cold) ends.

The generation of a direct-current electromotive force by heating the junction of two dissimilar metals is known as *thermoelectric action,* and the device that permits this action to take place is known as a *thermocouple.*

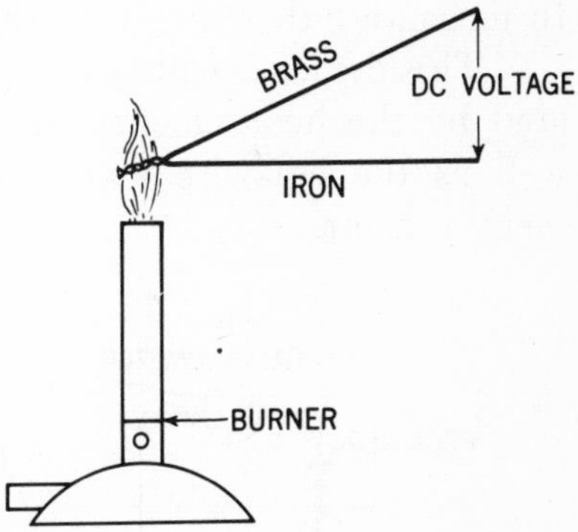

If we connect the thermocouple to a sensitive direct-current meter of the D'Arsonval type and calibrate the scale in degrees of temperature instead of in units of electric current, we have an instrument known as a *pyrometer,* which is used to measure the temperature of heated objects.

Any two dissimilar metals will function as a thermocouple,

Fig. 31-29. *Diagram illustrating the principle of a thermocouple.*

but it has been found that if we use a wire made of an alloy of bismuth and one made of an alloy of antimony for our thermocouple, we get the greatest possible voltage per degree of temperature difference.

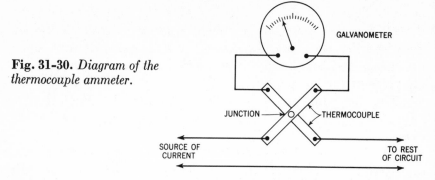

Fig. 31-30. *Diagram of the thermocouple ammeter.*

Now, we know that an electric current passing through a conductor will heat that conductor in proportion to the square of the current ($P = I^2R$; P represents heating effect). (Note that this is the same as the power formula.) So if we pass a current through the junction of a thermocouple, that junction will be heated in proportion to the square of the current, and this heat will generate an electromotive force. If we now attach to the cold ends a sensitive galvanometer that is properly calibrated, we can obtain the value of that current. The direction of the external current flow will have no effect upon this instrument; therefore, it can be used to measure either direct or alternating current.

This device is called a *thermocouple ammeter*. Since it is operated by the heating effect of the current, this type of meter, as well as the hot-wire ammeter, can be used for radio-frequency measurement.

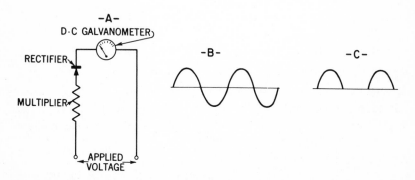

Fig. 31-31. *A—Circuit of the half-wave rectifier-type a-c voltmeter.*
B—Waveform of the applied voltage.
C—Waveform of the voltage entering the galvanometer.

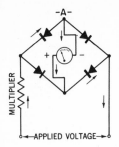 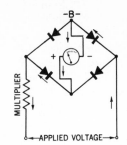

Fig. 31-32. *Circuit of the full-wave bridge rectifier. A—Current flow during one alternation. B—Current flow during the next alternation.*

The Rectifier-Type Meter. A common type of meter used in radio work for measuring low-frequency alternating currents and voltages is the *rectifier-type* instrument. We saw how a crystal rectifier in our crystal detector changed alternating current to direct current. A somewhat similar type of rectifier may be used to change alternating current into direct current, and then the direct current is fed into a standard direct-current moving-coil meter. The most common rectifiers used in these instruments are the *copper-oxide* and *selenium* types. A simple rectifier-type voltmeter is shown in Figure 31-31. Note that the rectifier is of the half-wave type.

A somewhat better circuit is that of the full-wave *bridge* rectifier shown in Figure 31-32. Note that during both alternations, the current flows through the galvanometer in the same direction.

If the multiplier is omitted, the instrument becomes an alternating-current milliammeter. Its range may be extended by placing shunts across the entire circuit.

SUMMARY

1. (a) An electric current is accompanied by a **magnetic field** and, (b) conversely, a changing magnetic field produces a **dielectric field** and sets up a voltage in a conductor within the changing magnetic field.
2. An **induced voltage** is set up in a conductor in the presence of a magnetic field by any change in their relation which causes magnetic lines of force to cut through the conductor.
3. **Alternating-current generators** consist of conductors made to pass rapidly through magnetic fields. The current alternates because the electromotive force is set up in one direction when the conductor cuts into the field and in the opposite direction when the conductor cuts out of the field.

4. The *direction* of the current induced in any conductor or coil is determined by Lenz's law, which states that the induced current and accompanying magnetic field are in such a direction as to oppose the force which produces them.
5. For *measuring alternating currents* we use the same units, volt, ampere, and ohm, that are used in direct-current systems. But modification in the use of these units is required because of fluctuation, change of direction, and impedance in alternating currents.
6. *Impedance* means the total opposition to the flow of alternating current.
7. *Instantaneous values* for electromotive force and current in alternating-current circuits are best described by the *sine curve,* which is a graph plotted from a revolving *radius vector* or from tabulated data.
8. Both currents and electromotive forces are commonly represented by *vectors.* When two electromotive forces or two currents that are out of phase are to be added, a parallelogram is constructed with the vectors as sides. The diagonal drawn to scale represents the *resultant* of the two vectors.
9. Alternating-current meters must be built on principles different from the principles governing direct-current meters. Several types that work by magnetic effects are practical. For radio work, the *heating effect* of the alternating current is often used to operate a sensitive direct-current meter which is not in the alternating-current circuit. The heating effect is utilized by means of (a) a hot wire which expands in proportion to the heat and (b) a thermocouple which sets up a direct current between two dissimilar metals—also in proportion to the temperature. The rectifier principle may also be used.

GLOSSARY

Alternating Current: A current or voltage continually changing in magnitude and periodically reversing its direction.
Angle of Rotation: The angle in degrees made by the armature of a generator in rotating from its starting point.
Cycle: The voltage variation created as the armature of a generator goes through one cycle or 360° of rotation, which may be graphed as a sine curve.
Direct Current: A current maintained in one direction through a circuit.
Electromagnetic Induction: The production of a voltage in a conductor when it cuts across magnetic lines of force.
Frequency: The number of cycles per second of an alternating current.

Generator: A device in which a coil rotates in a magnetic field and creates a voltage across its ends.

Impedance: The total opposition to the flow of alternating current in a circuit.

Phase: The instantaneous value in degrees of a cycle of alternating voltage or current.

Phase Angle: The angle of lead or lag between similar phases of two sine curves.

Power Factor: The fraction by which we multiply the apparent power of a circuit to get the true power.

Sine Curve: The graph which shows the variations of a pure alternating current or voltage.

Vector: The representation of a quantity by a line that indicates its magnitude and direction.

QUESTIONS AND PROBLEMS

1. Under what circumstances may a magnetic field produce a voltage?
2. Explain the left-hand rule for direction of the induced voltage.
3. Explain the use of Lenz's law in determining the polarity of a coil pushed over the end of a bar magnet. State the law.
4. How could we increase the strength of an induced electromotive force in a coil pushed over a bar magnet?
5. What are the characteristics of a direct current? Of an alternating current?
6. Describe the construction of an alternating-current generator.
7. Explain how a sine wave is generated by an alternating-current generator.
8. Draw a sine wave of alternating-current voltage and explain what its changes mean.
9. What is meant by an alternating-current cycle?
10. At what positions in degrees of an alternating-current cycle are the values zero; at what positions maximum?
11. What is the sine of an angle? How is it related to the sine curve of voltage change produced by an alternating-current generator?
12. How do we express the frequency of an alternating current?
13. Explain what is meant by maximum, average, and effective value of an alternating-current voltage. How may they be derived from one another?
14. When is an alternating-current voltage said to be in phase with its current? Indicate this relation by sine curves.
15. What is meant by a vector? What two conditions does it describe?

16. Represent vectorially an alternating-current voltage leading its current by 90°. By 45°. Represent these also by a sine-curve picture.

17. What accounts for the difficulty of adding together the voltages of two alternating-current generators feeding into a single line? How are these difficulties overcome?

18. What is meant by impedance? In what unit is it measured?

19. State Ohm's law for alternating-current circuits.

20. Why can we not always state that Power $= I_{effective} \times E_{effective}$ in alternating-current circuits?

21. How is the power factor of a circuit calculated?

22. When will the apparent and true power of an alternating-current circuit be equal?

23. Derive the result of mixing a direct-current voltage of 10 volts with an alternating-current voltage of 5 volts maximum.

24. What are the components of a fluctuating direct current?

25. Why can't we use direct-current meters in an alternating-current circuit?

26. Describe the iron-vane type of alternating-current meter.

27. Describe the inclined-coil meter.

28. Describe the dynamometer type of alternating-current meter.

29. Describe the operation of the hot-wire ammeter.

30. Describe the thermocouple type of alternating-current meter.

31. Describe the bridge rectifier-type alternating-current meter.

32

Inductance, Inductive Reactance, and Impedance

> **PROBLEM 1.** *What are the factors involved in inductance?*
>
> **PROBLEM 2.** *What are the effects of self-induction upon electromotive force, current, and resistance?*
>
> **PROBLEM 3.** *How do we measure self-inductance and mutual inductance?*
>
> **PROBLEM 4.** *How are inductors coupled for various purposes?*

Lenz's Law and Counter Electromotive Force. From Lenz's law, we have learned that when an induced current is set up in a moving conductor, the current always flows in such a direction that it forms a magnetic field opposing the motion of the conductor. Let us now see how we must modify this law to take into account a stationary conductor that is cut by a moving magnetic field.

If a current is passed through a coil of wire, a magnetic field is built up around this coil. As this field expands, it cuts across the conductors or turns of the coil itself, inducing a second current in them. Lenz also discovered that the direction of this induced current is such that it will oppose the original current. In other words, the direction of the induced current is such that it will tend to reduce the original current, and thereby tend to oppose the *expansion* of the magnetic field. When the original current reaches a steady level, the magnetic field becomes stationary and no longer cuts across the turns of the coil. There is no longer an induced current in this coil.

Now let us see what happens when the original current begins to decrease. The magnetic field around the coil starts to collapse. In so doing, it cuts across the turns of the coil, and once again a second current is induced in the coil. The direction of the induced current again opposes the change of the original current which is decreasing. Thus, it tends to keep current flowing in the coil for a time after the original current has ceased. The induced current, therefore, tends to oppose the *collapse* of the magnetic field.

We can now expand Lenz's law to state that *an induced current (or the induced voltage which sets the current flowing) is always in such a direction as to oppose the current or the magnetic-field change that is producing it.* For this reason, an induced voltage is often referred to as *counter electromotive force* or *back electromotive force.*

Idea of Inductance. The property of a circuit which opposes any change in the current flowing in it is called its *inductance.* Since this opposition is caused by voltages induced in the circuit itself by the *changing magnetic field,* anything that affects the amount of magnetic flux must also affect this inductance.

The unit used to measure the inductance of a circuit is called the *henry* (h). The henry can be defined as being the inductance present when a current change of one ampere per second in a circuit produces an induced electromotive force of one volt. The symbol used for inductance is L.

In radio work, it is often convenient to employ the *millihenry* (mh), which is 1/1000 of a henry, and the *microhenry* (μh), which is 1/1,000,000 of a henry.

Self-Inductance. When the effect of inductance is such as to oppose any change in current in the circuit where the changing current is flowing, the term *self-inductance* is applied to the phenomenon. Except when currents of extremely high frequency are flowing through them, the self-inductance of straight wires can be neglected. But the self-inductance of coils, especially when wound on magnetic materials, can be very great, the amount being determined by the number of turns, the size, the shape, the type of windings, and other physical factors.

The inductance of such coils (sometimes called *inductors*) can be calculated in henrys (or millihenrys or microhenrys) from special formulas which you may find in Bulletin 74 of the United States Bureau of Standards; we need not study or use these formulas here. Inductors used for radio-frequency work generally have cores of air or other nonmetallic materials. Examples are the tuning coil and the radio-frequency choke shown in Figures 8-3 and 23-13. The tuning coil has an inductance of approximately 300 microhenrys and the radio-frequency choke 2.5 millihenrys. This radio-frequency choke consists of about 300 turns of No. 36 cotton-covered wire on a ½-inch wooden dowel.

When used for audio-frequency work, the inductors are usually wound on special iron cores which multiply the inductance of the coil many thousands of times. Thus, the filter choke described in Figure 18-2, has an inductance of 30 henrys.

Inductors in Series and Parallel. Inductors, like resistors, can be connected in series, in parallel, or in combinations of series and parallel circuits. The total inductance of several inductors connected in series (provided the magnetic field of one inductor cannot act upon the turns of another) is equal to the sum of the inductances of the individual inductors. In a formula:

$$L_{total} = L_1 + L_2 + L_3 + \cdots \text{ and so forth.}$$

If two or more inductors are connected in parallel (provided there is no interaction or *coupling* of their magnetic fields), we can find the total inductance from the following formula,

$$\frac{1}{L_{total}} = \frac{1}{L_1} + \frac{1}{L_2} + \frac{1}{L_3} + \cdots \text{ and so forth,}$$

or

$$L_{total} = \frac{1}{\dfrac{1}{L_1} + \dfrac{1}{L_2} + \dfrac{1}{L_3} + \cdots \text{ and so forth}}.$$

This relation is similar to that between resistors in parallel.

As in the case of resistors, the total inductance of inductors connected in a series-parallel circuit may be obtained by first finding the inductance of the inductors in parallel and then adding this inductance to the inductance in series with it as though it were a straight series-inductor circuit.

Inductive Reactance. In Chapter 31, we learned that the impedance of an alternating-current circuit is the total opposition that circuit offers to the flow of current. Where only pure resistance is present in the circuit, the impedance is equal to the resistance. But we have seen that the presence of an inductor in the circuit causes a counter electromotive force to be built up which further opposes the flow of current. Under such conditions, the impedance of the circuit is greater than the resistance.

The factor which, in an alternating-current circuit, causes the impedance (Z) to be larger than the resistance (R) is called the *reactance* (X). Since this reactance is due to the presence of inductance, we call it the *inductive reactance*. To show that it is inductive reactance, we add the subscript L to the symbol for reactance (X) and get X_L as the symbol for inductive reactance.

This method of adding a subscript to identify an electrical value is commonly used. Thus, the current (I) flowing through the inductor is shown as I_L. The voltage (E) across the inductor becomes E_L. This notation is not restricted to inductors. The voltage across a capacitor may be designated as E_C, the resistance of an inductor R_L, and so on.

Since impedance represents an opposition to the flow of current and has the ohm as its unit, the inductive reactance, which increases the impedance, also has the ohm for its unit.

The inductive reactance depends upon the magnitude of the induced voltage. This magnitude, in turn, depends upon two factors: the inductance of the circuit (L) and the rate or frequency (f) at which the current (and, therefore, the magnetic field) is changing.

The formula for inductive reactance is
$$X_L = 2\pi f L$$
where X_L is the inductive reactance in ohms, f is the frequency in cycles per second, and L is the inductance in henrys.

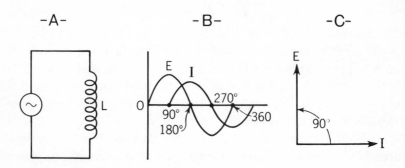

Fig. 32-1. *A—Circuit containing inductance only.*
　　　B—Sine curves showing how current (I) lags 90° behind the voltage (E).
　　　C—Vector diagram showing the same thing.

The factor 2π is necessary to make the result come out in ohms. π is a constant, equal approximately to 3.14. 2π therefore equals 6.28. Notice that the higher the frequency (f) the greater the inductive reactance.

Of course, it is impossible to have a circuit without some resistance in it. Even heavy copper or silver bars have some resistance in them. But for theoretical purposes, we may assume such a circuit with inductance only. In such a circuit, the impedance will be equal to the inductive reactance.

We know that Ohm's law for alternating-current circuits is expressed by the following formulas:

$$I = \frac{E}{Z}, \qquad E = I \times Z, \qquad Z = \frac{E}{I},$$

where Z is the impedance.

Substituting inductive reactance for impedance, we get for a theoretical circuit with inductance only

$$I = \frac{E}{X_L}, \qquad E = I \times X_L, \qquad X_L = \frac{E}{I}.$$

Effect of Inductance on the Phase Relationship of Voltage and Current. We have seen that inductance is the property of a circuit which opposes a change of current. Since in an alternating-current circuit the current and voltage are continually changing, you can see that one of the effects of inductance is to cause a continuous opposition to the change in current. As a result of this opposition, the current changes are delayed in relation to the voltage changes during the cycle. We describe this phase relation of voltage and current in an inductive circuit by saying *the current changes lag behind the voltage changes.*

In a pure inductive circuit—that is, a circuit with no resistance, the current will lag 90° behind the applied voltage (Fig. 32-1). But since there always must be some resistance present, the current may approach but never reach a 90° lag.

Alternating-Current Circuits with Inductance and Resistance in Series. In an alternating-current circuit where resistance and inductance are connected in series, the impedance (Z) is equal to the combined effect of the resistance (R) and the inductive reactance (X_L). Since R and X_L are both given in ohms, you might suppose that, to get their combined effect in series, the two would merely be added. You would be wrong, however, because not only does inductive reactance oppose the flow of current, but it also causes the current to lag behind the voltage. Thus, the corresponding instantaneous values of voltage and current do not occur at the same time. It is for this reason that the effects of R and X_L cannot be added arithmetically. We have devised another method for calculating the impedance—that is, the combined effect of resistance and inductive reactance in series.

Draw a right triangle as in Figure 32-2. Let the horizontal side represent the value of R expressed in ohms, and let the vertical side of the triangle represent the value of X_L in ohms. Both lines are drawn to the same scale. The hypotenuse (the side opposite the right or 90° angle) then represents Z. To find Z, we square R (multiply $R \times R$) and X_L (multiply $X_L \times X_L$). We add these two squares together and then find the square root of the sum. This square root is the value of Z.

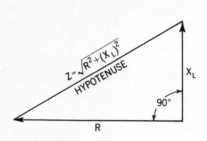

Fig. 32-2. *Diagram showing how to add resistance (R) and inductive reactance (X_L) in series.*

This computation is based upon the well-known formula for a right triangle: *The square of the hypotenuse equals the sum of the squares of the sides.* Using the right-triangle formula, let us work out a problem, based on Figure 32-2. Assume R to be equal to 8 ohms and X_L equal to 6 ohms. The square of 8 is 64 ($8 \times 8 = 64$), and the square of 6 is 36 ($6 \times 6 = 36$). Adding these two figures together, we obtain 100. The square root of 100 is 10 ($10 \times 10 = 100$). Thus, Z is equal to 10 ohms.

Mutual Inductance. Our discussion of inductance, inductive reactance, and impedance has been directed so far chiefly toward a single coil and the effect of changing magnetic fields·upon the current, the electromotive force, and the impedance of one coil. When an induced voltage in one circuit is the result of current changes in another circuit, the term *mutual inductance* is used to describe the relationship. The same unit, the *henry,* that is used for measuring self-inductance is also used for measuring mutual inductance. The symbol for mutual inductance is M. Like self-

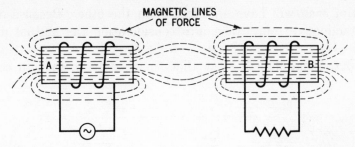

Fig. 32-3. *Diagram showing magnetic coupling between two inductors.*

inductance, the amount of mutual inductance depends solely upon
the physical components that go to make up the circuit. Owing
to the fact that mutual inductance represents the effect of one
circuit on another circuit, the two circuits are said to be *coupled*
together by mutual inductance. The presence of mutual inductance is sometimes indicated by the term *magnetic coupling,* for
it is the magnetic field of one circuit that induces a voltage in the
other circuit.

Magnetic Coupling. Mutual inductance is often employed to
transfer electrical energy from one circuit to another. If we have
an alternating current flowing in one inductor, a magnetic field
that expands and collapses in step with the alternating current is
created around that inductor. Assume that this field cuts across
the turns of another coil. Then an induced voltage is set up in
that coil.

If all the lines of force of that magnetic field cut across all
the turns of the second coil, we say we have *maximum coupling.*
Since this condition can never be obtained in practice, an expres-
sion to give the degree of coupling is used. Maximum coupling is
considered *100 per cent coupling,* or, as it is often called, *unity
coupling.*

If only half the lines of force cut all the turns or if all the
lines of force cut half the number of turns, the degree of coupling
is said to be 50 per cent. Only when the two coils are wound on the
same iron core does the coupling approach 100 per cent.

Inductance of Coupled Inductors. We have seen (page 373)
that the inductance of two inductors in series, whose fields are not
coupled, can be expressed by the formula,

$$L_{total} = L_1 + L_2$$

But when the coils are magnetically coupled, the magnetic

field of each will have an effect upon the other. Because of this interaction, we must take into consideration the mutual inductance (M).

Examination will show that there are two ways to connect

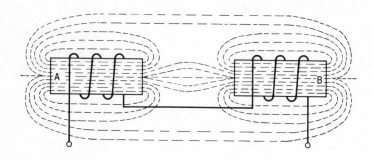

Fig. 32-4. *Inductors in series with their magnetic fields aiding each other. Note the windings are in the same direction on both coils.*

the inductors in series. Figure 32-4 shows them connected so that the two magnetic fields aid each other. Since the magnetic fields are helping each other, the formula for the total inductance becomes

$$L_{total} = L_1 + L_2 + 2M$$

From this formula, we can see that the effect of mutual inductance is to increase the total inductance.

The two inductors may also be connected in series in such a way that the magnetic fields oppose each other. Figure 32-5

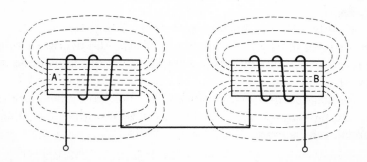

Fig. 32-5. *Inductors in series with their magnetic fields opposing each other.*

shows this circuit. Under such conditions, the formula for the total inductance becomes

$$L_{total} = L_1 + L_2 - 2M$$

Thus the effect of the mutual inductance is to decrease the total inductance.

A similar relation holds true for two inductors connected in parallel. If the magnetic fields aid each other, the formula for the total inductance becomes

$$L_{total} = \cfrac{1}{\cfrac{1}{L_1 + M} + \cfrac{1}{L_2 + M}}$$

Where the magnetic fields oppose each other, the formula becomes

$$L_{total} = \cfrac{1}{\cfrac{1}{L_1 - M} + \cfrac{1}{L_2 - M}}$$

The Transformer. We have stated that mutual inductance is often employed to transfer electrical energy from one circuit to another. One example of this practice is the antenna coupler described in Chapter 10, in which electrical energy flowing in the antenna-ground circuit is transferred to the tuning circuit. Other examples are the radio-frequency transformer employed in the tuned radio-frequency receiver, the intermediate-frequency transformer of the su-

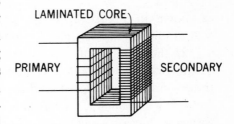

Fig. 32-6. *Diagram showing laminated core of a transformer.*

perheterodyne receiver, the audio-frequency transformer used to couple the audio-frequency amplifier stages, and the power transformer used in the B eliminator.

Transformers used for radio-frequency and intermediate-frequency work usually have air or special powdered-iron cores. Those used for audio-frequency work usually have iron cores. Transformers usually have two windings, a *primary* and a *secondary*. Alternating current (or fluctuating direct current, which as we have seen has an alternating-current component) is fed into the primary winding, and we get an alternating electromotive force induced in the secondary by mutual inductance.

The degree of coupling between the primary and secondary of a transformer wound with a core of air or other nonmagnetic substance is very low. Transformers wound on closed iron cores, such as shown in Figure 32-6, however, have a high degree of coupling, often approaching 100 per cent.

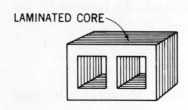

LAMINATED CORE

Fig. 32-7. *Another form of transformer core which permits closer coupling of the coils wound one over the other on the center arm.*

When the primary and secondary are wound on an iron core, the coils are well insulated from the core and from each other. There are several methods of constructing iron-core transformers. One method commonly used is to construct a core which consists of a large number of thin insulated strips or layers, called *laminations* (Fig. 32-6). Another method which gives a somewhat higher degree of coupling is to use a laminated core as shown in Figure 32-7. Here, the primary and secondary are wound one on top of the other on the center arm of the core.

If the number of turns of the secondary is greater than that of the primary, we get a greater number of turns cutting across the moving lines of force, and thus a greater induced electromotive force. We call such a transformer a *step-up* transformer. The ratio between the voltage of the primary (E_p) and the voltage of the secondary (E_s) is equal to the ration between the number of turns of the primary (T_p) and the number of turns of the secondary (T_s) at 100 per cent coupling. This relationship can be expressed as follows:

$$\frac{E_p}{E_s} = \frac{T_p}{T_s}$$

Thus, a step-up transformer with a greater number of secondary turns (T_s) will have induced in that secondary a greater voltage (E_s).

Let us try an example. A power transformer is required to deliver 330 volts alternating current across the secondary winding. Assume that the primary winding of 1,000 turns is connected across the 110-volt alternating-current line. How many turns must we have in the secondary winding?

Substituting our known values in the above formula, we get

$$\frac{110}{330} = \frac{1,000}{T_s}.$$

Cross-multiplying gives us

$$110 \times T_s = 1,000 \times 330 = 330,000.$$

Dividing both sides by 110, we get

$$T_s = 3,000 \text{ turns.}$$

A transformer may have its secondary winding with fewer turns than the primary winding. The voltage across the secondary will be less than that across the primary. We call such a transformer a *step-down* transformer.

Assume we wish to get 11 volts alternating current instead of 330 volts from the transformer described above. Now substitute our known values in our formula,

$$\frac{110}{11} = \frac{1,000}{T_s}.$$

Cross-multiplying and dividing by 110, we get

$$T_s = 100 \text{ turns.}$$

We call the ratio between the voltage across the primary and the voltage across the secondary the *voltage ratio* of the transformer. The ration between the number of turns in the primary and the number of turns in the secondary winding is known as the *turns ratio*. The voltage ratio is equal to the turns ratio.

Voltage and Current Relations in a Transformer. In step-up transformers, we obtain a larger voltage output than we put in— but we have to pay for it in terms of current. Theoretically, with 100 per cent coupling, there is no loss or gain of electrical power. The power in the secondary is equal to the power in the primary —practically there are some losses, but the transfer of energy from primary to secondary obeys the law that the power in each is equal to $E \times I$.

Thus, in the example of the step-up transformer previously described, assume we apply the voltage across the secondary (330 volts) to a load resistor of 110 ohms. Since $I = E/R$, the current flowing in the secondary circuit would be 3 amperes. The power consumed in this circuit ($P = E \times I$) would be 990 watts. Since we assume a perfect transformer, the power consumed by the primary circuit, too, is 990 watts. Thus, using the power formula, you can see that 9 amperes flows in the primary. Hence, although the voltage in the secondary is stepped up three times, the current flowing in the primary is three times that of the secondary.

Since the turn ratio between the primary (T_p) and secondary (T_s) is as one is to three $\left(\dfrac{T_p}{T_s} = \dfrac{1}{3}\right)$, and since the current in the secondary (I_s) is to the current in the primary (I_p) as one is to three $\left(\dfrac{I_s}{I_p} = \dfrac{1}{3}\right)$, by substitution we get $\dfrac{I_s}{I_p} = \dfrac{T_p}{T_s}$.

If, in the example just cited, the load resistor were made 330 ohms, only one ampere of current would flow in the secondary circuit. Thus, 330 watts would be consumed. This means that the primary circuit, too, would consume 330 watts, and 3 amperes of current would flow in that circuit.

Note that the three-to-one relationship still holds for the currents. Note, too, that it is the power consumption of the secondary circuit that determines the power consumption of the primary.

Power Losses in a Transformer. Losses in the transformer are of two kinds. There is a *copper loss* which is due to the resistance of the wire (I^2R). The other loss is an *iron loss*, due to the iron in the core.

The iron loss may be divided into two parts. Since the core is in the magnetic field, it is magnetized. But the alternating current causes the iron core to change the polarity of its poles in step with the frequency. A certain amount of energy is required to reverse the alignment of the molecules of the core. This energy comes from the electrical source and, therefore, is a loss. We call this the *hysteresis loss*. This loss may be partially overcome by using certain alloys of steel (such as an alloy of silicon and steel) that are easy to magnetize and demagnetize.

The other iron loss is due to the fact that an electric current is induced in the iron core by the changing magnetic field of the coils wound upon it. This induced current is called the *eddy current*. Since the eddy current must come from the electrical source, it, too, is a loss. We can reduce the loss due to eddy currents by making the core of the transformer from thin iron sheets, insulated from one another, instead of using a solid piece of iron. These thin sheets are called *laminations*.

SUMMARY

1. The *inductance* (L) of a conductor (usually a coil) is the property which tends to oppose any change in a current flowing in the conductor, regardless of the origin of this current.
2. Inductance is measured in *henrys*. One henry is the inductance possessed by a coil when one volt of electromotive force is induced by a current changing in the coil at the rate of one ampere per second.
3. *Inductive reactance* (X_L) is the name given to the opposition to an alternating current furnished by an inductor, above and beyond that of its resistance.
4. The total opposition in ohms of an inductor is called *impedance* (Z). This property is the combined resistance of the wire as a conductor (R) and of the inductive reactance (X_L).
5. In measuring currents and voltages in inductors, instantaneous values must be used because of the rapidly changing magnetic fields. Inductive reactance is found to be measurable in ohms by the formula $X_L = 2\pi f L$, which means that the inductive reactance in ohms is 2π times the frequency times the number of henrys of inductance.
6. The effect of the counter electromotive force due to self-inductance of a coil is to make the current *lag* 90° behind the voltage. This relationship may be shown graphically by sine waves and by vectors.
7. The combining of the wire resistance and the inductive reactance of a coil is achieved by using the right-triangle formula, that the square of the hypotenuse equals the sum of the squares of the sides. In formula form, it appears as

$$Z = \sqrt{R^2 + X_L^2}.$$

Impedance
$$= \sqrt{\text{resistance (squared)} + \text{inductive reactance (squared)}}.$$

8. *Mutual inductance* results from the interaction of the induced currents in two coils coupled magnetically.
9. The transfer of energy from primary to secondary in transformers conforms to the law of the conservation of energy. The product $E \times I$ in the primary is equal to $E \times I$ in the secondary. It follows that in step-up transformers, the current in the secondary will be smaller than in the primary; in step-down transformers, the current in the secondary will be greater than in the primary.
10. The *coupling* of two inductors magnetically is increased in proportion to the degree of cutting of the coils by the magnetic lines of force. This coupling is increased by the use of iron cores.

11. *Transformers* are devices for coupling two coils magnetically. Most transformers with iron cores use *laminated cores* to reduce the losses by eddy currents.

GLOSSARY

Copper Losses: Losses in a transformer due to heat dissipation resulting from ohmic resistance of the wires.

Counter (or Back) Electromotive Force: The voltage developed in a coil resulting from self-induction which is counter, or against, the impressed voltage.

Coupling: The transfer of energy from one circuit to another.

Coupling, Magnetic: Another name for mutual inductance.

Coupling, 100 Per Cent: The complete linkage of all the lines of force from one inductor with another.

Coupling, Unity: Another name for 100 per cent coupling.

Eddy Current Losses: Losses resulting from the inducing of useless currents in the core of a transformer.

Henry: The unit of inductance or mutual inductance.

Hysteresis Loss: The losses in a transformer due to the reluctance of the molecules of the core to turn around as the current through the coil reverses in direction.

Inductance: That property of a coil which makes it resist and oppose any current change through it.

Inductive Reactance: The opposition to alternating current offered by an inductor above and beyond that of its pure resistance.

Inductor: The name for a coiled conductor.

Iron Losses: The losses in a transformer resulting from hysteresis and eddy current losses in the magnetic core.

Mutual Inductance: The inductance developed by the magnetic linkage of the field of one coil with a second coil.

Self-Inductance: Same as inductance.

Voltage Ratio: The ratio between the voltage across the primary and the voltage across the secondary of a transformer.

QUESTIONS AND PROBLEMS

1. What effect does an alternating current have in passing through a coil? What is the effect called?
2. State Lenz's law as it applies to an alternating current through a coil.
3. Define what is meant by the inductance of a coil. In what units is it measured?
4. What are the subdivisions of the fundamental unit of inductance and what are their magnitudes?
5. What factors determine the amount of self-inductance of a coil?
6. State where inductors are used in radio receivers.
7. What is the total inductance of two inductors connected in series if there is no magnetic linkage?

8. What is the total inductance of inductors connected in parallel if there is no magnetic linkage?

9. Why is the impedance of a circuit with a coil greater than just the ohmic resistance alone of the wires making up the coil?

10. What is the significance of inductive reactance and in what unit is it measured?

11. Upon what two factors does the inductive reactance of a coil in a circuit depend?

12. How is inductive reactance calculated? Give the units of the factors used in your formula.

13. What is Ohm's law for a purely inductive circuit (that is, a coil assumed to have no ohmic resistance)?

14. What unusual phenomenon occurs between the phase relations of the impressed voltage and impressed current in an inductive circuit? How great will this effect be in an inductive circuit theoretically containing no ohmic resistance?

15. What is the effect of the introduction of ohmic resistance (R) in the circuit of the latter part of Question 14?

16. What is the method of computing the Z of a circuit containing X_L and R? Why must it be obtained in this way?

17. Under what circumstances will mutual inductance appear in a circuit containing two coils in series? How does it influence the total inductance of the circuit?

18. What is meant by unity coupling between two inductors?

19. What is the formula for the total inductance of two inductors connected in series with mutual inductance M in the series-aiding condition? In the series-opposing condition?

20. Answer Question 19 for two inductors in parallel.

21. Where in the radio receiver are transformers used? Describe the type of each example.

22. Describe the structure of a transformer. What may its input-voltage type be, and what type of voltage is its output?

23. What is the average degree of magnetic coupling in an efficiently constructed iron-core transformer?

24. What are eddy currents and how are they reduced in a transformer?

25. Upon what factors does the step-up or step-down condition of the voltages of a transformer depend? Represent this relationship mathematically.

26. What is meant by the voltage ratio of a transformer?

27. How is the current ratio of a transformer related to the voltage ratio? To the turns ratio?

28. What is the approximate condition of power dissipation in the primary and secondary circuits of a perfect transformer?

29. What are copper losses in transformers?

30. What is meant by hysteresis losses of a transformer?

31. What are the iron losses of a transformer?

33

Capacitance and Capacitive Reactance

The Capacitor. A capacitor, we have been told, consists of two conductors separated by a dielectric (insulator). The dielectric may be a vacuum, or air, or mica, or wax paper, or oil, or certain chemicals such as aluminum oxide, or, in fact, any material which will not permit electric current to flow through it readily.

Assume that we have a capacitor consisting of two metal

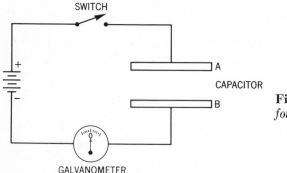

Fig. 33-1. *Capacitor ready for charging.*

plates separated by a vacuum. Now connect this capacitor in series with a battery, a switch, and an ammeter (Fig. 33-1). The ammeter is of a type which has the zero point in the center of the scale. Thus current flowing through it in one direction causes the pointer to deflect to the right, and current in the opposite direction deflects the pointer to the left.

Charging a Capacitor. Now close the switch. The positive pole of the battery, having a deficiency of electrons, pulls electrons off plate A of the capacitor, leaving a positive charge on that plate. The negative pole of the battery, having an excess of electrons, forces electrons to flow onto plate B of the capacitor, which receives, therefore, a negative charge. The meter shows this flow of electrons by the pointer's deflecting to the right, as seen in Figure 33-2.

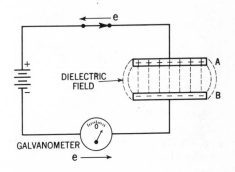

Fig. 33-2. *Capacitor being charged.*

The opposing charges on the plates of the capacitor set up a dielectric field or electrostatic field between them through the vacuum, as shown by the dotted lines. The electrical energy that flowed through the circuit is stored in this dielectric field, and current continues to flow until this field reaches the end of its ability to store electrical energy. When this limit is reached, the pointer of the ammeter drops back to zero, indicating that no more current is flowing, and we say that the capacitor is *charged.*

From Figure 33-2, you see that when the capacitor is charged, the electromotive force created by the dielectric field is exactly equal and opposite to the electromotive force of the

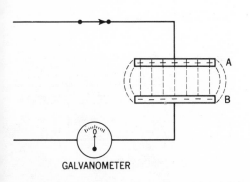

Fig. 33-3. *Capacitor fully charged. The battery has been removed.*

battery. Hence no current flows. Now remove the battery (Fig. 33-3).

Discharging the Capacitor. Since we have no closed circuit, no current flows even though the capacitor is still charged. If we now complete our circuit by connecting in a resistor in the place of the battery as in Figure 33-4, electrons stream from plate B where

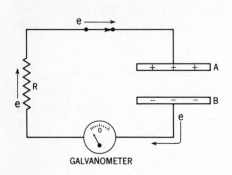

there is an excess of electrons, through the circuit and onto plate A, where a deficiency of electrons exists. We say that the capacitor is *discharging*. The pointer of the ammeter will indicate that the current is flowing in a direction opposite to that in which it flowed when the capacitor was being discharged.

GALVANOMETER

Fig. 33-4. *Capacitor discharging through resistor (R).*

Conditions Affecting the Storage of Energy by a Capacitor. The amount of electrical energy that the dielectric field of this capacitor can store depends upon three conditions.

1. The larger the area of the plates facing each other, the more the electrical energy that can be stored in the dielectric field.

2. The closer the plates are to each other, the more the electrical energy that can be stored in the dielectric field.

3. The nature of the dielectric makes a difference in the amount of energy that can be stored. This principle needs to be demonstrated.

An Experiment with the Dielectric. Suppose we connect the capacitor and the battery in the circuit again as in Figure 33-2. Now, while the capacitor is in this charged condition (Fig. 33-2), let us change the material of the dielectric by inserting a sheet of

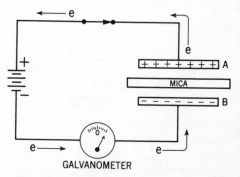

GALVANOMETER

Fig. 33-5. *The effect of placing a dielectric (such as mica) between the plates of a fully-charged capacitor.*

mica between the plates. The meter indicates that more current flows for a short time in the same direction as before (Fig. 33-5).

Apparently, more electrical energy has been stored in the dielectric field. Where did this increased capacitance come from, since the electromotive force of the battery remained constant?

For the answer, we have to go back to our electron theory. One explanation based on this theory is the following: Each atom of the sheet of mica consists of a nucleus around which are re-

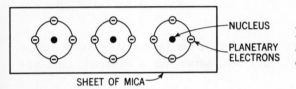

Fig. 33-6. *Normal arrangement of the atoms of a sheet of mica.*

volving the planetary electrons (Fig. 33-6). When the sheet of mica is placed in the dielectric field between the two plates, the planetary electrons of the atoms tend to move up the field toward the plate with a plus (+) charge. But since the electrons of the atoms of the elements in mica are not readily separated from their nuclei, it is supposed that these electrons rotate in distorted orbits around their nuclei, as shown in Figure 33-7.

This distortion of the orbits of these electrons changes the dielectric field within the various atoms of the mica, and tends to neutralize the field caused by the charge of the plates of the capacitor. Thus, the total dielectric field becomes the field created by the charge on the capacitor plates plus the dielectric fields around the atoms of the mica. As a result, the electromotive force created by the charged dielectric field causes more electrons to flow out of plate A and more onto plate B until the original balance is re-established. For these reasons, the ammeter showed that more current was flowing.

Another way to state what was just explained is to say that more electrical energy is stored in the distorted orbits of the electrons of the dielectric. So, in addition to the size and closeness of the plates of the capacitor, we have a third condition that determines the amount of electrical energy a capacitor can store— namely, the amount of energy that can be stored in the dielectric. This quantity is called the *dielectric constant* and depends upon the material used as a dielectric.

Fig. 33-7. *Distortion of the orbits of the planetary electrons of the atoms of the mica as a result of charging the capacitor plates.*

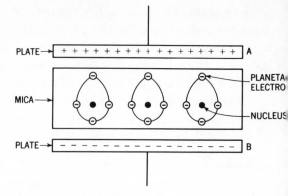

If the dielectric constant for air is taken as 1, mica has a constant of from 3 to 7, and wax paper has a dielectric constant of from 2 to 3.2.

The Variable Capacitor. Capacitors may be fixed or variable. The *variable capacitor,* as used to tune our simple crystal receiver (Fig. 8-3), may have plates of brass or aluminum. These plates may be rotated to vary the area of the plates facing one another, and the ability of the capacitor to store electrical energy is thus varied. Quite often, the plates are arranged in two sets of several plates each. The plates in each set are connected together. This gives the same effect as though we had a capacitor with larger plates, and thus we get a greater total effect. The stationary set of plates is called the *stator* and the rotary set the *rotor.* Air is usually the dielectric in variable capacitors.

Fixed Capacitors. A commonly used type of *fixed capacitor* is one with tin foil or brass plates and with thin sheets of mica for dielectric. A capacitor of this type is called a *mica capacitor.* See Fig. 6-2A. This type capacitor also is used as the grid capacitor in the triode detector circuit (Fig. 15-14). Such fixed capacitors usually are encased in bakelite or other insulating materials to protect them from moisture. To increase the capacitance, the plates are arranged in sets just as in the variable capacitor.

A fixed capacitor of greater capacitance can be made by placing a strip of waxed paper between two strips of tin foil about an inch wide and several feet long. As we know, the large area of the tin-foil plates will permit this capacitor to have a large capacitance. To save space, the whole is rolled up and encased in cardboard. This is called a *paper capacitor* (Fig. 6-2B). Such a capacitor may be used as a bypass capacitor (Fig. 23-12).

Electrolytic Capacitors. Another fixed capacitor commonly used in power supplies is the *electrolytic capacitor* (Fig. 18-16). In such a capacitor, a sheet of aluminum is kept immersed in a borax solution (called the *electrolyte*). An extremely thin coating of aluminum oxide and oxygen gas forms on the surface of the aluminum. If we consider the aluminum as one plate of the capacitor and the borax solution as the other, the coating of the aluminum oxide and oxygen gas, which will not conduct electricity, becomes the dielectric. The aluminum need not be a straight sheet but may be folded over many times or loosely rolled to give a greater effective area. Because the "plates" are separated by an extremely thin dielectric, the capacitance of such a capacitor is very high. Care must be taken, however, to connect the aluminum plate to the positive (+) side of the line; otherwise, the dielectric will be punctured and the capacitor destroyed. A variation of this type of electrolytic capacitor (called a *wet* type because of the solution) is the *dry* type. Although this capacitor is not strictly dry, it is so called because instead of the liquid electrolyte, a gauze saturated with borax solution is used. This *dry* electrolytic capacitor has a definite advantage in that the solution cannot spill.

Electrolytic capacitors are usually used where large capacitances are required, as in the case of the filter system of the B eliminator (Fig. 18-2).

The Breakdown Voltage of Capacitors. In addition to capacitance, another factor in the rating of capacitors is the *breakdown voltage*. If the electromotive force across the plates becomes great enough, an electron stream may be forced through the dielectric in the form of a spark. This spark burns a hole through the dielectric, and thus ruins its insulating property and destroys the capacitor. In the case of capacitors using paper, mica, or glass as dielectrics, this puncture is fatal to the capacitors. If air, borax solution, or oil is used as the dielectric, the breakdown heals itself when the electromotive force is removed. Care must be taken to operate the capacitor at a value which will not cause a breakdown. This value usually appears on the label on the capacitor.

The breakdown value depends upon the material of the dielectric and upon its thickness. The greater the thickness, the more electromotive force it can stand. But the greater the dielectric thickness, the smaller the capacitance. Capacitors with thicker dielectrics (greater breakdown value) must compensate for this condition by having a greater plate area if the capacitance is to be the same as that of a capacitor with a thin dielectric. Thus capacitors that can stand greater electromotive forces are usually bulkier.

How Do Capacitors Lose Energy? Losses of electrical energy in capacitors fall into three classes. First, there is the *resistance loss* resulting from the resistance of the plates of the capacitor and the wires leading to it. This loss is usually quite low, for the plates of the capacitor are large. The wire losses can be kept down by using heavy wire and good joints.

Then there is the *leakage loss*. No matter how good an insulator we have, some electrons are bound to leak through it. This loss can be reduced by choosing material for the dielectric which offers a high resistance to the flow of electrons. Mica is such a substance. Waxed paper is fairly efficient.

Finally, there are the *dielectric losses*. These fall into two groups. When alternating current is applied to a capacitor, the orbits of the electrons of the dielectric are constantly being distorted. The energy to perform this work must come from the electrical source, and thus represents a loss. We call this the *dielectric hysteresis loss*.

The other dielectric loss arises from the fact that some of the electrical energy remains in the dielectric after the capacitor has discharged. This residual loss is called the *dielectric absorption loss*. Certain substances, like mica, if used as dielectrics, will keep these dielectric losses low.

What Is Capacitance? From Figure 33-2, we can see that as we charge a capacitor, the dielectric field builds up a counter electromotive force which opposes the original electromotive force. The greater the electromotive force, the stronger the dielectric field and the greater the counter electromotive force. (We must take care, however, not to exceed the breakdown limit of the capacitor.) Thus, the capacitor acts to oppose any change in the voltage. This property of a circuit which opposes any change in voltage is known as *capacitance*. In direct-current circuits where the voltage is continuous and does not vary, capacitance, therefore, does not enter into their functioning. But in alternating-current circuits, the voltage is constantly changing, and here capacitance is just as important as inductance.

Measurement of Capacitance. The terms *capacity* and *capaci-*

tance are often used interchangeably, but *capacitance* is the preferred form. Let us study the measurement of capacitance.

The unit used to measure the capacitance of a circuit is the *farad* (f), named in honor of the English scientist Faraday. The farad can be defined as the amount of capacitance present in a capacitor when one coulomb of electrical energy (6.28×10^{18} electrons) is stored on the plates when one volt of electromotive force is applied. The symbol used for capacitance is C.

From this definition, we can see that

$$C \text{ (in farads)} = \frac{Q \text{ (in coulombs)}}{E \text{ (in volts)}}.$$

For practical use, the farad is too large a value to be conveniently handled. Accordingly, we use the microfarad (μf), which is one one-millionth of a farad, and the micromicrofarad ($\mu\mu$f), which is one one-millionth of a microfarad.* Thus, the value of the grid capacitor used in the triode detector is 0.00025 microfarad (μf), or 250 micromicrofarads ($\mu\mu$f). The capacitor used in the filter circuit of the B eliminator may have a capacitance of 8 microfarads (μf).

Calculation of the Capacitance of a Capacitor. We have seen that the capacitance of a capacitor is directly proportional to the total area of the plates that are exposed to the dielectric, inversely proportional to the thickness of the dielectric, and directly proportional to the dielectric constant.

Scientists have evolved the following formula to compute the capacitance of a capacitor:

$$C = \frac{0.0885 \times K \times S \times (N - 1)}{t}$$

where C is the capacitance in micromicrofarads ($\mu\mu$f), K is the dielectric constant, S is the area in square centimeters of one side of one plate, N is the total number of plates, and t is thickness of the dielectric in centimeters.

Let us try an example. Calculate the capacitance of a capacitor having two tin-foil plates each 2.5 cm wide and 250 cm long. The wax paper which separates these plates has a thickness of 0.25 cm and a dielectric constant of 2.

---

* Some manufacturers, in stamping parts, have abbreviated *micro-* by *m* rather than μ. This might cause confusion, since one mf is a millifarad, properly understood. Hence, we use μ for *micro-*.

Substituting our values in the above formula, we get

$$C = \frac{0.0885 \times 2 \times 625 \times 1}{0.25} = 442.5.$$

Thus, the capacitance of this capacitor is 442.5 micromicro-farads ($\mu\mu f$), or 0.0004425 microfarad (μf).

Capacitors in Series. When two or more capacitors are connected in series, the total capacitance is less than that of the smallest capacitor in the circuit. Figure 33-8 shows why. You can see that the effect of connecting two capacitors A and B in series, each with a dielectric thickness of d, is the equivalent of having one

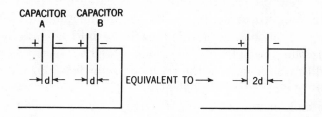

Fig. 33-8. *Diagram showing the effect of two capacitors in series.*

capacitor whose dielectric thickness is $2d$. The two center plates of the capacitors in series really do not add to the capacitance in any way, because the charges produced on them are electrically opposite and, therefore, neutralize each other. The effect, then, is the same as though the two inner plates were eliminated. Since the effect of connecting capacitors in series is to produce the equivalent of one capacitor with a thicker dielectric, the total capacitance is less than that of the smallest capacitor.

The formula by which we find the total capacitance of capacitors connected in series is

$$C_{total} = \frac{1}{\dfrac{1}{C_1} + \dfrac{1}{C_2} + \dfrac{1}{C_3} + \cdots \text{ and so forth}}$$

Since the effect of connecting capacitors in series is to produce the equivalent of one capacitor with a thicker dielectric, the breakdown voltage is increased. We must not assume, however, that connecting two capacitors, each with a breakdown voltage of 500 volts, will produce a capacitor with a breakdown voltage of

1,000 volts. We have seen that in the direct-current circuit, the voltage drop across resistors in series depends upon the resistance of each one. Likewise, the voltage across each capacitor depends upon its impedance. Should a 1,000-volt electromotive force be divided so that the voltage drop across one 500-volt capacitor is 300 volts and that across the other 500 volt capacitor is 700 volts, the latter will break down. The full 1,000 volts will then be applied to the second capacitor, which will also break down. Only if the voltage drop across each is equal to that across the other (that is, if the impedances of the two capacitors are equal), is it safe to put 1,000 volts across the two in series.

Capacitors in Parallel. Connecting several similar capacitors in parallel is the equivalent of having one capacitor whose plate area is equal to the total plate area and whose dielectric thickness is the equivalent of that of one of them. You may see why this is so from Figure 33-9. The area of plate No. 1 of capacitor A is added to the area of plate No. 1 of capacitor B. Similarly, the area of plate No. 2 of capacitor A is added to the area of plate No. 2 of capacitor B. The dielectric thickness has remained the same. Since the plate areas of capacitors A and B have been added and the dielectric thickness has remained the same, the capacitance

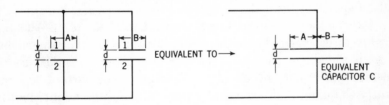

Fig. 33-9. *Diagram showing the effect of two capacitors in parallel.*

of the equivalent capacitor (C) is equal to the capacitance of A plus the capacitance of B. This can be expressed in the formula:

$$C_{total} = C_1 + C_2 + C_3 + \cdots \text{ and so forth}$$

The breakdown voltage of capacitors in parallel is that of the lowest breakdown voltage of any of them.

Direct Current Applied to Capacitors. A capacitor in series with a direct-current circuit will block the current, since in effect there is an insulator inserted in series with the circuit. But the moment the switch is closed, there will be a flow of electrons to one plate of the capacitor and from the other plate. Thus, in effect, there will be a flow of current in the direct-current circuit except through the dielectric (Fig. 33-2). This flow will continue until the counter electromotive force of the capacitor is equal to the electromotive force of the battery. This equilibrium comes about very quickly. Then the current flow ceases.

Also, we know that the effect of capacitance is to oppose any change in voltage. Thus, if our voltage is fluctuating, the capacitor tends to oppose the rise and fall of this voltage. The effect is, thus, to produce a steady electromotive force. Now we can understand the smoothing or leveling action of the capacitors in the filter circuit of the B eliminator (Fig. 18-2).

Another common use for capacitors in a direct-current circuit, although not related to radio, is to protect contact switches of ignition systems in automobiles. An ignition circuit has an inductance in series with a source of direct current. When the circuit is broken by the switch, inductance tends to keep the current flowing. This current manifests itself in the form of a hot spark across the contact points of the switch. In time, they may be burnt up. We connect a capacitor across these contact points; the electrical energy set flowing by the inductance goes to charge the capacitor, and no sparking results.

Capacitors in Alternating-Current Circuits. As in the case of the direct-current circuit, alternating current cannot flow through the dielectric of a capacitor connected in series. But in the alternating-current circuit, the voltage and current are constantly changing and periodically reversing. So just about the time the current has ceased flowing into the plates of the capacitor, an alternation or half cycle has been completed, and the current is ready to reverse anyway, so the electrons that have just entered one plate come back out and go through the external circuit and into the other plate of the capacitor. This process continues for each reversal of the alternating current.

Except for the dielectric, then, current is flowing in all parts of the circuit. Meters and lamp bulbs placed in the circuit will indicate this flow. It is common practice to say that alternating current will flow through a capacitor.

Capacitive Reactance. The effect of a capacitor is to build up a counter electromotive force which opposes the flow of current.

Thus capacitance, like inductance, increases the impedance of an alternating-current circuit. This factor which increases the impedance is called the *capacitive reactance*. Its symbol is X_C and its unit is the ohm.

The amount of capacitive reactance depends on the value of capacitance and the frequency. The formula for capacitive reactance is

$$X_C = \frac{1}{2\pi fC} = \frac{1}{6.28fC}$$

where X_C is the capacitive reactance in ohms, f is the frequency in cycles per second, C is the capacitance in farads, and 2π is the constant necessary to make the result come out in ohms. Since π is approximately equal to 3.14, $2\pi = 6.28$. Note here that the higher the frequency, the smaller the capacitive reactance.

If we were to have a circuit which had only capacitance, the impedance (Z) would be equal to the capacitive reactance (X_C). If we substitute X_C for Z in our Ohm's law for alternating-current circuits (see page 357), we get

$$I = \frac{E}{X_C}, \qquad E = I \times X_C, \qquad X_C = \frac{E}{I}$$

Effect of Capacitance on Phase Relationship of Voltages and Current. The effect of capacitance on the phase relation of voltage and current is opposite to that of inductance; *the voltage lags behind the current*. This lag is due to the counter electromotive force of the capacitor. Thus, the current reaches its peak before the voltage (Fig. 33-10).

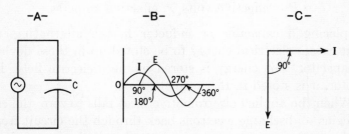

Fig. 33-10. *A—Circuit containing capacitance only.*
    B—Sine curves showing how voltage (E) lags 90° behind the current (I).
    C—Vector diagram showing the same thing.

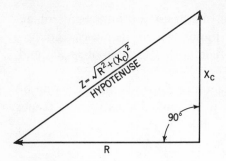

Fig. 33-11. *Diagram showing how to add resistance (R) and capacitive reactance (Xc) in series.*

As in the case of inductance, the maximum phase angle for capacitive circuits is 90°. Although this maximum can never be obtained in practice, it can be approached much more closely with capacitors than with inductors.

Alternating-Current Circuits with Capacitance and Resistance in Series. As in the case of the alternating-current circuit with inductance and resistance in series, when capacitance and resistance are in series, the impedance (Z) is equal to the combined effect of the resistance (R) and the capacitive reactance (Xc). Here, too, you do not simply add R and Xc, but you must add them by the right-triangle method (page 376).

Let R be one side of a right triangle and Xc the other. Then Z is equal to the hypotenuse. From this we get the following formula:

$$Z = \sqrt{R^2 + (X_c)^2}$$

Finding the Value of the Power Factor. We have seen that, in a direct-current circuit,

$$P \text{ (power)} = E \times I$$

We also know that in an alternating-current circuit containing nothing but resistance,

$$P = \text{effective volts} \times \text{effective amperes.}$$

But placing a capacitor or inductor in the alternating-current circuit causes electrical energy to be stored up in these devices. In the capacitor, this energy is stored in the dielectric field. In the inductor, it is stored in the magnetic field.

When the applied electromotive force falls to zero, the capacitor begins to discharge electrons back through the circuit from the negative to the positive plate. As the current falls to zero, the magnetic field around the inductor collapses, and a counter electromotive force is induced.

In both cases, electrical power is sent back into the source.

Thus, the true power is less than the apparent power. We may describe this condition by saying that:

True power = apparent power × power factor.

Let us go back to our right-triangle representation of Z in terms of R and X_C. In Figure 33-12, θ is the phase angle. It is the relationship between the resistance (R) and the impedance (Z) which causes the true power to be less than the apparent power. Thus the power factor is equal to R/Z. In the above triangle, R is the side adjacent to angle θ, and Z is the hypotenuse.

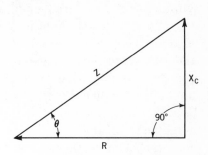

Fig. 33-12. *Diagram showing the calculation of the power factor.*

From trigonometry, we learn that the adjacent side divided by the hypotenuse is known as the *cosine* of the included angle θ (abbreviated to cos θ). Since R/Z is the power factor, our formula now becomes

True power = apparent power × cos θ.

The cosine of θ never exceeds 1.

The Effects of Radio Frequencies. In alternating-current circuits, the frequency of the electric current plays an important part. Household current has frequencies up to 60 cycles per second; audio frequencies go up to 15,000 cycles per second; radio frequencies may run as high as millions of cycles per second.

A study of the formulas indicates that the inductive reactance of a coil or the capacitive reactance of a capacitor varies greatly with variations of frequency. Thus, a coil which has a low inductive reactance at 60 cycles per second may have an inductive reactance 100 times as great at radio frequencies. A capacitor that offers little capacitive reactance at radio frequencies may offer a tremendous capacitive reactance at 60 cycles.

Even the resistance of a straight wire is affected by the frequency of the current flowing through it. It has been found that at high frequencies, the electrons traveling through a wire tend to travel near the surface, rather than the center, of the wire. The effect—namely, increased resistance—is as though we were using a thinner wire. This effect is called the *skin effect.*

The various losses which we have seen are present in the inductor and capacitor, such as the eddy current and hysteresis losses, also are increased as the frequency increases. This is the reason why inductors with laminated-iron cores are not usually employed for radio-frequency work.

We encounter another difficulty at radio frequencies. A straight wire, carrying* a current, has a magnetic field around it and, therefore, has a certain amount of inductance. At low frequencies, its inductive reactance is negligible, but as we approach the higher frequencies, this inductive reactance increases and must be taken into account. We then refer to the *distributed* or *stray* inductance of the wire. A radio set will often fail to function properly owing to the stray inductance of the wires connecting the various parts.

Likewise, two wires running close to each other form a capacitor. At low frequencies, the impedance offered by such a capacitor is very high, and a negligible amount of electrical energy is transferred from one wire to another. But at radio frequencies, the impedance becomes smaller, and appreciable quantities of electrical energy may thus be transferred to circuits where they do not belong. This effect is called the *distributed* or *stray* capacitance. You will recall that the internal capacitance of the triode, although too small to cause trouble at audio frequencies, is great enough to set up a feed-back in the radio-frequency amplifier (Chap. 23).

SUMMARY

1. *Capacitors* are devices for storing energy in the form of electrostatic charges.
2. *Capacitance* of a capacitor is determined by the area of the plates, distance between plates, and the nature of the dielectric.
3. Capacitor types include **fixed** (mica, paper, electrolytic) and **variable.**
4. Capacitors are rated for their **breakdown voltage,** or the ability to withstand high electromotive forces. This ability is determined by the nature and thickness of the dielectric.
5. The unit of measurement of capacitance is the **farad.** A farad is the amount of capacitance present when one coulomb of electrical energy is stored in a capacitor under the pressure of one volt.
6. When capacitors are connected *in series,* capacitance is less for the combination than the capacitance of the smallest capacitor.

7. Capacitors *in parallel* give a combined capacitance equal to the sum of the capacitances of the several capacitors.
8. In direct-current circuits, no current flows through a capacitor, but a momentary current develops until the electromotive force across the capacitor equals the applied electromotive force.
9. Strictly speaking, no current really goes through a capacitor in an alternating-current circuit, but since the current on both sides of the capacitor is constantly changing, there is at all times a current in all parts of such circuits except in the dielectric itself.
10. The effect of capacitance on phase relationship is to cause the voltage to lag 90° behind the current.

GLOSSARY

Breakdown Voltage: The voltage across a capacitor at which a spark will jump through the dielectric.

Capacitance: The property of a capacitor to store a charge and to oppose any voltage change across it.

Capacitve Reactance (X_C): The opposition to the passage of alternating current resulting from the holding-back-of-voltage effect of a capacitor.

Dielectric Absorption Loss: Loss of power in the dielectric of a capacitor due to the retention of some of the energy of atomic distortion by the dielectric after the capacitor has been discharged.

Dielectric Constant: A constant for an insulator telling the relative amount of energy that can be stored in it in the form of a distorted electronic orbit as compared with air.

Dielectric Field: The field of energy stored in the dielectric of a charged capacitor.

Dielectric Hysteresis Loss: Loss of power in the dielectric of a capacitor due to the reluctance of the atomic orbits to change their states of distortion.

Dielectric Losses: Power losses in the dielectric of a capacitor.

Electrolytic Capacitor: A capacitor with plates of aluminum and borax solution and a dielectric of aluminum oxide and oxygen.

Electrostatic Field: Same as the dielectric field.

Farad: The unit of capacitance of a capacitor.

Leakage Loss: Loss of power by electronic leakage through the dielectric of a capacitor.

Mica Capacitor: A capacitor with a mica insulator.

Micro-: 1/1,000,000.

Micromicro-: 1/1,000,000,000,000.

Paper Capacitor: A capacitor with a paper dielectric.

Skin Effect: The increase of resistance of a wire over its ohmic resistance with high frequency due to the tendency of current to travel only over the surface or skin of the wire.

Stray or Distributed Capacitance: The capacitance between the turns of wire of a coil, of importance when the coil is conducting a very high-frequency current.

Stray or Distributed Inductance: The inductance of a straight wire conducting very high-frequency currents.

QUESTIONS AND PROBLEMS

1. What is the basic structure of all capacitors?
2. State the electronic behavior during the charging of a capacitor with a battery.
3. What happens to the electrical energy flowing in a circuit as it charges up a capacitor?
4. What is the relation between the voltage across a charged capacitor and that of the charging battery?
5. Upon what three factors does the amount of energy that can be stored in a charged capacitor depend?
6. Explain what is meant by the dielectric constant of the dielectric of a capacitor.
7. What is meant by a variable capacitor? How is this variation accomplished?
8. What is a mica capacitor and where might it be used in receivers?
9. Describe the structure of a paper capacitor.
10. Describe the structure of an electrolytic capacitor. Account for its high capacitance.
11. What care is necessary in the use of an electrolytic capacitor?
12. A capacitor was ruined when too high a voltage was placed across its plates. Explain what happened internally.
13. Upon what factors does the breakdown voltage of a capacitor depend?
14. What are the three classes of losses in a capacitor?
15. How does a capacitor act to oppose any voltage change across it?
16. Explain the meaning of capacitance of a capacitor and give the units in which it is measured.
17. Relate the capacitance, quantity of charge, and charging voltage for any capacitor in a formula, and give the units of measurement for each.
18. Calculate the total capacitance of three capacitors in parallel, one being 100 μf, the other 10 μf, and the third 800 $\mu\mu$f.
19. Calculate the total capacitance of a 10-μf, a 20-μf, and a 40-μf capacitor connected in series.

20. What is the effect on breakdown voltage of connecting two capacitors of equal capacitance in series?
21. When will current flow from a battery into a capacitor cease?
22. Precisely what is meant when we say that alternating current is flowing through a capacitor in the circuit?
23. What is the name given to the opposition to flow of alternating current by a capacitor, and in what unit is it measured?
24. How does the change of frequency affect the reactance of a capacitor? How does increasing the capacitance of a capacitor affect its reactance when the frequency is kept constant?
25. State Ohm's law for a purely capacitive circuit supplied with an alternating current.
26. What effect does a capacitor in an alternating-current circuit have upon the phase relationship of the voltage and the current? What is the maximum phase difference angle?
27. Calculate the total holding-back effect of an alternating-current circuit containing a capacitor whose reactance is 4 ohms and a resistor of 3 ohms.
28. Why is the true power dissipation of a circuit containing a resistor and capacitor different from that of the apparent power? How is the former obtained from the latter?
29. What is meant by power factor? Give two ways in which it may be found.
30. What is the largest power factor possible? Account for this.
31. As the frequency of current is increased, what effects occur in the inductors and capacitors in the circuit?

34

Resonant Circuits and Tuning Principles

PROBLEM 1. *How is resonance shown by vectors?*

PROBLEM 2. *How is resonance usually brought about in a receiver?*

PROBLEM 3. *What are the characteristics of series and parallel resonant circuits?*

PROBLEM 4. *How do we calculate the values for the different factors in a tuning circuit?*

PROBLEM 5. *How are filters for various frequency ranges designed?*

Vector Representation of Resonance. We have already learned that the use of vectors furnishes us with a convenient means for picturing the relationship of currents and voltages in alternating-current circuits. Thus, if an alternating-current circuit has nothing but inductance in it, the vector diagram appears as in Figure 34-1.

We know that the length of the voltage or electromotive-force (E) vector is independent of the length of the current (I) vector, and that the length of each vector depends upon the scale selected for each. Thus, if we select a scale of, say, 100 volts per inch for the voltage vector, if this vector is one inch long, it represents 100 volts. If it is 2 inches long, it represents 200 volts.

At the same time, we may use a scale of, say, one ampere per inch for the current vector. Thus, if this vector is 2 inches long, it represents 2 amperes.

Thus, from Figure 34-1, we can tell the strength of voltage and current. We can also tell that the voltage leads the current in this circuit. The *angle of lead* (the *phase angle*) is 90° (since we always read vector diagrams in a counterclockwise direction).

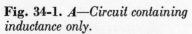

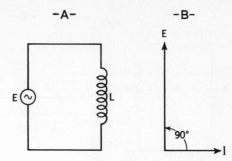

Fig. 34-1. *A—Circuit containing inductance only.*

B—Vector diagram showing current (I) lagging 90° behind voltage(E).

If the alternating-current circuit has nothing but capacitance in it, the vector diagram appears as in Figure 34-2. Here, you can see, the current leads the voltage. The phase angle is 90° once again.

Pure resistance (R), in an alternating-current circuit, has no effect on the phase relationship between current and voltage. Thus,

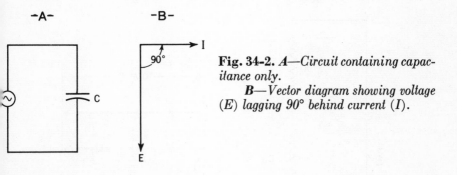

Fig. 34-2. *A—Circuit containing capacitance only.*

B—Vector diagram showing voltage (E) lagging 90° behind current (I).

if our circuit has nothing but resistance in it, the vector diagram shows us that the voltage and current are in phase (Fig. 34-3).

Another use of the vector diagram is to enable us to add voltages and currents in alternating-current circuits. If we have two resistors in series, it is a simple arithmetical problem to add the voltages across each of the resistors in order to calculate the total voltage supplied by the source (Fig. 34-4). Since the connection in this diagram is a series connection, the current (I) is the same throughout the whole circuit.

If, however, we have an inductor and a resistor in series, we cannot simply add the voltage across each to give us the total voltage. We must take into consideration the fact that inductance

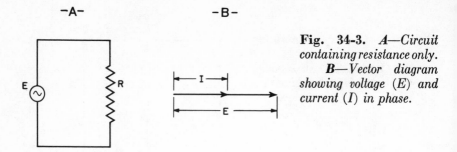

-A-   -B-

Fig. 34-3. *A—Circuit containing resistance only.*
B—Vector diagram showing voltage (E) and current (I) in phase.

affects the phase relationships. This situation appears in the vector diagram of Figure 34-5. Note that I and E_R are in phase, but that I and E_L are 90° out of phase.

To obtain the total voltage supplied by the source, we must make use of the parallelogram method described in Chapter 31.

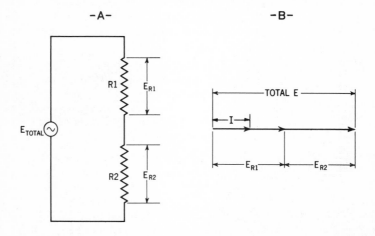

Fig. 34-4. *A—Circuit containing two resistors (R_1 and R_2) in series. The voltage drop across each (E_{R1} and E_{R2}), when added together, will give the total voltage (E) of the circuit.*
B—The vector diagram picturing the above.

Here, too, the current is the same throughout the whole circuit. The same procedure can be followed if capacitance and resistance appear in the circuit. The vector diagram appears in Figure 34-6.

Representing Tuned Circuits by Vectors. When capacitance and inductance both appear in a circuit, we call such a hookup a *tuned*

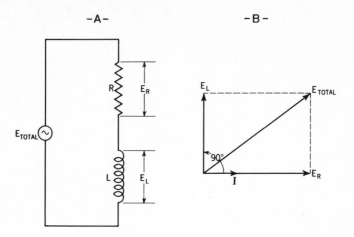

Fig. 34-5. *A—Circuit with resistance (R) and inductance (L) in series.*
B—Vector diagram showing how the voltage drop across the re-sistor (E_R) is added to the voltage drop across the inductor (E_L).

circuit. We have encountered such tuned circuits throughout our examination of the radio receiver.

We may use the same procedure as above to show the effect of capacitance and inductance in the tuned circuit. The diagrams in Figure 34-7 picture this.

Since the vector for the voltage across the inductor is 180° from the vector for the voltage across the capacitor, they are on the same straight line. Since they are in opposite directions, we may

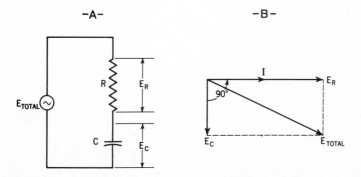

Fig. 34-6. *A—Circuit with resistance (R) and capacitance (C) in series.*
B—Vector diagram showing how the voltage drop across the re-sistor (E_R) is added to the voltage drop across the capacitor (E_C).

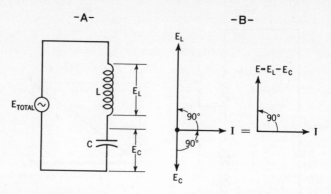

Fig. 34-7. *A—Circuit diagram with inductance (L) and capacitance (C) in series.*

          B—Vector diagrams showing E_L greater than E_C.

subtract one from the other to get the total voltage. We may assume, for example, a vector for E_L larger than that for E_C. The result then is as if we had nothing in the circuit but an inductor whose voltage vector is the difference between vector E_L and vector E_C. If E_C is made larger than E_L, the result is as if we had nothing but a capacitor in the circuit (Fig. 34-8).

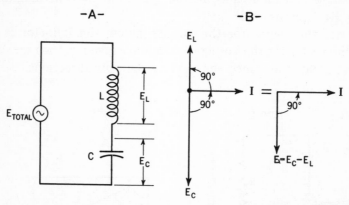

Fig. 34-8. *A—Circuit diagram with inductance (L) and capacitance (C) in series.*

          B—Vector diagrams showing E_C greater than E_L.

If E_L is equal to E_C, they cancel each other out, and the net result is zero. We now have

$$E_L = E_C, \qquad E_L - E_C = 0$$

From the formula $E = I \times X_L$, we may determine that the voltage across the inductor (called here E_L) is equal to the product of the current (I) and the inductive reactance (X_L). Thus, $E_L = I \times X_L$. Similarly, we may determine from the formula $E = I \times X_C$ that the voltage across the capacitor (E_C) is equal to $I \times X_C$.

Since $E_L = E_C$, then $I \times X_L = I \times X_C$. The inductor and capacitor are connected in series and, therefore, the current (I) flowing through them is the same. We may therefore cancel out I, and we get

$$X_L = X_C$$

Also, from the formula $E_L - E_C = 0$, we get $(I \times X_L) - (I \times X_C) = 0$. Dividing through by I,

$$X_L - X_C = \frac{0}{I} = 0$$

So when E_L is equal to E_C, the inductive reactance (X_L) is equal to the capacitive reactance (X_C). Like the voltages, the reactances act in opposition and, therefore, cancel each other out. The net reactance of the circuit is zero. We call this condition *resonance*.

Impedance at Resonance. Since this circuit contains merely an inductor and a capacitor, the impedance (Z) of the circuit is equal to the net reactance. Thus, Z becomes equal to zero. Since $I = E/Z$, at resonance $I = E/0$. Since any number divided by zero is equal to infinity, then $E/0$ is equal to infinity, and the current flowing through a circuit at resonance is infinitely great. Although this ideal does not exist in practice, the current at resonance may reach very large values.

The reason that the current is not equal to infinity at resonance is the presence of a certain amount of resistance in every circuit. Thus, when X_L and X_C cancel out, Z is not equal to zero but actually it is equal to the resistance found in the circuit, and the current, therefore, is limited.

Since the impedance Z is equal to the square root of the sum of the square of the resistance (R) plus the square of reactance (X), we can show this formula as follows:

$$Z = \sqrt{R^2 + X^2}$$

Thus, if the reactance is inductive, the formula becomes

$$Z = \sqrt{R^2 + (X_L)^2}$$

and if the reactance is capacitive, it becomes

$$Z = \sqrt{R^2 + (X_C)^2}$$

If, however, the reactance is due to inductance and capacitance in series, we see that these two reactances tend to oppose each other. Thus, the formula becomes

$$Z = \sqrt{R^2 + (X_L - X_C)^2}$$

Note that we subtract X_C from X_L because here we assume X_L to be the larger. If X_C is the larger, we subtract X_L from it.

At resonance, $X_L - X_C$ becomes zero. Our formula now is

$$Z = \sqrt{R^2 + 0}, \quad \text{or} \quad Z = R$$

This resistance is almost entirely found in the wire that goes to make up the coil or inductor. We can make this resistance very small by winding our coil with a few turns of heavy wire, but a small amount of resistance still remains. But for our theoretical discussion at this point, we assume that there is no resistance in the circuit.

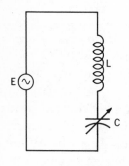

Assume that the circuit shown in Figure 34-9 is at resonance and the frequency of the generator is kept constant. Then $X_L = X_C$, $X_L - X_C = 0$, $Z = 0$, and the current (I) is very great. If we keep the inductance (L) constant and vary the capacitor (C) so that X_C becomes *larger* or *smaller*, the condition of resonance is destroyed. X_L no longer equals X_C. $X_L - X_C$ no longer equals

Fig. 34-9. *Use of a variable capacitor to vary the resonant frequency of the circuit.*

zero. Z likewise is no longer equal to zero, but quickly assumes sizeable proportions, and the current (I) is proportionally reduced. This can be shown by the graph in Figure 34-10. Note how quickly the current falls at a change in capacitance.

Tuning for Resonance. We can now understand what happens in our radio receiver as we turn the dial that controls the variable capacitor. We say that a certain radio station, say WOR, comes in at a certain "point on the capacitor." What we mean is that at this certain "point on the capacitor," the capacitance is such that, together with the inductance of a fixed coil or inductor, the tuning circuit is resonant to radio signals of a particular frequency—namely, the frequency of station WOR (710 kc). Current set flowing in the tuning circuit by WOR's radio wave will be at its maximum.

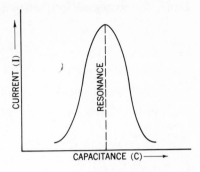

Turning the dial (and thereby changing the capacitance) throws the circuit out of resonance. The current quickly dies down, and we no longer hear that station. Of course, the

Fig. 34-10. *Graph showing the effect on the current (I) as the capacitance of the variable capacitor of Figure 34-9 is changed. The inductance and frequency are kept constant.*

same thing would occur if the capacitor were kept constant and the inductor varied. Although some radio receivers tune by means of changes in inductance, most sets use variable capacitors.

How Frequency Affects Resonance. In addition to being dependent upon the values of L and C, the condition of resonance also depends upon the frequency (f). We know that $X_L = 2\pi f L$, and

$$X_C = \frac{1}{2\pi f C}$$

(pages 374 and 397). If X_L equals X_C (at resonance), then

$$2\pi f L = \frac{1}{2\pi f C}$$

Multiplying both sides of this equation by f, we get

$$f^2 \times (2\pi L) = \frac{1}{2\pi C}$$

Dividing both sides by $2\pi L$, we get

$$f^2 = \frac{1}{(2\pi)^2 \times L \times C}$$

Taking the square root of both sides, we get

$$f = \frac{\sqrt{1}}{\sqrt{(2\pi)^2 \times L \times C}} = \frac{1}{2\pi \sqrt{L \times C}}$$

Thus, the resonant frequency (f_r) is

$$f_r = \frac{1}{2\pi \sqrt{L \times C}}$$

This condition holds at resonance only, and we can see that any change in the frequency will upset this condition.

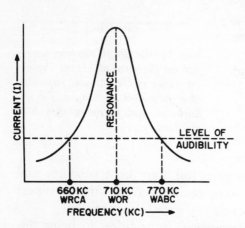

We can now plot frequency against current to show this relationship (Fig. 34-11). Thus, if our tuning circuit is resonant to a radio signal whose frequency is, say, 710 kc, signals at that frequency will set a large current flowing in the tuner. Signals whose frequencies fall below or above 710 kc will not be able to cause any appreciable currents to flow in the tuning circuit, and thus the signals will not be heard (Chap. 4).

Fig. 34-11. *Curve of a resonant circuit showing the relationship of current (I) to changes in frequency. The inductance and capacitance of the circuit are kept constant.*

Voltage Gain of a Resonant Circuit. There is another feature we should note about a resonant circuit. While the voltage drop across the complete circuit $(E_L - E_C)$ is equal to zero at resonance, the voltage drop across the inductor (E_L) and that across the capacitor (E_C) are not zero, but may be very large. It is only because they are equal and opposite at resonance that they cancel each other out. In fact, E_L and E_C may be many times as great as the voltage delivered by the source, since $E_C = I \times X_C$ and $E_L = I \times X_L$, and I may be very large owing to the condition of resonance. This feature makes it possible to obtain considerable voltage amplification of radio signals of that particular frequency to which the circuit is resonant. You can now understand why a stage of tuned radio-frequency amplification can give more voltage amplification than an untuned stage (Chap. 23).

Examination of the formula

$$f_r = \frac{1}{2\pi \sqrt{L \times C}}$$

shows us that for a given frequency, the factor $L \times C$ must be equal to a certain quantity if the circuit is to be resonant to that frequency. Thus, L may be large and C small or C large and L small, provided their product is the same (pages 28-30).

Calculating the Capacitance Needed for Resonance. Let us try a problem. Assume that the tuner in Chapter 6, consists of an inductor whose inductance is 300 microhenrys and a variable capacitor whose maximum capacitance is 0.00035 µf. To what value must we set our variable capacitor so that our circuit will receive the radio wave broadcast by station WOR (710 kc)? (In electrical language we mean, at what value of our capacitor will the tuning circuit be in *resonance* with a transmitting station whose frequency is 710 kc?)

From our formula, we see that at resonance

$$f_r = \frac{1}{2\pi \sqrt{L \times C}}$$

where f_r is in cycles per second, L is in henrys, and C is in farads. Thus, f_r is equal to 710 kc, or 710,000 cycles, and L is equal to 300 microhenrys or 0.0003 henry. Substituting these values, we get

$$710{,}000 = \frac{1}{6.28 \sqrt{0.0003 \times C}}$$

Multiplying both sides by 6.28, we get

$$710{,}000 \times 6.28 = \frac{1}{\sqrt{0.0003 \times C}}$$

or

$$4{,}458{,}800 = \frac{1}{\sqrt{0.0003} \times \sqrt{C}}$$

Since the $\sqrt{0.0003}$ is equal to 0.01732, then

$$4{,}458{,}800 = \frac{1}{0.01732 \sqrt{C}}$$

Multiplying both sides by 0.01732, we get

$$\frac{1}{\sqrt{C}} = 77,226$$

or

$$\sqrt{C} = \frac{1}{77,226} = 0.000,0129$$

Then $C = 0.000,000,000,166$ farad. This magnitude may be expressed more conveniently as 0.000,166 µf. This means, then, that our variable capacitor must be set so that its capacitance is 0.000,-166 µf to receive station WOR.

An Example to Show Voltage Amplification. It was stated that the tuned circuit at resonance may give us a certain amount of voltage amplification. Let us try another problem to see how this works out.

Figure 34-12 shows the circuit described in the above problem. You recognize the P and S coils as the primary and secondary, respectively, of the antenna coupler. Across the secondary is placed the input voltage, or electromotive force, induced in it from the

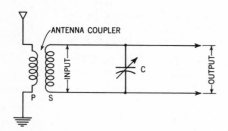

Fig. 34-12. *The tuning circuit of the radio receiver as a resonant circuit.*

primary by the current produced by the radio wave from a station such as WOR cutting across the antenna-ground system. The output of the tuner is the voltage developed across the capacitor (C) which places the electrical charges on the grid of the following tube. The ratio of output to input voltage—that is, the number of times the input voltage must be multiplied to become as great as the output voltage—is the amplification gain of the tuned circuit.

From the previous problem we know that the frequency (f) is 710,000 cycles per second, and the capacitance (C) of the capacitor for this station is 0.000,166 µf (0.000,000,000,166 farad). Let us further assume that the input voltage is 0.001 volt and that the resistance of the secondary is 10 ohms.

The impedance of the capacitor can be found from the following formula:

$$X_c = \frac{1}{2\pi \times f \times C}$$

where X_c is expressed is ohms, f in cycles per second, and C in farads.

Substituting our known values, we get

$$X_c = \frac{1}{6.28 \times 710,000 \times 0.000,000,000,166}$$

$$X_c = \frac{1}{0.00074} = 1,351 \text{ ohms.}$$

Since at resonance X_c and X_L drop out, the current flowing in the tuned circuit may be found by the following formula:

$$I = \frac{E}{R} = \frac{0.001 \text{ volt}}{10 \text{ ohms}} = 0.0001 \text{ ampere.}$$

The voltage across the capacitor (E_c) is equal to the product of the current (I) and the reactance of the capacitor (X_c). Thus,

$$E_c = I \times X_c = 0.0001 \text{ ampere} \times 1,351 \text{ ohms} = 0.1351 \text{ volt.}$$

But the voltage developed across the capacitor is the output voltage of the circuit. Thus, you see that we get a voltage amplification of 135 (that is, the voltage across the capacitor divided by the input voltage is $0.1351 \div 0.001 = 135$) from this circuit at resonance.

No Energy Is Created by Voltage Gains. The voltage gain of this circuit is no violation of the principle of the conservation of energy. Electrical energy is alternately exchanged between the inductor and the capacitor. The only power dissipated is that which is converted into heat by the resistance of the circuit. This loss is the only power which the primary is called upon to supply.

If electrical energy is drawn from the tuner, for example, to supply the crystal detector and phones, the voltage across the secondary output will drop to a value consistent with the available input power.

Series Resonant Circuits. We may picture our resonant circuit very simply as in Figure 34-13. Here the inductor, the resistance of the inductor, and the capacitor are pictured as being in series with the electrical source. We call such a circuit a *series resonant circuit*.

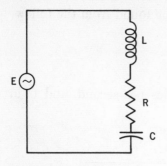

Fig. 34-13. *The series resonant circuit showing inductance, capacitance, and resistance in series.*

Let us list some of the things we know about this circuit. At resonance, X_L is equal and opposite to X_C. These two reactances cancel each other out. The opposition to the flow of current, or impedance (Z), then becomes equal to the resistance (R). If R is small, the current (I) flowing through the circuit becomes quite great. *Thus, the characteristic effect of a series resonant circuit is to permit to flow through the circuit a large amount of current whose frequency is in resonance with that of the resonant circuit.*

Since the source of electrical energy, here the alternating-current generator, is in series with the circuit, its impedance will help cut down the amount of current in the circuit. It becomes necessary, therefore, to keep the impedance of the source as low as possible.

How Resistance Reduces Selectivity. In Chapter 10 it was stated that the effect of resistance in the tuner is to reduce the selectivity of the receiving set. Let us see if we can explain how this happens.

We know that at resonance X_L and X_C are equal and opposite, and that Z is equal to R. Assume that the value of R is small, and

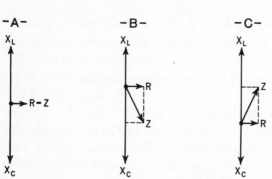

Fig. 34-14. *Vector diagrams showing effect of frequency changes on a resonant circuit when the resistance (R) is small.*

A—Resonance.

B—Frequency reduced. Slightly off resonance.

C—Frequency increased. Slightly off resonance.

let us draw a vector diagram to picture this condition (Fig. 34-14-A).

Figure 34-14-B shows what happens as the frequency is reduced. X_C becomes larger and X_L smaller. The circuit is now some-

Fig. 34-15. *Vector diagrams showing the effect of frequency changes on a resonant circuit when the resistance (R) is large.*
A—Resonance.
B—Frequency reduced. Slightly off resonance.
C—Frequency increased. Slightly off resonance.

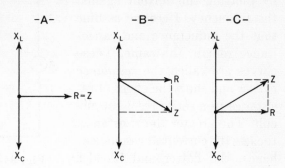

what off resonance. The impedance (Z) is increased and, therefore, the current flowing through the circuit is reduced.

Figure 34-14-C shows what happens as the frequency is increased. X_C becomes smaller and X_L larger. The circuit is somewhat off resonance, and the current flowing through the circuit is reduced again.

Now let us see what happens if the resistance is large. Figure 34-15-A shows the condition of resonance. Note that Z is larger than it appears in Figure 34-14-A.

Figures 34-15-B and C show the vector diagram for the circuit made slightly off resonance by reducing the frequency in Figure B and increasing the frequency in Figure C. In both cases, Z appears larger than the Z at resonance.

But note this. In Figure 34-14, when the circuit was off resonance, the impedance became *much* larger than was the impedance at resonance. In Figure 34-15, the impedance, when the circuit was off resonance, became only *slightly* larger than was the impedance at resonance.

Thus, the *difference* between the amounts of current flowing through the circuit in the resonant and off-resonant conditions is much greater when the resistance in the circuit is small than when it is large.

We can now show this relationship in a graph (Fig. 34-16)

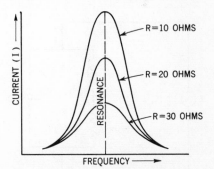

Fig. 34-16. *Resonance curves showing changes produced by changes in resistance (R). Inductance and capacitance are kept constant.*

by plotting the current against the frequency. Here we assume that the inductance and capacitance remain the same. These curves are called the *resonance curves* and show the effect of resistance in a series resonant circuit. The greater the resistance, the less the current at resonance; hence, the flatter and broader the curve. Compare these curves with the tuning curves of Figures 10-1 and 10-2.

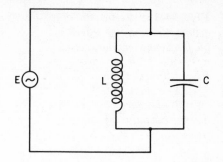

Fig. 34-17. *The parallel resonant circuit with inductance (L) and capacitance (C) in parallel.*

Parallel Resonant Circuits. In addition to the series form, the resonant circuit may assume a parallel form. This is shown in Figure 34-17. We call this a *parallel resonant circuit.* In a series circuit, the current is uniform, and the voltages across the circuit elements are added vectorially to yield the total potential drop across the circuit. In a parallel circuit, however, the voltage across each branch is the same, and the separate branch currents are added to yield the total current through the circuit.

The current flowing from the alternating-current generator in Figure 34-17 divides when it comes to the junction of the two branches of the circuit. Part of the current flows through the inductive branch and part through the capacitive branch. The amount of current that will flow through each branch depends upon the impedance of each. The greater proportion of the current will flow through the branch offering the smaller impedance.

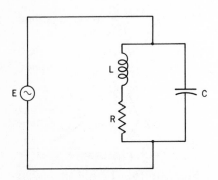

Fig. 34-18. *The parallel resonant circuit. The resistance is usually found in the inductive branch of the circuit.*

At low frequency, the inductive reactance of L is low, the capacitive reactance of C is high, and more current tends to flow in the inductive branch. At high frequencies, the reverse is true, and more current tends to flow in the capacitive branch.

At a certain frequency (resonance), the inductive reactance is equal to the capacitive reactance. The current flowing in each branch is then the same.

But inductance causes the current to lag 90° behind the voltage, whereas capacitance causes it to lead the voltage by 90°. Thus, the currents flowing in each branch are 180° apart (90° + 90°). This is the same as saying that they are flowing in opposite directions. Since at resonance the currents are thus equal and opposite, they tend to cancel out, and the net result for the complete parallel resonant circuit is that there is *no flow of current from the generator*. We may say that the effect of a parallel resonant circuit is the same as an infinitely great resistance placed in series with the source of electrical energy. *Thus, the characteristic effect of a parallel resonant circuit is to offer a tremendous resistance to a current whose frequency is in resonance with that of the resonant circuit.*

As in the case of the series resonant circuit, the presence of a small amount of resistance in the circuit causes us to modify our theoretical results. This resistance is almost completely due to the resistance of the wire which goes to make up the inductor. Our circuit for parallel resonance becomes that shown in Figure 34-18. At resonance, the impedance of the *L* branch of the circuit is slightly greater than that of the *C* branch, and although the net result is equivalent to a very large resistance in series with the source, it is not an infinitely great resistance, and a certain small amount of current does actually flow through the circuit.

At resonance, then, the impedance of the parallel resonant circuit becomes very great. As we vary our frequency to a smaller or larger value than the resonant frequency, the impedance of the circuit quickly drops, and more and more current flows. We can picture this by plotting *impedance* against *frequency*. The result (Fig. 34-19) is similar to the resonance curve for the series resonant circuit that we obtained when we plotted *current* against *frequency* (Fig. 34-11).

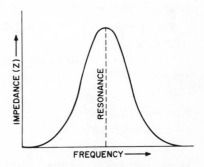

Fig. 34-19. *Resonance curve for the parallel resonant circuit with impedance (Z) plotted against the frequency (f). C and L are kept constant.*

We have seen that the presence of resistance in the inductive branch of the resonant circuit upset the balance and permitted current from the generator to flow in the circuit. The greater this resistance, the more current flows in the circuit. The result of resistance, then, is to flatten and broaden the resonance curve shown in Figure 34-19.

In the parallel resonant circuit, except for the presence of resistance as noted above, the currents flowing through the branches of the circuit are equal and opposite. Thus, we may state that

$$I_L = I_C, \qquad I_L - I_C = 0$$

From this relation we may see that, although the net result is that no current flows from the generator, the current flowing from the inductor to the capacitor (I_L) and back again (I_C) may be quite large.

When we discussed the series resonant circuit, we stated that at resonance, the current flow is at its maximum. But in the case of the parallel resonant circuit, we saw that the current flow from the generator at resonance is at its minimum. For this reason, we often call the parallel resonant circuit the *antiresonant circuit.*

It has been found that the maximum transfer of power occurs when the impedance of the load (the circuit) matches the impedance of the source (the generator) (pages 512-514). Thus, since the impedance of the series resonant circuit is very small, we should keep the impedance of the generator small, too. The impedance of the parallel resonant circuit, however, is very high. It is important, therefore, that the impedance of the source be likewise kept high.

The Q of a Resonant Circuit. Examination of the resonance curves in Figure 34-16 shows us that the less resistance we have in the circuit, the sharper the curve. This statement means that the difference in current strength at the resonant frequency and current strength at a frequency slightly off resonance is very marked. Another way of saying the same thing is that the *selectivity* is good. The selectivity is, thus, determined by the amount of resistance in the circuit. The less the resistance, the better the selectivity.

The resistance in a resonant circuit is almost exclusively lodged in the coil. This resistance (R) is the effective alternating-current resistance and includes the resistance of the wire, the loss

due to distributed capacitance, and the loss due to the skin effect
of alternating current. In a well-designed coil, R is due almost
entirely to skin effect. The less the resistance of a coil, the better
it is.

This "goodness" or merit of the coil may be expressed by the
ratio between the inductive reactance (X_L) and the resistance (R).
The symbol for this ratio is the capital letter Q. It is helpful to
associate Q with quality.

$$Q = \frac{X_L}{R}$$

Since X_L is equal to $2\pi f L$, then

$$Q = \frac{2\pi f L}{R}$$

The loss in a coil due to distributed capacitance and to the skin
effect is roughly proportionate to the frequency. The inductive
reactance (X_L) is directly proportionate to the frequency. For
these reasons, the Q of a coil remains fairly constant over a wide

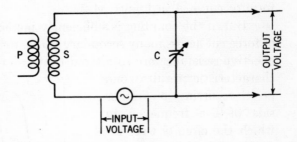

Fig. 34-20. *Series resonant circuit to show the
amplification gain of a
tuned circuit.*

range of frequencies. Typical radio inductors have Q's of the order
of 100 to 800, depending upon the nature of the service for which
they are designed. The Q is sometimes called the *figure of merit*.

At resonance in a parallel tuned circuit, the net resistance
(R_0) is Q times the reactance of either one of the branches. Thus,

$$R_0 = X_C \times Q = X_L \times Q$$

The current through either the inductor or capacitor at resonance
is Q times the net line current. In series resonant circuits, the
voltage across either the inductor or capacitor is equal to Q times
the net voltage across the complete circuit.

If we consider the secondary circuit of Figure 34-12 a series resonant circuit as shown in Figure 34-20, we see that Q times the net voltage across the complete circuit (the input voltage) is equal to the voltage across the capacitor (the output voltage). From this we may infer that Q is equal to the amplification gain of the tuned circuit.

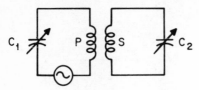

Fig. 34-21. *One method of coupling one tuned circuit to another.*

Coupled Circuits. In radio work, one tuned circuit is often coupled to another, as in Figure 34-21. The over-all frequency characteristic—that is, the relationship between frequency and current flowing in the secondary for a given voltage across the primary—can be shown by a graph like that in Figure 34-11. If each circuit is independently tuned to the same frequency and then the circuits are *loosely* coupled—that is, if all the lines of force around the primary coil cut across a few of the secondary turns, or if a small percentage of the lines of force cut across all the secondary turns—the over-all frequency characteristic assumes the form of curve A in Figure 34-22.

But, if the coupling is sufficiently increased so that many lines of force cut across many secondary turns, the over-all reactance and effective resistance are so altered that a double-humped frequency characteristic results, one peak occurring on either side of the frequency to which the circuits were individually tuned (Fig. 34-22, curve B).

We call this condition *tight* coupling. One method of achieving it is to wind the secondary coil directly over the primary. You will readily see why such a curve is usually not desired for radio tuning: two frequencies (that is, two radio stations) would come in

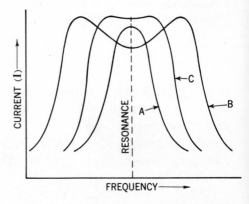

Fig. 34-22. *Resonant curves showing the effect of coupling.*
A—Loosely coupled.
B—Tightly coupled.
C—Compromise between A and B.

with equal strength for any one setting of the variable capacitor.

In practice, a compromise is often struck between very loose and very tight coupling to permit nearly uniform energy transfer over a particular restricted range of frequencies (Fig. 34-22, curve *C*). You can now see how we eliminated sideband cutting in the superheterodyne receiver (Chap. 26, Fig. 26-11).

As shown in Figure 34-16, resistance in any circuit also tends to flatten out the curve that shows the frequency char-

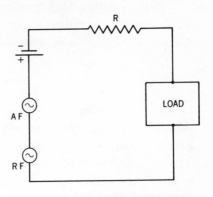

Fig. 34-23. *A battery, a low-frequency (AF) generator, and a high-frequency (RF) generator supplying current to a load through a resistor (R).*

acteristic, and thus tends to reduce the selectivity of our circuit. However, note that in coupling we can broaden the curve without greatly reducing the current value.

Action of Filters. Electrically, *filters* are used to separate currents of certain frequencies from those of other frequencies. For our discussion here, we may consider direct current as having a zero frequency.

Assume that you have as an electrical source a battery supplying direct current (zero frequency), a generator of alternating current of audio frequency (low frequency), and a generator of radio-frequency current (high frequency). Assume that they are all connected in series and supply current to a load through a resistor connected in series (Fig. 34-23). Let us neglect the impedance of the source.

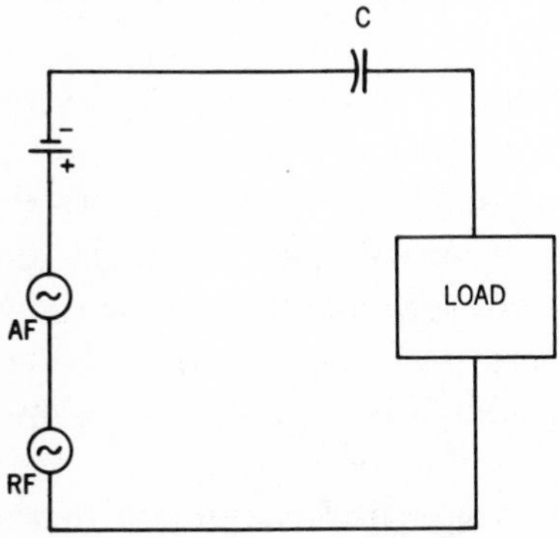

The resistor will not have any filtering action, because it impedes equally all currents that pass through it, regardless of frequency.

Fig. 34-24. *The resistor of Figure 34-23 has been replaced by a capacitor (C).*

Now, assume that you replace the resistor with a capacitor (Fig. 34-24). The direct current will be filtered out because the capacitor offers infinite impedance to its passage. Since

$$X_C = \frac{1}{2\pi f C}$$

at low frequencies the capacitor offers a definite impedance to the flow of current. Thus, it will impede the passage of audio-frequency current considerably. The impedance to the radio-frequency current, however, will be very small, since when f reaches a large size, the value of the fraction becomes very small.

If now an inductor replaces the capacitor (Fig. 34-25), the direct current will be only slightly impeded, owing to the small resistance of the coil. Since $X_L = 2\pi f L$, the impedance to the audio frequency will be considerably more than that to the direct current. But the impedance to the radio frequency may be so

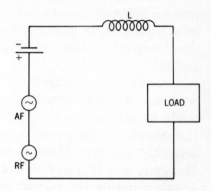

Fig. 34-25. *The current is now being fed to the load through an inductor (L).*

great that most of the radio-frequency current will be held back. We now can understand the action of the radio-frequency choke coil in Figure 23-13, where the radio-frequency currents are held back from the audio-frequency amplifier.

Low-Pass Filter. Now let us connect the capacitor across the load (Fig. 34-26). None of the direct current will flow through the capacitor. Since the capacitor offers a fairly high impedance to the audio-frequency current, very little of it will pass through, and most of it will flow into the load. Radio-frequency current, however, will find that the capacitor offers it an easy path, and very little will flow through the load. We call this arrangement a *low-pass* filter since it passes the low frequencies on to the load. Another example of the use of a low-pass filter is shown in the tone control pictured in Figure 25-1. Stray radio-frequency current is bypassed to the ground through the capacitor in Figure 23-13, by means of this filter system.

High-Pass Filter. In Figure 34-27, we have replaced the capacitor across the load by an inductor. Now the direct current and the audio-frequency current will pass through the inductor, very little going to the load. The radio-frequency current, however, will find that L offers a very high impedance to its passage, and most of the current will flow through the load. We call this arrangement a *high-pass filter*. In Figure 25-3 arm B of the tone control is an example of such a filter.

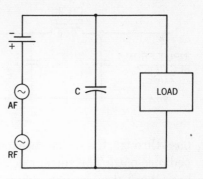

Fig. 34-26. *The capacitor (C) is now in parallel with the load and acts as a low-pass filter—that is, the low-frequency currents can pass to the load.*

Power-Supply Filters. Let us see how these principles apply to the filter system of our power supply (Chap. 18). This consists of a choke coil and two capacitors connected as in Figure 34-28. In this circuit, the inductor and capacitors are very large, the choke coil being 30 henrys and the capacitors 8 μf each. You will also remember that the current flowing into the filter system is a full-wave pulsating direct current delivered by a full-wave rectifier from the 60-cycle alternating-current line. This pulsating direct current may be resolved into its two components, a direct current and a 120-cycle alternating current (Fig. 34-29).

As this pulsating direct current enters the filter system, the direct-current component flows through, impeded only by the resistance of the choke coil. The alternating-current component, although at a fairly low frequency, finds the impedance of the 30-henry choke quite high. Most of the alternating current, therefore, is blocked and must

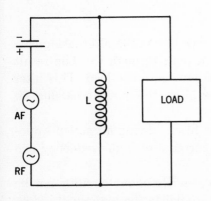

Fig. 34-27. *The inductor (L) is now in parallel with the load and acts as a high-pass filter—that is, the high-frequency currents can pass to the load.*

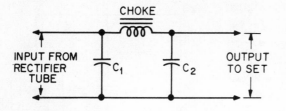

CHOKE

INPUT FROM
RECTIFIER C_1 C_2 OUTPUT
TUBE   TO SET

Fig. 34-28. *The filter circuit of the power supply.*

pass through C_1, which, because of its large value, offers a low-impedance path. The current flowing through the choke coil, therefore, has almost the complete direct-current component and very little of the alternating-current component (Fig. 34-30).

Fig. 34-29. *Waveform diagram showing the pulsating direct current from the full-wave rectifier tube broken down into its two components, a steady direct current which goes to the radio set and a 120-cycle alternating current which is filtered out.*

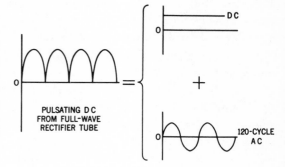

PULSATING D C
FROM FULL-WAVE
RECTIFIER TUBE

DC

+

120-CYCLE
A C

The impedance of the load further blocks the alternating-current component, which again finds a path through C_2. The result is that only a steady direct current flows into the load. This filter system is an example of a low-pass filter, the current passing, in this case, having zero frequency.

Figure 34-31 shows a high-pass filter, having an action opposite to that described above: only currents of high frequency can pass through.

Filter Action of Resonant Circuits. Resonant circuits can be made to serve as filters in a manner similar to the individual inductors and capacitors discussed above. The series resonant circuit offers a very low impedance to currents of the particular frequency to which it is tuned and a relatively high impedance to currents of other frequencies.

The parallel resonant circuit, on the other hand, offers a very high impedance to currents of the particular frequency to which it is tuned and a relatively low impedance to currents of other frequencies.

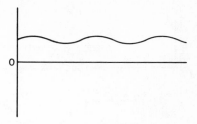

Fig. 34-30. *Waveform of the pulsating direct current after it passes through half of the filter section. The second half of the filter irons out this slight ripple.*

Assume that the resonant circuits in Figure 34-32 are tuned to the same frequency, say, that of WOR (710 kc). Currents of all frequencies flow into the filter network from the antenna. As they approach parallel resonant circuit No. 1, current whose frequency is 710 kc finds that this circuit offers it a very high impedance. Very little of this current flows through the parallel resonant circuit and most of it flows on to the series resonant circuit. Currents of other frequencies, however, find parallel resonant circuit No. 1 an easy path, and most of these currents flow to the ground.

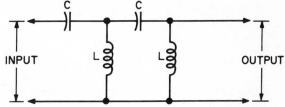

Fig. 34-31. *Circuit of a high-pass filter.*

The Band-Pass Filter. The series resonant circuit offers a low-impedance path to current whose frequency is 710 kc. Currents of other frequencies, however, are stopped and forced to flow back to the ground through parallel resonant circuit No. 1.

The current that passes through the series resonant circuit is predominantly of the 710-kc frequency, along with a very small amount of some nearby frequency.

Once again the parallel resonant circuit, now circuit No. 2, offers a high impedance to the 710-kc current and forces it to flow on to the set. The stray currents whose frequencies are not 710 kc find this circuit an easy path to the ground. The net result is that only currents whose frequency is 710 kc will find their way to the set. We call this complete circuit a *band-pass filter*.

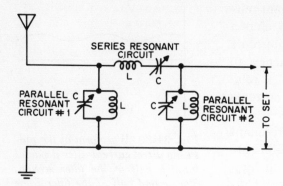

Fig. 34-32. *Diagram showing how series and parallel resonant circuits are used to allow signals of only one band of frequencies to pass. The band-pass filter.*

The Band-Elimination Filter. The situation shown in Figure 34-33 is the exact opposite of the one we have just considered. If all three resonant circuits are tuned to, say, 710 kc, any current whose frequency is 710 kc is stopped from passing through and will be forced to flow to the ground. Currents of all other frequencies will pass through to the set.

We call this a *band-elimination* or *band-stop filter.* It is used under conditions where it is desired to keep a powerful station, such as WOR, from interfering with reception of other stations.

Fig. 34-33. *Diagram showing how series and parallel resonant circuits are used to stop signals of one band of frequencies from passing. The band-stop filter.*

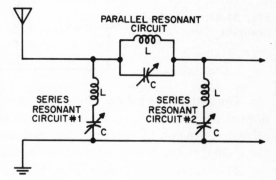

SUMMARY

1. **Capacitors** and **inductors** may be connected together to form a circuit that is resonant to a definite frequency.
2. At resonance, the voltage drop across the capacitor (E_C) is equal and opposite to the voltage drop across the inductor (E_L). Thus, $E_C = E_L$ and $E_C - E_L = 0$, for a series resonant circuit.

3. From the above, we can see that the *capacitive reactance* (X_C), at resonance, is equal to the *inductive reactance* (X_L) and that $X_C - X_L = 0$.
4. The *series resonant circuit* offers very little impedance to currents of the resonant frequency.
5. The *parallel resonant circuit* offers very high impedance to currents of the resonant frequency.
6. Selectivity in a receiver is improved by (a) reducing the resistance (R) of the tuning circuit and (b) by loose coupling between the primary and secondary of the antenna coupler.
7. The *figure of merit* of an inductor is expressed by the letter Q, which is the ratio between the inductive reactance (X_L) and the resistance (R) of the coil. Thus, $Q = X_L/R$.
8. Some of the principles operative in filter systems are (a) resistors impede equally the flow of direct and alternating currents, regardless of frequency, (b) capacitors block the flow of direct current completely. The impedance of a capacitor is greater for low-frequency (af) than for high-frequency (rf) currents, and (c) the impedance offered by inductors to high-frequency currents is greater than to low-frequency currents.

GLOSSARY

Antiresonant Circuit: A parallel resonant circuit.
Filter: A circuit containing inductors and capacitors used to separate currents of different frequencies.
Loose Coupling: Coupling between coils in which few lines of force from the primary cut across the secondary.
Parallel Resonant Circuit: A resonant circuit in which the generator is in parallel with a coil and with a capacitor.
Resonance: That condition of a circuit containing inductance, capacitance, and resistance in which $X_L = X_C$ and the total reactance is zero.
Series Resonant Circuit: A resonant circuit in which a generator, a capacitor, a coil, and a resistor are all in series.
Tight Coupling: Coupling between coils in which many lines of force from the primary cut across the secondary.
Tuned Circuit: A circuit containing a capacitor, a coil, and a resistor in series.

QUESTIONS AND PROBLEMS

1. State the effect on the current-voltage phase angle of a purely inductive circuit, a purely capacitive circuit, and a purely resistive circuit. Show this vectorially.

2. Show how the impedance is determined vectorially in a circuit containing an inductor and a resistor in series.
3. Do the same for a capacitor and a resistor in series as in Question 2.
4. Show vectorially how to obtain the impedance of an alternating-current circuit containing a capacitor, an inductor, and a resistor in series.
5. When, in the circuit of Question 4, the voltages across the coil and capacitor are equal, what can be said about their reactances? Give proof.
6. When, in the circuit of Question 4, the voltages across the coil and capacitor are equal, what is the sum of their reactances? Give proof.
7. What is the magnitude of the current flowing through a circuit containing an inductor and a capacitor in series, and no resistor, when the condition of resonance exists? Give proof.
8. Interpret the resonance curve in Figure 34-11 from the point of view of tuning for a station.
9. Derive the formula for the resonant frequency of a tuned circuit and give the units for the various factors.
10. Explain how the voltage across the coil of a circuit containing an alternating-current generator, a capacitor, a resistor, and a coil in series at resonance may be many times larger than the voltage of the generator.
11. Describe the characteristics of a series resonant circuit.
12. Explain vectorially why resistance in a series resonant circuit reduces the selectivity of that circuit.
13. Describe the characteristics of a parallel resonant circuit.
14. In a series resonant circuit, the source generator must have a very low impedance for maximum power transfer. Explain why.
15. Why must the generator have a high impedance for maximum power transfer in a parallel resonant circuit?
16. What is meant by the Q of a coil and how is it calculated?
17. What type of coupling is desirable to avoid side-band cutting? Explain why.
18. Illustrate a low-pass filter by means of a circuit diagram.
19. Illustrate a high-pass filter by means of a circuit diagram.
20. Explain how the filter system of a power supply acts as a low-pass filter.
21. Explain the operation of a band-pass filter.
22. Explain the operation of a band-elimination filter.

35

The Electromagnetic Wave

> **PROBLEM 1.** *What is the nature of an electromagnetic wave?*
>
> **PROBLEM 2.** *How are radio waves produced in a transmitting station?*
>
> **PROBLEM 3.** *How is the radio wave transmitted (a) by ground wave and (b) by sky wave?*
>
> **PROBLEM 4.** *How does the ionosphere affect the sky wave?*
>
> **PROBLEM 5.** *How are static and fading caused and corrected?*

How the Radio Wave Is Produced. The term *electromagnetic wave* covers a whole series of phenomena such as radio waves, heat waves, light waves, X rays, and gamma rays (the rays emitted by such substances as radium). These waves or rays all may be called forms of radiant energy and seem to differ chiefly in their wave lengths and, hence, frequencies.

We will deal now only with the radio waves, which, as you will note, comprise a very wide range of frequencies. Little is known about the nature of electromagnetic waves. We do know that they represent a form of energy, but all else is in the realm of theory.

The Quantum Theory. One school of thought holds that these rays are minute bundles of energy, shot off into space like bullets out of a gun. According to the Planck-Einstein theory, the flow of an alternating current through a conductor tends to force some of the electrons in the outer orbits, or rings of the atom, to take up positions in the inner orbits. In the process, bundles of energy, called *quanta*, are emitted. It is these quanta that radiate out into space, producing the radio wave.

Although considerable evidence supports the quantum theory, there are some facts which this theory does not explain. We have assumed in this book that the radio wave is a wave motion through the medium of the ether. The student must be warned that all explanations of the radio wave are purely theoretical and that further research may produce new theories. As a matter of fact, many scientists tend to hold to a theory that combines the quantum and wave theories.

How Is an Electromagnetic Wave Produced? According to the wave theory, this is what happens in a transmitting station which broadcasts radio signals. Assume that you have a generator capable of producing an alternating current whose frequency is, say, 500,-000 cycles per second. Two vertical wires (called a *dipole* antenna) are attached to the brushes of the generator (Fig. 35-1).

During one half cycle, electrons stream into one of the vertical wires (negative charge) and out of the other (positive charge). Since the two wires have opposite electrical charges, we may consider them as the opposite plates of a capacitor with the surrounding air as the dielectric. As a result, a dielectric field (also called the *electric* or *electrostatic* field) is set up between them. The lines of force are shown in Figure 35-1, and the arrowheads indicate the direction of this field, from negative to positive.

As the generator voltage dies down to zero, this dielectric field collapses back into the wires. But before the outermost line of force shown in the drawing can reach the wires, the generator begins to go through the second half-cycle and another dielectric field begins to form. This field is now in the opposite direction.

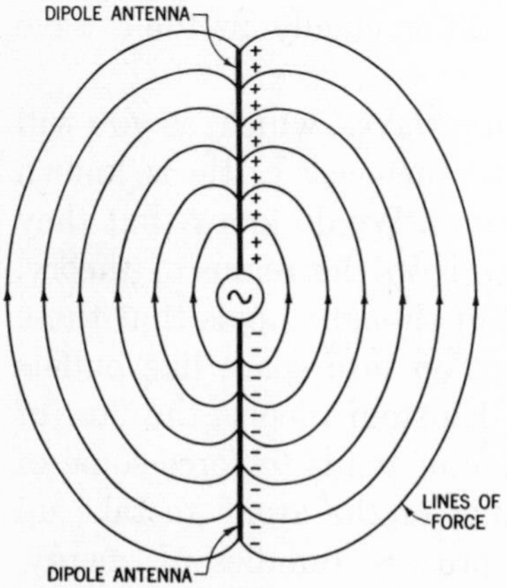

The line of force remaining from the first field is pushed out by the second field and becomes detached from the wire (Fig. 35-2). This process repeats itself, and the result is a radiating stream of lines of force that move out through space at the rate of 186,000 miles per second (Fig. 35-3).

Fig. 35-1. *Diagram of the dielectric field around a dipole antenna.*

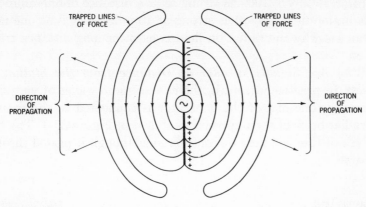

Fig. 35-2. *Diagram showing how lines of force are prevented from returning to the antenna.*

We have learned earlier in our study that a moving dielectric field produces a magnetic field. This magnetic field is at right angles to the dielectric field. Thus, we have a dielectric field, with an accompanying magnetic field, radiating through space. This combined radiation is called the *radio wave*. This is, therefore, an electromagnetic wave and, like light, is a form of radiant energy.

The Radiation Field. We must not, however, confuse this *radiation* field with the field around a conductor carrying an electric current. To differentiate between the two, we call the latter the *induced* field. The induced field, at a distance of 10 miles from the

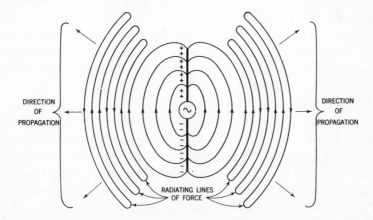

Fig. 35-3. *Diagram showing how the trapped lines of force are radiated or propagated.*

generator, is only 1/1000 as strong as at a distance of one mile. But the radiation field is 1/10 as strong at 10 miles as it is at one mile. We can see why the radiation field is used for long-distance transmission.

Why Are Signals Weaker as Distance from the Station Increases? In practice, except in the case of radio waves of very high frequencies, one end of the generator is connected to the ground. The radiation field then appears as shown in Figure 35-4. The bottom half of the field may be considered as though it passed through the earth.

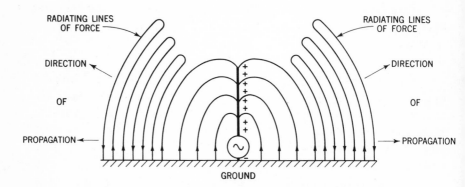

Fig. 35-4. *How lines of force are radiated when one end of the generator is connected to the ground.*

The higher the frequency of the generator, the stronger the radiation field. There is some radiation at frequencies of 25 and 60 cycles per second, but highest efficiency is obtained at 50 kc or over. Thus, with the ordinary type of transmitting antenna, the radiation field at a given point is about 25,000 times as strong at 1,500 kc as it would be at 60 cycles per second.

The radiation field spreads out in all directions somewhat like the larger and larger circles formed by ripples in a pond when a stone is thrown in. Since the total energy of the field is constant, the further away the wave gets from the generator, the more it is spread out and the weaker it gets. You will notice that water waves, too, get weaker the further they get from the source of disturbance (the stone thrown into the pond).

Another factor that weakens the radiation field is the absorption of energy by the earth. Eddy currents and dielectric losses cut it down considerably. Thus, intervening hills or buildings may prevent a signal from being received strongly.

As the radiation field (that is, the radio wave) sweeps across the receiving antenna, it induces a voltage, or electromotive force, in the antenna-ground system. This voltage is extremely small. It has been estimated that the electromotive force induced in the average receiving antenna by radiation from a nearby transmitting station of average power is usually about 50 microvolts (0.00005 volt). Signals from distant stations are correspondingly weaker. You can now see the necessity for radio-frequency amplification in our receiver.

The Radio Wave Is Transmitted by Ground Wave and Sky Wave. When a radio wave leaves the transmitting antenna, it

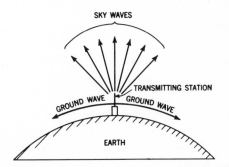

Fig. 35-5. *Diagram showing how a transmitting station sends out ground and sky waves.*

spreads out in all directions. One portion travels along the surface of the earth and is, accordingly, called the *ground wave*. Another portion is radiated out into the sky and is appropriately called the *sky wave* (Fig. 35-5).

The Ground Wave. As the ground wave travels over the surface of the earth, energy is absorbed by the earth, and the signal gets weaker and weaker the further it goes. This loss of energy results from the fact that electric currents are induced by the radio wave and set flowing in the earth. Naturally, the better electricity-conducting portions of the earth over which the radio wave travels require less energy to set these induced currents flowing than portions that are poor conductors. Thus, less energy is lost by the radio wave in traveling over good conductors. We can see, therefore, why the ground wave can travel further over ocean water (a relatively good conductor) than over land.

From our study of inductance, we know that the higher the frequency, the greater the amount of induced voltage. We may, therefore, expect that radio waves of higher frequencies will lose more power by the absorption of the earth than will radio waves of lower frequencies.

For this reason, radio waves of lower frequencies (50 to 550 kc) are used for ground-wave transmission over distances up to about 1,000 miles. Radio waves whose frequencies lie in the broadcast band (535 to 1,605 kc) are usually effective over distances of about 50 to 200 miles. Of course, the energy received at any station also depends upon the power of the transmitting station that is sending the signal. At frequencies above 1,605 kc, the ground wave can be received only at distances of about 15 to 20 miles.

The Sky Wave and the Ionosphere. The sky wave travels outward into the sky and would never return to earth were it not for the *Kennelly-Heaviside Layer.* This layer was named for the two scientists who first studied it. Today, this region of the atmosphere beyond the stratosphere is called the *ionosphere* and has been found to consist of several layers of *ionized* gases.

When a gas (such as air) exists under a very low pressure, it is relatively easy to knock out one or more electrons from its molecules. Such a molecule or atom having a deficiency of electrons is called an *ion.* An atom or group of atoms that has lost one or more electrons has a positive charge. Ions can be attracted or repelled by electric forces, just as any other charged bodies are attracted or repelled.

Fast-moving particles, such as electrons and cosmic rays from outer space, can knock off electrons from molecules of a gas under low pressure. In addition, certain types of radiations, such as ultraviolet rays from the sun, may also knock off these electrons.

Ions tend to lose their charges. They constantly recombine with free electrons to re-form the original molecules. That is why this ionization is negligible at low altitudes. Below 60 miles, any volume of air contains so many molecules of the various gases that any molecule which may have lost an electron almost immediately recovers it from a neighbor. Moreover, the ultraviolet rays of the sun are absorbed by the upper air, and comparatively few get down to a distance less than 60 miles above the surface of the earth.

On the other hand, the further up we go, the rarer the air gets—that is, there are fewer molecules in any volume. Beyond a distance of 200 miles from the earth's surface, there probably are so few molecules that ionization is virtually nil. So we see that the ionosphere is a layer or region beginning at about 60 miles beyond the surface of the earth and extending to about 200 miles beyond the surface of the earth.

The ionosphere is believed to consist of several layers which ionize in different ways. We know that different gases *ionize* at different pressures. Also, the different gases that constitute the air have different densities, and at greater distances from the earth, there are more molecules of the lighter gases and fewer of the heavier ones. This condition results in the ions forming layers within the ionosphere at different altitudes, depending upon the gases present (Fig. 35-6). These layers are constantly shifting from day to day, from month to month, and from year to year. The ions also are constantly recombining with electrons, and new ions are being formed. Climatic conditions and solar and stellar dis-

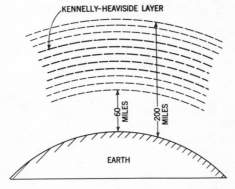

Fig. 35-6. *Diagram showing the Kennelly-Heaviside layer above the surface of the earth.*

KENNELLY-HEAVISIDE LAYER

60 MILES

200 MILES

EARTH

turbances also cause these layers to change position. In addition to the great mobility of the layers, the absence of ultraviolet rays from the sun at night causes the whole ionosphere to rise.

How the Sky Wave Gets Back to Earth. The effect of the ionosphere on the sky wave is threefold. (1) A certain portion of the wave penetrates it and never returns to the earth. (2) A portion of the wave is absorbed by this layer. (3) Another portion is reflected back to the earth, where it may be received.

The angle at which the sky wave must strike the ionosphere to penetrate it depends upon the density of the layer and the frequency of the wave. This angle is known as the *critical angle.* It is the angle between the sky wave and the antenna transmitting it (Fig. 35-7). Waves that strike the ionosphere at angles less than

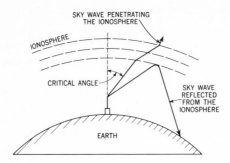

Fig. 35-7. *Diagram showing the critical angle. Sky waves of a certain frequency, striking the ionosphere at an angle less than the critical angle, penetrate and do not return to earth.*

the critical angle penetrate and never return. Those that strike the ionosphere at angles greater than the critical angle are reflected back to earth, as shown in Figures 35-7 and 35-8. The greater the frequency of the sky wave, the greater the critical angle. When

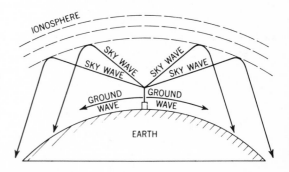

Fig. 35-8. *Diagram showing reflection of the sky waves from the ionosphere.*

the sun is directly overhead, the ionosphere is at its densest. This condition increases the critical angle. For this reason, too, the critical angle is greater in daytime than at night. Seasonal changes in the ionosphere position and changes in its density resulting from sunspot activity also determine this angle.

The absorption of part of the sky wave depends upon the density of the ionosphere. Increased ionization of the air resulting from sunshine, sunspot activity, and the like, all tend to increase the absorption.

Skip Distance and Skip Zones. The portion of the sky wave that is reflected to the earth does not come straight down, but is

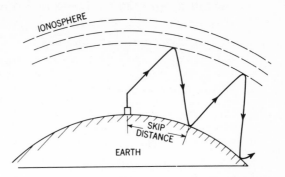

Fig. 35-9. *Diagram showing what is meant by skip distance.*

reflected at an angle that corresponds to the angle at which that particular wave strikes the ionosphere. Figure 35-8 illustrates this principle. The wave, after being reflected from the ionosphere, strikes the earth, then bounces back from the earth, and is again reflected toward the earth from the ionosphere (Fig. 35-9). This process continues until the radio wave is completely absorbed.

The distance between the transmitter and the point where the sky wave first reaches the earth after being reflected from the ionosphere is called the *skip distance*. Skip distances of several hundred miles are common at the higher frequencies.

It is possible that there may be a gap between the furthest point reached by the ground wave and the point where the sky wave is reflected to earth (Fig. 35-10). This gap is known as the

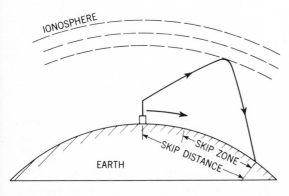

Fig. 35-10. *Diagram showing what is meant by skip zone. In this zone no signals are received.*

skip zone and is responsible for the peculiar fact that a signal may be received at a great distance from the transmitting station, whereas an operator whose receiver is nearer to the transmitter may hear nothing.

Effect of Frequency on Transmission of the Radio Wave. The Federal Communications Commission has divided the radio wave spectrum into the following channels:

Very low frequency (VLF)............. 10 to 30 kc
Low frequency (LF)................... 30 to 300 kc
Medium frequency (MF).............. 300 to 3,000 kc
High frequency (HF)................. 3,000 to 30,000 kc
Very high frequency (VHF)............ 30,000 to 300,000 kc
Ultrahigh frequency (UHF)............ 300,000 to 3,000,000 kc
Superhigh frequency (SHF)............ 3,000,000 to 30,000,000 kc

At low frequencies (30 to 300 kc), the ground wave is extremely useful for distances up to about 1,000 miles. The energy loss caused in passing over the earth is low, and since we do not depend upon the ionosphere, transmission is stable and practically unaffected by daylight and seasonal changes.

For transmission over distances ranging from 1,000 to about 8,000 miles, we must depend upon the sky wave. When the frequency is low, the amount of absorption by the ionosphere is low. However, this absorption increases as we raise the frequency, and the use of sky waves whose frequencies are about 550 kc is possible only at night.

At frequencies which lie in the broadcast band (535 to 1,605 kc), the earth losses of the ground wave limit its use to about 200 miles. Owing to absorption by the ionosphere, sky waves at these frequencies are not effective in daytime. But at night, when this absorption is reduced, transmission up to 3,000 miles is possible. At about 1,400 kc, absorption of the sky wave reaches its maximum. From there on, increases in frequency result in decreases in absorption, until the very high frequencies are reached (above 30 mc).

At frequencies of 1,600 kc to 30 mc, ground losses become so great that transmission of the ground wave is limited to about 15 miles. The sky wave, however, may reach distances as far away as 12,000 miles from the transmitter. As is the case for all sky waves, however, transmission at these frequencies is unstable as a consequence of constant changes in the ionosphere.

Frequencies Above 30 Mc. At frequencies above 30 mc, the ground losses are so high as to completely eliminate the ground wave. At these frequencies, the critical angle becomes so great that practically all of the sky wave penetrates the ionosphere and is not reflected to earth. Under freak conditions of the ionosphere, the sky wave may bounce back, and then transmission may occur over long distances. But such conditions are rare and do not last very long.

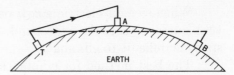

Fig. 35-11. *Diagram illustrating transmission above 30 mc. Radio waves from transmitting station (T) can be received at receiving station (A), but not at (B). The curvature of the earth interferes.*

Transmission of such waves, therefore, is possible normally only in a straight line from the transmitting antenna to the receiving antenna. In this respect, then, these radio waves resemble light waves. The distance we can transmit in a straight line is limited by the curvature of the earth's surface (Fig. 35-11). Thus, transmission is possible between the transmitting station T and receiving station A, but not receiving station B. Of course, if we raise the antennas or place them on top of a hill, greater distances can be covered. Changes in atmospheric conditions, due to changes in temperature, air pressure, and moisture, sometimes seem to increase slightly the distance over which these waves may be sent, by slightly bending the waves toward the ground. Waves that normally, in straight-line transmission, would pass above the receiving antenna are bent down to strike it. Transmission at these frequencies is quite stable, and signals are affected very little by outside disturbances.

Interferences with Reception of Radio Waves. Radio waves suffer from interferences of two types. One such type of interference is called *static,* and is manifested as hissing, clicking, and crackling noises heard in the receiver. These noises may become great enough to make transmission impossible. The other type is called *fading,* and is manifested in undesirable changes in the intensity or loudness of the signal in the receiver.

Preventing Static. Static falls into two categories. There is *man-made static* and *natural static,* or *atmospherics.*

Man-made static is generated by most electrical devices. Ignition systems, diathermy machines, sparking brushes on motors and generators—all may cause interference with radio reception. In fact, almost any device that produces an electric spark can generate static. This static may be radiated into space and be picked up by nearby antennas, or may be sent directly into the receiver through a common power supply.

Whenever an electric spark occurs, a train of radio waves is sent out over a fairly wide band of frequencies. For this reason, static is difficult to eliminate.

The best method for eliminating man-made static is to kill it at the source. If the brushes of a motor are sparking, cleaning them will eliminate this source of static. Another method of prevention is to place a filter system between the machine that is at fault and the power lines. The filter will bypass the radio-frequency currents to the ground. Figure 35-12 shows such a filter. The radio-frequency currents are prevented from entering the power lines by the choke coils, and they take the easy path to the ground through the capacitors.

Eliminating Static by Changes in the Receiver. Where we cannot filter out static or where static is radiated into space, other methods of elimination are used. Since static is a form of radio

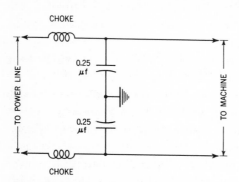

Fig. 35-12. *Filter circuit to prevent radio-frequency currents set up by a sparking machine from traveling back into the power lines.*

wave, a selective tuner may help in tuning it out. The use of a directional antenna, such as a loop, will eliminate some of the static, if the source of the noise is not in the same direction as the transmitting station.

Man-made static falls into two classes: the *impulse* type and the *hiss* type. The impulse type consists of separate and distinct pulses of very high amplitude. These pulses are of very short duration. The hiss type consists of a series of pulses, so close together that they overlap to produce the hiss. For the reduction of the hiss type of static, we employ the methods outlined above.

The impulse type of static may be eliminated by yet another method. Since the impulses consist of high-amplitude pulses of very short duration, we can get rid of them if the receiver is made to go dead for the extremely short interval that the static impulses are present. Because this interval is so minute, there is no noticeable interference with the signal.

A form of automatic volume control is used. As the loud impulse comes in, the amplification factor of the receiver is reduced to zero, and nothing is heard. After the impulse has passed, the set returns to normal (Chap. 24). This automatic volume control must, of necessity, be extremely quick-acting.

Natural static, or atmospherics, consists of radio waves generated from such natural sources as thunderstorms. Such waves are usually responsible for the crackling and crashing sometimes heard in the receiver. They are present at most of the frequencies and diminish in strength as the frequency increases. For this reason, transmission at high frequencies suffers little from this form of interference. At the ultrahigh frequencies, static is rarely present except during local thunderstorms.

Static may be transmitted like any other radio wave. At low or broadcast frequencies, static from far places is absent in the receiver owing to the absorption of the sky wave. But at night, this absorption is diminished, and the sky-wave static may cover great distances. Atmospherics may be reduced by the methods used to reduce the hiss type of man-made static—namely, by employment of a selective receiver and a directional antenna.

Causes of Fading. Fading, the second source of interference, is caused by the interaction of two parts of the same radio wave. At a certain distance from the transmitter, both the ground wave and the sky wave may be received. Because each wave travels a different path, it is possible that they may be received simultaneously or slightly out of step. If they come in together, they reinforce one another, and the signal is louder. If they are out of step, they tend to neutralize one another, and the signal dies down (Fig. 35-13).

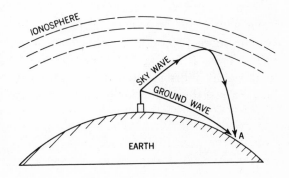

Fig. 35-13. *Diagram showing how fading is produced. The ground wave and the sky wave arrive at the same point (A) out of step (out of phase) and tend to neutralize each other. This condition causes the signal to fade out.*

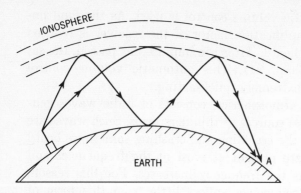

Fig. 35-14. *Another cause of fading. Here two sky waves arrive at the same point (A) out of step.*

Another cause of fading is the ionosphere. Because of variations in the sky wave due to changes in the ionosphere, the signal in the receiver may get louder and weaker. Fading may also be caused by the interaction of two sky waves. One sky wave may reach the receiver in one hop, while the other, hitting the ionosphere at a different angle, may arrive in two hops (Fig. 35-14). Here, too, fading may or may not occur, depending upon whether or not the two sky waves arrive in step.

Violent changes in the ionosphere, during a condition known as an *ionosphere storm,* cause severe fading, especially among frequencies higher than 1.5 mc. These storms may last as long as several weeks and are believed to be due to vigorous sunspot activity.

The most common means of overcoming fading is the use of automatic volume control. As the signal drops, the gain of the tube is raised, and the level of reception is maintained. Automatic volume control is not very effective, however, where the fading is extreme.

Another method used to overcome fading is known as *diversity reception.* It has been found that fading does not usually occur at two different places at exactly the same time. Accordingly, two or more receiving antennas are used, spaced some distance apart. Thus, if fading occurs in one, the other may still receive the loud signal. This method is not yet very practical for home use because a rather complicated type of receiver must be used.

SUMMARY

1. Radiant energy is transmitted by **electromagnetic waves.** Heat, light, radio, and gamma rays are forms of radiant energy differing, as far as we are able to judge, chiefly in frequency and wave length.
2. Radio waves exhibit properties of both electricity and magnetism, or, more precisely stated, radio waves have both a dielectric field and a magnetic field at right angles to each other. Also the electric and the magnetic vectors both are at right angles to the direction of propagation.
3. Radio waves may be produced at a transmitting station by alternating-current generators attached to a dipole antenna or to an antenna wire and ground. Electrons are set moving in the antenna, which may be considered as a sort of capacitor. A dielectric field is set up between the two wires of a dipole, or between the wire and ground for the grounded antenna. At each alternation, the new dielectric field is formed and collapses. Successive waves of lines of dielectric force are sent out into space at the speed of 186,000 miles per second.
4. *Radiation fields* increase in strength in proportion to frequency, but all radio waves lose intensity with distance.
5. The radio wave consists of two parts: a **ground wave** and a **sky wave.**
6. Ground waves travel only comparatively short distances because their energy is absorbed by the earth. Radio waves with frequencies of 50 to 550 kc travel up to distances of 1,000 miles under favorable conditions. But frequencies in the broadcast band (535 to 1,605 kc) are effective as ground waves only for about 50 to 200 miles.
7. Sky waves travel out into space to the ionosphere, which is a region beyond 60 miles from the earth's surface in which are ionized gases. Sky waves are reflected from the ionosphere to the earth when the angle between the vertical and their direction of propagation is greater than the **critical angle.** The critical angle is the angle below which the waves penetrate the ionosphere.
8. The sky wave is reflected to earth at varying distances from the transmitting station. For any particular case, the distance between the transmitter and the place where the reflected sky wave first reaches the earth is called the **skip distance.**
9. Frequencies above 30 mc are **very high, ultrahigh,** and **superhigh** frequencies. Such radio waves are not reflected from the ionosphere and can be transmitted only in a straight line between the transmitting antennas to the receiving antenna.
10. Static is a form of interference with radio reception due to oscillatory discharges from some other source than radio sta-

tions. *Man-made* static may come from all kinds of electrical devices which produce sparks. *Natural* static comes from lightning or other electrical disturbances.

11. Man-made static should be controlled at the source by filtering systems, but some help can be provided in receivers by selective tuning or by quick-acting automatic-volume-control devices.

12. *Fading* is sometimes caused by neutralization of parts of the same wave slightly out of step when received by way of the ground and the sky or by one reflection and two reflections. Sun spots and disturbances in the ionosphere from whatever causes may produce fading.

13. The most common method of correcting fading is by automatic volume control.

GLOSSARY

Critical Angle: The angle between a vertical transmitting antenna and the sky wave, which determines whether a radio wave will penetrate the ionosphere or be redirected to earth.

Diversity Reception: Reception with several antennas in different places to overcome fading.

Fading: The falling off of intensity of the pickup from the radio wave.

Ground Wave: The portion of a radiated field about a transmitter antenna that travels along the ground.

Induced Field: The magnetic field around a current-carrying conductor.

Ionosphere: A series of layers of ionized air in the upper regions which reflect back to earth radiated sky waves.

Kennelly-Heaviside Layer: Another name for the ionosphere.

Quantum: A unit bundle of energy assumed to be radiated from a transmitting antenna and making up the radio wave.

Radiated Field: The field of energy radiated from an antenna consisting of an electrostatic field at right angles to a magnetic field.

Skip Distance: The distance between a transmitting antenna and the point where the sky wave returns to earth.

Skip Zone: The region between the end of the ground wave and the point where the sky wave returns to earth in which no signal for the station is received.

Static: Hissing, clicking, cracking noise in receivers which may have a natural or man-made origin.

QUESTIONS AND PROBLEMS

1. Name several types of electromagnetic waves.
2. Explain the wave theory of electromagnetic radiation from a dipole antenna.
3. Describe the nature of a radiated radio wave.
4. Differentiate between the radiation field and the induction field around an antenna.
5. How does the radiation field vary with the frequency of its generating current?
6. What accounts for the weakening of the radiation field as it spreads from the source?
7. How does the earth affect radio waves of high frequencies?
8. Describe the origin of the ionosphere, and its behavior.
9. How does the ionosphere affect the sky wave?
10. What is the relation between the frequency of a sky wave and its critical angle?
11. Illustrate by means of a diagram what is meant by skip distance and skip zone.
12. Explain the fact that a station may be heard by a receiver at a great distance while a receiver closer to the station cannot get that station.
13. Explain the transmission behavior of the following ranges of frequencies: 50 to 550 kc; 550 to 1,600 kc; 1,600 kc to 30 mc; above 30 megacycles.
14. What two conditions serve to interfere with radio reception under normal conditions? How do they arise?
15. Draw a circuit to eliminate man-made static fed in through the power line. Explain how it works.
16. How may a quick-acting automatic-volume-control system eliminate the impulse of man-made static?
17. By what method may natural static effects in the receiver be reduced?
18. What occurs during ionosphere storms and what effect does it have on radio reception?
19. What is the most common means of overcoming fading in modern receivers?
20. What is diversity reception and what is its purpose?

36

Radio Antennas

PROBLEM. *What principles are involved in adapting antennas for purposes of transmission and reception of radio signals?*

Antenna Characteristics. In our discussion of resonant circuits (Chap. 34), we considered circuits containing concentrated, or *lumped,* inductance and capacitance as represented by inductors and capacitors. There are, however, important tuned circuits where the inductor and capacitor do not appear. These circuits utilize the distributed inductance and capacitance, which are inevitable even in a circuit containing a single straight wire. An antenna is such a circuit.

The function of the antenna of a transmitter is to radiate the strongest possible radio wave from a given transmitter. To accomplish this, it becomes important that there be the maximum power transfer from the transmitter to the antenna. This immediately suggests that the antenna must be a tuned circuit in *resonance* with the transmitter.

We can show why this is so if we consider Figure 36-1, where the antenna is represented by its equivalent tuned circuit coupled to the transmitter. When the tuned circuit is in resonance with the transmitter, the inductive reactance (X_L) and capacitive reactance (X_C) cancel each other out, leaving only the small ohmic resistance (R) of the wire.

Since the current (I) flowing in the tuned circuit is equal to the voltage (E) divided by the impedance (Z), and since the impedance of this resonant circuit is equal to the small ohmic resistance (R), it can be seen that at resonance the current is at its

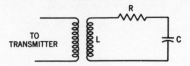

Fig. 36-1. *Diagram showing the equivalent circuit of an antenna coupled to the transmitter. L is the inductance, C is the capacitance, and R is the ohmic resistance of the wire.*

maximum value. Thus, since the power is equal to the square of the current times the resistance ($P = I^2 \times R$), at resonance, therefore, we have the maximum power delivered to the tuned circuit or antenna.

Standing Waves. When the antenna is fed, or *excited,* by a radio-frequency generator (the transmitter), we find that at certain points along the antenna, separated by distances corresponding to half the wavelength of the output of the generator, the current, when measured, will always be about zero. We call these points *current nodes.* At points halfway between the nodes, we find that the current is always at some maximum value. We call these points *current antinodes,* or *loops.* We also find that at the point of a current node, there will be a voltage loop, and at the point of a current loop, there will be a voltage node. Between their respective nodes and loops, the distribution of current and voltage along an antenna is *sinusoidal* in form—that is, in the form of a sine curve (Fig. 36-2).

The reason for this phenomenon is the presence of *standing,* or *stationary,* waves. We may best understand how standing waves are produced, perhaps, by considering a water wave. Assume that a stone is thrown into a still pond of water a short distance from the shore. We can picture what happens by consulting Figure 36-3.

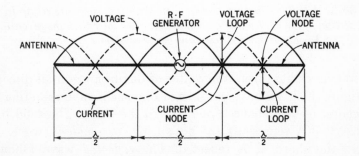

Fig. 36-2. *Sinusoidal distribution of current and voltage along an antenna. The Greek letter* lambda (λ) *is the symbol for the wavelength.*

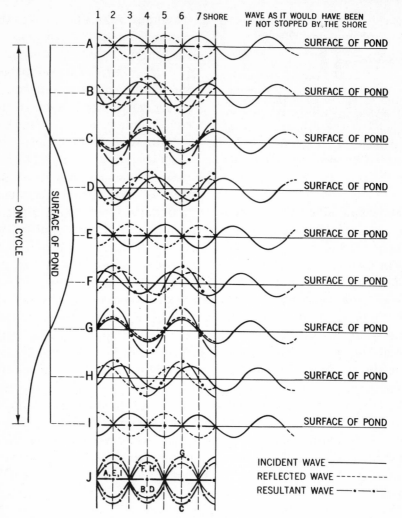

Fig. 36-3. *A to I—Diagram showing how standing waves are set up in water. Each section of the diagram is an eighth of a cycle later than the preceding one. J—The combined resultant waves of A to I.*

Waves radiate from the center of disturbance in all directions. In Figure 36-3, we have considered one such wave radiating from the center of disturbance (point 1) to the shore. The solid line in Figure 36-3-A represents the advancing, or *incident,* wave. As it strikes the shore, it is reflected. The *reflected* wave (shown in dotted lines) really is a continuation of the original wave except that its direction has been reversed at the point where it was reflected. Thus, the reflected wave is the mirror-image of the original wave, as it would have been had it not been reflected by the shore.

You will notice that at all points, the reflected wave is 180° out of phase with the incident wave. Thus, any pressure exerted on the water particles owing to the passage of the incident wave would be neutralized and canceled by the reflected wave. We show the resultant by the dot-and-dash line.

In Figure 36-3-B, we show what happens an eighth of a cycle later. The incident and reflected waves are in phase at certain points and out of phase at others. Where they are in phase, they reinforce one another, with a resulting greater pressure exerted on the water particles at that point. Where they are out of phase, they tend to neutralize one another, and complete neutralization takes place at points where they are 180° out of phase. Once again, the resultant of these two waves is shown by the curve indicated by the dot-and-dash line.

Figure 36-3-C to I are successive eighth-cycles apart. An examination of the resultant waves of the complete figure (A to I) shows some interesting facts. Note that a zero point (node) always occurs at points 1, 3, 5, and 7. Further, note that these nodes are a half wavelength apart. Also note that antinodes, or loops, also occur a half wavelength apart and mid-way between the nodes (points 2, 4, 6, and the shore) (Fig. 36-3-J).

The combined action of the incident and reflected waves, then, is to produce a resultant wave that seems to stand still. The particles of water are moving up and down (except at the nodes), but the crests of the waves have no forward or backward motion. We call such a wave a *standing,* or *stationary; wave.*

At the point where the water waves strike the shore, the particles of water lose their motion. But at this point, the pressure becomes greatest. Since our resultant waves show a maximum point, or loop, at this point (Fig. 36-3-J), you can see that the standing waves are depicting *pressure* rather than *motion* of the water particles. It follows, then, that wherever we have a *pressure loop,* there we shall find a *motion node,* and wherever we find a *pressure node,* there we shall find a *motion loop* (Fig. 36-4).

Similarly, when a wave of electrical energy is fed from a radio-frequency generator into an antenna that is in resonance with it, we get standing waves along the wire of the antenna. These are

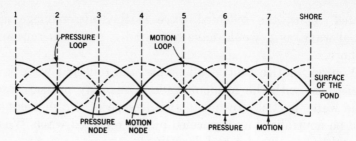

Fig. 36-4. *Diagram showing standing waves of pressure and motion in water.*

standing waves of *current* (corresponding to *motion*) and of *voltage* (corresponding to *pressure*).

In Figure 36-5, we show a common type of antenna, called a *doublet,* or *dipole.* It consists of an elevated, straight piece of wire, with the radio-frequency generator (the transmitter) attached to the center. Since the flow of electrons (current) must cease at the ends of the antenna, we can readily see that our standing current wave must end in nodes.

Since the electrons are piled up at the ends of the antenna where there is practically no current flow (the current nodes), the electrical potential (voltage) therefore becomes maximum. At the point of a current loop, the electrons are in greatest motion, and the piling up of electrons (giving rise to electrical potential, or voltage) is least, approaching zero. Thus, we can see that wherever a current node appears, there will be a voltage loop, and wherever we have a current loop, there will be a voltage node.

So if we are to have current nodes at the ends of our antenna,

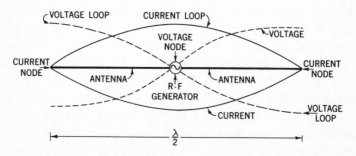

Fig. 36-5. *Diagram showing standing current and voltage waves on a half-wavelength doublet antenna.*

we must also have voltage loops at these points. We may see by inspection, then, that the shortest length we can make our doublet antenna is a half wavelength (Fig. 36-5).

Calculating the Length of the Antenna. In describing the natural frequencies of the tuned circuits discussed in Chapter 34, it is customary to talk about their frequencies (cycles per second). In the case of the antenna, however, it is more convenient to talk about the wavelength.

We can see the relationship between the frequency and wavelength if we examine the following equation:

$$\text{Wavelength (in meters)} = \frac{300{,}000{,}000}{\text{frequency (in cycles per second)}}.$$

The 300,000,000 represents the number of meters a radio wave will travel in one second. Thus, if our transmitter generates a wave

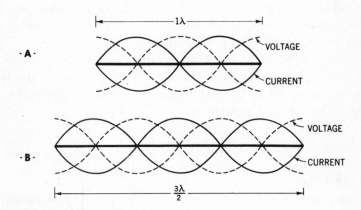

Fig. 36-6. *A—Full-wave antenna, showing distribution of standing waves of current and voltage.*
    B—One-and-one-half wave antenna.

whose frequency is 7,500,000 cycles per second (7.5 megacycles), the wavelength is

$$\text{Wavelength} = \frac{300{,}000{,}000}{7{,}500{,}000} = 40 \text{ meters.}$$

Our half-wavelength (*half-wave*) antenna would be 20 meters long.
    Scientists have found that the velocity of an electric current

in a conductor (the antenna in this case) is approximately 5 per cent less than the velocity of the radio wave. So although it is customary to consider the half-wave antenna as being the same length as half the radiated wave, in practice the antenna is made 5 per cent shorter. Thus, the half-wave antenna for a 40-meter wave would be 19 meters long. The symbol for wavelength is the Greek letter *lambda* (λ).

We have stated that our elevated-wire antenna has on it a standing wave with current nodes and voltage loops at each end. Although the half-wave antenna is the shortest that will satisfy this requirement, you may readily see that any such antenna whose length is an integral number (whole number) times the half wavelength will meet this condition also. Thus, we may have the full-wave antenna, one-and-one-half-wave antenna, and so forth (Fig. 36-6).

The elevated-wire antenna is called a *Hertz* antenna after Heinrich Hertz, the man who invented it. As you shall see later in this chapter, there are a number of different methods of connecting this antenna to the transmitter.

Another type of antenna in common use is the *Marconi* antenna invented by Guglielmo Marconi. Here, one end of the transmitter is connected to the antenna wire and the other end to the ground. The ground acts as a sort of electrical mirror, and thus the shortest type of Marconi antenna may be a quarter-wave in length (Fig. 36-7).

Since the bottom of the Marconi antenna is at ground potential, care must be taken to have a voltage node at that point. Because of this, we can use only *odd* multiples of the quarter-wavelength. Thus, the length of the Marconi antenna may be $\dfrac{\lambda}{4}, \dfrac{3\lambda}{4}, \dfrac{5\lambda}{4}$, and so forth (Fig. 36-8).

The advantage of the Marconi type antenna over the

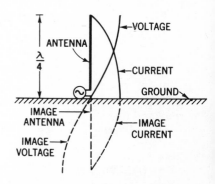

Fig. 36-7. *The quarter-wave Marconi antenna, showing current and voltage distribution. Note that this antenna corresponds to the half-wave Hertz antenna. Only half the current and voltage waves is shown here for the sake of simplicity.*

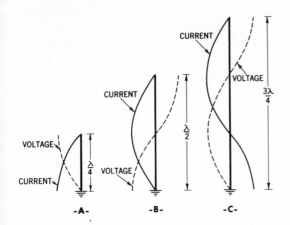

Fig. 36-8. *Marconi-type antennas of different lengths.*

A—Quarter-wave. Note that the voltage node is at the ground.

B—Half-wave. Note that the voltage loop is at the ground. This length cannot be used.

C—Three-quarter wave. The voltage node is at the ground again.

Hertz type is that the length of the former is half that of the latter. Although this does not mean much at the high frequencies (short wavelengths), it becomes important at the long wavelengths, especially if we wish to construct a vertical antenna.

Harmonics. Although circuits having lumped constants (inductors and capacitors) resonate at only one frequency, circuits having distributed inductance and capacitance (such as the antenna) may resonate readily at frequencies that are twice, three times, four times, and other integral multiples of the original frequency. The original frequency is called the *fundamental* frequency. Since the new frequencies are in *harmonic relationship* to the fundamental frequency, they are called *harmonics*. Thus, an antenna which was designed to resonate at 1,000 kc may also be used to radiate radio waves whose frequencies are 2,000 kc (called the second harmonic), 3,000 kc (third harmonic), and so forth.

The Hertz antenna may be operated at the fundamental or at any harmonic frequency. Figure 36-9 shows the current distribution on a half-wave antenna at the fundamental, second har-

Fig. 36-9. *Current distribution on a half-wave Hertz antenna at the fundamental, 2nd harmonic, and 3rd harmonic frequencies. Only half the current wave is shown for the sake of simplicity.*

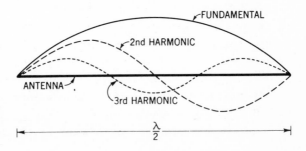

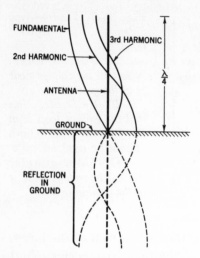

Fig. 36-10. *Voltage distribution on a quarter-wave Marconi antenna at the fundamental, 2nd harmonic, and 3rd harmonic frequencies. Only half the voltage wave is shown for the sake of simplicity. Note the voltage loop at the ground for the 2nd harmonic.*

monic, and third harmonic frequencies.

The Marconi (or grounded) antenna, however, can be operated only at its fundamental and *odd* harmonics (third, fifth, seventh, and so forth). You will recall that there must be a voltage node at the grounded end. This occurs only at the fundamental and odd harmonic frequencies. Figure 36-10 makes this clear.

Loading. We often desire to use an antenna to radiate waves of various frequencies. Of course, we may lengthen or shorten our antenna so that it is always in resonance with the transmitted frequency. But this plan is not always practical.

We may accomplish the same result by inserting an inductor or capacitor in series with the antenna. Assume that the antenna is too short for the signal frequency. In this situation, the natural frequency of the antenna is higher than the signal frequency. When an inductor is inserted in series with the antenna, the total inductance (the distributed inductance of the antenna plus the inductance of the inductor) becomes greater. This increased inductance reduces the natural frequency of the antenna until it is in resonance with the signal frequency (Fig. 36-11-A).

On the other hand, if the antenna is too long (that is, the natural frequency of the antenna is lower than the signal frequency), a capacitor is connected in series with the antenna. Since two capacitances in series (the capacitance of the capacitor and the *distributed capacitance* of the antenna) give a total which is smaller than either, the natural frequency of the antenna is increased until once again it is in resonance with the signal frequency (Fig. 36-11-B).

The process of lengthening or shortening the antenna by

electrical means is called *loading*. (The student is advised to review Chapter 34 if he has any difficulty in following the above discussion.)

Antenna Impedance and Radiation Resistance. From our study of the characteristics of alternating-current circuits, we saw that the impedance (Z) was obtained by dividing the voltage (E) by the current (I) (page 357). At the ends of our half-wave Hertz antenna (Fig. 36-5), we find a maximum voltage and a current that is nearly zero. Thus, the impedances at these points are relatively great. At the center of the antenna, however, the current is at its maximum, and the voltage approaches zero. Thus, we have a point of low impedance. The impedances along the antenna vary from the maximum at the ends to nearly zero at the center.

A resistor dissipates electrical power in the form of heat. Our antenna uses up power by radiating it away in the form of a radio wave. Hence, it acts like a resistor drawing power from the generator. This *assumed* resistor, because it is a result of the power radiated, is called the *radiation resistance*. The radiation resistance of the half-wave Hertz antenna has been found to be about 73 ohms. (The radiation resistance of a quarter-wave Marconi antenna is about 36 ohms.)

Radiation resistance is measured at a current loop. Since this current loop occurs at the center of our half-wave Hertz antenna, and since the E/I value at this point is nearly zero, we may say that the impedance at the center of the half-way Hertz antenna is about 73 ohms.

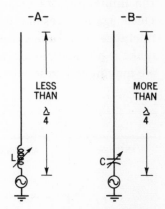

Fig. 36-11. *A—Adding inductance to an antenna to increase its effective length.*

B—Adding capacitance to an antenna to decrease its effective length.

We have stated that the current drops to *nearly* zero at the ends, and the voltage is *nearly* zero at the center of our half-wave Hertz antenna. No matter how high we may raise our antenna, there will always be some capacitance between it and the ground. Thus, as the current reaches the ends of the antenna, there is set up an *end effect* whereby a little current flows into the end capacitance. Thus, there is a small current flowing at the current nodes.

Similarly, the voltage at the center does not pass through
zero, but drops to a low, but finite, value at the point where the
reversal of polarity takes place (the voltage node) because
the ohmic resistance of the antenna is not zero, but some low
value. Energy, therefore, is consumed, and there must be some
voltage present to force the current to flow.

In summation, then, we see that the impedance at the center
of the half-wave Hertz antenna is about 73 ohms, rising gradually
as we approach the ends, which have a relatively high impedance.

Transmission Lines. Heretofore, we had spoken vaguely about
connecting the antenna to the radio-frequency generator (the
transmitter). Obviously, it is quite impractical to locate our transmitter next to the antenna, especially since we try to erect the
antenna so that it is clear of obstructions and high in the air.
You can see that some type of radio-frequency *transmission line*
is needed to convey the radio-frequency power from the output
of the transmitter to the antenna.

If we consider the half-wave doublet antenna of Figure 36-5,
the transmission line may be merely an extension of the wires connecting the radio-frequency generator to the antenna (Fig. 36-12).

It is quite essential that the transmission line should carry
power from the radio-frequency generator to the antenna with
the minimum loss of such power in the transmission line itself.
Once again a resonant circuit is suggested. The distributed inductance and capacitance of the wires of the transmission line
make it a tuned circuit, and if we make this line of suitable length,
we may have it resonate at the frequency of the generator. You see
that we may treat the *resonant
transmission line* as we do the
antenna. Since the transmission
line is at resonance, standing
waves of current and voltage
will be found along its length.

The difficulty is that our
transmission line will radiate a
radio wave just as the antenna.
This is undesirable, since power
radiated away by the transmission line means that much less
to reach the antenna. This diffi-

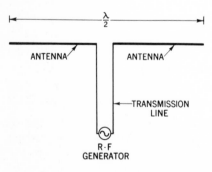

Fig. 36-12. *Transmission line
connecting the r-f generator to the
antenna.*

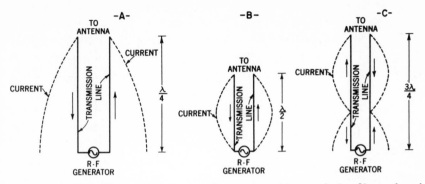

Fig. 36-13. *Standing waves of current on resonant transmission lines of various lengths.*

A—The quarter-wave resonant transmission line. The voltage wave and half the current wave have been omitted for the sake of simplicity.

B—The half-wave transmission line.

C—The three-quarter wave transmission line. Note that the current wave for the lower third of the transmission line really should be shown on the inside of the wires of the line. This would indicate that the flow of current in the lower third of the transmission line is opposite to the flow in the upper two-thirds of the line. For the sake of simplicity, however, the wave is depicted by the curve on the outside of the line. The arrows, however, show the true direction of the current flow in each part of the line. The same note should be applied to the subsequent figures.

culty is overcome by spacing the two wires of the transmission line close to each other (from 2 to 6 inches) and arranging the standing waves on each wire in such a way that they cancel each other out.

Figure 36-13-A shows how this is done. Here we have taken our half-wave doublet antenna of Figure 36-5 and doubled it back on itself. For the sake of simplicity, we have omitted the voltage wave and half the current wave.

Note that the half-wave antenna now has become a quarter-wave transmission line. The current is flowing away from the generator in one wire of the transmission line and toward the generator in the other, as indicated by the arrows. Thus, the current wave on each wire is equal and opposite to the other. Cancellation of the standing waves results, and there is no radiation.

Like the antenna, resonant transmission lines may be constructed that are multiples of the quarter wavelength. Figures 36-13-B and C show the half-wave and three-quarter-wavelengths.

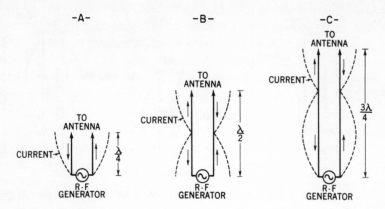

Fig. 36-14. *Resonant transmission lines terminating in a current loop.*
A—The quarter-wave line.
B—The half-wave line.
C—The three-quarter-wave line.

Unlike the antenna, the transmission line does not terminate in free space, but is connected to the antenna. It is not necessary, therefore, that we have a current node at its end. The line may terminate in a current loop and the current can flow onto the antenna (Fig. 36-14).

At this point, a question might arise. If we examine Figures 36-13-B and 36-14-B, we find in both cases we have a half-wave resonant transmission line connecting the radio-frequency generator to the antenna. Nevertheless, one transmission line has current nodes at each end, but the other has current loops. What determines whether we have a node or loop at the ends?

The answer lies in the type of generator used. If the generator be of a high-impedance type, the end of the transmission line which connects to it must have a current node. If it is a low-impedance-type generator, the transmission line has a current loop at the end connecting to it. This will become clearer when we discuss methods of coupling the transmitter to the transmission line.

Although the loss of power due to radiation by a resonant transmission line may be cut down by canceling out the effects of the current and voltage standing waves, the presence of these waves, nevertheless, introduces certain other losses. The power loss due to the resistance of the wire ($P = I^2 \times R$) may become quite high at the points of current loops. In high-powered transmitters, the voltage at the voltage loops may become great enough to cause sparks to jump from one wire to another or to adjacent objects. Obviously, we should try to eliminate the standing waves.

If our transmission line were of infinite length, there could be no standing waves, because we never could get a reflected wave from the far end. Meter measurements along the line would show a gradual decrease in current and voltage. But at each point along the line, the ratio of voltage to current (which is the impedance at that point) would be the same. This impedance is called the *surge* or *characteristic impedance* of the line and its symbol is Z_0.

The characteristic impedance is quite independent of the frequency of the current, depending only on the inductance and capacitance per unit length of line. We may determine its value from the following formula:

$$Z_0 = \sqrt{\frac{L}{C}}$$

where Z_0 is the characteristic impedance, L is the inductance per unit length of line, and C is the capacitance of the same length of line. For a type of line often used to feed a half-wave antenna, the value of the characteristic impedance is about 500 ohms.

Of course, a line of infinite length is only a theory. But if we have a line of *finite* length terminating in a resistance equal to the characteristic impedance, all the energy of the incident wave would be absorbed, and there would be no reflected nor standing wave.

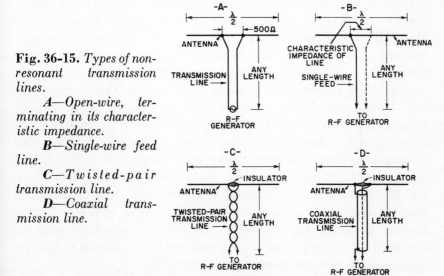

Fig. 36-15. *Types of non-resonant transmission lines.*

A—Open-wire, terminating in its characteristic impedance.

B—Single-wire feed line.

C—Twisted-pair transmission line.

D—Coaxial transmission line.

We have noted that the half-wave Hertz antenna has impedances which range from about 73 ohms at the center to very large values at the ends. If we terminate our transmission line at points on the antenna which correspond to the characteristic impedance of the line (about 500 ohms for the line mentioned above), the antenna would act as the terminating resistance. Under such condition, all the energy would be absorbed by it. There would be no standing waves on the transmission line (Fig. 36-15-A). We call such a line a *nonresonant transmission line*. The line may be of any length.

In practice, we may test this line for standing waves by passing over its length a flashlight lamp attached to a loop of wire about 6 inches in diameter. If any standing waves exist along the transmission line, the loop will absorb some electrical energy, which will light the lamp. Current loops will be indicated by an increase in brightness of the lamp. Should this occur, the points on the antenna to which the line is attached may be varied until the characteristic impedance (Z_0) is obtained. The lamp then will fail to increase in brightness over the full length of the line.

A variation of the nonresonant transmission line shown in Figure 36-15-A is the *single-wire feed* system. Here, only one wire connects the transmitter to the antenna. The capacitance of the antenna in relation to the ground gives us the electrical equivalent of the missing wire. The single wire is attached to a point on the antenna whose distance from the center is sufficient to enable the transmission line to terminate in its characteristic impedance (Fig. 36-15-B). Although a good ground connection is always desirable, special care should be taken to have a good ground connection for a transmitter using this type of transmission line.

Another nonresonant transmission line is the *twisted-pair* line. This type of line consists of two insulated wires twisted around each other. An advantage of this line is its greater flexibility than the parallel-wire line shown in Figure 36-15-A. This is important in installations where the transmission line does not run in a straight line, but has to curve around obstructions. Since the characteristic impedance of a twisted-pair line is about 73 ohms, it may be connected directly to the center of the half-wave doublet antenna (Fig. 36-15-C). Any slight discrepancy may be corrected by moving the points where the line connects to the antenna a little distance away from the center.

Still another type of nonresonant transmission line is the *concentric* or *coaxial* line. This type of line consists of a copper wire or tube running through the center of another, and larger, tube. Insulated spacers are placed inside the line to keep the inner wire or tube in the exact center of the large tube. The outer tube acts as a shield, and thus there can be no radiation. The diameter of the outer tube depends upon the power used and varies from about ⅜ inch for low power to about 3 to 4 inches for high-power broadcast stations. Since the characteristic impedance for a coaxial line having an outer tube of about ⅜ inch diameter is about 75 ohms, we may connect this type of line directly to the center of the half-wave doublet antenna (Fig. 36-15-D).

Impedance Matching. Usually, though not always, we desire to transfer the maximum power from one circuit to another. As you will see on pages 512-514, when a generator feeds into a load, the maximum amount of power is transferred when the resistance or impedance of the generator and that of the load are equal. If we consider the exciting circuit as the generator and the excited circuit as the load, to obtain the maximum transfer of power, the resistance or impedance of the exciting circuit must equal the impedance of the excited circuit. This is called *impedance matching*.

When we excite the transmission line, the input impedance of the line must match the output impedance of the transmitter for maximum power transfer. Similarly, the output impedance of the transmission line must match the input impedance of the antenna.

Coupling the Transmitter to the Transmission Line. To connect the output of the transmitter to the input of the transmission line, we use a *coupling network*. One form of such a network is the air-core transformer. If we connect the primary in the transmitter-output circuit and the secondary in the transmission line-input circuit, we may vary the coupling of the primary and secondary until maximum power transfer between the two circuits occurs, and thus impedance matching is achieved.

Another use of this coupling system is to isolate the transmission line and antenna from the large direct-current voltages at the output of the transmitter. Still another use is to tune to resonance the circuits connected by this system. To do this, the primary and secondary may consist of variable inductors. More common, however, is to tune these coils by means of variable capacitors (Fig. 36-16).

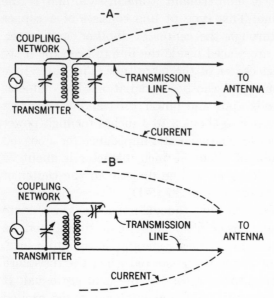

Fig. 36-16. *A—Coupling network with a current node at input end of the transmission line.*

B—Coupling network with a current loop at input end of the transmission line.

The primary circuit of the coupling network consists of the output circuit of the transmitter. As you shall see in Chapter 40, this is a parallel resonant circuit. The secondary circuit couples the transmission line to the output of the transmitter. The secondary circuit may be either a series or parallel resonant circuit, depending upon whether a current loop or node is to appear at the input end of the transmission line.

In our discussion of resonant circuits, we saw that a series resonant circuit (pages 415-416) is a low-impedance circuit which permits a large current to flow through it. Thus, if we have a *current loop* (maximum current) at the input end of the transmis-

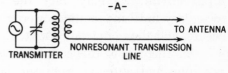

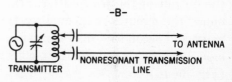

Fig. 36-17. *Coupling the nonresonant transmission line to the transmitter.*

A—Inductive coupling.

B—Capacitive coupling.

sion line, we must have a *series resonant circuit* to tune the line. On the other hand, a *current node* (minimum current) requires a *parallel resonant circuit* (pages 418-420) to tune the line. You see, therefore, that the type of circuit used to tune the secondary of the coupling network depends upon the distribution of standing waves on the transmission line (Fig. 36-16).

In the case of nonresonant transmission lines, the secondary of the coupling network need not be tuned. The input impedance of the line is pure resistance (usually about 500 ohms for the parallel-wire type), and we may use the system shown in Figure 36-17-A.

A variation of this method is the *direct-* or *capacitive-coupling* method shown in Figure 36-17-B. Here the line is tapped to the output coil of the transmitter through fixed capacitors. These capacitors are used merely to block the direct-current voltages in the output circuit of the transmitter from reaching the transmission line and antenna. Coupling may be varied by changing the taps of the coil.

Matching the Transmission Line to the Antenna. As in the case of coupling the input end of the transmission line to the transmitter, the output end of the transmission line must be impedance-matched to the antenna. Thus, if a half-wave Hertz antenna is fed at its center (point of a current loop or low impedance), the output end of the resonant transmission line feeding it also must terminate in a current loop (low impedance). If this transmission line is a quarter-wave long (or any odd multiple of the quarter-wave), its input end (the end coupled to the transmitter) terminates in a current node (high impedance). This indicates the need for a parallel-resonant tuning system (Fig. 36-18-A).

Should we use a resonant transmission line that is an even number of quarter-waves long, the input end of the line terminates in a current loop (low impedance). This necessitates a series-resonant tuning circuit (Fig. 36-18-B).

When the half-wave Hertz antenna is fed at the center (current loop), we say it is *center-fed* or *current-fed*. Another method of feeding the Hertz antenna is to connect the resonant transmission line to the end of the antenna. Here, one wire of the transmission line goes to the end of the antenna, and the other terminates on an insulator alongside. In this instance, the line connects into the antenna at a current node (high impedance). The stand-

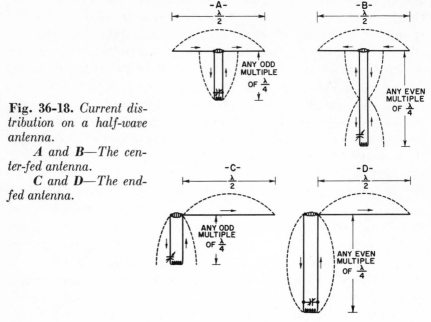

Fig. 36-18. *Current distribution on a half-wave antenna.*

*A and **B**—The center-fed antenna.*

*C and **D**—The end-fed antenna.*

ing wave of current on the transmission line, too, must terminate at this point in a current node to insure proper impedance matching. Here, too, we may use a transmission line that is any multiple of the quarter wavelength. If the line is an odd multiple of the quarter wave, the input end terminates in a current loop (low impedance). This requires a series-resonant tuning circuit (Fig. 36-18-C). If it is an even multiple of the quarter wave, the input end terminates in a current node (high impedance), necessitating a parallel-resonant tuning circuit (Fig. 36-18-D).

The *end-fed* Hertz antenna is also called the *voltage-fed* antenna, since the transmission line is connected at a point of voltage loop or maximum. Another name for this type is the *Zeppelin* or *Zepp* antenna, since it was used first on the Zeppelin dirigible.

We have seen how the nonresonant transmission lines may be connected to the Hertz antenna (Fig. 36-15). Yet another method makes use of the *quarter-wave stub*. A resonant transmission line, a quarter-wave long, is connected to the Hertz antenna, just as any other resonant transmission line. The end corresponding to the input end of the line, however, is left open. A nonresonant line, coupled to the transmitter, is connected to this quarter-wave stub at a point where the impedance on the stub equals the characteristic impedance of the nonresonant line. The stub acts as a sort of transformer, coupling the nonresonant line to the antenna (Fig. 36-19).

The Marconi antenna, too, may be connected to the transmission line in a number of different ways. Generally, nonresonant transmission lines are used. Figure 36-20-A shows the antenna inductively coupled to the transmitter. Since the coupling coil increases the natural frequency of the antenna, a capacitor may be inserted to bring it back again to its desired value. Figure 36-20-B shows the twisted-pair line being used. In Figure 36-20-C, the coaxial line is used. A variation is shown in Figure 36-20-D. Here, the transmission line is terminated on a point on the antenna where the impedance is equal to the characteristic impedance of the line, thus insuring impedance matching.

Resistance and Power in the Antenna. Resistance in an antenna is of two types. One is the *radiation resistance* arising from the fact that it is the function of the antenna to radiate power supplied it by the transmitter. The other is the *ohmic* or *loss* resistance, which is inherent in the wires that go to make up the antenna. This loss can

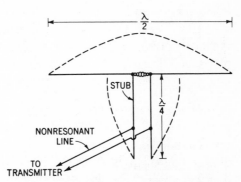

Fig. 36-19. *Current distribution on an antenna using quarter-wave matching stub.*

be kept very low by the use of heavy wire or copper tubing and carefully constructed joints. As a matter of fact, this resistance can be kept so low as to be negligible.

In addition to loss of power due to the loss resistance and radiation resistance, there are other losses due to absorption of power by nearby structures, pipes, and so on. For this reason, the antenna should be kept as far as possible from such objects. Other losses occur from slight leakage across insulators supporting an antenna. An attempt should be made to connect the insulators at low-voltage points on the antenna. In the case of the grounded (Marconi) antenna, the resistance of the ground introduces still another loss; hence a good ground connection is essential.

We may calculate the electrical power in the antenna by multiplying the square of the maximum current (at a current loop) by the assumed radiation resistance of the antenna:

$$P = I^2 \times R$$

Radiation Characteristics. If we erect a vertical antenna and measure the field strength of the wave radiated from it in a circle which has the antenna at its center, we find that this field is equally strong at all points on this circle. Thus we can draw a pattern of the *radiation characteristics* of this antenna by means of a circle (Fig. 36-21-A). This pattern is known as the *radiation pattern*. Since this is the pattern we would draw upon the ground if we were above the antenna looking down, we call it the *horizontal pattern*. It is the pattern of the radio waves radiated parallel to the ground.

If we were to draw the pattern of the radiated waves which are not horizontal to the ground, we would get a pattern as appears in Figure 36-21-B. This figure is called the *vertical pattern*

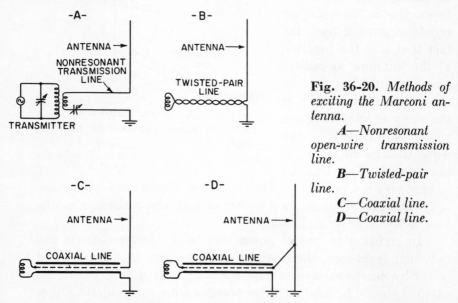

Fig. 36-20. *Methods of exciting the Marconi antenna.*

A—Nonresonant open-wire transmission line.

B—Twisted-pair line.

C—Coaxial line.

D—Coaxial line.

of radiation. To understand what it means, you must assume that the distance from the center of the antenna to the curve, along any particular line, represents the relative field strength in that direction. Thus, if line OA is twice as long as OB, the field strength in the direction of OA is twice as strong as in the direction OB.

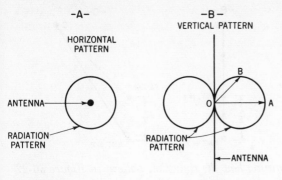

Fig. 36-21. *Radiation pattern of a vertical antenna.*
A—The horizontal radiation pattern.
B—The vertical radiation pattern.

Although the pattern in Figure 36-21-B appears in two dimensions, the actual pattern is three-dimensional. To get this, you must rotate the figure about the antenna as an axis. You would then get a sort of doughnut with practically no hole and the antenna running through it at the center.

Antennas in Arrays.
These patterns are for a single vertical, half-wave antenna. To obtain radiation which has directional effects, two or more such antennas may be combined. The simplest combination or *array* consists of two vertical, half-wave antennas spaced a half wavelength apart. Equal currents are fed into each antenna in step (in phase) with each

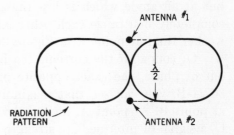

Fig. 36-22. *The horizontal pattern of two vertical half-wave antennas, a half wave apart, with their currents in phase.*

other so that the currents reach their maximum in the same direction at the same instant. Figure 36-22 shows the horizontal pattern of such an array.

To understand how we arrive at this pattern, examine Figure 36-23. In Figure 36-23-A, since the currents in both antennas are in phase and since the distances the two radio waves travel in reaching point A are the same, the two waves arrive in step or phase and reinforce each other, giving a strong signal.

In Figure 36-23-B the wave from antenna No. 2, arriving at point B, has traveled a half wavelength farther than the radio wave from antenna No. 1. Since a half wavelength represents 180°,

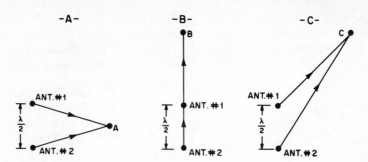

Fig. 36-23. *Diagrams explaining how the radiation pattern in Figure 36-22 is formed.*

the currents set flowing by the two radio waves at point B are equal, but in opposite directions. Thus, they neutralize each other, and no signal is heard.

In Figure 36-23-C the two radio waves arrive out of phase, but at an angle which is less than 180°. They, therefore, do not completely neutralize each other, and the signal is heard, though weaker than at point A in Figure 36-23-A.

Of course, if the currents fed into the two antennas are 180° out of phase, the exact opposite of the above results. In Figure 36-24-B, you can see that maximum signal strength will be had at point B. At point A, no signal will be heard, whereas at point C, a signal of intermediate strength will be received. Figure 36-24-A shows the pattern for this array.

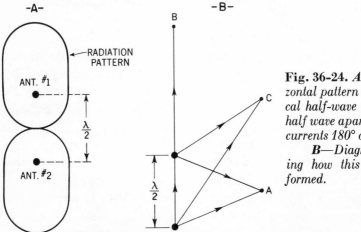

Fig. 36-24. *A—The horizontal pattern of two vertical half-wave antennas, a half wave apart, with their currents 180° out of phase.*

B—Diagram showing how this pattern is formed.

Other directional patterns may be obtained by spacing the antennas differently, using currents with different phase differences, and using more antennas in the array. Of particular interest is the array shown in Figure 36-25. Here the two half-wave an-

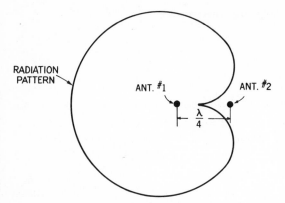

RADIATION
PATTERN

ANT. #1   ANT. #2

$\frac{\lambda}{4}$

Fig. 36-25. *Unidirectional pattern (cardioid) for two vertical, half-wave antennas, a quarter wave apart with currents 90° out of phase.*

tennas are spaced a quarter wavelength apart, and the current is fed into them 90° out of phase. The resulting pattern is called the *cardioid* or *undirectional* pattern because most of the energy is transmitted in one direction.

The half-wave horizontal antenna has characteristics comparable to those of the vertical antenna. But the vertical pattern of the horizontal antenna resembles the horizontal pattern of the vertical antenna, and vice versa (Fig. 36-26).

Horizontal antennas may also be arranged in arrays to get a wide variety of directional patterns.

Some of the radio waves radiated by the antenna strike the ground and are reflected upward. This reflected energy affects the vertical pattern of the antenna (Fig. 36-27). The effect is as

Fig. 36-26. *Radiation pattern of a horizontal antenna. Note that it is the opposite of the vertical antenna.*
A—Vertical pattern.
B—Horizontal pattern.

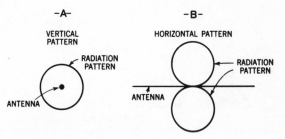

-A-

VERTICAL PATTERN

RADIATION PATTERN

ANTENNA

-B-

HORIZONTAL PATTERN

RADIATION PATTERN

ANTENNA

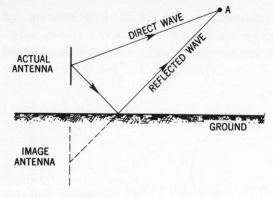

Fig. 36-27. *Diagram showing the effect of the ground upon the vertical radiation pattern of an antenna.*

if there were an *image* antenna located beneath the surface of the ground and transmitting a simultaneous signal. We may treat the actual antenna and image antenna as though they formed an array, and thus determine the resulting pattern.

Let us examine the radiation characteristics of the loop as a transmitting antenna. Since the dimensions of the loop usually are small compared to the wavelength, we may consider the current at any instant as flowing in one direction (Fig. 36-28-A).

We may, therefore, regard the two vertical arms as an array of two vertical antennas, less than a wavelength apart and with the currents flowing in *opposite phase* to each other (one current is up when the other is down). This gives us the horizontal pattern shown in Figure 36-28-B.

The top and bottom parts of the loop are equivalent to two horizontal antennas, also 180° out of phase. Their pattern is also a figure eight, this time vertical (Fig. 36-28-C). You can now see

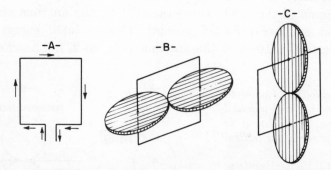

Fig. 36-28. *A—Current flow in a loop antenna.*
B—Pattern for the vertical arms of the loop.
C—Pattern for the horizontal arms of the loop.

why the loop will not radiate any signals in directions toward which its flat sides are pointed.

The Receiving Antenna. We have seen that the purpose of the transmitting antenna is to radiate the radio wave. And to insure maximum power transfer, the antenna is treated as a resonant circuit tuned to the frequency of the radio wave. The purpose of the receiving antenna is to obtain the maximum power transfer from the radio wave. Thus the receiving antenna, too, should be a resonant circuit tuned to the frequency of the radio wave.

To construct such a resonant receiving antenna in the ordinary broadcast band (535 to 1,605 kilocycles) is not very practical. For example, a half-wavelength of the radio wave broadcast by station WOR (710 kc) is equal to about 211 meters (approximately 232 yards). Since the power of the broadcast transmitter is generally quite large, most broadcast receivers do not use the resonant antenna but, rather, a self-contained loop antenna. Where the receiver is a considerable distance from the transmitting station, a raised wire about 100 feet long generally suffices.

However, in the FM broadcast band (88 to 108 megacycles), in the regular television band (54 to 216 megacycles), and in the ultra-high-frequency television band (470 to 890 megacycles), the resonant antenna does become practical. For example, in the regular television band, half-wavelengths range from 0.7 to 2.75 meters. Hertzian, or dipole, antennas of these lengths can be constructed and erected very easily.

Receiving Antennas Used for Television. Let us consider a dipole receiving antenna to be used in the regular television band. It must cover a range from 54 to 216 megacycles, divided into twelve channels of 6 megacycles each. The frequency allocations of these channels are as follows:

Channel	Frequency (mc)	Channel	Frequency (mc)
2	54-60	8	180-186
3	60-66	9	186-192
4	66-72	10	192-198
5	76-82	11	198-204
6	82-88	12	204-210
7	174-180	13	210-216

Because it is impractical to put up an antenna for each channel, we use a type that is tuned to the geometric center of the band and that is wide-band enough to encompass the entire band. To find the geometric center of the band, we take the square root of the product of the band limits. Thus, the geometric center of the regular television band ($\sqrt{54 \times 216}$) is 108 megacycles.

A rule-of-thumb method for finding the length of a half-wave dipole antenna that is tuned for a certain frequency is expressed in the following formula:

$$\frac{468}{\text{Frequency (in mc)}} = \text{Length of half-wave dipole (in feet).}$$

Thus, a half-wave dipole antenna resonating at 108 megacycles should be 4.3 feet long (486/108).

This dipole antenna is illustrated in Figure 36-29-A. The antenna for television receivers generally is mounted horizontally. It is center-fed with the two elements placed end-to-end and a few inches apart. As is true of all half-wave Hertz antennas, its impedance at center is about 73 ohms. Thus it can be connected to a nonresonant, flexible, coaxial cable whose characteristic impedance, too, is 73 ohms. The input section of the television receiver then must have an impedance of 73 ohms to match the cable.

The antenna must receive signals from a very wide band (54

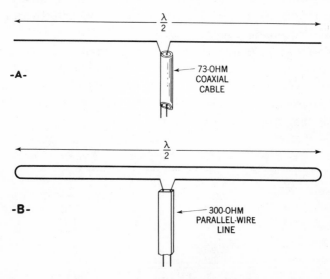

Fig. 36-29. *A—The simple dipole.*
B—The folded dipole.

to 216 megacycles). From our study of resonant circuits (Chapter 34) we learned that the higher the resistance in that circuit, the less the selectivity and the broader the tuning curve becomes. To increase the resistance of the dipole antenna, we can increase the diameter of the elements. This is practical up to a certain point. Then the antenna becomes unwieldy.

The Folded-Dipole Antenna. Another method for effectively increasing the resistance of the antenna is to place another element equal in size to the full length of the antenna parallel to it and a few inches away. Then, because the current at the ends of such antennas is equal to zero (see Fig. 36-5), the ends can be joined without danger of short circuit. This is the *folded-dipole* antenna illustrated in Figure 36-29-B.

The center-impedance of this folded-dipole antenna is about four times that of the simple dipole, namely, about 300 ohms. The antenna usually is connected to the receiver through a 300-ohm, flexible, parallel-wire line. The wires are spaced about ⅜ inch apart and are encased in a plastic ribbon. The input section of the television receiver, too, should have an impedance of 300 ohms.

Other Broad-Band Antennas. There are several other methods for increasing the resistance of the antenna and, hence, its broad-band qualities. An antenna that is quite popular is the *double-V* type, illustrated in Figure 36-30-A. The double wire of each vee increases the effective diameter of each element and, thus, increases the resistance of the antenna. The angles formed by the vees determine this resistance and they can be adjusted to give the antenna an impedance of 300 ohms to match the 300-ohm parallel-wire line.

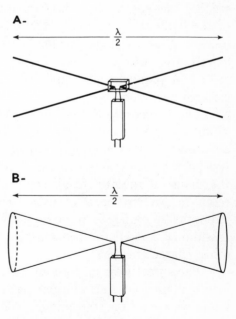

Fig. 36-30. *A—The double-V antenna.*
B—The double-cone antenna.

Another broad-band antenna is the *double cone* type illustrated in Figure 36-30-B. This type acts like the double-V antenna. It can be constructed of sheet metal, wire screening, or metal rods held together with a wire frame. There are a great many variations of the above types of antenna.

Using Two Antennas to Cover the Band. As you see, the wide band of frequencies to be covered by a single antenna presents quite a problem. Often, this problem is met by dividing the entire frequency band in two. The lower half encompasses channels 2, 3, 4, 5, and 6, covering a frequency range from 54 to 88 megacycles. The upper half includes channels 7, 8, 9, 10, 11, 12, and 13, covering a frequency range from 174 to 216 megacycles. Two separate antennas are used, each tuned to the geometric center of its half of the band. Thus each antenna need not tune as broadly as one that would cover the entire band.

The geometric center of the lower half of the band ($\sqrt{54 \times 88}$) is 69 megacycles. Applying our rule-of-thumb equation

$$\left(L \text{ (feet)} = \frac{468}{\text{Frequency (mc)}} \right)$$

we find the length of the half-wave dipole to cover this lower half of the band to be 6.8 feet. Similarly, the geometric center of the upper half of the band ($\sqrt{174 \times 216}$) is 194 megacycles and the length of a half-wave dipole is 2.4 feet. The two antennas are connected in parallel and signals from both are led to the receiver through a common line.

The Directivity Pattern of the Dipole Antenna. Since the television receiving antenna has small physical size, we can take full advantage of its directional properties. Just as the *radiation pattern* of a transmitting antenna indicates the relative strengths of the signals it radiates to all compass points around it, so the *directivity pattern* of a receiving antenna indicates the relative strengths of signals it receives from all compass points around it (assuming that all the transmitters are identical in power and all other characteristics).

The directivity pattern of an antenna used for receiving is identical to what its radiation pattern would be if the same antenna were used for transmitting. Thus the directivity pattern of a half-wave dipole receiving antenna is the same as the radiation pattern of the same antenna used as a transmitter. (See Fig. 36-

26-B.) Signals are received best from transmitters located perpendicular to the length of the antenna. Note, too, that signals from transmitters on both sides of the antenna are received equally well. One advantage of antennas of small physical size is that they can easily be mounted on rotators and so turned for best reception from each of a number of different transmitting stations.

The Use of Reflectors and Directors. We may change the directivity pattern of a receiving antenna by the use of *parasitic elements.* For example, one such parasitic element is the *reflector* illustrated in Figure 36-31-A. This reflector is a simple rod about

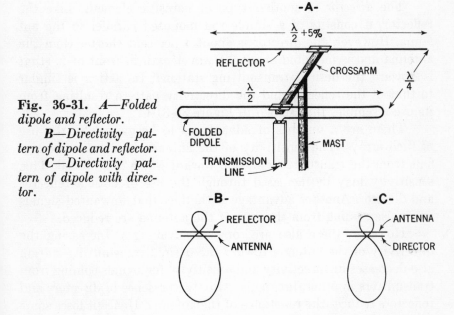

Fig. 36-31. *A—Folded dipole and reflector.*

B—Directivity pattern of dipole and reflector.

C—Directivity pattern of dipole with director.

5 per cent longer than the antenna mounted parallel to it and a quarter wavelength behind it (that is, away from the desired transmitting station). The directivity pattern resulting from such an array is shown in Figure 36-31-B.

The signal coming from the desired transmitting station in front of the array strikes first the antenna and then its reflector. Current is induced in both. As a result, the reflector re-radiates the signal, which is picked up by the antenna. Thus there are two currents set flowing in the antenna, one from the transmitter and one from the reflector. Because of the size of the reflector.and its distance from the antenna, the two currents are in phase and augment each other. Hence, the receiver obtains a stronger signal than if there had been no reflector.

Signals coming from the back of the array (either from another transmitter or as reflections of the original desired signal) strike first the reflector and then the antenna. Again two currents are induced in the antenna. But this time the currents are out of phase and tend to cancel each other. Thus signals coming from behind the array are received weaker than if there had been no reflector. You see now the reason for the directivity pattern shown in Figure 36-31-B.

The *director* is another type of parasitic element. Like the reflector, it consists of a simple rod mounted parallel to the antenna. However, the director is about 4 per cent shorter than the antenna and is mounted about 0.1 wavelength in front of it (that is, toward the desired transmitting station). Its action is similar to that of the reflector and the directivity pattern resulting from its use resembles that shown in Figure 36-31-C.

There are a number of advantages to be gained by the use of such arrays. The sensitivity of the antenna is increased to signals from the transmitting station toward which it is aimed. This sensitivity may be increased through the use of both a reflector and director. Another advantage is the fact that unwanted signals and noise coming from the rear of the antenna are reduced.

However, there also are some disadvantages. Increasing the directivity of the antenna toward the desired transmitting station also decreases its directivity and sensitivity for signals coming from transmitters in other directions. Also, the presence of directors and reflectors reduces the resistance of the antenna. Hence it loses some of its broad-band characteristics.

SUMMARY

1. The antenna is a resonant circuit, coupled to the transmitter, and is used to radiate the radio wave. Tuning of the antenna is performed by adjusting its length so that it conforms to the wavelength (which is a function of the frequency) of the radio wave.

2. A characteristic of the antenna is the presence of standing waves of current and voltage along its length. These standing waves are

sinusoidal in form and have nodes and antinodes (or loops) a half wavelength apart, respectively. A current node appears at a point where there is a voltage loop, and a voltage node appears at a point of current loop.

3. Antennas fall into two main types—the elevated or Hertz antenna and the grounded or Marconi type. The Hertz antenna has a current node at each end, but the Marconi type has a current loop at the grounded end. The radiation resistance is about 73 ohms for the Hertz antenna and 36 ohms for the Marconi type. The Hertz antenna may be operated at any harmonic frequency, and the Marconi type may be operated at any odd harmonic of the fundamental frequency.

4. A transmission line is used to couple the antenna to the output of the transmitter. This line may be of a resonant or nonresonant type.

5. The resonant transmission line has standing waves of current and voltage along its length. The nonresonant line is terminated in its characteristic impedance and, therefore, has practically no standing waves.

6. The input end of the transmission line is coupled to the output of the transmitter through a coupling network. The output of the transmission line is impedance-matched to the antenna. The half-wave Hertz antenna may be either center-fed (current-fed) or end-fed (voltage-fed).

7. Antennas may be arranged in arrays to produce various types of characteristic patterns.

GLOSSARY

Antinodes: Regions along an antenna or resonant line where the current or voltage is maximum.

Center Feed: A method of coupling the transmission lines of a transmitter to the center of the half-wave antenna.

Current-Fed Antenna: Another name for a center-fed half-wave antenna.

Dipole Antenna: A center-fed Hertz antenna.

Distributed Inductance and Capacitance: Capacitance and inductance distributed almost uniformly throughout a resonant circuit.

End Feed: A method of coupling one wire of the transmission line to one end of a half-wave antenna, allowing the other wire of the transmission line to be free.

Feeder Lines: The lines coupling a transmitter to an antenna.

Folded Dipole Antenna: A center-fed Hertz antenna with another element of equal length placed parallel to it and a few inches apart, the ends of the antenna and the other element being joined.

Fundamental Frequency: The lowest frequency to which an antenna is resonant.

Harmonics: Simple whole-number multiples of the fundamental frequency.

Hertz Antenna: A simple ungrounded antenna.

Horizontal Radiation Pattern: Pattern of radiation from an antenna as viewed from above.

Loading: Adding capacitance or inductance to an antenna to make it resonant for various frequencies.

Loops: Same as antinodes.

Lumped Inductances and Capacitances: Capacitance and inductance concentrated in definite parts of a resonant circuit.

Marconi Antenna: A simple grounded antenna.

Nodes: Regions along an antenna or resonant line where the current or voltage is zero.

Nonresonant Transmission Line: A transmission line that is terminated in its characteristic impedance, hence there are no standing waves.

Radiation Pattern: The horizontal and vertical pattern of radiation of radio waves from an antenna.

Radiation Resistance: Energy radiated by an antenna is equivalent to energy dissipated in a resistor. The radiation resistance is the value of this equivalent resistance.

Reflector: A parasitic element slightly longer than the antenna mounted parallel and a quarter wavelength behind it.

Resonant Transmission Lines: Transmission lines resonant to the transmitted frequency.

Standing Wave: An electrical wave in an antenna or resonant line, with fixed nodes and loops.

Transmission Lines: Lines connecting the transmitter to the antenna—that is, feeder lines.

Vertical Radiation Pattern: Pattern of radiation from an antenna as viewed from the ground.

Voltage-Fed Antenna: Same as an end-fed antenna.

QUESTIONS AND PROBLEMS

1. Differentiate between lumped inductances and capacitances, and distributed inductances and capacitances.
2. What must be the frequency relationship between the antenna and transmitter to insure maximum radiation of the radio wave?
3. Describe the current and voltage distribution along a half-wave Hertz antenna.
4. Describe the current and voltage distribution along a quarter-wave Marconi antenna.

5. State the formula for conversion of frequency into wavelength, and give the units for each factor.
6. What is the relationship between the size of a Hertz antenna and the wavelength of the radio wave radiated by it?
7. What is the relationship between the size of a Marconi antenna and the wavelength of the radio wave radiated by it?
8. At what harmonic frequency may we operate the Hertz antenna? The Marconi antenna?
9. Explain what is meant by "loading an antenna."
10. What is meant by "radiation resistance"?
11. Name the two main types of transmission lines and give the characteristics of each.
12. Explain what is meant by "characteristic impedance" of a line.
13. How would you test a transmission line for standing waves?
14. Name three types of nonresonant transmission lines.
15. List two advantages of the nonresonant transmission line over the resonant line.
16. What is meant by "impedance matching"?
17. Draw a diagram of the coupling network between the output of the transmitter and the input of a resonant transmission line which has a current loop at its input end.
18. Describe two methods of coupling a nonresonant transmission line to the output of a transmitter.
19. By means of a diagram, show how you would connect a center-fed, half-wave Hertz antenna to a half-wave resonant transmission line. Show the standing waves of current.
20. Repeat the above, but this time show a half-wave Hertz antenna being end-fed by a half-wave resonant transmission line.
21. What is meant by the "radiation pattern" of an antenna?
22. How does a folded dipole differ from a simple dipole antenna?
23. Explain the use of a director and reflector with a folded dipole antenna.

37

Radio-Tube Characteristics

PROBLEM 1. *How do we show by graphs the characteristics of radio tubes?*

PROBLEM 2. *How do we use the characteristic curves of tubes to calculate plate current, plate resistance, or amplification factors?*

PROBLEM 3. *How do we calculate power output and voltage amplification?*

The Diode in Operation. From our previous studies, we have learned that the basic principle of the radio tube is that a heated filament or cathode shoots off electrons which are attracted to a positively charged plate and are made to flow through the plate circuit (Chap. 27).

The simplest type of radio tube is the two-electrode *diode,* containing a cathode and plate. We have learned before that if the plate is charged positively, the electrons will be attracted to it and will flow in the plate circuit. If the plate is charged negatively, the electrons will be repelled and no current will flow in the plate circuit.

If we connect our diode as in Figure 37-1, and keep the current from the filament battery constant, we are able to see the relationship between changes in the B or plate voltage and the number of electrons attracted to the plate (that is, the amount of plate current as measured by the milliammeter).

Plotting the Diode Characteristic Curve. If we plot our findings on a graph, we get a curve similar to that of Figure 37-2. This curve is called the *characteristic curve* of the diode. Arrange the circuit as shown in Figure 37-1 with a clip on one of the leads to the B battery. Connect a voltmeter across the part of the B bat-

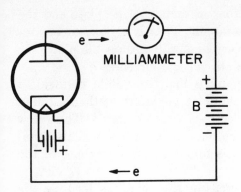

Fig. 37-1. *Circuit to show relationship between plate current and plate voltage.*

tery which is successively connected to furnish the voltage for the plate. Begin with a low voltage and successively attach the movable clip to higher and higher voltages. Each time a new voltage is used, record the reading of the voltmeter and the milliammeter. When the table is complete—say with eight or ten readings—transfer the data to the graph as follows: Mark off on the vertical axis (Y) the units of current in milliamperes. On the horizontal axis (X), mark off units of volts. For each volt reading, put a ruler on the point corresponding to it on the horizontal axis; draw a faint line upward from this point. Now find the point on the Y axis that corresponds to the reading of the milliammeter taken for the specific voltage, and with the ruler, draw a faint line horizontally. Where this line of the current level crosses the vertical line indicating the voltage, make a dot. Continue to plot each reading of voltmeter and milliammeter in the same way. When all the dots are located on the chart, connect the points by a continuous line. This line is the course or curve of the current under the influence of changing voltage on the plate.

Notice that, except for the bends at the bottom and top, the curve is a straight line bearing upward and to the right. This means that an increase in the plate voltage causes an

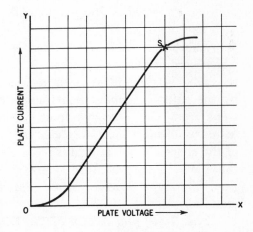

Fig. 37-2. *Graph showing the characteristic curve of the diode.*

increase in the number of electrons attracted to the plate and the current set flowing in the plate circuit. That is to say, except for the very low voltages and the very high voltages on the plate, the plate current increases as the plate voltage increases.

When the charge on the plate is low (low plate voltage), a space charge, produced by a cloud of electrons, gathers around the cathode and repels new electrons being emitted. Thus, few electrons reach the plate, and the plate current is low. This situation accounts for the bend that is found in the lower end of the curve.

As the plate voltage is increased, the electrons forming the space charge are attracted to the plate, and the number of electrons reaching the plate each second is increased. Soon a point is reached (point *S* on the curve) where *all* the electrons being emitted by the cathode are immediately attracted to the plate. Increasing the plate voltage beyond this point cannot increase the plate current because the cathode is not able to send out electrons any faster. This point is called the *saturation point* of the tube. The amount of current flowing in the plate circuit when the saturation point is reached is called the *saturation* or *emission* current.

Reducing the Space Charge. If the space charge were not present to repel electrons coming from the cathode, then the same plate current could be produced at a lower plate voltage. One method for making this space charge small is to make the distance between the cathode and plate small. This method is used in tubes such as type 35Z5-GT.

Another method is to introduce a small amount of mercury, which becomes vaporized when the tube is in use. The space inside the tube is thus filled with mercury atoms. Electrons shot off by the cathode collide with these atoms and tear off other electrons from the mercury atoms, thus *ionizing* them. Since these mercury *ions* are positively charged, they neutralize the electrons of the space charge, and thus more electrons are made available to the plate. Tubes of this type are called *mercury-vapor rectifiers*. The type 83 tube is an example with a filament type of emitter.

The Rectifying Action of the Diode. We can use the characteristic curve to show what happens if the steady direct voltage of the B battery is replaced with an alternating voltage (Fig. 37-3). In this figure, we have combined two graphs into one. First, there is the graph for the alternating-voltage input to the diode. Then, there is the graph for the characteristic curve of the tube. The action of the alternating voltage in the diode produces the rectified output, a series of direct-current pulses. We learned the importance of this phenomenon and explained it in some detail when we discussed the diode detector and the power supply (Chaps. 14 and 18).

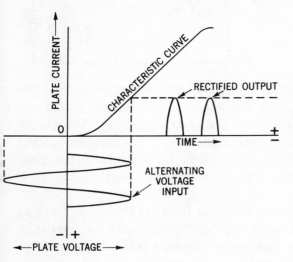

Fig. 37-3. *How the characteristic curve of the diode is used to show the relationship between voltage input and the current output.*

Subletters on Symbols. At this point, mention should be made of a sort of shorthand used by scientists. We know that the symbol for voltage or potential difference is E, the symbol for current is I, and for resistance the symbol R is used. If we wish to denote the potential difference between the plate and the cathode, we use the symbol E with the subscript p. Thus, the new symbol becomes E_p. Similarly, the plate current becomes I_p. The filament voltage is E_f, and the filament current is I_f. Grid voltage becomes E_g and grid current I_g. This system is logical and saves using many unnecessary words.

The Characteristic Curve of the Triode. The *triode* contains a third electrode, the grid, between the filament and the plate (Chap. 15). This grid acts upon the electron stream as a sort of valve, and small variations in grid voltage cause large variations in plate current.

We may obtain the characteristic curve of the triode by means of a circuit shown in Figure 37-4. Variations in the voltage of the grid battery produce variations in plate current. By plotting one

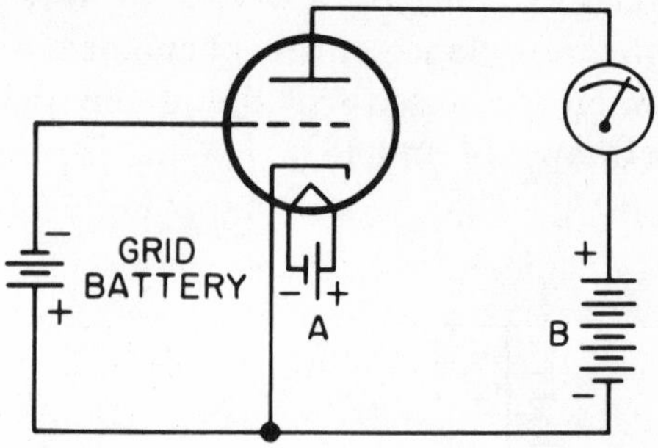

Fig. 37-4. *Hookup for obtaining the characteristic curve of a triode.*

set of values against the other, we may get the characteristic curve shown in Figure 37-5. From this curve, you will notice that a certain amount of current flows in the plate circuit even though the grid may be charged somewhat negatively. We previously learned the cause of this condition: The stream of electrons to the plate is not cut off completely until an appreciable negative charge is placed on the grid.

You will note also that the bend found in the diode curve at the saturation point toward the top of the curve is practically missing. The reason for this greater linearity is that modern tubes using indirectly heated cathodes as emitters can furnish more electrons than can be conducted away by the plate at the applied potentials, and therefore the plate current continues to mount with increases in the plate voltage (that is, within the limits normally encountered in radio work).

The Effect of Grid Bias Shown by a Curve. We learned that if the grid ever becomes positive, it will attract some of the electrons shot out by the filament or cathode. This electron stream will cause a current to flow in the grid circuit. This current will interfere with the incoming signal, and distortion will result. The C battery is used to place a negative charge or bias on the grid to prevent the flowing of any grid current. The incoming signal makes the negative charge on the grid *more negative* or *less negative*. These variations of the negative charge on the grid produce the variations in plate current.

The effect of the grid bias can be shown graphically by use of the characteristic curve of the tube (Fig. 37-6). Figure 37-6-A shows the effect of having too low a grid bias. Note that the output curve differs from the input signal. This difference indicates distortion and is due to the fact that a portion of the positive half-cycle of the signal is great enough to overcome the grid bias, and the grid becomes positive. The grid bias must be negative enough to be larger than the peak of the positive half-cycle of the signal.

Figure 37-6-B shows the distortion resulting from making the grid bias too large. The signal operates at the bend or *knee* of the characteristic curve, and part of the bottom loop is cut off. Although this effect is not desirable where we seek to amplify the signal, it is the desirable condition for detection (Chap. 15). You will recall that we strive to remove the bottom loop to give us the result shown in Figure 15-10. The result of having too large a grid bias is *grid-bias detection*.

Figure 37-6-C shows the correct grid bias to be used for the amplifier tube. It is neither too large nor too small. The output closely resembles the input signal. You will notice that we operate on the straight-line portion of the curve.

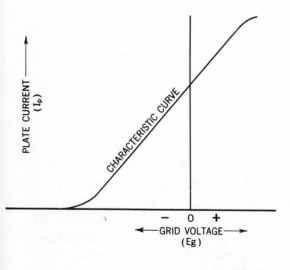

Fig. 37-5. *The grid-voltage–plate-current characteristic curve for a triode.*

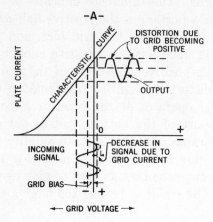

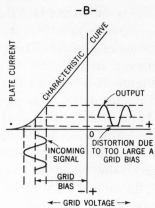

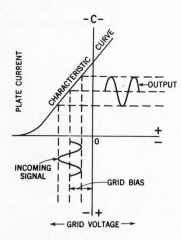

Fig. 37-6 *A—Graph showing the effect of too little grid bias.*

B—Graph showing the effect of too much grid bias.

C—Graph showing the effect of the proper grid bias.

Transfer Characteristic Curves. In Figure 37-5, we have the characteristic curve formed when variations of grid voltage (E_g) are plotted against corresponding variations of plate current (I_p). This curve is called the E_g-I_p or *transfer characteristic* curve. You will note that the potential difference between the plate and cathode (E_p) remained constant. If we change the E_p and again plot the E_g-I_p curve, we get a second curve resembling the first and lying nearly parallel to it. If, on the same graph, we plot the curves for a number of different plate voltages, we get a *family* of transfer characteristic curves. The family of such curves for a triode such as the 6J5 tube is shown in Figure 37-7.

Plate Characteristic Curve. From this family of curves, we may obtain the proper grid bias to be used for a particular tube operating at a particular plate voltage.

There is another tube relationship that may be expressed by a characteristic curve. If we keep the grid voltage (E_g) constant and vary the plate voltage (E_p), we get corresponding variations of plate current (I_p). The curve showing this relationship is called the *plate characteristic* curve. If we take different values of grid voltage, we are able to obtain a *family* of plate characteristic curves (Fig. 37-8). The tube used in this illustration is the same as for Figure 37-7.

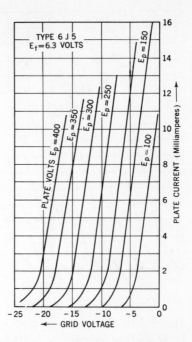

Fig. 37-7. *Family of transfer or mutual-characteristic curves for the triode (type 6J5).*

Static and Dynamic Characteristics. So far, in our consideration of the characteristic curves of the tube, we took a tube with no load in the plate circuit—that is, with only the B battery and meter. This is called the *static* condition of the tube, and the curves so obtained are called the *static characteristic curves*. But in practice, the output of the tube feeds into a load such as the primary of the coupling transformer or plate resistor. If in our diagram, we represent this load by a resistor (R) (assumed to be the equivalent of the load) and plot our curves anew, we get characteristic curves that reflect more accurately the operating conditions of the tube. These curves are called the *dynamic characteristic curves*. Figure 37-9 shows how we obtain these curves.

Figure 37-10 shows the relationship between the static curve of a typical triode (type 6J5) compared to two dynamic curves for the same tube under different conditions of load (25,000 ohms and 100,000 ohms). In all three cases, the applied B voltage (250 volts) was the same.

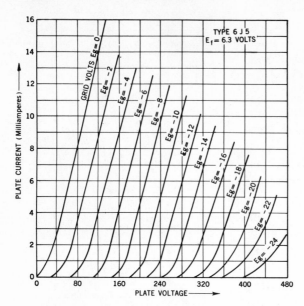

Fig. 37-8. *Family of plate characteristic curves for the 6J5 triode.*

Under static conditions (no load), the entire B voltage is applied to the plate of the tube. But if a load resistor is inserted in the plate circuit, a voltage drop will occur across that resistor as the plate current flows through it. As a result, the applied voltage to the plate will be less than the B voltage (250 volts) by the amount of this voltage drop. The higher the resistance of the load resistor, the greater the voltage drop across it, and the less the applied voltage to the plate of the tube.

This is indicated by the flattening of the dynamic curves. The higher the load resistor, the flatter the curve. Note that at the point of no-plate-current flow, all three curves coincide. This is because with no flow of plate current there is no voltage drop across the load resistors and the grid is sufficiently negative to stop the flow of plate current.

Fig. 37-9. *Circuit for obtaining the dynamic characteristic curves of a triode.*

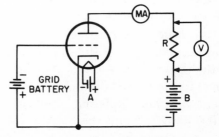

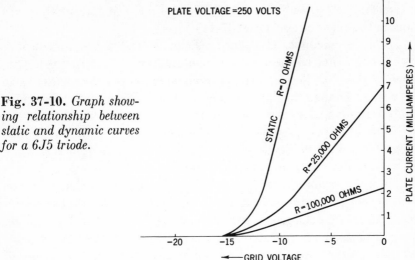

Fig. 37-10. *Graph showing relationship between static and dynamic curves for a 6J5 triode.*

How We Use the Characteristic Curves. An examination of the family of curves shown in Figure 37-8 shows us the interrelation of the grid-bias voltage, the plate voltage, and the plate current. Knowing any two values will give us the third. Thus, if we know we are to apply a grid bias of —8 volts to the 6J5 tube and place 250 volts on the plate, we can determine the plate current that will flow during the maximum signal swing. Here is how.

Along the plate-voltage axis (the horizontal axis) pick out the point representing 250 volts. From this point, draw a line vertically upward until it intersects the curve marked $E_g = -8$. This curve is the characteristic curve of the tube for a —8-volt grid bias. From the point of intersection, draw a horizontal line parallel to the horizontal axis until it

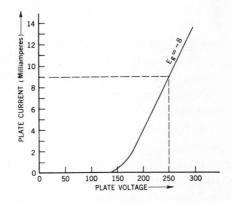

Fig. 37-11. *Plate-current–plate-voltage characteristic curve for the 6J5 triode. Grid bias is —8 volts.*

reaches the plate-current axis (the vertical axis). At this point of intersection, the plate current will read 9 ma, the current that will flow in the plate circuit (Fig. 37-11).

Plate Resistance. The *plate resistance* (R_p) is the alternating-current internal resistance of a vacuum tube—that is, the resistance of the path between the cathode and the plate. It is the ratio of a small change in plate voltage to the corresponding change in plate current and is expressed in *ohms,* the unit of resistance.

For example, assume that a change of 0.001 ampere is produced by a plate voltage variation of 10 volts. Since $R = E/I$, then $R_p = 10$ volts/0.001 ampere $= 10,000$ ohms.

Amplification Factor. We have seen that a small change in the grid potential produces a change in the plate current that is equivalent to a large change in the plate voltage. Thus, an increase of, say, 10 volts in the plate voltage may produce an increase of 0.001 ampere in the plate current. Assume that this same increase of 0.001 ampere in the plate current can be accomplished by decreasing the negative grid potential only 0.1 volt. The ratio, then, between the increase of plate voltage (10 volts) and the decrease of grid voltage (0.1 volt) required to produce the same increase in plate current (0.001 ampere) is called the *amplification factor* of the tube. In this case, it would be found by dividing the 10 volts by the 0.1 volt. This operation gives us an amplification factor of 100 for this imaginary tube.

The symbol for amplification factor is the Greek letter *mu* (μ). You will recall that we discussed the amplification factor of the tube (Chap. 27). We discovered that it is an indication of the suitability of the tube for voltage-amplification purposes.

Transconductance. The ratio between a small change in plate current and the change in grid potential producing it, all other voltages remaining constant, is called the *plate-to-grid transconductance,* or simply *transconductance.* Thus, in the tube taken for our example, the 0.001 ampere increase in plate current was produced by a decrease of 0.1 volt in the grid potential. The transconductance of the tube would then be 0.001 ampere/0.1 volt or 0.01.

You will recall that by Ohm's law, resistance is equal to the quotient of voltage divided by current. But to compute transconductance, we divide *current* by *voltage.* This is, in a sense, the reciprocal of the resistance. Accordingly, the unit for transconductance is the *mho,* which is the unit for resistance (ohm) spelled backwards.

Thus, the transconductance for our tube becomes 0.01 mho. In practice, the mho is too large for easy handling. Accordingly, we use the micromho, which is one one-millionth of a mho. Thus, our transconductance becomes 10,000 micromhos.

Transconductance is also known as *mutual conductance,* and its symbol is G_m. A tube with a high transconductance produces large plate-current variations corresponding to small variations in grid potential.

The plate resistance, amplification factor, and transconductance are interrelated. The amplification factor is essentially a product of the other two. Thus,

$$\mu = R_p \times G_m$$

where μ is the amplification factor, R_p is the plate resistance, and G_m is the transconductance, in mhos.

Power Output. We can represent the circuit of the radio tube shown in Figure 37-12-A by its equivalent circuit in Figure 37-12-B. In Figure 37-12-A, E_g is the signal voltage applied to the grid of the tube, and R is the resistance of the load. Since the signal voltage (E_g) multiplied by the amplification factor (μ) gives us the corresponding change in the plate voltage, in Figure 37-12-B the alternating-current generator marked μE_g represents the changing plate voltage. R_p stands for the plate resistance of the tube, and R for the resistance of the load. Since they both are in series, the total resistance offered to current flowing in the plate circuit is $R_p + R$.

We must remember that current *changes* in the plate circuit resulting from the signal provide the power of the signal in the load. These current changes are caused by the changing plate voltage (μE_g). Since, from Ohm's law, $I = E/R$, then:

$$I_p = \frac{\mu E_g}{R_p + R}$$

The voltage drop (E_R) across the load (R) is equal to the resistance times the current flowing through it. Then,

$$E_R = R \times \frac{\mu E_g}{R_p + R}$$

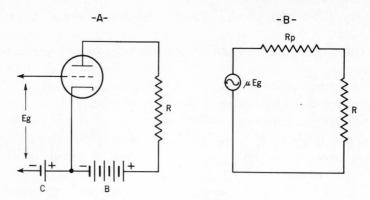

Fig. 37-12. *A—Circuit of the triode as an amplifier.*
B—The equivalent circuit of A.

The power in watts is equal to volts times amperes ($P = E \times I$). We, therefore, get for the power in the load (power output), in watts

$$P = E_R \times I_p$$

Substituting for E_R and I_p, we get

$$P = \frac{R \times \mu E_g}{R_p + R} \times \frac{\mu E_g}{R_p + R} = \frac{R \times \mu^2 E_g^2}{(R_p + R)^2}$$

Later in our study we shall show that the power output for any given signal input voltage is maximum when the plate and load resistance (R_p and R) are equal. The formula for the *maximum power output* then becomes

$$P = \frac{\mu^2 E_g^2}{4R_p}$$

The above formula applies when we deal with average values of voltage and currents. If we wish to express it in terms of a signal voltage having a *peak* value of e_g, it becomes

$$P = \frac{\mu^2 e_g^2}{8R_p}$$

(The use of e_g instead of E_g for the peak signal voltage indicates that we are dealing with an *instantaneous* value of voltage—that is, the instant the voltage is at its peak. This instantaneous value is indicated by the use of the small letter.)

Thus, for a type 2A3 tube having an amplification factor (μ) of 4.2 and a plate resistance (R_p) of 800 ohms, if the peak value of e_g is 45 volts, the maximum power output may be determined as follows:

$$P = \frac{\mu^2 e_g^2}{8R_p} = \frac{(4.2)^2 \times (45)^2}{8 \times 800} = 5.6 \text{ watts.}$$

Power Sensitivity. A convenient method for the comparison between tubes is to compare their *power sensitivity,* which is the ratio between the power output and the square of the signal-voltage input. This relationship may be expressed in the following formula:

$$\text{Power sensitivity} = \frac{\text{power output}}{(\text{input signal volts})^2}.$$

Power sensitivity is expressed in mhos, power output is expressed in watts, and the input signal volts are the root-mean-square (rms) values.

Plate Dissipation. As electrons emitted by the cathode strike the plate, a certain amount of heat is generated. Since this heat energy is taken from the electrical energy, it represents a loss of power. This loss of power is called *plate dissipation.* It is the difference between the power supplied to the plate of the tube and the power delivered by the tube to the load.

Plate Efficiency. It should be remembered that the tube itself does not generate power. It is the B battery that supplies the power fed into the load. The tube acts as a sort of valve in which variations in signal voltage applied to the grid circuit allow more or less power to be drawn from the B battery and expended in the plate circuit.

The ratio, at full signal voltage, of the alternating-current power output to the average direct-current power input is called the *plate efficiency.* Since the average direct-current power input is the product of the average direct-current plate voltage times the average direct-current plate current, then

$$\text{Plate efficiency (\%)} = \frac{P}{E_p \times I_p} \times 100,$$

where E_p and I_p are, respectively, the average numbers of direct-current plate volts and direct-current plate amperes, and P is the power output in watts.

Voltage Amplification. We have seen that the plate current (I_p) flowing through the load resistance (R) in Figure 37-12-A causes a voltage drop in R varying directly with the plate current. The ratio of this voltage variation produced in the load resistance to the input signal voltage (E_g) is the *voltage amplification* or *gain*, provided by the tube. Thus,

$$\text{Voltage amplification} = \frac{E_R}{E_g}$$

But we have seen that

$$E_R = \frac{R \times \mu E_g}{R_p + R}$$

Then,

$$\text{Voltage amplification} = \frac{\dfrac{R \times \mu E_g}{R_p + R}}{E_g} = \frac{\mu \times R}{R_p + R}$$

Thus, in our type 2A3 tube, which has a $\mu = 4.2$ and an $R_p = 800$ ohms, if we assume a load resistance of 2,500 ohms, then,

$$\text{Voltage amplification} = \frac{4.2 \times 2,500}{800 + 2,500} = \frac{10,500}{3,300} = 3.2.$$

Tetrode. In Chapter 27, it was pointed out that as the electrons emitted by the cathode strike the plate, they cause a secondary emission of electrons from the plate, owing to the force of impact. The presence of a positively charged screen grid near the plate causes some of those secondary electrons to be attracted to the screen grid, resulting in a loss for the plate. In Figure 37-13, we see a graph which illustrates this phenomenon.

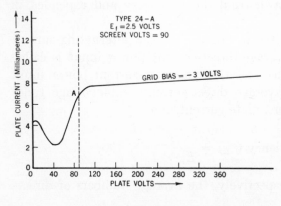

Fig. 37-13. *Plate-current —plate-voltage characteristic curve for the tetrode (type 24-A).*

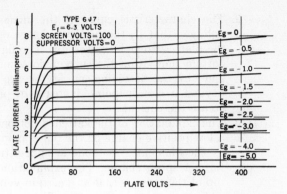

Fig. 37-14. *Family of plate-current—plate-voltage characteristic curves for the pentode (type 6J7).*

The graph is for the type 24-A tube with 90 volts applied to the screen grid. The dip in the graph indicates the fact that when the plate voltage is below that of the screen grid (90 volts), many of the secondary electrons are going to the screen grid. But when the plate voltage is increased above the 90-volt mark (as shown by A on the graph), the greater positive charge on the plate attracts most of these electrons and the graph becomes normal.

Pentode. One of the effects of the secondary emission from the plate is to limit the available alternating-current output voltage, since true amplifier action does not extend below point A of the graph in Figure 37-13. This defect is remedied in the pentode by the introduction of the suppressor grid, which herds the secondary electrons back to the plate.

In Figure 37-14, you will see a family of curves for the type 6J7 pentode. Note that the dip is not present.

It is suggested that you review the chapter on types of tubes (Chap. 27) and that you study the characteristics and curves of various types of tubes as given in the manuals issued by the various tube manufacturers.*

SUMMARY

1. The *characteristic curves* of vacuum tubes are graphs showing the relation between two of their variables plotted on the X and Y axes. The data for the curve are supplied by the readings of voltmeters and milliammeters.

* See, for example, the receiving tube manuals issued by the Radio Corporation of America, of Harrison, N. J., and the Sylvania Electric Products, Inc., of Emporium, Pa.

2. The characteristic curve of the **diode** shows how as the plate voltage (that is, the positive charge on the plate) is increased, the plate current increases. (a) The flat part of the curve at the bottom shows that the current does not respond to low voltages, and (b) the flattening out at the top of the curve shows that beyond a certain point, increase in plate voltage does not increase the current.

3. The explanation of the flattened bottom of the curve is that with a low positive charge on the plate, many of the electrons emitted by the filament or cathode are not attracted to the plate; hence form a space charge. The explanation of the flattening of the top of the curve is that at a certain voltage, all the electrons possible to be given off by the filament or cathode are being attracted to the plate; hence no more electron flow can take place from the filament or cathode to plate, regardless of how great a charge is put on the plate.

4. The point on the curve, corresponding to a certain plate voltage and yielding a certain current, above which no increase in plate voltage will increase the current, is called the **saturation point** of the tube.

5. The reduction of space charge in a diode is aided by (a) reducing the distance between plate and filament or cathode and (b) by the use of mercury vapor in the tube.

6. For **triodes,** curves may be made to show relations between any two factors when other factors are kept constant. For example, we may plot the relation between the signal swing on the grid and the plate-current changes, the plate voltage being kept constant.

7. The characteristic curves of tubes are used for calculations of the various values we sometimes need to know in order to build or repair a radio receiver.

GLOSSARY

Amplification Factor (μ) : The ratio between the change of plate voltage and the change of grid voltage required to give the same plate-current change.

Characteristic Curve: A graph showing the relationship between two variables of a tube, when one is made to undergo many changes.

Dynamic Characteristic Curves: Characteristic curves obtained under operating conditions of a tube.

Emission Current: The current flowing when the saturation point of a tube is reached.

Ion: An atom with a positive or negative charge.

Mercury-Vapor Rectifier: A tube in which mercury vapor fills the inner space instead of its being a vacuum.

Mutual Conductance: The ratio between a small change in plate current and the change in grid voltage producing it.

Plate Characteristic Curve: A characteristic curve whose two variables are plate current and plate voltage.

Plate Dissipation: The loss of power in the form of heat at the plate of a tube.

Plate Efficiency: The ratio at full signal voltage of alternating-current power output to the average direct-current power input.

Plate Resistance (Rp): The alternating-current internal resistance of a radio tube.

Power Sensitivity: A measure of the power controlled in the plate circuit by a given input grid voltage change.

Saturation Current: The plate current flowing when the saturation point is reached.

Saturation Point: The condition of operation of a tube where further increases of plate voltage cannot produce any greater plate current.

Space Charge: The charge produced by the emitted electrons as they fill the space within the tube between cathode and plate.

Static Characteristic Curves: Characteristic curves obtained not under operating conditions.

Transconductance: Same as mutual conductance.

Transfer Characteristic Curve: A graph with two variables: grid voltage and plate current, plate voltage being kept constant.

Voltage Amplification or *Gain:* The ratio of voltage variation across the load resistor to input signal voltage.

QUESTIONS AND PROBLEMS

1. What is the basic principle of operation of a radio tube?
2. What does the characteristic curve of a diode tell us about its operation?
3. What condition accounts for the lower bend of a diode characteristic curve?
4. What condition accounts for the upper bend of a diode characteristic curve?
5. Explain two ways in which the space charge within a diode might be reduced.
6. What function does the control grid serve in the triode?
7. State the meanings of E_p, I_p, E_f, I_f, E_g, I_g.
8. Why is the upper bend of a triode characteristic curve usually not shown for modern tubes?
9. When a negative bias is placed on the grid of a triode audio-frequency amplifier, what is the function of the input signal on the grid? What is the effect on plate current?
10. What effect occurs when grid bias of a tube is too low? When it is too large?

11. What does the transfer characteristic curve tell us about a tube? What condition of the tube must be kept constant?

12. What does a plate characteristic curve tell us about a tube? What condition must be kept constant in securing such a curve?

13. Differentiate between the static and dynamic conditions of a tube.

14. How does a changing plate current affect the plate voltage?

15. How is the plate resistance of a tube computed?

16. What is the significance of the amplification factor?

17. What may be learned from the transconductance of a tube? In what units is transconductance measured?

18. Relate amplification factor, plate resistance, and transconductance in one formula.

19. When considering a tube as a generator feeding into a load, what is the formula for its voltage output?

20. State the general formula for the voltage drop across the load of a tube in the plate circuit, using μ, E_g, R, and R_p. State the general formula for power dissipated in the load.

21. When will the maximum power output occur for a tube? How may the power output be computed at that time?

22. What is the significance of the power-sensitivity rating of a tube?

23. What is the source of power developed from a tube?

24. What is meant by the voltage amplification, or gain, of a tube?

25. What effect has secondary emission within the tube?

38

Radio-Tube Amplifiers

PROBLEM 1. *What are the general principles governing the use of radio-tube amplifiers?*

PROBLEM 2. *What are the characteristics of circuits using audio-frequency amplifiers?*

PROBLEM 3. *How do radio-frequency amplifiers differ from audio-frequency amplifiers?*

General Principles. Radio-tube amplifiers fall into two broad categories. Those which are used to amplify currents whose frequencies lie between approximately 30 and 15,000 cycles per second are called *audio-frequency amplifiers*. The other group is used to amplify currents whose frequencies lie above 15 kc and is called *radio-frequency* amplifiers.

Amplifiers may be designed to serve two functions. One type has as its chief purpose to give a greatly magnified reproduction of the input signal without regard to the power delivered. We call it a *voltage amplifier*. There is another type whose chief purpose it is to deliver a relatively large amount of power to such a load as a loudspeaker or a transmitting antenna. An amplifier of this type is called a *power amplifier*.

Generally speaking, the last stage of any amplifier system (whether audio-frequency or radio-frequency) is a power stage, since it is connected to the loudspeaker (in the case of the audio-frequency amplifier) or to the antenna (in the case of the radio-frequency amplifier). The intermediate stages, sometimes called the *driver* stages, are usually voltage amplifiers for audio-frequency work and power or voltage amplifiers for radio-frequency amplification in the transmitter. The radio-frequency amplifiers in the receiver are of the voltage type.

Audio-Frequency Amplifiers. The *audio-frequency amplifier* is one that is suitable for amplifying signal voltages whose frequencies lie within the audible range—that is, from approximately 30 to 15,000 cycles per second. The amplifier must amplify, without undue discrimination, all the frequencies lying in this range. For this reason, we use nonresonant circuits to couple the various stages.

Audio-frequency amplifiers are classified also according to the operating conditions under which the tubes work. The classifications in general use are class A, class AB, and class B. These classes are covered by definitions drawn up by the Institute of Radio Engineers.

A *class A amplifier* is an amplifier in which the grid bias and signal grid voltages are such that plate current in a specific tube flows at all times.

A *class AB amplifier* is an amplifier in which the grid bias and signal grid voltages are such that plate current in a specific tube flows for appreciably more than half the electrical cycle but less than the entire cycle.

A *class B amplifier* is an amplifier in which the grid bias is approximately equal to the cutoff value, so that the plate current is approximately zero when no signal grid voltage is applied, and so that plate current in a specific tube flows for approximately half of each cycle when a signal grid voltage is applied.

Frequency and Phase Distortion. Before entering further discussion of the various classes of audio-frequency amplifiers, it might be well to consider the problem of *distortion*. Because the function of the amplifier is to produce an output whose form, as nearly as possible, coincides with that of the signal input, we must strive to cut distortion to a minimum.

First of all, there is distortion arising from the inability of the amplifier to amplify equally all frequencies of the audio range. This distortion is especially pronounced at both ends of the audio range and manifests itself by the fact that sounds whose frequencies lie at the low and high ends (low-pitched and high-pitched sounds) are not reproduced with the same relative volume as are sounds lying in the middle register. Careful selection of the component parts of the amplifier, together with the methods of tone control described in Chapter 25, can reduce this distortion to a point where it is not objectionable. This type of distortion is called *frequency distortion.*

Another form of distortion, called *delay* (or *phase*) *distortion,* results from the effects of transmission of different frequencies at different speeds, giving a relative phase shift over the frequency range in the output. This type of distortion does not concern us here and is important only in cases where ultrahigh-frequency and transmission-line work is considered.

Nonlinear Distortion. There is another type of distortion that takes place in the tube itself. It is caused by the improper selection of grid bias, which forces the tube to operate under conditions represented by the curved, or *nonlinear,* portion of the characteristic curve (Fig. 37-6). For this reason, it is called *nonlinear distortion.* Thus, Figure 37-6-A shows the distortion to the plate-current curve due to too *low* a grid bias, and Figure 37-6-B shows the distortion due to too *high* a grid bias.

Let us see how this distortion affects the signal. When too low a grid bias is used, the tops of the curve are flattened. When too high a grid bias is used, the bottoms of the curve are flattened. It can be shown, mathematically, that any periodic curve (that is, a curve that periodically repeats itself, as is the case here), regardless of shape, can be reduced to a number of simple sine curves of various amplitudes and phase relationships, but all in harmonic frequency relationship.

Here is what this statement means. Suppose you were to strike middle *C* of the piano. The frequency of that note is 256 cycles per second. Now, assume that you were to play the same note on a violin. The frequency is the same, but the note sounds different. You are able to distinguish between a note on the piano and the same note on the violin. What makes the difference?

The answer is that the difference is due to *overtones,* or *harmonics.* When middle *C* is played on the piano or violin, we not only get frequencies of 256 cycles per second (called the *fundamental frequency*) but at the same time sounds are produced whose frequencies are two, three, or more times as great. These sounds are called *overtones,* or *harmonics,* and they are said to be in *harmonic relationship* with the fundamental frequency (that is, they are frequencies produced by multiplying the fundamental frequency by a whole number such as 2, 3, 4, 5, and so forth).

The harmonic whose frequency is twice the fundamental is called the *second harmonic;* three times the fundamental frequency produces the *third harmonic;* and so forth. The piano and violin differ in that they produce these harmonics in different proportions and strengths. That is why *C* on the piano sounds different from *C* on the violin.

When dealing with sound, these harmonics are not considered distortions, but are really part of the distinguishing feature, or quality, of the sound. But in electrical circuits, harmonics are distortions and produce waveforms which are different from the original. Let us see how that occurs.

How Harmonics Produce Distortion. Assume we have a sine curve which we will consider the fundamental, and its second harmonic which lies entirely below the zero axis (Fig. 38-1). You can see that by adding the two curves together, we get a new curve with the tops flattened. But this new curve resembles the curve of Figure 37-6-A. Thus, we can consider the curve resulting from too low a grid bias as being produced by the fundamental frequency plus its second harmonic. Now you can see how the harmonics cause distortion of the signal.

If we were to take the second harmonic to be entirely above the zero line, we would get a curve like Figure 37-6-B (Fig. 38-2). Here, the curve resulting from too high a grid bias is produced by the fundamental frequency plus its second harmonic.

Similarly, we can break down any distortion of the signal

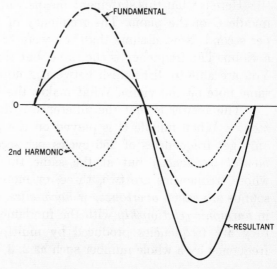

Fig. 38-1. *Graph showing the effect of adding the fundamental to the second harmonic which is below the X axis.*

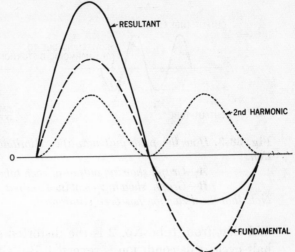

Fig. 38-2. *Graph showing the effect of adding the fundamental to the second harmonic which is above the X axis.*

waveform as being due to the presence of harmonics (second and higher) of the fundamental. These harmonics rapidly decrease in strength as their frequencies differ from the fundamental. Thus, the second harmonic may be strong enough to cause distortion in the audio-frequency amplifier, and steps must be taken to eliminate it, but harmonics of the order of the third or higher usually are negligible.

Sometimes, as we shall see later when we consider the transmitter, we deliberately seek to generate these harmonics.

Correcting Nonlinear Distortion. The remedy for nonlinear distortion is to choose correct grid-bias and plate-voltage values so that the tube may be operated on the straight portion of the curve. The *push-pull amplifier* (pages 233-234) also serves to reduce nonlinear distortion, especially second-harmonic distortion. You will recall that each tube in the push-pull arrangement operated on different half-cycles of the signal; while one tube was handling the positive half-cycle, the other was handling the negative half-cycle.

You will also recall that both tubes simultaneously delivered their outputs to the center-tapped primary of the output transformer (Fig. 27-4). These two outputs were added together to give the total output of the stage of amplification.

Now let us see how the second-harmonic distortion is removed (Fig. 38-3). From Figure 38-3-A, you can see that during the first half-cycle, the output from tube No. 1 is the undistorted signal,

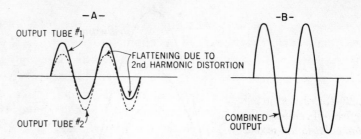

 OUTPUT TUBE #1

FLATTENING DUE TO
2nd HARMONIC DISTORTION

OUTPUT TUBE #2

COMBINED
OUTPUT

Fig. 38-3. *How the push-pull amplifier eliminates second-harmonic distortion.*

A—*Graph showing output of each tube.*

B—*Graph showing combined output of the output transformer. Note that the distortion has been eliminated.*

and that from tube No. 2 is the distorted signal. During the next half-cycle, this condition is reversed. But since the two outputs are added together, the *total* output for each half-cycle is the same and therefore the over-all effect is to produce an output signal whose waveform closely resembles that of the input signal.

Of course, this method eliminates only second-harmonic (and other *even*-harmonic) distortion. But as we have seen, harmonics beyond the second are so weak as to have little effect.

Overloading Causes Distortion. There is another form of distortion caused by *overloading* the tube. We may select the proper grid bias for our tube, but if a signal comes in that produces too great a swing of the grid potential, the grid may be driven positive on the positive half-cycle, and to the point of *cutoff* (the point where the negative charge on the grid gets so great as to stop en-

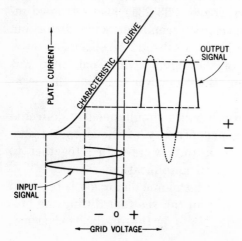

Fig. 38-4. *Distortion of the signal due to overloading.*

tirely the flow of electrons from the cathode to the plate) on the negative half-cycle (Fig. 38-4). This condition results in a flattening of the tops and bottoms of the output curve. The remedy is to choose a tube which has a longer straight-line characteristic or else to use an input signal without so great a swing.

Still another form of distortion arises through the use of a load in the plate circuit whose resistance is too low. If you turn to Figure 37-10, you will see that the less the load resistance, the more the characteristic curve is bent. This condition, in turn, reduces the length of the straight-line portion of the curve, and thus a nonlinear distortion may be introduced. The remedy for the difficulty is to use a load whose resistance is suited to the tube.

The Class A Amplifier. In the *class A amplifier,* a radio tube is used to reproduce grid-voltage variations across a load in the plate circuit. These variations closely resemble in form the input-signal voltage impressed on the grid, but are of greater amplitude. The reproduction is accomplished by using a suitable grid bias, so that the tube operates on the straight-line or linear portion of the characteristic curve. At no time does the grid go positive (Fig. 38-5).

The class A amplifier produces high-fidelity amplification. As a voltage amplifier, it may be used to provide the high-voltage grid swing necessary to operate the power stage.

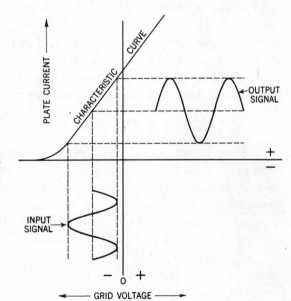

Fig. 38-5. *Graph showing relationship between the input and output signals in a class A amplifier.*

As a power amplifier, it sacrifices high voltage gain for relatively large power output (Chap. 27). Power tubes of the triode type in class A service are characterized by low power sensitivity, low plate efficiency, and low distortion. Pentodes in class A are characterized by high power sensitivity, high plate efficiency, and relatively high distortion.

Faithful reproduction may be obtained by using a single class A tube in the output stage. Greater power may be obtained by hooking two such tubes in parallel or push-pull (Chap. 27). The push-pull arrangement has the added advantage of eliminating any second-harmonic distortion that may be present.

The Class AB Amplifier. A *class AB amplifier* employs two tubes connected in push-pull with a higher negative grid bias than is used in a class A stage. Class AB amplifiers are subdivided into two classes: *class AB₁*, wherein the peak signal voltage applied to each grid is not greater than the negative grid-bias voltage, as a result of which there is no flow of grid current, and *class AB₂*, wherein the peak signal voltage slightly exceeds the negative grid-bias voltage and, consequently, there is a flow of grid current during a small portion of the cycle (Fig. 38-6).

More power output can be obtained from the class AB amplifier than from the class A amplifier. The reason is that a greater grid swing is possible with the class AB than with the class A amplifier. The operating point is shifted to the low end of the characteristic curve, and a greater grid swing is possible with class AB before the grid goes positive or the top bend of the curve is reached (Fig. 38-7). Since we can use larger grid potentials (e_g) in the class AB amplifier, the power output is increased, since

$$\text{Power output} = \frac{\mu^2 e_g^2}{8R_p}$$

Examination of the output signal curves (Fig. 38-6) shows that part of the bottom loops has been cut off. If a single tube were used, this would create a great deal of distortion (especially of the second-harmonic type). But we have already seen (Fig. 38-3) how two tubes in push-pull eliminate this distortion.

In the case of class AB₂ amplification, the grid goes positive for a small portion of the cycle (Fig. 38-6-B). This condition causes a loss of power due to the flow of grid current. This power loss, plus the power consumed by the input transformer, must be furnished by the preceding stage of amplification (the driver stage).

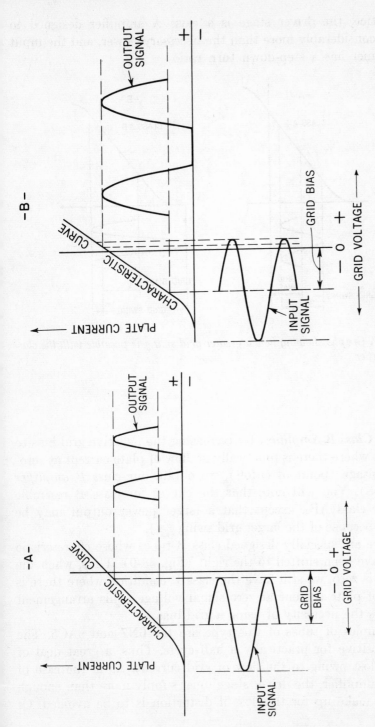

Fig. 38-6. A—Graph showing relationship between input and output signals in a class AB_1 amplifier. B—Graph showing relationship between input and output signals in a class AB_2 amplifier.

In practice, the driver stage is a class A amplifier designed to furnish considerably more than the necessary power, and the input transformer has a step-down turn ratio.

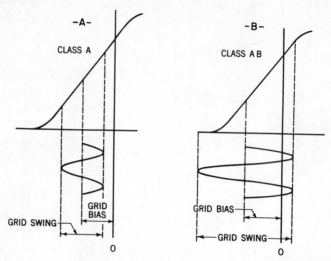

Fig. 38-7. *Graphs showing how a greater grid swing is possible with the class AB amplifier.*

The Class B Amplifier. By increasing the negative grid bias to the point where there is practically no flow of plate current at zero-signal voltage (point of cutoff), we obtain our *class B amplifier* (Fig. 38-8). You will note that the curves for class B resemble those for class AB_2, except that a larger power output may be obtained because of the larger grid swing (e_g).

There are specially designed class B tubes whose charcteristic curves have been shifted to the right (Fig. 38-9). Thus, when the grid bias is zero, we still have the class B condition where there is no flow of plate current at zero-signal voltage. This arrangement eliminates the necessity of using a grid bias.

Examples of tubes of this type are the 6N7 and 6AC5. The grid is positive for practically a half-cycle. Thus, a great deal of power is lost owing to the flow of grid current. As in the case of the AB_2 amplifier, the driver stage must supply more than enough power to make up for this loss if distortion is to be avoided. Of course, the greater grid swing permissible enables the class B amplifier to deliver a greater power output. Again, like class AB, the class B amplifier can only be operated in a push-pull circuit.

    Grid-Bias Voltage. It might be well to say a few words here about how we obtain the *grid-bias voltage,* which is so important in determining how the amplifier tube will operate. One method is the *cathode-resistor bias method* (Fig. 38-10). Here a resistor, shunted by a fixed capacitor, is connected to the cathode of the tube. The voltage drop across the resistor supplies the necessary grid-bias voltage (pages 155-156).

This method is used extensively in both the audio- and radio-frequency amplifiers of the radio receiver. It is also employed in low- and medium-powered public-address systems and low-powered transmitters.

Another method for obtaining the grid-bias voltage is by the use of *batteries* or a separate *rectifier and filter system.* This method has the advantage of furnishing a steady, constant bias under all conditions of operation. It is not usually employed in receivers that obtain their power from the house power lines, since

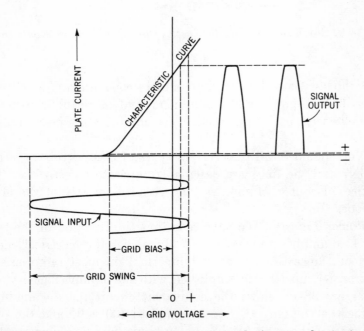

Fig. 38-8. *Graph showing relationship between the input and output signals in a class B amplifier.*

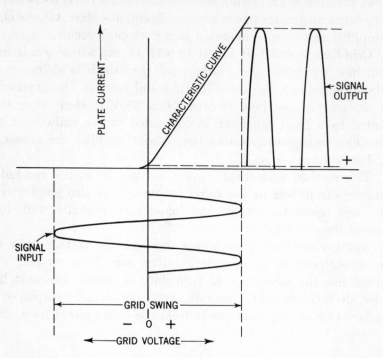

Fig. 38-9. *Graph showing how the special class B tubes operate on zero grid bias.*

the cathode-resistor bias method is more convenient. But portable receivers, high-power audio amplifiers, and powerful transmitters make extensive use of this method for obtaining the necessary grid bias.

You should recall that certain types of class B tubes (such as the 6N7 and the like) are designed to operate at zero bias. This practice, of course, eliminates the necessity for any of the above methods.

Power Transfer. We have seen that the function of the radio tube is to amplify the signal and to transfer the electrical energy to a load. Since this energy is quite small in most radio circuits, this transfer must be accomplished with maximum efficiency.

Figure 38-11 shows the equivalent circuit for the amplifier. Assume the voltage (μE_g) to be equal to 100 volts and the plate resistance of the tube (R_p) to be 10 ohms. If we assume the load resistance (R) to be one ohm, then the total resistance of the circuit $(R_p + R)$ is equal to 11 ohms. From Ohm's law we can determine the current (I) flowing through the circuit as being

$$I = \frac{E}{R} = \frac{100 \text{ volts}}{11 \text{ ohms}} = 9.09 \text{ amperes.}$$

The voltage drop across the load resistor (R) can be determined as follows:

$$E_R = I \times R = 9.09 \text{ amperes} \times 1 \text{ ohm} = 9.09 \text{ volts.}$$

The power in the load then becomes

$$P_R = I^2R = (9.09)^2 \times 1 = 82.62 \text{ watts.}$$

If we assume different values for the load resistance, we can draw up the table shown in Figure 38-12. From this table, we can draw the following conclusions:

1. The higher the load resistance (R), the greater the voltage drop across the load (E_R). Thus, if we are operating the amplifier as a *voltage* amplifier, we should have the load resistance as high as is feasible.

2. If we are interested in the *power* output, the maximum transfer of power occurs when the load resistance (R) is

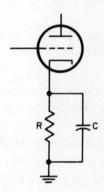

Fig. 38-10. *The cathode-resistor method for obtaining grid bias.*

equal to the resistance of the source (R_p). We shall see later that there are some modifications of this rule.

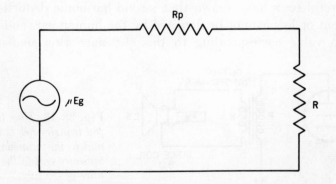

Fig. 38-11. *The equivalent circuit for an amplifier.*

μE_g (volts)	R_p (ohms)	R (ohms)	I (amperes)	E_R (volts)	P_R (watts)
100	10	1	9.09	9.09	82.62
100	10	5	6.66	33.30	221.77
100	10	10	5.00	50.00	250.00
100	10	20	3.33	66.60	221.77
100	10	100	0.90	90.00	81.00

Fig. 38-12. *Table showing power and voltage relationships as the load resistor (R) is changed.*

These rules apply not only to radio tubes, but also to any circuits where electrical power is transferred from one circuit to another.

Impedance Matching in Audio-Frequency Circuits. So far, we have considered the load as if it were a pure resistance, but this is not always the case. The load may be the primary of a coupling or an output transformer. Accordingly, the load may present an impedance rather than a resistance.

Since the impedance varies with variations of frequency, distortion may appear if the impedance of the load is made equal to the impedance of the source. It has been found that making the load impedance twice as great as the plate resistance (R_p) gives us an output that contains less than 5 per cent of second-harmonic distortion.

Careful tests have shown that second-harmonic distortions of 5 per cent or less cannot be detected by the human ear, and so we call the value corresponding to this the *maximum undistorted*

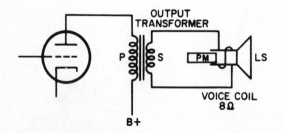

Fig. 38-13. *How the output transformer is used to match the impedance of the voice coil to the resistance of the tube.*

power output. Examination of the table in Figure 38-12 shows that the effect of making the load twice the resistance of the plate drops the power output about 10 per cent. Since variations of power output which are less than 25 per cent cannot be detected by the human ear, this power loss is negligible. Thus, manufacturers of radio tubes specify that a load impedance about twice as great as the plate resistance be used for maximum undistorted power output.

Example of Impedance Matching. The principles of impedance matching must be used in every circuit where electrical energy is transferred. Assume that we have a type 6BC4 tube acting as a class A power amplifier and that we wish to deliver the output to the voice coil of a dynamic speaker. The plate resistance of the type 6BC4 tube is 4,800 ohms and the impedance of the voice coil is, say, 8 ohms (Fig. 38-13).

For the maximum undistorted power output, the impedance of the load must be about twice the plate resistance, or about 9,600

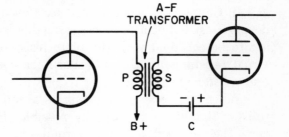

Fig. **38-14.** *How the audio-frequency trans- former is used to match the output of one tube with the input of the next.*

ohms. Obviously, the 8-ohm voice coil cannot be coupled directly to the tube.

Use is made here of an output transformer. The primary of this transformer supplies the load to the tube, and its impedance, therefore, is made to equal about 9,600 ohms, which is the necessary value to insure the maximum undistorted power output.

The power is transferred to the secondary of the transformer by mutual inductance. This secondary now becomes the source of electrical power to the voice coil of the speaker. Since maximum power transfer is achieved when the impedance of the source equals the impedance of the load, the impedance of the secondary is made the same as that of the voice coil—namely, 8 ohms.

The same principle is employed wherever an audio-frequency transformer is used to couple the output of one tube to the input of another (Fig. 38-14). The impedance of the primary is two or more times the plate resistance. If the first tube is used as a voltage amplifier, we want this impedance to be as high as possible. But the higher the primary impedance, the more it cuts down the voltage from the B+ that can be put on the plate. Some compromise value is chosen.

The impedance of the secondary must match the input impedance of the second tube. If this tube is used as a class A amplifier, there is no flow of grid current and, therefore, the impedance of the grid (input) circuit is very high. Thus, the impedance of the secondary of the audio-frequency transformer must be very high, too.

Resistance Coupling of Audio-Frequency Amplifier Stages. To pass the signal from one stage of amplification to another, means of *coupling* must be devised. In general, there are three methods of coupling: *resistance* coupling, *impedance* coupling, and *transformer* coupling.

In Chapter 17, we discussed *resistance coupling*. The coupling device consisted of a *plate resistor* (this is the load resistor and is not to be confused with the plate resistance R_p, which is the internal resistance of the tube itself), a *coupling capacitor,* and a *grid resistor* (Fig. 38-15).

When the tube is operating as a voltage amplifier, the plate resistor should be as large as possible. But this resistance cuts down the plate voltage. A compromise figure is arrived at with the use of a plate resistor whose resistance is up to ten times as great as the plate resistance of the tube (R_p).

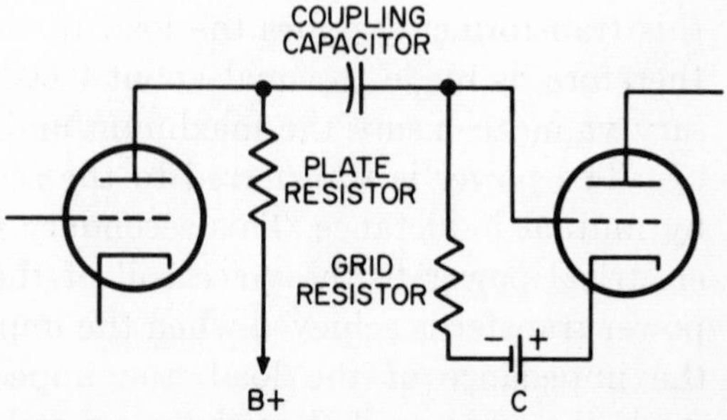

Fig. 38-15. *Resistance coupling for audio-frequency amplification.*

The coupling capacitor must keep the large positive charge from the B battery off the grid of the second tube and, at the same time, offer a minimum impedance to the signal voltage. This requirement calls for a large value for this capacitor, usually about 0.01 µf. If the capacitor is made too large, the charge on the grid will take too long a time to leak off through the grid resistor. The coupling capacitor must keep direct-current leakage to a minimum.

The grid resistor helps keep the signal voltage charges on the grid of the tube. For this reason, it must be made as large as possible. But too large a resistance will prevent the charges from leaking off the grid fast enough. A value of about 500,000 ohms (0.5 megohm) is usually chosen for the grid resistor.

At low frequencies (about 50 cycles per second), the amplification for a resistance-coupled audio-frequency amplifier falls off because of the high reactance offered by the coupling capacitor. At high frequencies, the amplification falls off, too, because the capacitance between the grid and cathode of the second tube offers a low reactance. Since the grid-and-cathode circuit is in parallel (or shunt) with the signal input, a good deal of the signal is lost through this path. For intermediate frequencies, the response is fairly uniform.

Resistance-coupled audio-frequency amplification has the advantage of low cost and relative freedom from distortion. Its chief disadvantage is that a high B voltage is needed to overcome the high resistance of the plate resistor.

Impedance Coupling. The *impedance-coupled* audio-frequency amplifier is an attempt to overcome this disadvantage. A large inductor (called a *choke coil*) is used instead of the plate resistor. This coil gives the high impedance load needed by the voltage amplifier, and at the same time, the low direct-current resistance needed to place a large positive charge on the plate.

The remainder of the circuit is similar to that of the resistance-coupled amplifier. The frequency response, too, is similar to that of the resistance-coupled amplifier, though using an inductor instead of a resistor introduces a slightly greater distortion of the signal.

Coupling by a Transformer. The *transformer-coupled* audio-frequency amplifier has been discussed (Chap. 17). Amplification falls off at low frequencies because the impedance of the primary (the load) decreases with the frequency. The low grid-cathode capacitive reactance causes a falling off of amplification at the high frequencies.

Inverse Feedback. In Chap. 16 we saw how some of the output voltage was fed back to the input circuit of the tube to be reamplified, and thus give us a greater output. We called this *regenerative feedback.* Now it is possible to feed this voltage back in such a way that it does not aid, but tends to cancel, the signal input. The feedback is then out of step (180° out of phase) with the incoming signal. We call this *degenerative* or *inverse feedback* (also known as *negative feedback*). Such feedback is of no value to us in the regenerative detector, but it is frequently used in audio-frequency amplifiers to reduce distortion. Figure 38-16 shows such a circuit.

You will notice that this is the circuit for an ordinary resistance-coupled audio-frequency amplifier. The last tube is a beam power tube. The inverse feedback is obtained from the plate of the last tube and is fed back to the control grid of the same tube through capacitor C and resistor R. The amount of voltage feedback depends on the values of R and R₁ as well as the plate re-

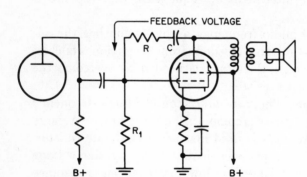

Fig. 38-16. *Circuit showing inverse feedback in the audio-frequency amplifier. The values of R and R₁ determine the amount of feedback.*

sistance of the tube. Capacitor C is a blocking capacitor to keep the B+ voltage off the grid of the tube.

If distortion is present owing to the presence of unwanted frequencies in the output, the inverse feedback tends to cancel out these unwanted frequencies in the input signal, and thus they are not present (at least in so great a degree as otherwise) in the final output signal. Again, if distortion is present owing to the fact that the amplifier had amplified some frequencies more than others, the inverse feedback represses to a greater degree, in the input signal, those frequencies that were overamplified. Thus, the final output signal shows a more even frequency range. Of course, the effect of inverse feedback is to reduce the over-all amplification, but modern high-*mu* tubes can compensate for this defect.

We have a second method for producing inverse feedback. Keep in mind that this occurs when the feedback is 180° out of phase with the incoming signal. This incoming signal appears as a potential difference between the grid and cathode of the tube. Thus the grid and cathode are 180° out of phase with each other. Also, the output signal appears as a potential difference across the primary of the output transformer. Thus the top and bottom of

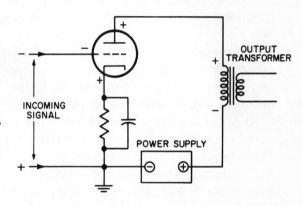

Fig. 38-17. *Circuit of an amplifier, showing the phase relationships between the various points. Except for the power supply, the + and − do not indicate the polarity of these points, but, rather, the direction in which these points are swinging.*

this primary winding are 180° out of phase with each other. Also, the grid and plate of the tube are 180° out of phase with each other.

Assume, now, that a signal enters the tube in such a manner that the grid swings toward the negative and the cathode toward the positive. The plate, too, will swing toward the positive, as will the top of the primary of the ouput transformer. The bottom of the primary winding will swing toward the negative (Fig. 38-17).

This negative signal will be delivered to the cathode (180° out of phase, since the cathode is swinging positive) through the power supply, cathode resistor, and cathode bypass capacitor. Normally, the large cathode bypass capacitor irons out the variations of the feedback signal, and thus the effect of the inverse feedback is lost. If we eliminate this cathode bypass capacitor, on the other hand, the signal variations are restored and the inverse feedback reduces distortion.

The Radio-Frequency Amplifier. The *audio-frequency* amplifier differs from the *radio-frequency* amplifier in a number of ways. First of all, the range of frequencies that must be covered by the audio-frequency amplifier lies between about 30 and 15,000 cycles per second. The radio-frequency amplifier amplifies signals whose frequencies may lie between 15 kc and upward of 300 mc.

But whereas the audio-frequency amplifier must handle its full frequency range at one time, the radio-frequency amplifier is called upon to handle only one frequency at a time (or at most, a very narrow band of frequencies). For this reason we deal with nonresonant or untuned circuits when we consider the audio-frequency amplifier, whereas we deal with resonant or tuned circuits when we consider the radio-frequency amplifier (Chaps. 23 and 26).

Harmonics Do Not Distort in Radio-Frequency Amplifiers. Another difference is that the chief bugaboo of the audio-frequency amplifier is harmonic frequency distortion. Because of this we can operate a single tube only in class A. Tubes must be operated in push-pull for class AB and class B. In the case of the radio-frequency amplifier, however, harmonic distortion has very little effect because of the selectivity of the tuned circuit. The second harmonic of a 500-kc signal, for example, is 1,000 kc. It would have to be a poorly tuned circuit, indeed, to pass both the fundamental (500 kc) and the second harmonic (1,000 kc).

Flywheel Effect. There is still another difference. In the case of the audio-frequency amplifier, the *whole* input signal must be faithfully reproduced in amplified form. This requirement means that the tube must amplify the whole input signal curve or else two tubes must be used in push-pull, each tube operating on half the curve, both halves being added together in the out-put transformer.

In the case of the radio-frequency amplifier, we have the current oscillating in the tuned circuit. It is not necessary that power be supplied to this oscillating current during its complete cycle of oscillation. It is enough that a short pulse, in step with the oscillation, of course, be given to the oscillating current. The effect is the same as if you would push a child in a swing. You do not have to push during the whole swing. It is enough to give a slight push during a small portion of the swing to keep the child going. This effect is known as the *flywheel effect*.

Thus, we need not have plate current flowing during the whole cycle. All we need are short pulses of plate current in resonance with the oscillations of the tuned circuit (Fig. 38-18). This is another reason why a single tube can be operated as a radio-frequency amplifier of any class.

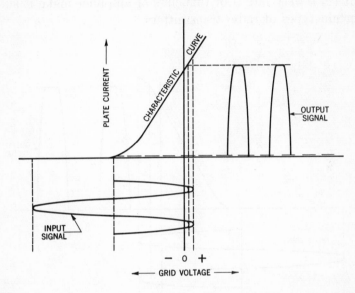

Fig. 38-18. *Distortion of the output signal in a class B amplifier. While this distortion would prevent us from using a single tube in class B as an audio-frequency amplifier, we can do so in the radio-frequency amplifier because of the "flywheel" effect.*

The Class C Amplifier. We have classified our amplifiers by the amount of grid bias placed on the tube. This amount, in turn, determined the portion of the characteristic curve upon which the tube operated. Accordingly, there is still another class of amplifier to be considered.

According to standards set by the Institute of Radio Engineers, a *class C amplifier* is an amplifier in which the grid bias is appreciably greater than the cutoff value, so that the plate current in each tube is zero when no alternating grid voltage is applied, and so that plate current in a specific tube flows for appreciably less than half of each cycle when an alternating grid voltage is applied. Figure 38-19 shows this graphically.

Here you see why class C amplification is not suitable for audio-frequency work. Not even the push-pull hookup can overcome the distortion, because the output-signal curve represents less than half the input-signal waveform. But in the radio-frequency amplifier, the flywheel effect of the tuned circuit supplies the missing portions of the cycle. The high efficiency and high power output (e_g is very large) of this class of amplifier make it suitable for certain types of radio transmitters.

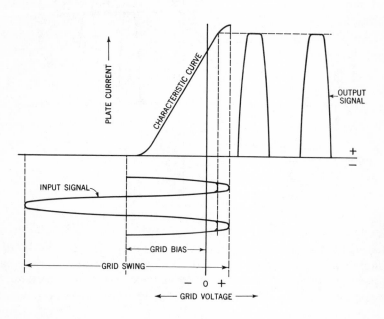

Fig. 38-19. *Graph showing relationship between the input and output signals in a class C amplifier.*

The grid swing is great enough to drive the grid to such a positive condition that the saturation point of the characteristic curve is reached. The plate current then is limited by this point. But the saturation point is controlled by the emission of electrons from the cathode and the plate voltage applied to the tube. Modern transmitting tubes are constructed to supply adequate electronic emission. We may, therefore, use extremely high plate voltages, and the plate current will be proportional to the plate voltage.

The Radio-Frequency Amplifier in the Receiver. In the receiver, radio-frequency amplifiers are employed to produce the tremendous voltage amplification needed to transform the minute voltages induced in the antenna-ground system by the passing radio wave into signals of sufficient strength to pass through the detector and audio-frequency stages of the system. Thus, the radio-frequency amplifier in the receiver is a *voltage amplifier*.

If we examine the circuit of a stage of radio-frequency amplification (Fig. 38-20), we note that the resistance between the grid and cathode of the tube is in parallel (or shunt) with the tuned circuit which feeds into the input of the tube.

In Chap. 34, we saw that the effect of a resistance across a resonant circuit is to reduce the *selectivity* of the tuned circuit. We may consider a tube that draws grid current as equivalent to a resistor across the input circuit: the higher the current, the lower the resistance. If the grid draws no current, the tube then presents an infinite input resistance. Since this condition is desirable, we must operate our tube so that the grid draws no current —namely, in class A operation.

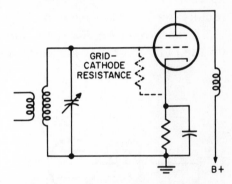

Fig. 38-20. *Diagram showing that the grid-cathode resistance of the tube is in parallel with the tuned circuit.*

The Radio-Frequency Amplifier in the Transmitter. Because efficiency and large power output are desirable in radio transmitters, class B and C amplifiers are usually employed. Harmonic distortions are filtered out by the tuned circuits, and the flywheel effect of the oscillating currents supplies the portions of the cycle that are missing as the result of the large grid bias used in class C.

The radio-frequency amplifier may consist of a single-tube stage (called a single-ended stage) or may consist of stages where the tubes are connected in parallel or push-pull for greater power output. As we have seen, the single-tube stage is not confined to class A operation, as in the case of the audio-frequency amplifier, but may be operated in any class.

When the tube is operated as a class B amplifier, the signal-voltage swing is such that during the positive half of the swing (the time during which plate current flows), the tube operators over the whole linear section of the characteristic curve (Fig. 38-8). For this reason, the class B amplifier is often called a *linear amplifier*. The output current is proportional to the input voltage.

The final stage of the transmitter is called upon to deliver power to the antenna. Thus, this stage is always a *power* stage. Since this final stage is a class B or C amplifier, there is a loss of power due to the grid being driven positive with the accompanying flow of grid current. This power loss must be made up in the intermediate or driver stages. For this reason, the driver stages, too, are usually operated as *power* amplifiers.

Grid Bias for the Radio-Frequency Amplifier. Grid-bias voltage for the radio-frequency amplifiers used in radio receivers is usually

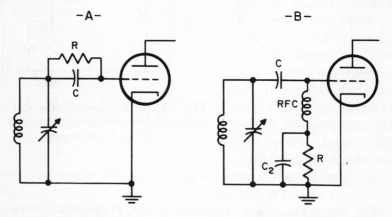

Fig. 38-21. *Methods of obtaining grid bias by the grid-leak-capacitor method.*
A—Series method.
B—Shunt or parallel method.

obtained by means of the *cathode-resistor bias* method (Fig. 38-10), described in Chapter 20. In the transmitter, a favorite method for obtaining the grid-bias voltage is the *grid leak-capacitor* method (Fig. 38-21-A), described in Chap. 15. This method is used only for class B or C amplifiers—that is, only where there is a flow of grid current owing to the fact that the grid has been driven positive. Current flowing through the resistor R causes a voltage drop, and it is this that biases the grid of the tube. Capacitor C acts as a blocking capacitor to keep the bias on the grid of the tube. Figure 38-21-A shows the *series* arrangement of such a system.

In Figure 38-21-B is shown the *parallel* arrangement of such a system. Current flowing through R creates the voltage drop that places the bias on the grid of the tube. Capacitor C is a blocking capacitor. The radio-frequency choke coil (RFC) and the capacitor (C_2) connected across the grid-leak resistor (R) are used to filter out variations of voltage, and thus a steady bias voltage is applied to the grid.

This grid-leak-capacitor method for obtaining grid bias suffers from one serious drawback. The bias voltage is obtained only when there is a flow of grid current. When the grid-current flow stops, the grid bias of the tube is reduced to zero. Examination of Figure 38-19 shows what happens to the plate current when the grid bias becomes zero. The plate current shoots right up and may reach a very high value. This, in turn, causes the plate to be bombarded heavily by the electron stream from the cathode. If this condition continues for any considerable period of time, the plate turns red-hot and may even burn up.

Because of this danger, transmitters (especially high-power ones) often use *batteries* or a separate *rectifier and filter system* to supply the necessary grid-bias voltage to the tubes. This plan has the advantage that a steady bias voltage is delivered under all conditions of operation, and thus the danger of too great a plate current is removed. Many transmitters use both batteries and the grid-leak method. The batteries furnish an irreducible minimum of bias voltage, thus insuring the safety of the tubes. The grid-leak supplies the voltage needed in excess of this minimum amount.

Coupling Radio-Frequency Amplifiers. As in the case of audio-frequency amplifiers, radio-frequency amplifiers may be resistance-coupled, impedance-coupled, and transformer-coupled. The fact that we are able to use tuned circuits in the radio-frequency amplifiers, however, is a distinct advantage and we accordingly modify our circuits to this end. Figure 38-22 shows a typical stage of resistance-coupled audio-frequency amplification. Capacitor C is the blocking capacitor which prevents direct-current plate voltage from the previous stage from flowing onto the grid. R prevents the input signal from being shorted through the bias supply. R_1 is the load resistor, and C_1 is the coupling capacitor which passes on the

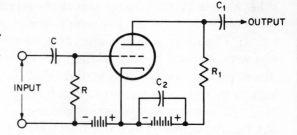

Fig. 38-22. *A stage of resistance-coupled audio-frequency amplification.*

alternating-current signal voltage, but keeps the direct-current plate voltage off the grid of the following tube. C_2 is a bypass capacitor.

Figure 38-23 shows changes made to operate the amplifier as a radio-frequency amplifier using tuned circuits. (It should be noted that the stage of amplification shown in Figure 38-22 could be operated as a radio-frequency amplifier as well as an audio-frequency amplifier.) In place of R, a radio-frequency choke coil (RFC) has been inserted. At high frequencies, the impedance of

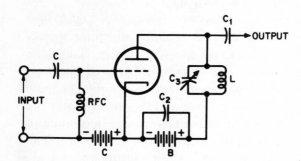

Fig. 38-23. *A stage of radio-frequency amplification. Note the resemblance to the audio-frequency stage in Figure 38-22.*

this choke coil becomes quite high. In place of the load resistor (R_1), a *parallel-resonant tuned circuit* (often called a *tank*) is inserted. From our studies of resonant circuits (Chap. 34), we learned that the impedance of such a resonant circuit is very high. By matching the impedance of the tank circuit to the plate resistance (R_p) of the tube, we are able to get the maximum power output. But if any unwanted frequencies come through, the impedance of the tank circuit falls off rapidly, and the power output at these unwanted frequencies dies down. Thus, harmonic distortion is eliminated.

Transformer coupling may also be employed, using tuned circuits for the primary and secondary of the transformer. Transformers for radio-frequency currents are usually made with cores of air to avoid large losses of electrical power because of hysteresis and eddy currents (Chap. 32). In the receiver, it should be noted, successful use has been made of a radio-frequency transformer having a core of finely divided iron powder.

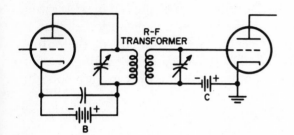

Fig. 38-24. *Circuit of a transformer-coupled radio-frequency amplifier.*

Figure 38-24 shows the circuit for a transformer-coupled radio-frequency amplifier. The tank circuit comprising the primary of the radio-frequency transformer is a *parallel-resonant* circuit providing the high impedance needed for the load for the first tube. The tuned circuit comprising the secondary of the transformer is a *series-resonant* circuit (Chap. 34). The impedance of such a circuit is very low, and thus very little of the signal voltage is lost. Other methods of coupling, variations of the above two, will be discussed when we consider the radio transmitter.

Neutralization. Studying the radio-frequency amplifier for the receiver (Chap. 23), we saw how *neutralization* was needed to overcome undesired feedback arising out of the interelectrode capacitance between the grid and plate of the triode. The capacitance between the grid and plate of the tube sets up a voltage which feeds back some of the electrical energy from the plate to the grid, setting up oscillations

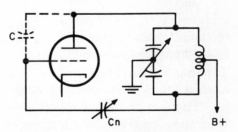

Fig. 38-25. *Circuit of a radio-frequency amplifier showing the neutralizing capacitor* (C_n). *This is an example of plate neutralization.*

and other disturbances. If we send into the grid a voltage that is equal in magnitude and opposite in direction or phase (180° out of phase) to the voltage set up by the interelectrode capacitance, the two voltages cancel each other out, and no feedback results. This suppression illustrates the principle of *neutralization*.

Figure 38-25 shows how it is accomplished. Note that the variable capacitor in the tank circuit has a peculiar form. In reality, it is two variable capacitors in series, with their center going to the ground. Note also that the B+ goes to the center tap of the coil. The net effect of this hookup is to produce a condition similar to that which exists across the center-tapped primary of the output transformer of a push-pull audio-frequency stage of amplification (Fig. 27-4). The voltages at both ends of the tank coil are opposite in direction (180° out of phase).

If some of the voltage from the bottom end of the coil is fed through a small variable capacitor (C$_n$), called a *neutralizing capacitor,* onto the grid of the tube, neutralization is achieved. The neutralizing capacitor controls the amount of voltage so fed to insure that it is just enough to neutralize that arising from the capacitance of the electrodes. Since this neutralizing voltage comes from the plate circuit, this method is called *plate neutralization.*

Neutralizing voltage may also be drawn from the grid circuit and deposited on the plate. Such a method is shown in Figure 38-26. This method is called *grid*

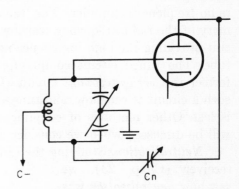

Fig. 38-26. *Circuit showing grid neutralization.*

neutralization, and operates the same as plate neutralization.

There is another method which is called *direct plate-to-grid neutralization.* Here, use is made of the fact that the voltage drop across an inductor is 180° out of phase with the drop across a capacitor in that same circuit (pages 406-409). If an inductor (L) is placed across the plate and grid of the tube, the voltage drop across it will be exactly *opposite* to the voltage drop across the grid and plate of the tube. This is so because of the capacitive effect of plate and grid. If the inductor is carefully chosen, the voltage drop across it will also be *equal* to the voltage drop across the grid and plate. Thus, the two voltages will cancel each other out, and no feedback will result (Fig. 38-27). The capacitor (C) in series with the inductor (L)

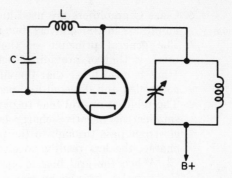

Fig. 38-27. *Circuit using direct plate-to-grid neutralization.*

is used to keep the B+ off the grid of the tube.

In modern practice, however, radio-frequency amplifiers using screen-grid tubes do not have to be neutralized. At radio frequencies, the grid-to-plate capacitance of the screen-grid tube is negligible.

SUMMARY

1. *Vacuum-tube amplifiers* may be classified under two headings: (1) *audio-frequency* and (2) *radio-frequency.*
2. Another classification is based on their function: (a) *voltage amplifiers* magnify the input signal without regard to the power delivered and (b) *power amplifiers* deliver a large amount of power to a load—usually loudspeakers or antennas.
3. Audio-frequencies lie between 30 and 15,000 cycles, and radio frequencies range from 15 kc up.
4. Amplifying tubes are classified by the Institute of Radio Engineers as *A, AB, B,* and *C,* according to the operating conditions for which they are adapted.
5. Briefly, these types are defined in terms of grid bias, alternating grid voltages, and plate current as follows:
A *class A amplifier* is a tube in which some plate current flows at all times.
A *class AB amplifier* is a tube in which plate current flows during less than the entire cycle but during more than half of it.
A *class B amplifier* is a tube in which plate current is approximately zero when no exciting grid voltage is applied; hence, plate current flows only during half of each cycle.
A *class C amplifier* is one in which the grid bias is greater than the cutoff value, so that plate current flows for less than half of each input cycle applied to the grid.

6. Class C amplifiers are used in certain types of radio-frequency amplifiers in transmitters, but not in audio-frequency work.

7. The general principle of the rating and use of amplifying tubes is that of providing such a negative charge on the grid (that is, grid bias) that the current in the plate circuit may be controlled and directed for specific purposes.

8. The relation of grid bias to plate current is as follows: (1) The smaller the negative charge on the grid, the more readily do electrons pass through to the plate. (2) The larger the negative charge, the less readily do electrons pass through to the plate. (3) When the grid bias is small, the alternating voltages from the signal impressed on the grid make it easy for electrons to flow during the positive half of the cycle and may even permit some current to flow during the the negative half of the cycle.

9. In general, when using an amplifier as a *voltage* amplifier we should have the resistance of the load as high as feasible; when *power* amplification is desired, the load resistance should be about twice the plate resistance (R_p) of the tube.

GLOSSARY

Audio-Frequency Amplifier: A tube amplifying frequencies from about 30 to 15,000 cycles per second.

Class A Amplifier: A tube amplifier so biased that plate current flows at all times during the input voltage cycle.

Class AB Amplifier: A tube amplifier so biased that plate current flows for more than half but not all of the input voltage cycles.

Class B Amplifier: A tube amplifier so biased that plate current flows for only half of the input voltage cycle.

Class C Amplifier: A tube amplifier so biased that plate current flows for less than half of the input voltage cycle.

Degenerative Feedback: Feedback of energy from the plate circuit to the grid circuit in such phase relationship as to weaken the input signal.

Delay Distortion: Distortion due to transmission of different frequencies at different speeds resulting in phase shifting.

Distortion: Change of waveform in the output of a tube as compared with the input.

Frequency Distortion: Unequal amplification of different frequencies by an amplifier.

Impedance Matching: Adjusting load impedance to generator impedance to get maximum power output.

Inverse Feedback: Same as degenerative feedback.

Negative Feedback: Same as inverse feedback.

Nonlinear Distortion: Distortion due to tube operation on the bends of a characteristic curve.

Overloading: Allowing too large a signal voltage swing on the grid, resulting in distortion.

Phase Distortion: Same as delay distortion.

Power Amplifier: An amplifier designed primarily to furnish power to a power-consuming device or circuit.

Radio-Frequency Amplifier: An amplifier designed to amplify frequencies above 15,000 cycles per second.

Second Harmonic: A frequency twice the fundamental frequency.

Third Harmonic: A frequency three times the fundamental frequency.

Voltage Amplifier: An amplifier designed primarily to get a maximum voltage amplification from voltage on grid to voltage across plate load.

QUESTIONS AND PROBLEMS

1. What are the two broad categories of tube amplifiers? Explain each.
2. What two purposes might an audio-frequency amplifier serve in a receiver?
3. Driver stages are usually amplifiers of what type? What type of tube amplifier do they usually feed into?
4. What types of amplifiers are the radio-frequency stages of a tuned radio-frequency receiver?
5. Why are audio amplifier stages coupled together with non-resonant circuits?
6. Differentiate by diagram between a class A, a class AB, and a class B audio amplifier.
7. List and describe the different forms of tube amplifier distortion.
8. What distortion results when grid bias is too low?
9. What type of distortion is remedied by use of a push-pull amplifier? How is this accomplished?
10. What distortion effect results from overloading an amplifier?
11. What distortion effect results from using too low a plate resistor?
12. Describe the characteristics of a class A amplifier.
13. Describe the characteristics of a class AB amplifier.
14. Differentiate between a class AB_1 and a class AB_2 amplifier.
15. Describe the characteristics of a class B amplifier.
16. How is the distortion resulting from flow of grid current overcome in the class AB_2 amplifier? In the class B amplifier?
17. What practical methods are used to obtain grid bias?
18. What determines whether a tube will operate as a class A, AB_1, AB_2, or B amplifier?

19. Complete the following statements: The higher the load resistance of a tube amplifier, the greater the ——————— of the tube. The greatest power transfer from a tube to a load occurs when ———————.

20. To obtain less than 5 per cent second-harmonic distortion with maximum undistorted power output, how large must be the plate resistance as compared with the load impedance?

21. From the point of view of maximum undistorted power output, what is the function of an output transformer?

22. List and describe three types of coupling circuits. Give the advantages and disadvantages of each type.

23. Explain the operation and purpose of a degenerative amplifier.

24. Differentiate a radio-frequency amplifier from an audio-frequency amplifier from the point of view of function.

25. Why are resonant circuits used with radio-frequency amplifiers?

26. Why is harmonic distortion a negligible problem with radio-frequency amplifiers?

27. What are the characteristics of a class C amplifier and where is it used?

28. A radio-frequency amplifier whose grid draws current corresponds to what condition in a radio receiver?

29. What class of amplifiers are usually used in radio-frequency stages of amplifiers?

30. Why are driver stages in a transmitter coupled to the final power stage? Why are they sometimes power amplifiers?

31. What danger is met in using grid leak and capacitor grid bias in a transmitter?

32. In place of a load resistor, what might be used in the plate circuits of radio-frequency stages in a transmitter?

33. What is the purpose of neutralization of a triode radio-frequency amplifier?

34. List and describe the methods of neutralization of a triode radio-frequency amplifier.

39

Radio-Tube Oscillators

> PROBLEM. *How are radio tubes made to serve as oscillators?*

What Is an Oscillator? In addition to serving as rectifiers, detectors, and amplifiers, radio tubes may serve as *oscillators*. As such, they act as generators of alternating current, usually of high frequency and constant, equal amplitude. We call such a high-frequency alternating current a *continuous radio-frequency* or *carrier* current. When modulated by audio currents originating in the microphone, the carrier current becomes the *modulated radio-frequency current*. This current, in turn, produces the *modulated radio wave* that is radiated by the transmitting antenna and is intercepted by the receiving antenna. In short, radio tubes as oscillators generate the high-frequency currents for transmitters in modern radio and television broadcasting as well as in modern radio and television receivers.

Oscillators in the Superheterodyne and Regenerative Receiver. We made the acquaintance of the radio-tube oscillator in our discussion of the superheterodyne receiver (Chap. 26). It was used to generate the continuous radio-frequency current which was used to beat against the incoming signal to produce the intermediate beat-frequency current which was fed into the intermediate-frequency amplifiers.

Before we studied the superheterodyne receiver, we met the radio-tube oscillator (in a somewhat disguised form) as the regenerative detector (Chap. 16). Plate current was fed back to the tuning circuit, by means of a tickler coil, to be reamplified, and thus to produce a louder signal. You will recall that unless this feedback was carefully controlled, the tube would start to *oscillate* and transmit a signal that could be received over a distance of several blocks.

The Simple Oscillator Circuit. In its essence, the oscillator consists of a coil and capacitor hooked together (Fig. 39-1). Assume that the capacitor is charged. Electrical energy is contained in the *dielectric* or *electrostatic* field of the capacitor. The capacitor starts to discharge. Electrons flowing through the coil set up a *magnetic* field. The energy of the dielectric field is then converted into the energy of the magnetic field. As the current starts to die down, the magnetic field about the coil collapses, and its energy is changed back into dielectric-field energy as the capacitor is charged once more, this time with opposite polarity.

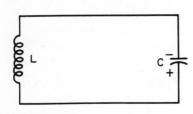

Fig. 39-1. *A simple oscillatory circuit.*

The back-and-forth swings of the electrons (called *oscillations*) continue at an extremely rapid rate and, were it not for the presence of resistance in the circuit, these oscillations would continue indefinitely. Thus, an alternating current of extremely high frequency circulates through the circuit, and this frequency is determined by the value of the inductance and capacitance. As we have seen,

$$f = \frac{1}{2\pi \sqrt{L \times C}}$$

where f signifies frequency. The frequencies considered here are *radio frequencies* (15 kc to 300 mc and more). We can vary the frequency of this alternating current by changing the values of L or C. In practice, we usually use a variable capacitor to give us our frequency changes.

How the Oscillator Works. The next step is to amplify this alternating current. A class C amplifier (page 521) is hooked across the capacitor (Fig. 39-2). The oscillating radio-frequency current in the coil-capacitor circuit (called the *tank*) causes a radio-frequency voltage (the *signal* or *excitation* voltage) to be placed across the input of the tube. Grid bias is furnished by the voltage

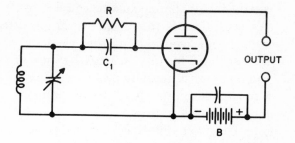

Fig. 39-2. *A class C amplifier is hooked across the simple oscillatory circuit.*

drop across the grid leak (R). As a result, the signal, in greatly amplified form, appears at the output of the tube (Chap. 38).

A question now arises. Since some resistance is always present in every circuit and since energy is dissipated in this resistance, what keeps the oscillations going? The answer to our question is *feedback.* You will recall that in the case of the regenerative detector (Chap. 16) some energy from the plate circuit was fed back to the tuning circuit by mutual inductance. The same principle is used here (Fig. 39-3).

Coil L_1 corresponds to the tickler coil of the regenerative detector feeding back energy from the output, which overcomes the effect of resistance and keeps the oscillations going. Since this is a class C amplifier, plate current flows only during a small portion of the cycle. But it is not necessary that energy be fed into the tank during the *complete* cycle of oscillation. It is enough that *short pulses,* in step with the oscillations, be fed in (pages 520-521).

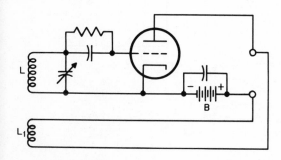

Fig. 39-3. *The output is fed back into the oscillatory circuit by means of an inductor* (L_1).

Merely setting a current oscillating in the tank circuit does not make a transmitter. The signal so set up must be passed on, amplified, and ultimately radiated out as a radio wave. In other words, the oscillator must be coupled to the rest of the transmitter. We shall discuss this matter of transmitters later in Chapters 40 and 41, but keep in mind that electrical energy will be drained off the oscillator for this purpose. Because of this drain, feedback from the plate must not only provide for losses resulting from resistance, but must also provide for power handed on by the oscillator to the rest of the transmitter.

The next question that arises is, what makes the oscillator *self-starting?* In the case of the regenerative detector, the incoming signal started a current flowing in the tuning circuit. But there is no incoming signal here. The *grid-leak bias* does the trick for us. Since, at the start, there is no grid current flowing, the voltage drop across the grid leak is zero. Hence, the grid bias, also, is zero. If you examine the characteristic curve for the class C amplifier (Fig. 39-4), you will notice that when grid bias goes to zero, the plate current becomes quite great. This current, starting to flow through the feedback coil (L_1) of Figure 39-3, induces a voltage in the tank circuit which starts the oscillations. Once started, these oscillations are kept going, as we have seen above.

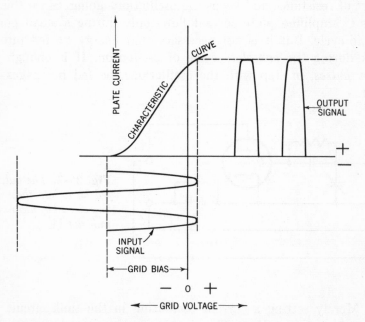

Fig. 39-4. *Graph showing how plate current goes up as the grid bias approaches zero.*

Another question is, what makes the peak amplitude of each cycle of this oscillating current equal to its neighbor? Well, let us see what happens if the amplitude of the radio-frequency current oscillating in the tank circuits starts to die down. In Figure 39-4, the signal voltage across the input of the tube starts to drop, and the grid bias (because of the voltage drop across the grid leak) also goes down. But as the grid bias approaches zero, the plate current goes up. Thus, more current is fed back to the tank through coil L_1 and the radio-frequency current rises back to its normal level.

The amplitude of the radio-frequency current cannot go up because the plate current in the output is limited, as shown by the top bend of the curve in Figure 39-4. Since the feedback depends upon the plate current, the feedback, too, is limited, as shown by the same bend of the curve. So, if the radio-frequency current in the tank circuit rises, its losses rise, too, but the feedback cannot go beyond its maximum value. The mounting losses quickly reduce the radio-frequency current to its original value. You can see now why the amplitudes of the peaks of the radio-frequency current oscillating in the tank circuit are all of the same value.

We have stated that the frequency of this oscillating radio-frequency current depends upon the values of inductance (L) and capacitance (C) in the tank circuit and is determined by the following formula:

$$f = \frac{1}{2\pi \sqrt{L \times C}}$$

Actually, this formula is not strictly true. If we consider the plate resistance of the tube (R_p) and the resistance (R) of the tank circuit, including the resistance introduced into the tank circuit when it is coupled to a load, the formula for frequency becomes

$$f = \frac{1}{2\pi} \sqrt{\frac{1 + \dfrac{R}{R_p}}{L \times C}}$$

where R/R_p values are very small, usually much less than unity; nevertheless, in the interest of frequency stability, we should seek to keep the value of R as low as possible. Quite obviously, the load should be kept as low as possible. Thus, the oscillator should not be coupled directly to a radiating system such as an antenna.

For a particular frequency (which fixes the product of $L \times C$) and for a given Q (pages 420-422), the value of R can be reduced

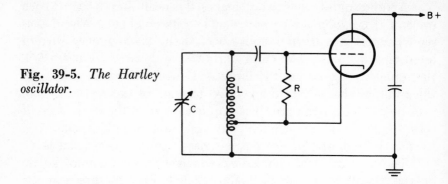

Fig. 39-5. *The Hartley oscillator.*

and stability thus increased by using a low L (that is, a low L-to-C ratio). The smaller the inductance, the smaller the dimensions of the coil, and the lower the inherent resistance.

   Types of Oscillator Circuits. Although radio-tube oscillators may take many forms, they fall into two general types depending upon how feedback is accomplished. One type depends upon the inductive coupling between two coils to give us the required feedback. The simple oscillator shown in Figure 39-3 is of this type. A variation of this simple oscillator that is in wide use is the *Hartley* oscillator shown in Figure 39-5.

   The novelty of this circuit lies in the fact that coil L is, in reality, two coils in one. Thus the whole coil is the inductor of the tank circuit, and the bottom part of coil L may be considered as the feedback coil corresponding to coil L_1 of Figure 39-3. The frequency of the oscillating current is determined by the values of L and C. Output from this oscillator is obtained by inductive or capacitive coupling to coil L.

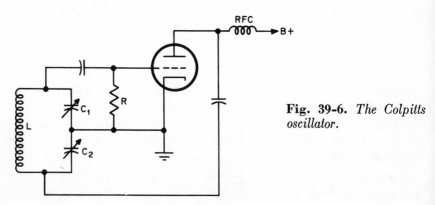

Fig. 39-6. *The Colpitts oscillator.*

A variation of the Hartley oscillator is the *Colpitts* oscillator shown in Figure 39-6. It is quite similar to the Hartley, except that the tap is not on the coil, but on the capacitor. This is accomplished by using two tuning capacitors, C_1 and C_2. Just as with the Hartley circuit, where the amount of feedback is controlled by varying the tap point on the coil, so the feedback in the Colpitts circuit is con-

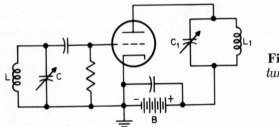

Fig. 39-7. *The tuned-grid tuned-plate oscillator.*

trolled by varying the ratio of the capacitances of C_1 and C_2. The total capacitance of the tank circuit is the combined capacitances of C_1 and C_2, connected in series.

The second type of oscillator depends upon the capacitance between the grid and plate of the tube to couple the feedback to the tank circuit. An example of this type is the *tuned-grid tuned-plate* oscillator shown in Figure 39-7.

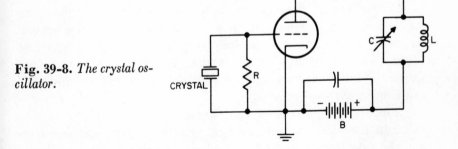

Fig. 39-8. *The crystal oscillator.*

In this circuit, the frequency of the oscillating current is determined jointly by the $L \times C$ of the grid circuit and the $L_1 \times C_1$ of the plate circuit. Hence its name: *tuned-grid tuned-plate*. The plate circuit should be tuned to the same resonant frequency as the grid circuit, and feedback is accomplished through the electrodes of the tube. At high radio frequencies, the grid-to-plate capacitance of the tube provides sufficient coupling, but at lower radio frequencies, a small capacitor may be needed across these two electrodes of the tube to provide the necessary feedback coupling. Output from this oscillator is obtained by inductive or capacitive coupling to coil L_1.

The *crystal oscillator* shown in Figure 39-8 is a variation of the tuned-grid tuned-plate oscillator. Certain crystalline substances possess the property of converting electrical energy to mechanical energy, and vice versa. We already have met such a crystal in the Rochelle-salt phonograph pickup (pages 129-131). The quartz crystal is another. If a mechanical stress is applied to the crystal, a dielectric field appears between its faces (voltage across the crystal). Conversely, when a voltage is applied to electrodes on two parallel faces of the crystal, a mechanical strain occurs in the crystal. As you already know, we call this the *piezoelectric* effect.

Thus, electrical energy applied to two parallel faces of the crystal produces a mechanical strain in the crystal. This strain, in turn, produces a dielectric field which, in turn, again produces a strain. This process goes on. At the natural period of the mechanical vibrations of the crystal, the two actions may be made mutually self-sustaining by feeding back a sufficient portion of electrical energy to replenish the energy which is lost as heat during each cycle.

The effect in the crystal circuit, then, is that we have an oscillating current whose frequency is determined by the natural frequency of the crystal. This frequency, in turn, is determined by the mechanical structure of the crystal. Quartz crystals can be cut whose natural frequency may be hundreds of thousands, and even millions, of cycles per second.

Since we may consider the quartz crystal as a tuned circuit, you can now see the resemblance between the crystal oscillator and the tuned-grid tuned-plate oscillator. Quartz-crystal oscillators are noteworthy for their remarkably steady frequency output. Output from the oscillator shown in Figure 39-8 may be obtained by coupling to coil L.

Another type of oscillator that is widely used is the *electron-coupled* oscillator whose circuit is shown in Figure 39-9. It uses a

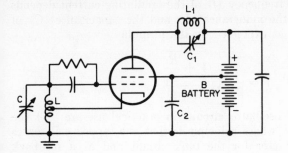

Fig. 39-9. *The electron-coupled oscillator.*

tetrode tube and actually combines the standard Hartley oscillator and a class C amplifier. The screen grid acts as a sort of plate and, together with the cathode and control grid, forms a triode which functions in the oscillator circuit. Thus, the flow of electrons within the tube varies in step with the oscillations in the tank circuit composed of capacitor C and coil L. The actual plate of the tube has no effect on these oscillations. However, since the screen grid is open-meshed, most of the electrons flow through it to the actual plate of the tube.

The output from this oscillator is taken off across a load, consisting of the tuned circuit made up of capacitor C_1 and coil L_1, which are placed in the actual plate circuit of the tube. The oscillator and output circuits are coupled by the electron stream within the tube; hence the name *electron-coupled*. Since the effect of the screen grid is to shield the oscillations in the oscillator section from the effect of the load, the frequency stability is rather good.

SUMMARY

1. An *oscillator* is a circuit for generating alternating currents, usually of high frequency.
2. Oscillations are started in a circuit by a strong plate current fed back to, and setting up induced voltages in, a *tank,* or tuned oscillator circuit.
3. Once started, oscillations of electrons in an oscillator would continue indefinitely except for resistance.
4. The supply of energy to overcome the losses and to keep the oscillations going is furnished by the feedback circuit.
5. A class C amplifier usually is used with this so-called tank, or oscillator circuit.

6. In all cases, the frequency (f) of the oscillating current depends primarily upon the inductance (L) and the capacitance (C) of the tank circuit as expressed by the formula

$$f = \frac{1}{2\pi} \sqrt{\frac{1 + \dfrac{R}{R_p}}{L \times C}}$$

7. Several types of oscillator circuits in practical use are: (1) the *Hartley* oscillator, whose principle is that one tapped coil serves both as the inductor for the tank circuit and as a feedback coil from the plate circuit; (2) the **Colpitts** oscillator; (3) the **tuned-grid tuned-plate** oscillator. (4) The **quartz-crystal** oscillator, which depends on the piezoelectric effect. (5) The **electron-coupled** oscillator.

GLOSSARY

Carrier: An alternating current of radio frequency and equal amplitude.

Colpitts Oscillator: An oscillator employing capacitive feedback coupling instead of inductive feedback coupling as used in the Hartley oscillator.

Continuous Radio Frequency: Same as the carrier.

Crystal Oscillator: A tuned-grid tuned-plate oscillator, employing a crystal as a tuned-grid circuit.

Electron-Coupled Oscillator: A stable oscillator in which a standard oscillator and output circuit are electron-coupled within a tube.

Feedback: Coupling of energy from the plate circuit to the input or grid circuit of a tube.

Hartley Oscillator: An oscillator in which feedback is accomplished by mutual inductance.

Oscillator: A circuit used to generate alternating currents, usually of high frequency.

Piezoelectric Effect: The effect whereby certain crystals develop a voltage across their faces when mechanically stressed and become mechanically stressed when a voltage is placed across them.

Tank: An LC circuit in which the electrons oscillate.

Tuned-Grid Tuned-Plate Oscillator: An oscillator in which feed back is by plate-to-grid capacitance and in which the plate and grid circuits each contain an LC circuit.

QUESTIONS AND PROBLEMS

1. Describe the behavior of a tube as an oscillator.
2. What is the function of a tube oscillator in the superheterodyne receiver?

3. How may a regenerative receiver be made to oscillate?
4. In essence, what is an oscillator? Why must energy be fed into it continually?
5. What is it that determines the oscillation frequency of a resonant circuit?
6. What function does feedback perform in an oscillator?
7. Explain how the simple regenerative oscillator is made self-starting and how oscillations of equal amplitude are maintained.
8. Why shouldn't an oscillator be coupled directly to a radiating system such as an antenna?
9. Draw a simple Hartley oscillator circuit.
10. Draw the circuit of a simple Colpitts oscillator.
11. Draw the diagram of a tuned-grid tuned-plate oscillator and describe its operation.
12. What is the principle of operation of a crystal oscillator?
13. Draw the circuit of a crystal oscillator.
14. Draw the diagram of an electron-coupled oscillator and describe its operation.

40

The Continuous–Wave (CW) Transmitter

PROBLEM 1. *How are telegraph code signals produced by radio transmitters?*
PROBLEM 2. *What principles are involved in continuous-wave transmitters?*

Kinds of Waves in Modern Transmitters. Modern radio transmitters radiate waves which may be of two general types. One type is the *continuous* or *unmodulated* radio wave whose waveform resembles the radio-frequency current oscillating in the tank of the oscillator discussed in Chapter 39. The amplitudes of all the cycles are equal and frequency is constant. There is nothing to distinguish one cycle from the next (Fig. 9-6).

The other type of radio wave is the *modulated* wave. In one type, the amplitudes of the peaks may vary from cycle to cycle. This type of modulated wave is called an *amplitude-modulated* (AM) wave. In another type of modulated wave, the amplitudes of the cycles remain constant, but the frequency is constantly changing. This is called a *frequency-modulated* (FM) wave. More will be said about these in the next chapter.

Radio Telegraphy. The continuous radio wave is used only for *radio telegraphy*—that is, for the transmission of short and long pulses or trains of waves to form the dots and dashes of a telegraphic code (Appendix). As the operator presses the key down (closes the key), a train of these continuous waves radiates from the antenna. When the key is raised (opened), the train of waves ceases. By keeping the key closed for a shorter or longer period of time, a *dot* (short train) or *dash* (long train) is radiated. Thus, if

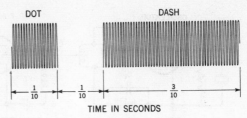

Fig. 40-1. *Diagram showing the relative duration of dots and dashes. The letter illustrated here is A (dot-space-dash or · —).*

it is desired to send the letter *A* (dot-space-dash or · —), the operator closes the key for a fraction of a second, opens it for the same length of time, and then closes it for a period three times as long as the first time (Fig. 40-1).

The frequency of the radio waves is *radio frequency;* the train forming the dot, although of 1/10-second duration, may contain thousands, or even millions, of cycles.

Why We Couple an Amplifier to the Oscillator. We may, of course, connect the oscillator directly to the antenna and radiate the radio wave. This, however, is rarely done. First of all, since the radio-frequency currents in the oscillator are relatively weak, very little power can be delivered to the antenna; the radiated wave, therefore, would be quite weak. Furthermore, as we learned in Chapter 39, putting a heavy load on the oscillator varies the frequency to which it is tuned. The antenna is such a heavy load. For these two reasons, then, it becomes important to feed the oscillations into a radio-frequency amplifier before we send the signal into the antenna. As we have learned in Chapter 38, the radio-frequency amplifier usually employed in the transmitter is of class C.

Methods of Coupling—Capacitive Coupling. There are a number of methods for coupling the oscillator to the radio-frequency amplifier. Simplest is the *direct* or *capacitive-couple* method (Fig. 40-2). Here, the *signal* or *excitation* is fed from the tank circuit of the oscillator, through the coupling capacitor (C), to the grid of the amplifier tube. The coupling capacitor also serves to keep the direct current of the oscillator off the grid of the amplifier tube.

Bias is supplied to the amplifier by means of the C battery feeding through the radio-frequency choke (RFC). The purpose of the choke coil is to supply a high impedance to the radio-frequency excitation, and thus to keep it from leaking off the grid of the tube. Capacitor C_1 across the B battery is used to offer an easy path for the radio-frequency current, which can, therefore,

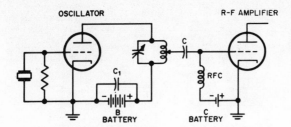

Fig. 40-2. *The direct or capacitive method of coupling the oscillator to the radio-frequency amplifier.*

avoid traveling through the B battery to the cathode in order to complete the plate circuit.

You will notice that the connection between the coupling capacitor (C) and the coil of the oscillator tank is adjustable. By changing the point on the coil where contact is made, the amount of excitation fed into the grid of the amplifier tube may be varied. This variation controls the grid swing of the tube. The adjustment should be varied until maximum excitation is achieved. (We shall see how to test for this maximum a little later.)

Inductive Coupling. Another method for coupling the oscillator to the radio-frequency amplifier is the *inductive method* (Fig. 40-3). Both tank circuits are tuned to the same frequency. Coupling takes place by mutual inductance. The coupling can be varied by moving the coils nearer together or further apart or by rotating one in relation to the other (pages 110-112). The degree of coupling will help determine the amount of excitation fed into the amplifier.

The inductive method of coupling introduces a difficulty. The distributed capacitance of the coils may produce an unwanted coupling effect upon each other. This undesirable feature may be reduced by placing the coils further apart, but doing this cuts down the efficiency of the transfer of excitation. However, by the use of *transmission lines,* the two coils may be kept a considerable dis-

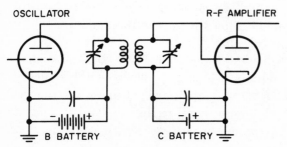

Fig. 40-3. *The inductive method of coupling the oscillator to the radio-frequency amplifier.*

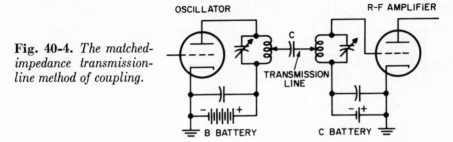

Fig. 40-4. *The matched-impedance transmission-line method of coupling.*

tance apart and yet be able to transfer the excitation from the oscillator to the radio-frequency amplifier. Figure 40-4 shows one type of such a transmission line.

The capacitor (C) is for the purpose of keeping the B-battery voltage off the grid of the amplifier, not for coupling. The connection to each coil is adjustable and should be varied until the proper excitation is achieved. Care should also be taken to adjust these connections (or *taps*) so that the impedances at each end of the transmission line are equal for the maximum transfer of power (pages 512-514). This method is called *matched-impedance* coupling.

Another type of coupling is known as *link* coupling (Fig. 40-5). Here use is made of an inductive link between the two tank circuits. The coupling ordinarily is made by a turn or two of wire closely coupled to the bottom ends of the coils of the tank circuits of the coupled stages. The link line is usually two closely spaced parallel wires or a twisted pair of wires connecting the loops. The advantage of this system is that, since the voltage between the link lines has been stepped down to a low value, radio-frequency losses due to capacitance between the lines are small. Also, because the link lines carry current in opposite directions, the counter elec-

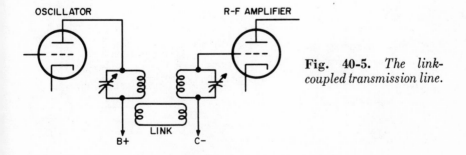

Fig. 40-5. *The link-coupled transmission line.*

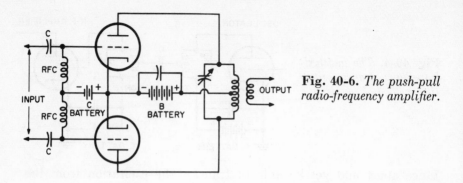

Fig. 40-6. *The push-pull radio-frequency amplifier.*

tromotive forces induced in each are canceled out, thereby removing undesired inductance of the two long lines. The amount of excitation fed into the amplifier may be varied by varying the number of loops at each end of the link and by varying the coupling between these loops and their respective tank coils.

The Push-Pull Amplifier. As in the case of the audio-frequency amplifier, the radio-frequency amplifier may be operated in *push-pull* for greater power output. The push-pull circuit may be operated as a class C amplifier. Figure 40-6 shows a typical circuit.

The push-pull amplifier may be coupled to the oscillator or driver amplifier in the same manner as the single-ended amplifier. Figure 40-7 shows the *direct* or *capacitive-coupled* method. Figure 40-8 shows the *inductive* method of coupling.

Transmission lines, too, can be employed for coupling. Figure 40-9 shows the *matched-impedance* method of coupling. In Figure 40-10 is shown the *link coupling* method.

Frequency Multipliers. Oscillators using a tuned tank in the grid circuit are called *self-excited oscillators*. An example of such an oscillator is the Hartley type shown in Figure 39-5. Oscillators

Fig. 40-7. *Direct or capacitive coupling for the push-pull radio-frequency amplifier.*

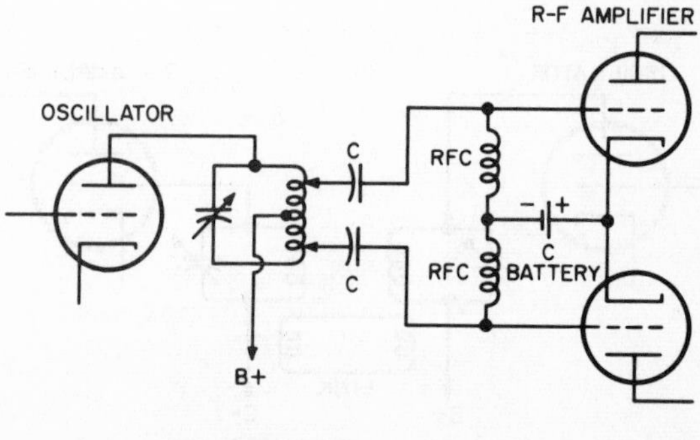

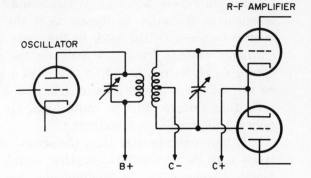

Fig. 40-8. *The inductive-method of coupling a push-pull radio-frequency amplifier to the oscillator.*

using crystals in the grid circuits are called *crystal oscillators* (Fig. 39-7). The frequency of the self-excited oscillator can be changed by varying the value of the coil or the capacitor or of both. But a crystal oscillates only at its natural frequency. The higher the frequency, the thinner the crystal must be.

To avoid the need for changing coils, capacitors, or crystals in the oscillator when change of frequency is desired, use is made of *frequency multipliers*. In the frequency multiplier, the harmonics of the fundamental frequency are deliberately produced. This practice is in contrast with the procedure of eliminating harmonics discussed in pages 505-506. Thus, if the oscillator frequency (the fundamental frequency) is, say, 3.5 mc, the second-harmonic output is 7 mc, and the third-harmonic output is 10.5 mc, and so on. Since harmonics drop off sharply in amplitude the further they are from the fundamental frequency, harmonics above the second are rarely used. For this reason, frequency multipliers are sometimes called *doublers*. Figure 40-11 shows a typical circuit.

The circuit of the frequency multiplier looks the same as that of the ordinary radio-frequency amplifier. There are several im-

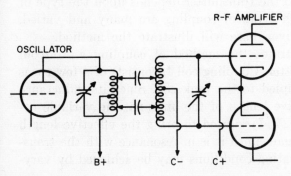

Fig. 40-9. *The matched-impedance transmission line method of coupling an oscillator to a push-pull radio-frequency amplifier.*

portant differences, however. Whereas the tank in the grid circuit is tuned to the same frequency as is the oscillator (the fundamental frequency), the tank in the plate circuit is tuned to the harmonic of that frequency (usually the second harmonic). To obtain a rich harmonic output, we need a high negative grid bias on the tube, considerably more than double the cutoff value. The excitation voltage must be quite high. (It is suggested that you review Chapter 38 on amplifiers.)

If harmonics greater than the second are desired, the doubler stage may be followed by another doubler, thus producing the fourth harmonic of the fundamental frequency. The push-pull amplifier is not suitable for second-harmonic output because this type of amplifier suppresses the second harmonic. However, the push-pull circuit may be used to produce the third and other odd harmonics.

Because the frequency of the plate circuit differs from the frequency of the grid circuit, frequency multipliers, even those employing triodes, do not have to be neutralized. In practice, since the output of the frequency multiplier is quite low, a final amplifier is used between the frequency multiplier and the antenna.

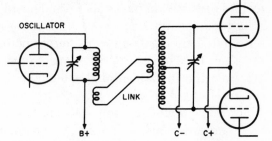

Fig. 40-10. *Method of coupling the oscillator to the push-pull radio-frequency amplifier by means of a link-coupled transmission line.*

Coupling the Transmitter to the Antenna. The method of coupling the antenna to the transmitter depends upon the type of antenna used. Although types of coupling are many and varied, the simple examples given here will illustrate the method.

Figure 40-12 illustrates the method of coupling a Marconi antenna to the transmitter. Coupling coil L consists of a few turns of wire inductively coupled to the tank coil. Since its inductance will increase the effective length of the antenna, the variable capacitor C (about 0.00025 μf) is used to bring the effective length of the antenna down again until it is in resonance with the transmitter. Maximum operating conditions may be achieved by varying the coupling between coil L and the transmitter tank coil.

Since variations in the load will change the resonant frequency of the plate tank of the transmitter, this tank must be returned to resonance after every change of coupling or of variable capacitor C. The ammeter is a radio-frequency type and indicates the current flowing into the antenna.

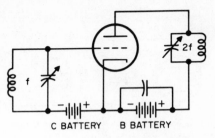

Fig. 40-11. *Circuit of the frequency multiplier. The plate tank circuit is tuned to a harmonic of the frequency to which the grid tank is tuned.*

Coupling to a Hertz half-wave antenna depends upon whether it is center-fed (current-fed) or end-fed (voltage-fed), and upon the length of the transmission line (pages 463-465). Figure 40-13 shows one method of coupling a center-fed antenna. When the two radio-frequency ammeters show similar readings, it indicates that the transmission line and antenna are being fed properly.

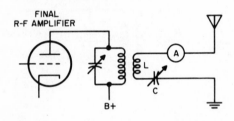

Fig. 40-12. *Method of coupling the final radio-frequency amplifier to a Marconi antenna.*

A circuit for coupling to an end-fed antenna is shown in Figure 40-14. In this case, L and C are adjusted so that the circuit is in resonance with the transmitter.

Keying the Transmitter. Since we are discussing continuous wave transmitters, which send dot-dash messages, we need a key in the circuit. The key is merely a device for closing and opening a circuit, but in radio transmitters, the key must be connected in the circuit with regard for certain precautions. A good keying system must fulfill four general objectives.

1. When the key is open, there must be no radiation from the antenna.

2. When the key is closed, there must be full power output from the transmitter into the antenna.

3. Keying should not cause clicks which may interfere with other stations.

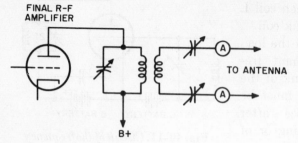

FINAL R-F
AMPLIFIER

TO ANTENNA

B+

Fig. 40-13. *One method of coupling the final radio-frequency amplifier to a center-fed Hertz antenna.*

4. Keying should not alter the transmitter frequency.

Radiation occurring when the key is open comes from two general sources. If the final amplifier of the transmitter is improperly neutralized, some energy may leak across from the grid to the plate of the tube, because of the capacitance between these

Fig. 40-14. *One method of coupling the final radio-frequency amplifier to an end-fed Hertz antenna.*

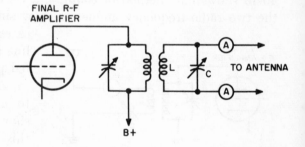

FINAL R-F
AMPLIFIER

L   C   TO ANTENNA

B+

two electrodes, and thus into the antenna. This creates a background signal, and the dots and dashes appear simply as louder portions of the continuous wave. The obvious remedy is proper neutralization.

Another source of this difficulty is the magnetic coupling that may exist between the final tank coil and other parts of the transmitter. The remedies are proper spacing of parts and shielding.

Key clicks occur because of sudden surges of high-frequency

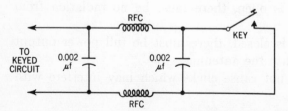

RFC

KEY

TO
KEYED
CIRCUIT

0.002
μf

0.002
μf

RFC

Fig. 40-15. *A filter used to eliminate key clicks.*

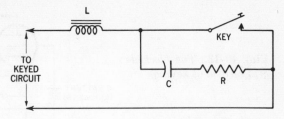

Fig. 40-16. *Another method used to eliminate key clicks. The lag circuit.*

electrical energy that may accompany the opening and closing of the key. There are numerous ways of eliminating them. Figure 40-15 shows one method. Since these surges are of radio frequency, the filter circuit shown above will filter them out.

Another bad effect that occurs when the key is opened and closed is the production of surges of currents which contain many new frequencies. These surges may cause interference with other stations. The effect is eliminated by a type of filter called a *lag circuit*, shown in Figure 40-16. The choke coil L (several henrys) causes a slight current lag and blocks the radio-frequency surges. As capacitor C (about 0.25 µf) is charged up, it absorbs the blocked energy. This energy, in turn, is then dissipated in the resistor R (about 100 ohms). This filter circuit and the one previously described are often connected together in a keying circuit, as shown in Figure 40-17.

In what stage should the key be placed? Since an open key is required to cut off all radiation, it may be placed in any stage and in any circuit of that stage which will make it inoperative, thereby breaking the radio-frequency signal chain to the antenna. It should be pointed out that if a stage is keyed, the succeeding stages must have sufficient fixed bias to prevent the flow of damaging currents, which would result from no grid-exciting signal.

Keying usually takes place in the *plate* or *grid* circuits of one of the radio-frequency amplifiers. Thus, keying in the plate circuit turns the plate voltage on and off. This method generally is not preferred because of the large voltages across the key. Keying in

Fig. 40-17. *Combined keying circuit.*

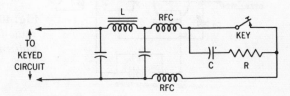

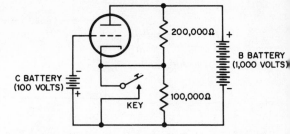

Fig. 40-18. *The blocked-grid method of keying.*

the grid circuit controls the excitation to the grid of the tube. Since the voltages involved in this circuit are relatively low, this method of keying is preferred.

Figure 40-18 shows such a method. Assume the circuit shown here. When the key is up, two thirds of the B voltage (1,000 volts), or 667 volts, is across the 200,000-ohm resistor. This statement means that 667 volts are on the plate of the tube. One third of the B voltage, or 333 volts, is across the 100,000-ohm resistor. Thus, the C-battery voltage (100 volts) plus the 333 volts supplies a negative bias of 433 volts to the grid of the tube. This bias is more than enough to cut off all plate current.

When the key is closed, the 100,000-ohm resistor is short-circuited. The full 1,000 volts are now applied to the plate of the tube. The negative grid bias drops to 100 volts (which we have assumed is the normal bias for the tube). Plate current now flows. This type of keying is known as the *grid-blocking* method.

Neutralizing the Radio-Frequency Amplifier. When the radio-frequency amplifier tube is a triode, we must neutralize the feedback that occurs through the capacitance between the grid and plate of the tube. We encountered this problem in the study of receivers (pages 183-184). Figure 40-19 shows the circuit employed to neutralize the amplifier tube in a transmitter.

Although the circuit shown here is for *plate neutralization,*

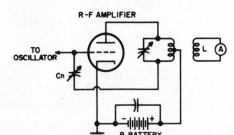

Fig. 40-19. *Circuit showing how a radio-frequency amplifier is neutralized.*

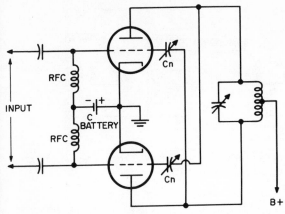

Fig. 40-20. *Circuit showing how neutralizing capacitors* (C_n) *are hooked up to neutralize a push-pull radio-frequency amplifier.*

the procedure about to be described applies to all types of neutralization.

First, operate the oscillator and amplifier normally. Next, remove the B voltage from the amplifier. Now adjust the neutralizing capacitor (C_n) until the radio-frequency miliammeter coupled to the plate tank coil of the amplifier through coil L gives a minimum reading. At this point, the capacitance of C_n and that between the grid and plate of the tube are such that potential variations coupled through them from the grid circuit into the plate tank circuit are equal and opposite.

To further check the neutralization, connect a direct-current milliammeter in the grid circuit of the radio-frequency stage being neutralized. With no plate voltage, there should be no movement of the meter pointer as the plate circuit is tuned through resonance if the stage is properly neutralized.

Thus, with direct-current voltage applied to the plate of the amplifier, feedback from the plate circuit to the grid circuit through the tube is exactly counterbalanced by that through C_n. The amplifier now is nonoscillatory. You may, therefore, replace the B voltage and the transmitter is ready for operation.

Like the single-ended radio-frequency amplifier, the push-pull radio-frequency amplifier employing triodes must be neutralized to prevent feedback. Two neutralizing capacitors are employed, connecting the grid of one tube with the plate of the other (Fig. 40-20). The neutralization procedure given above must be made for both tubes simultaneously, and the neutralizing capacitors should be adjusted each to approximately the same value of capacitance.

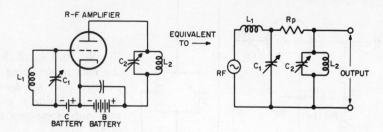

Fig. 40-21. *Diagram showing the equivalent circuit of a radio-frequency amplifier.* R_p *is the internal resistance of the tube.*

Testing for Resonance. The principle of resonance must be applied to continuous-wave transmitters. Let us investigate this problem now. In Figure 40-21 we have a diagram of the radio-frequency amplifier with its equivalent circuit. Note that the grid tank circuit (L_1 and C_1) is a *series* resonant circuit, but that the plate tank circuit (L_2 and C_2) is a *parallel* resonant circuit. Both of these tank circuits may be tested for resonance by connecting milliammeters in the grid and plate circuits as shown in Figure 40-22.

Since the grid tank circuit is a series resonant circuit, its impedance is lowest at resonance. Thus, when the *maximum* current flow occurs in the grid circuit (as shown by the milliammeter), the grid tank is at resonance.

On the other hand, the plate tank circuit is a parallel resonant circuit. At resonance, its impedance is at maximum. Thus, when the *minimum* current flow occurs in the plate circuit (as shown by its milliammeter), the plate tank is at resonance. The point of resonance is shown by a sharp dip in the plate current (Fig. 40-23).

The Absorption Frequency Meter. It is very important that the transmitter should operate only at that frequency for which

Fig. 40-22. *Diagram showing how direct-current milliammeters are hooked into the grid and plate circuits of the radio-frequency amplifier to test for resonance.*

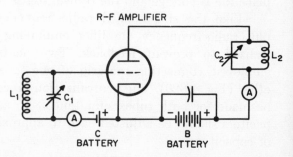

it was designed. We may calculate the values of all the parts needed for that particular frequency, but practice shows variations between the theoretical frequency and the actual frequency of the radiated waves. Variations of coupling and loading, as well as many other factors, all tend to create variations of frequency.

Thus, an instrument which checks the frequency of the transmitter is an essential part of the transmitting station. Such an instrument is the *absorption frequency meter,* a simple example of which appears in Figure 40-24.

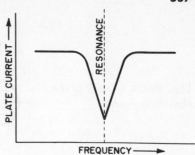

Fig. 40-23. *Graph showing the dip in plate current which indicates that the plate tank circuit is at resonance.*

This meter consists of a coil (L) and a variable capacitor (C), tunable over the frequency range of the transmitter. The coil is loosely coupled to the plate tank coil of the amplifier and when this meter is tuned to the frequency of the transmitter, a small amount of energy will be extracted from the tank.

This energy can be used to light the small flashlight lamp. When the frequency meter is tuned exactly to the transmitter frequency, maximum current will flow in the lamp. Thus, the brightness of the lamp indicates resonance.

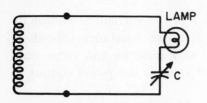

Fig. 40-24. *Circuit of the absorption frequency meter.*

The frequency meter is calibrated so that for the particular coil used, settings of the variable capacitor can be read directly as frequency. The frequency (as shown by the frequency meter) at which the lamp burns brightest is the frequency of the transmitter.

The Dummy Antenna to Measure Power Output. It is quite essential also to know the power output of a transmitter. The current flowing in the feeder lines (as shown by the ammeter in Fig. 40-12) cannot give us this information because the resistance of the antenna at the point measured is rarely known. Use, therefore, is made of a device known as a *dummy antenna* (Fig. 40-25).

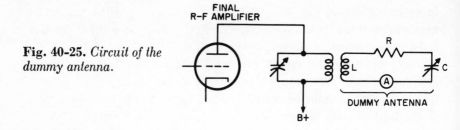

Fig. 40-25. *Circuit of the dummy antenna.*

This dummy antenna consists of a coil (L) which is inductively coupled to the plate tank coil of the final amplifier of the transmitter, a variable capacitor (C), a known resistor (R) of about 25 ohms, and a radio-frequency ammeter. The dummy antenna is tuned to the same frequency as is the transmitter. If we now take the reading of the radio-frequency ammeter, we can calculate the power in the dummy antenna from the following formula:

$$\text{Power} = I^2 \times R$$

where power is expressed in watts, I is the current as shown by the radio-frequency ammeter, and R is the resistance (about 25 ohms). Since the power in the dummy antenna can come only from the transmitter, this calculated value is the power output of the set.

The Continuous-Wave Receiver. In concluding the discussion of the continuous-wave transmitter, something must be said about the reception of telegraph signals. The receiver for continuous-wave radio-telegraphy presents a special problem. Since the carrier wave is unmodulated, it has no audio envelope to produce an audio note in the speaker. The receiver, therefore, must have incorporated in it a local radio-frequency oscillator, known as a

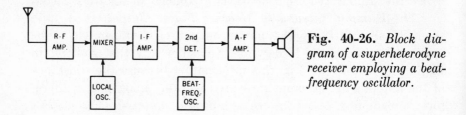

Fig. 40-26. *Block diagram of a superheterodyne receiver employing a beat-frequency oscillator.*

beat-frequency oscillator, similar to the type used in the super-heterodyne receiver (Chap. 26). This oscillator produces a radio-frequency current which beats against the incoming signal to produce a beat note whose frequency lies in the audio range.

Figure 40-26 shows the block diagram for such a receiver. It is identical with any superheterodyne receiver, except for the beat-frequency oscillator. For illustration, if the intermediate frequency is 455 kc, then the beat-frequency oscillator would send a signal to the second detector at 456 or 454 kc. The beat note would be, as a result, $456 - 455$ (or $455 - 454$), or one kilocycle. This is an audio-frequency note which excites the audio-frequency amplifier and produces a one-kilocycle note in the speaker.

SUMMARY

1. Radio waves sent out by transmitting stations may be either of two types: continuous (unmodulated) or modulated.
2. A continuous-wave transmitter is used to send the dot-and-dash signals of radiotelegraphy.
3. The signals are produced by a key momentarily closing an open circuit.
4. Both the dot and the dash consist of pulses, or trains, of many waves, but the dash is noticeably longer than the dot.
5. A radio-frequency amplifier must be coupled to the oscillator to produce greater energy for the antenna. This amplifier may be coupled by capacitive coupling or inductive coupling.
6. Change of frequency may be produced by a frequency multiplier, a system in which the tank in the grid circuit is tuned to the fundamental frequency while the tank in the plate circuit is tuned to a harmonic—usually the second harmonic.
7. The method of coupling the transmitter to the antenna depends upon whether the antenna is the Marconi or Hertz type, and whether it is current- or voltage-fed, as well as the length of the transmission line.
8. The key for sending must be connected so as to prevent radiation when open, and to provide full power without clicks when the key is momentarily closed.
9. In continuous-wave transmission, feedback due to grid-to-plate capacitance in a triode is usually prevented by neutralizing each tube carefully.
10. The frequency of the transmitter is checked by a circuit consisting of a coil, a small lamp, and a variable capacitor calibrated to read in frequencies. This coil is coupled inductively

to the plate tank coil and is tuned by means of the variable capacitor. The light is at its brightest when this circuit is tuned to resonance.

11. Power output is measured by a dummy antenna coupled to the transmitter.

GLOSSARY

Absorption Frequency Meter: A resonant circuit calibrated to check the transmitter frequency.

Continuous Radio Wave: A radio wave capable of inducing in a receiving antenna a radio-frequency alternating current of uniform amplitude.

Crystal Oscillator: An oscillator using a crystal in the grid circuit.

Doubler: A frequency multiplier generating the second harmonic.

Dummy Antenna: A nonradiating load, coupled to a transmitter, which may be used to measure the power output of the transmitter.

Frequency Multiplier: An amplifier whose output is some harmonic of its grid tank frequency.

Key Clicks: Radiations of noise due to surges of energy across the key as it is opened and closed.

Link Coupling: Coupling between two coils through the agency of two other coupling coils and a link line.

Self-Excited Oscillator: An oscillator using a tuned tank (LC circuit) in the grid circuit.

Single-Ended Amplifier: A one-tube amplifier stage.

QUESTIONS AND PROBLEMS

1. What two general types of waves are radiated by transmitters and where is each used?

2. How are dots and dashes produced in a radiated continuous radio wave?

3. Why don't we merely couple the oscillator to the antenna and send out a continuous radio wave?

4. Explain with the use of a diagram the operation of a radio-frequency amplifier coupled capacitively to an oscillator.

5. Substitute inductive coupling instead of capacitive coupling in Question 4.

6. What difficulty arises with inductive coupling and how is it remedied?

7. Explain with the use of a diagram the operation of a radio-frequency amplifier coupled to an oscillator by means of link coupling.

8. Show by diagrams a push-pull radio-frequency amplifier coupled to an oscillator by various coupling methods.
9. How may the frequency of the self-excited oscillator be varied?
10. What is the purpose of the frequency multiplier? Explain its operation.
11. Why may the push-pull frequency amplifier not be used as a frequency doubler?
12. Why is it not necessary to neutralize a frequency-multiplier stage?
13. Describe several methods of coupling the transmitter to the antenna.
14. List the four prime requirements for a good keying system.
15. What are the causes of and remedies for radiation from a continuous-wave transmitter when the key is open?
16. Illustrate one method of eliminating key clicks.
17. Why is keying in the plate circuit not very desirable?
18. Describe the grid-blocking method of keying.
19. Describe the step-by-step procedure in neutralizing a triode radio-frequency amplifier in a transmitter.
20. Describe the structure and use of an absorption frequency meter.
21. Describe the structure and use of a dummy antenna.
22. What special problem must the continuous-wave radio-telegraph receiver solve? How does it meet this problem?

41

The Modulated-Wave Transmitter

PROBLEM 1. *How is the carrier wave of a transmitter modified to transmit voice messages and music?*

PROBLEM 2. *What are the principles of transmission by amplitude modulation (AM) and frequency modulation (FM)?*

Two Methods of Modulation. We must not lose sight of the fact that the primary purpose of radio transmission is to convey ideas or intelligible signals from the sender to the receiver. Thus, merely to generate and radiate a continuous wave is meaningless, as meaningless as sending a letter that contains a blank sheet of paper. Something must be done to the radio wave if it is to convey a message.

In Chapter 40, we saw that if we break up the continuous wave into a series of short and long trains (dots and dashes), we can devise a code which will convey ideas to the person receiving the wave signal. In this chapter, we will deal with another method of saddling intelligence onto our winged carrier.

The continuous radio wave has two inherent characteristics which lend themselves to our purpose. These are the *frequency* and *amplitude* of the wave. Varying either of these characteristics according to a prearranged plan will permit us to "write" on the "blank sheet," the continuous radio wave.

This process of varying either the frequency or amplitude of the continuous carrier wave is called *modulation. Frequency modu-*

Fig. 41-1. *How the continuous carrier wave is modulated by the audiofrequency note.*

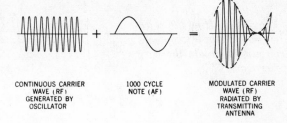

CONTINUOUS CARRIER
WAVE (RF)
GENERATED BY
OSCILLATOR

1000 CYCLE
NOTE (AF)

MODULATED CARRIER
WAVE (RF)
RADIATED BY
TRANSMITTING
ANTENNA

lation is a comparative newcomer to the radio field, and since it involves principles beyond the elementary stage, no attempt will be made here to go into details concerning its operation. At the end of this chapter, however, some of its basic principles will be discussed.

This chapter will deal primarily with *amplitude modulation,* which is characteristic of most broadcast stations. In essence, it is a process whereby audio-frequency fluctuations are impressed on the continuous radio wave in order to cause corresponding variations in the amplitude of this wave. Changing the wave in this manner is called *amplitude modulation,* and the changed radio wave is called an *amplitude-modulated radio wave.*

This modulated radio wave produced at the transmitting station is radiated by the transmitting antenna and received in the radio receiver. The detector in the receiver separates the audio-frequency variations from the carrier and passes on these audio-frequency variations to the audio-frequency amplifier, where they are built up to sufficient strength to operate the loudspeaker, thus giving back to us the original message delivered into the microphone at the transmitting station (Chap. 9).

In general, there are two types of audio-frequency variations used to modulate the carrier wave. One is a steady audio-frequency note (such as a 1,000-cycle note) (Fig. 41-1).

In the receiver, the detector removes the bottom half of the

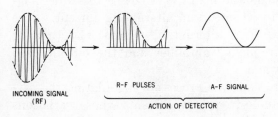

INCOMING SIGNAL
(RF)

R-F PULSES

A-F SIGNAL

ACTION OF DETECTOR

Fig. 41-2. *How the detector demodulates the incoming radio-frequency signal.*

Fig. 41-3. *How the voice currents in the microphone circuit modulate the carrier wave.*

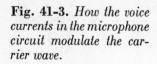

PLUS 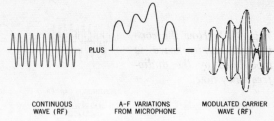 =

CONTINUOUS   A-F VARIATIONS   MODULATED CARRIER
WAVE (RF)   FROM MICROPHONE   WAVE (RF)

incoming signal, removes the radio-frequency carrier wave (demodulation), and leaves the original 1,000-cycle audio-frequency note (Fig. 41-2).

From the transmitting antenna, short and long trains of this modulated wave (corresponding to the dots and dashes of the code mentioned in Chapter 40) are radiated. This radiation results in short and long sounds coming from the loudspeaker of the receiving set. These sounds are the 1,000-cycle note, or whistle. This method of radio communication is called *interrupted continuous-wave* (ICW) *radio telegraphy*. Note that no beat-frequency oscillator is needed in the receiver in order to hear the signals.

You can see that other audio-frequency variations may be impressed on the carrier wave. Thus, the audio-frequency fluctuations caused by speech or music may be used to modulate the carrier wave (Fig. 41-3).

Demodulation in the detector causes the reproduction of the original audio-frequency variations. This method of radio communication is known as *radio telephony*.

The Modulator: How We Get the Audio-Frequency Variations. To modulate the continuous carrier wave in the transmitter for interrupted continuous-wave radio telegraphy, a number of different devices are used. Since we need a constant audio frequency (say, a 1,000-cycle note), any device which vibrates at that frequency, a tuning fork, for example, can be made to vibrate at its natural frequency in a magnetic field. As it cuts across this magnetic field, it will cause to be set up an alternating current whose frequency is 1,000 cycles. This alternating current may then be amplified by an audio-frequency amplifier and the output used to modulate the carrier wave.

Of greater interest to us is the process of modulating the carrier wave by means of audio-frequency currents whose variations conform to speech and music—that is, radio telephony. Refer to pages 19-20 and you will recall that sound waves, striking the telephone transmitter, cause corresponding variations in the electric current flowing in the transmitter circuit. It is this fluctuating electric current which we usually change into alternating currents of the same waveform as the original sound, amplify in the audio-frequency amplifier, and use to modulate the carrier wave. The audio-frequency amplifier used for this purpose is called the *modulator*. Except for certain variations which we will discuss later in this chapter, it is identical with the audio-frequency amplifier discussed in Chapter 17.

Side Bands. The combination of audio-frequency currents with the radio-frequency carrier current is, in essence, a heterodyne process similar to that which takes place in the mixer tube of the superheterodyne receiver (Chap. 26). We, therefore, get beat frequencies equal to the *sum* and the *difference* of the audio frequencies involved. Thus, for each audio frequency appearing in the modulating signal, two new radio frequencies appear, one equal to the carrier frequency *plus* the audio frequency, the other equal to the carrier frequency *minus* the audio frequency. These new frequencies are called *side frequencies,* since they appear on each side of the carrier. The groups of side frequencies representing a band, or group, of modulation frequencies are called *side bands*.

Let us assume that the oscillator of the transmitting set produces a carrier current whose frequency is 1,000,000 cycles per second. If we were to modulate this carrier by an audio-frequency current whose frequency is 1,000 cycles per second, we would get two new radio frequencies, 1,000,000 plus 1,000, or 1,001,000 cycles per second, and 1,000,000 minus 1,000, or 999,000 cycles per second. These two new frequencies are the side frequencies.

If instead of using a 1,000-cycle note to modulate our carrier current, we were to use audio-frequency currents created by sound waves whose frequencies range up to, say, 5,000 cycles per second, we would get, not two single side frequencies, but two whole bands of side frequencies. One band would lie between 1,000,000 and 1,005,000 cycles, whereas the other would lie between 1,000,000 and 995,000 cycles.

Thus, a modulated signal occupies a group of radio frequencies, or *channel*, rather than a single frequency as in the case of the unmodulated carrier. The *channel width* is twice the highest

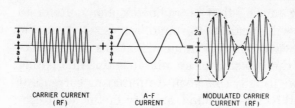

CARRIER CURRENT   A-F   MODULATED CARRIER
     (RF)   CURRENT   CURRENT (RF)

Fig. 41-4. *One hundred per cent modulation.*

modulation frequency. In the example given here, the channel width would be twice 5,000, or 10,000 cycles.

Percentage of Modulation. In the radio receiver, the audible output depends entirely upon the *amount of variation* in the carrier wave, not upon the strength of the carrier alone. We, therefore, seek to obtain the largest permissible variations in the carrier wave. Let us see how we do so.

You will note in Figure 41-4 that the amplitude of the carrier current is measured by the distance *a*. The amplitude of the audio-frequency current is assumed here to be the same value (*a*). Now consider the positive half (above the *X* axis) of the carrier current. If the audio-frequency current is added to it, the positive half-cycles of audio-frequency current will be added to the carrier current to produce the peaks in the modulated current curve. These peaks will be equal to *twice* the amplitude of the carrier current.

'The negative half-cycle of the audio-frequency current will cancel out the carrier current (since the amplitudes are equal and opposite) to produce the valley in the modulated current curve. At this point the resulting current is zero. The same thing happens to the negative half (below the *X* axis) of the carrier current.

This condition, where the carrier amplitude during modulation is at times reduced to zero and at other times increased to twice its unmodulated value, is called *100 per cent modulation*. It occurs when the peak amplitude of the audio-frequency current equals the amplitude of the unmodulated carrier current. The proportion

Fig. 41-5. *Undermodulation. Fifty per cent modulation.*

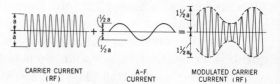

CARRIER CURRENT   A-F   MODULATED CARRIER
     (RF)   CURRENT   CURRENT (RF)

between the amplitude of the carrier and the peak amplitude of the audio-frequency current is called the *degree of modulation* and can be measured in percentages.

Thus, if the peak amplitude of the audio-frequency current is equal to *half* the amplitude of the carrier current, we say we have *50 per cent modulation* (Fig. 41-5).

If, on the other hand, the peak amplitude of the audio-frequency current exceeds the amplitude of the carrier current, we have a condition of *more than* 100 per cent modulation. We say we have *overmodulated* the carrier current (Fig. 41-6). You see that during a considerable period of time, the output is completely

Fig. 41-6. *Overmodulation. One hundred fifty per cent modulation.*

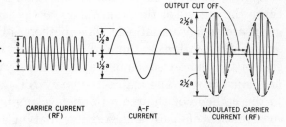

CARRIER CURRENT
(RF)

A-F
CURRENT

MODULATED CARRIER
CURRENT (RF)

cut off. The waveform of the signal heard in the loudspeaker of the receiver will not be equal to that of the original. In consequence, we have distortion.

Since we are seeking the greatest amount of variation, modulation less than 100 per cent means we are not getting the most efficient utilization of the radiated power. On the other hand, overmodulation produces distortion. It can be readily seen that 100 per cent modulation is desirable.

Power Relations in the Modulated Transmitter. The amount of power required to modulate a transmitter depends on the percentage and type of modulation. To modulate a carrier 100 per cent with a single tone (as in Fig. 41-4) requires an audio-frequency power equal to one half of the radio-frequency carrier power. Here is how it is calculated.

The peak amplitude of the modulated carrier current in 100 per cent modulation is twice that of the unmodulated carrier current. Since the power $P = I^2 \times R$, then if we assume the resistance (R) to be constant, the power of the peaks of the modulated carrier is *four times* (2^2) that of the unmodulated carrier. However, this value holds only for the peaks. It can be calculated mathematically that the average power of the modulated carrier is *one and one half times* that of the unmodulated carrier. Since this 50 per cent increase in power must come from the modulator, the audio-frequency power must be equal to one half the unmodulated carrier power.

With voice modulation (Fig. 41-3), the greater portion of the audio-frequency components will not modulate the carrier 100 per cent, so that the power increase is considerably less than for single-tone modulation.

Methods of AM Modulation. Perhaps the most common type of modulation is the method whereby the audio-frequency current is applied to the plate of one of the radio-frequency amplifiers to cause the output of the transmitter to vary in accordance with the audio-frequency variations. This method is known as *plate modulation.* Application of the audio-frequency voltage to the control grid of the radio-frequency amplifier is referred to as *grid* or *grid-bias modulation.* The audio-frequency voltage may be applied also to the cathode of the radio-frequency amplifier. This method is a combination of plate and grid modulation and is known as *cathode modulation.*

When a tetrode is used as a radio-frequency amplifier, modulation may be applied to the screen grid as well as to the plate. This method is a variation of plate modulation. Where a pentode is employed, modulation may be applied to the suppressor grid of the tube. This method is a variation of grid modulation.

Plate Modulation. Figure 41-7 illustrates plate modulation. The modulator consists of a stage of audio-frequency push-pull amplification. The tubes are operated in class A, AB, or B (Chap. 38). The only difference between the modulator stage and an ordinary audio-frequency stage of amplification lies in the fact that whereas the audio-frequency amplifier feeds into an *output transformer,* which, in turn, couples the loudspeaker to the amplifier, the modulator tubes feed into a *modulation transformer* that couples the audio-frequency variations to the plate circuit of the radio-frequency amplifier.

Note that the plate voltage to the radio-frequency amplifier is applied through the secondary of the modulation transformer. The audio-frequency voltages in this secondary vary this direct-current plate voltage, and the result is that a varying direct-cur-

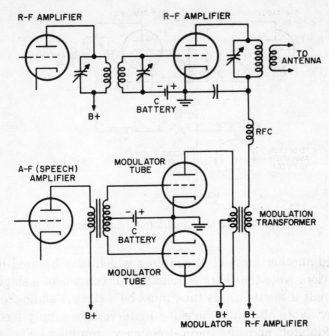

Fig. 41-7. *Plate modulation, transformer coupling. Neutralization is omitted for the sake of simplicity.*

rent voltage (varying in step with the audio-frequency variations) is applied to the plate of the radio-frequency amplifier. This variation causes the power fed into the antenna to vary with the audio-frequency variations, and hence a modulated wave is radiated.

The radio-frequency choke coil between the secondary of the modulation transformer and the plate tank of the radio-frequency amplifier is used to offer a high impedance to the radio-frequency currents, and thus keep them from flowing down into the plate-voltage supply. Note that separate plate-voltage supplies are indicated for the modulator and the radio-frequency amplifier. This practice is followed where powerful transmitters are employed. For low or medium power, the same plate-voltage supply may be used for both.

The audio-frequency amplifier driving the tubes of the modulator is an ordinary amplifier, such as the one illustrated in Figure 17-14.

This method of coupling the audio-frequency variations to the carrier is called *transformer coupling*. In Figure 41-8 is il-

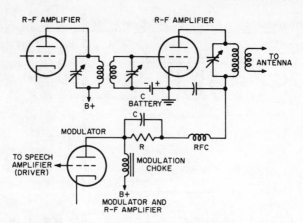

Fig. 41-8. *Plate modulation, choke coupling.*

lustrated another method of coupling which may be used in plate modulation. Note that here the modulator consists of a single tube. To prevent distortion, this tube must be a class A audio-frequency amplifier. Note also that the same plate-voltage supply feeds both the modulator and the radio-frequency amplifier. The voltage on the radio-frequency amplifier plate is constant as long as no signal current flows in the plate circuit of the modulator tube. As soon as such a signal current flows, it produces a large voltage drop across the modulation choke. This voltage drop will vary in step with the audio-frequency current of the modulator. As a result, the plate voltage on the radio-frequency amplifier, too, will vary in step with the audio-frequency current, and thus the output of the transmitter will be modulated at this audio frequency.

For 100 per cent modulation, the audio-frequency voltage applied to the r-f amplifier plate circuit must have a peak value equal to the direct-current voltage on the r-f amplifier before modulating (Fig. 41-4). To obtain this without distortion, the radio-frequency amplifier must be operated at a direct-current plate voltage *less* than the modulator plate voltage. The extent of the voltage difference is determined by the type of modulator tube used. To obtain this drop in voltage, the resistor R is employed. The capacitor C permits audio-frequency voltages to flow around this resistor. This method of modulation is called *choke-coupled plate modulation*.

Grid-Bias Modulation. In Figure 41-9 is shown the circuit for *grid-bias modulation*. Here, the audio-frequency voltages vary the grid-bias supply to the radio-frequency amplifier. This variation, in turn, varies the power output of this amplifier, which causes a modulated wave to be radiated. But results are obtained when the source of grid bias comes from batteries.

The modulator tube must be operated as a class A audio-frequency amplifier. Since we are varying the grid bias of the radio-frequency amplifier, we do not need as much power as is needed for plate modulation. The comparatively low power output of the class A audio-frequency amplifier is usually sufficient for our purpose. On the other hand, the carrier output of the transmitter that is grid-modulated is about one quarter that of the plate-modulated transmitter.

In What Part of the Transmitter Is Modulation Impressed? We have seen that the purpose of the modulator is to impress the audio-frequency variations upon the carrier. We must decide where, between the oscillator and the antenna, this coupling is to take place.

The oscillator should never be modulated because, as we have seen, change in load will seriously affect the frequency. Thus, modulation of the oscillator will cause the signal to wobble, spoiling the reception and causing interference with neighboring stations. As a matter of fact, in the interest of frequency stability, the transmitter should be modulated as far away from the oscillator as possible.

This requirement indicates that the final radio-frequency

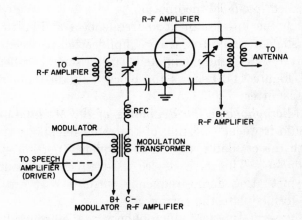

Fig. 41-9. *Grid modulation, transformer coupling.*

Fig. 41-10. *Block diagram showing the relationship of the components of a radio-telephone transmitter (high-level modulation).*

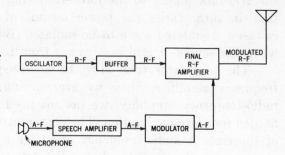

amplifier should be modulated. This final ampifier may be a class C amplifier with the advantage of greatest efficiency.

There is, however, a drawback to this procedure. Since the carrier is being modulated at the point of its greatest power, the audio-frequency power used to modulate it, too, must be at its maximum. Sometimes, a compromise is made by modulating that radio-frequency stage next to the final amplifier. Thus, less audio-frequency power is needed.

Since the final radio-frequency stage in such a setup amplifies the *modulated* carrier, it must be a *linear amplifier* (class B). If it were a class C amplifier, too much distortion would creep in. Thus, the advantage of the greater efficiency of class C amplification would be sacrificed. We would save in audio-frequency power at the cost of output power.

If we modulate the final radio-frequency amplifier, we call the modulation *high-level* modulation. Modulating in any other stage is called *low-level* modulation.

It is in the interest of good frequency stability to insert at least one stage of radio-frequency amplification between the oscillator and the tube being modulated. Such a stage is called a *buffer amplifier*. Figure 41-10 shows the block diagram for a radio-telephone transmitter.

The Microphone Is the Beginning of the Modulation System. As the radio-frequency portion of the radio-telephone transmitter starts with the oscillator, the audio-frequency portion starts with the *microphone*. This is a device used to change sound waves into the fluctuating audio-frequency currents that are amplified and used to modulate the carrier.

Five general types of microphones are in general use. The *carbon-grain microphone* consists of two carbon disks, one fastened

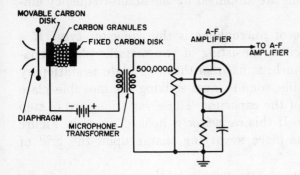

Fig. 41-11. *Hookup for the carbon-grain microphone.*

securely to the back of the microphone, and the other to a diaphragm. The space between these two disks is partly filled with carbon granules. As the sound waves strike the diaphgram, these carbon granules are pressed together with a varying pressure, depending upon the sound waves. This varying pressure on the granules changes the electrical resistance between the two disks. If this device is hooked up in a circuit such as that in Figure 41-11, the sound waves cause a fluctuating current to flow in the circuit.

This fluctuating current varies in step with the sound waves —that is, at audio frequency. By means of the transformer, this audio-frequency current places a fluctuating charge upon the grid of the amplifier tube. The 500,000-ohm potentiometer acts as a volume control (pages 128-129).

Another type of microphone is the *piezoelectric crystal* type. We have already met this crystal in a phonograph pickup in Chapter 17 (Fig. 17-17). If for the needle holder we substitute a diaphragm, then sound waves striking this diaphragm set up a fluctuating alternating voltage across the faces of the crystal.

Fig. 41-12. *Hookup for the capacitor microphone.*

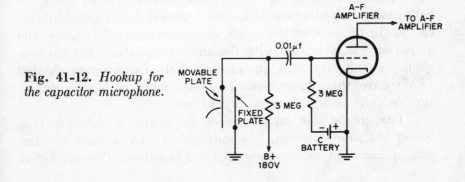

These voltage variations are amplified by the audio-frequency amplifier.

Still another type of microphone is the *capacitor* type. If a small air-spaced capacitor, consisting of two metallic plates separated by about 0.001 inch, is fixed so that one plate is stationary and the other is movable, sound waves striking the movable plate vary the capacitance of the capacitor. These variations are in step with the sound waves. If this capacitor is hooked up as in Figure 41-12, these variations place a varying charge upon the grid of the amplifier tube.

Still another type of microphone is the *ribbon* or *velocity* type. Here, a thin metallic ribbon (usually made of duralumin, an aluminum alloy) is suspended between the poles of a powerful permanent magnet. Sound waves striking this ribbon cause it to vibrate back and forth, cutting the magnetic field and setting up an alternating current in the ribbon. This ribbon is coupled to the tube of the audio-frequency amplifier by means of a transformer.

The *dynamic* microphone is a variant of the velocity type. Instead of a metallic ribbon, a small, light coil of wire moves across the magnetic field. In fact, if you were to speak into the cone of a small permanent-magnet dynamic speaker (Fig. 22-5), you would have a dynamic microphone.

Frequency Modulation (FM). As stated earlier in this chapter, messages may be conveyed by varying the frequency of the carrier wave in step with audio-frequency variations caused by speech or music. This method of radio communication is called *frequency modulation*. Although it is beyond the scope of this book to go into the procedure in detail, we shall attempt to outline the basic principles.

Figure 41-13 illustrates how the frequency-modulated carrier wave differs from the amplitude-modulated carrier wave. In both cases, the audio modulation is impressed on the unmodulated carrier. In the case of the amplitude-modulated (AM) wave, the *amplitude* varies in step with the audio modulation, but the frequency remains constant. In the case of the frequency-modulated (FM) wave, the *frequency* varies in step with the audio modulation, but the amplitude remains constant.

The greater the amplitude of the audio modulation (the louder the sound entering the microphone), the greater the frequency variation, or *deviation,* of the FM carrier. The number of

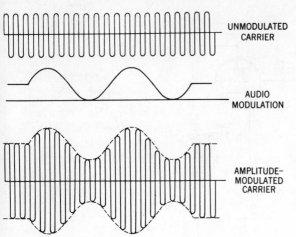

UNMODULATED
CARRIER

AUDIO
MODULATION

AMPLITUDE-
MODULATED
CARRIER

Fig. 41-13. *Comparison between the amplitude-modulated and frequency-modulated carrier.*

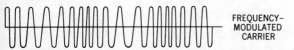

FREQUENCY-
MODULATED
CARRIER

such frequency variations per second is determined by the frequency of the audio modulation. In Figure 41-13, two cycles of audio modulation have been shown. Note that the frequency-modulated wave exhibits two sets of frequency deviations.

Another important difference between the two types of modulation lies in the matter of side bands. In the amplitude-modulated wave, the width of the side band is equal to the highest audio frequency (about 15 kc). Thus, the band width of the transmitted signal has a maximum width of about 30 kc. In practice today, most broadcast stations operate on a band width of 10 kc, and thus the range of the audio signal heard in the speaker is limited to about 5 kc.

In the case of the frequency-modulated wave, there is no such limit, since the frequency of the audio signal does not vary the frequency of the wave, but rather the number of frequency deviations per second. Modern FM transmitters operate on a band width of 150 kc, thus permitting a frequency deviation of 75 kc to each side of the carrier frequency. To get the necessary wide channels and prevent one station from interfering with another, extremely high frequencies are employed, usually around 100 mc. This high frequency makes it necessary to transmit in a direct line

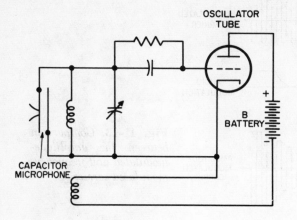

Fig. 41-14. *Theoretical circuit of the frequency-modulation transmitter.*

rather than in accordance with the ordinary AM broadcasting procedure (pages 440-441).

An idea of how frequency modulation is produced is illustrated in Figure 41-14. You will recognize this diagram as the regenerative oscillator with a capacitor microphone across the grid tank circuit. As sound strikes the capacitor microphone, the capacitance varies with the sound. The louder the sound, the greater the variation in capacitance. The frequency of the sound determines the number of such variations per second. This capacitance variation, in turn, varies the total capacitance of the tank circuit, thus varying the frequency of the oscillator.

In practice, this method of frequency modulation is not employed, and the illustration is used merely to show the principle involved. It is beyond the scope of this book to discuss the actual circuits employed.

To receive the frequency-modulated signal, we may employ the ordinary superheterodyne receiver, but with a number of im-

Fig. 41-15. *The discriminator circuit.*

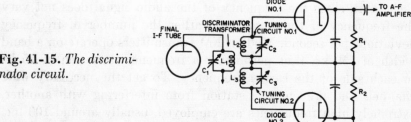

portant changes. In the AM receiver, the tuned circuits are required to pass a 10-kc band, and hence selectivity is desirable. The tuned circuits of the FM receiver, on the other hand, are required to pass a 150-kc band. Thus, they cannot be too selective. Resistance is deliberately added to broaden the tuning curve.

Another difference is the intermediate frequencies employed. AM receivers generally employ frequencies around 455 kc. FM receivers may use intermediate frequencies as high as 5 mc or higher.

Still another difference lies in the method of demodulation, or detection, employed. The AM receiver requires a demodulator whose output is determined by the *amplitude* of the signal. FM receivers require a demodulator whose output is determined by the *frequency* of the signal. This demodulator stage is called a *frequency discriminator*.

The circuit of one type of discriminator is shown in Figure 41-15. The primary of the discriminator transformer (L_1) is fed by the output of the final intermediate-frequency tube and is inductively coupled to two secondaries (L_2 and L_3). This primary is tuned to the intermediate frequency (assume it is 5,000 kc) by means of capacitor C_1.

Secondary L_2 is tuned to 75 kc *above* the intermediate frequency (5,075 kc) by means of capacitor C_2 and forms tuning circuit No. 1. Secondary L_1 and C_3 form tuning circuit No. 2, which is tuned to a similar amount *below* the intermediate frequency (4,925 kc).

Diode No. 1 acts as a detector for tuning circuit No. 1, and its output is developed across its load resistor R_1. Diode No. 2 performs a similar function for tuning circuit No. 2, and its output is developed across its load resistor R_2. R_1 is equal to R_2, and thus we have a balanced circuit.

If the output of the last intermediate-frequency stage is at the intermediate frequency (5,000 kc), equal voltages will be induced in L_2 and L_3, and the voltage drops across the load resistors R_1 and R_2, too, will be equal. Since the polarities of these voltage drops are in opposition to each other, the voltage drops will cancel out, and no signal will be passed to the audio-frequency amplifier.

But if the output of the last intermediate-frequency stage is higher than the intermediate frequency, a larger voltage will be developed across tuning circuit No. 1 and its load resistor R_1 than across tuning circuit No. 2 and its load resistor R_2. Thus, the voltage drops will no longer cancel out, and a signal will be passed to the audio-frequency amplifier. The greater the frequency difference, the greater will be the signal.

Similarly, if the frequency falls below the intermediate frequency, a signal of opposite polarity will be passed to the audio-frequency amplifier. Thus, the output of the discriminator stage is determined by the frequency of the signal. Since the frequency variations are determined by the audio modulation, the audio signal appears at the output of the discriminator stage to be amplified by the audio amplifier.

If the radio-frequency signal should contain amplitude as well as frequency modulation, such amplitude modulation would create a voltage variation across R_1 and R_2 that would interfere with the audio output of the discriminator stage. It is the function of the *limiter stage* to remove any amplitude modulation which may be present in the signal before it reaches the discriminator stage.

The final intermediate-frequency amplifier is operated as such a limiter stage. To do this, the tube is operated with a low plate voltage so that the positive half-cycle of the signal quickly brings the tube to saturation, and with a grid bias sufficient so that the negative half-cycle quickly cuts it off. As a result, this stage limits the amplitude of the signal it will pass.

One valuable function of the limiter is to eliminate static which usually increases the amplitude of the signal. Since the limiter action eliminates amplitude variations, the FM receiver is singularly free of static.

A more recent type of FM demodulator is that known as the

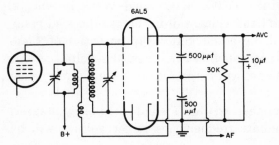

Fig. 41-16. *The basic circuit of the ratio detector.*

ratio detector whose basic circuit is shown in Figure 41-16. Coils L_1, L_2, and L_3 form the primary, secondary, and tertiary windings, respectively, of a transformer. The primary L_1 is part of the resonant circuit in the plate circuit of the last intermediate-frequency amplifier. The secondary L_2 is part of the resonant circuit in the input circuit of the ratio detector. The tertiary winding L_3 is closely coupled to the bottom of the primary winding. Both resonant circuits are tuned to the intermediate frequency.

Note that L_2, diode D_1, resistor R, and diode D_2 form a series circuit. If an unmodulated intermediate-frequency signal is impressed across L_2, current will flow through this circuit as indicated by the arrows and, as a result, a voltage drop will appear across R. Since capacitors C_1 and C_2 are connected in series across R, this voltage will appear across these capacitors. Since both capacitors are of equal value, this voltage will be divided equally between both capacitors.

Should the amplitude of the intermediate-frequency signal increase, the voltage across R (and, accordingly, C_1 and C_2) will increase, too. Should the amplitude of the signal decrease, the voltage will decrease. However, should any amplitude modulation appear in the signal, such amplitude changes, which are merely momentary changes, would be absorbed and ironed out by capacitor C_3, which is across resistor R and which, generally, is quite large (usually from 8 to 10 μf).

Thus, you see, we need no limiter stage to remove amplitude modulation from the signal. The effect of R and C_3, then, is to place a constant voltage across C_1 and C_2, a voltage that will vary only with signal strength, not with modulation. This voltage, as we have seen, is divided equally between C_1 and C_2.

Now what happens when the signal is frequency-modulated? Normally, the voltages across C_1 and C_2 would remain equal. But note that L_3, which is inductively coupled to L_1, has one of its ends connected to the middle of L_2 and the other end to the junction of C_1 and C_2. Thus, current flowing through L_3 has two parallel paths. One is through L_3, C_2, D_2, the bottom half of L_2, and back to L_3. The other is through L_3, the top half of L_2, D_1, C_1, and back to L_3. Because of phase differences resulting from inductive reactance, the current flowing in each of the two paths are unequal. Hence different voltages will appear across C_1 and C_2. These differences will vary as the frequency variations of the modulated signal.

Thus you see that, while the *total* voltage across C_1 and C_2 in series remains constant (its magnitude depending upon the signal strength), frequency modulation of the signal changes the *ratio* in which the voltage is divided between C_1 and C_2. Hence the name, ratio detector. Thus the variations in voltage across one of these capacitors (C_2, for example) will reflect the audio variations which frequency-modulated the carrier current at the transmitter.

A practical ratio-detector circuit is shown in Figure 41-17. Both diodes are contained in the envelope of a 6AL5 tube. The audio signals are taken from the junction of the two 500-$\mu\mu$f capacitors. Since the voltage across the 30,000-ohm resistor is determined by the strength of the signal, we can obtain automatic-volume-control voltage from the negative side of the resistor to be applied to the preceding tubes.

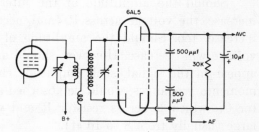

Fig. 41-17. *The practical circuit of the ratio detector.*

Modulation by the Effects of Light—Facsimile. The frequency-modulation transmitter may be affected by audio-frequency currents modified by light as well as by sound. If a beam of light, say about 0.01 inch in diameter, is passed over a picture or photograph, the beam will be reflected with a varying intensity according to whether the spot on the picture is light or dark. If the spot is light, much light will be reflected; if the spot is dark, little light will be reflected. This reflected light is caused to fall upon a *photoelectric cell,* a device which changes light waves into electric current. The brighter the light striking this photoelectric cell, the greater the current output of the cell.

As the beam of light traverses (or scans) the picture, the reflected light varies in intensity with the light and dark spots on the picture. The result is a fluctuating current output from the cell. If this fluctuating current is used to modulate the frequency of the carrier, the wave will then contain frequency variations in step with the fluctuating current.

At the receiving end, the fluctuating current operates a stylus that passes over a special chemically treated paper in step with the movements of the beam of light at the transmitting station. The effect of the current is to cause a black spot to appear on the paper, the density of the spot varying with the strength of the current. Thus, the picture is reproduced at the receiver. This process is called *facsimile transmission.*

SUMMARY

1. The continuous wave of a transmitter must be *modified* in some way to convey intelligible signals.
2. Two methods of *modulation* (modifying the continuous wave) are used: (a) *amplitude* modulation (AM) and (b) *frequency* modulation (FM).
3. The common method used by broadcasting stations was, until a few years ago, amplitude modulation. This method continues to be the practice generally, but a number of stations transmit also by frequency modulation.
4. In *amplitude modulation,* the carrier current is maintained at a constant frequency, and the sound currents are impressed on the carrier current so as to modify the amplitude. The pattern of such currents shows an envelope on the carrier current having fluctuations corresponding to the variations of the sound waves.
5. The process of amplitude modulation consists of using in the transmitter the principles of audio-frequency amplifier and the beat system of the superheterodyne receiver.
6. The ideal condition for amplitude modulation is to have the peak amplitude of the audio-frequency current equal the normal amplitude of the carrier current. In this case, the total amplitude at the peak will be two times the amplitude of the carrier current, or *100 per cent modulation.*
7. The power of the audio-frequency current will bring about this ideal condition when it is one half the unmodulated carrier power.
8. The modulation may be applied as audio-frequency voltage to the *plate,* to the *grid,* or to the *cathode* of the radio-frequency amplifier. For *plate modulation,* which is most common, the modulator is essentially a stage of push-pull amplification that feeds into a modulation transformer. This transformer couples the audio-frequency variation to the plate circuit of the radio-frequency amplifier.

9. The modulator should not be coupled to the oscillator stage. When the final radio-frequency amplifier is modulated, the system is called *high-level modulation*. Modulation at any other point is called *low-level modulation*.

10. Microphones have the function of impressing the energy of sound waves upon electric currents. This function is the reverse of the functions of loudspeakers. The principles used in microphones are: (1) to vary the resistance of the electrical circuit (carbon-granule type), (2) to vary the capacitance of a capacitor, thereby varying the amount of charge stored (capacitor type), (3) to induce a voltage across a conductor as it vibrates in a magnetic field (ribbon type or dynamic type), or (4) to create a varying voltage across a crystal by means of sound vibrations.

11. In the *frequency-modulation* system of transmission, the carrier current is maintained at a constant amplitude while the frequency is varied by the audio-frequency modulation.

12. One method of producing frequency modulation is to connect a capacitor microphone across the grid tank circuit of a regenerative oscillator. Here, the capacitance of the microphone varies the capacitance of the tank circuit, which in turn varies the frequency of the oscillator.

13. Frequency-modulated waves are usually transmitted in straight lines to receivers, and transmission is limited, therefore, to short distances.

GLOSSARY

Amplitude Modulation: Varying the amplitude of a carrier current with an audio-frequency signal.

Capacitor Microphone: A microphone operating on the principle of varying the thickness of the dielectric of a capacitor, thereby changing its capacitance and producing a varying voltage output.

Carbon Microphone: A microphone operating on the principle of varying the resistance of a container of carbon granules by means of sound waves.

Cathode Modulation: A form of modulation wherein the audio signal is fed into the cathode circuit of a radio-frequency amplifier.

Channel: A band of radio frequencies.

Crystal Microphone: A microphone operating on the principle of making sound waves vary the compression on a crystal, thereby producing a varying voltage across the faces of the crystal.

Discriminator: A detector in a frequency-modulation receiver which changes variations in the received carrier frequency into audio-frequency changes.

Facsimile Transmission: Transmission of pictures by radio.

Frequency Modulation: Varying the frequency of the carrier current in accordance with an audio-frequency signal.

Grid Modulation: A form of carrier modulation wherein the audio-frequency signal is fed into the grid circuit of a radio-frequency amplifier.

High-Level Modulation: Modulation of the final radio-frequency amplifier stage.

Interrupted Continuous Wave (ICW): Dots and dashes produced by intermittent transmitting of a carrier modulated continually by a single audio-frequency signal.

Limiter: A stage in a frequency-modulation receiver which limits all signals to the same amplitude.

Low-Level Modulation: Modulation of a radio-frequency amplifier stage before the last stage.

Microphone: A device to change sound into fluctuating audio-frequency currents.

Modulation: Variation of the frequency or amplitude of a continuous carrier current by means of an audio-frequency signal.

Modulator: An audio-frequency amplifier used to modulate a continuous radio-frequency current.

Overmodulation: A condition of modulation wherein the amplitude of the modulator current is greater than the amplitude of the continuous carrier current, resulting in distortion.

Per Cent Modulation: The percentagge of increase or decrease of peak amplitude of the unmodulated carrier.

Plate Modulation: A form of modulation wherein the audio-frequency signal is fed into the plate circuit of a radio-frequency amplifier.

Ratio Detector: A detector in a frequency-modulation receiver where frequency variations in the signal produce changes in the ratio in which the voltage is divided between two capacitors that form a voltage divider.

Side Bands: The range of frequencies on each side of the carrier frequency produced by audio-frequency amplitude modulation.

QUESTIONS AND PROBLEMS

1. By what two alterations of a continuous carrier wave may modulation be affected?
2. What two types of audio-frequency variations are used to modulate a carrier wave?
3. What is the interrupted continuous-wave method of radio transmission?
4. What is meant by radio telegraphy? By radio telephony?
5. In its fundamental form, what is a modulator?
6. How do side bands arise when a radio-frequency current is modulated in radio telephony?

7. What is the channel width when a radio-frequency current is modulated in radio telephony by audio-frequency signals up to 4,000 cycles per second? Show how you derived this.

8. What factor, in addition to the strength of the carrier from the transmitter, determines what the strength of the signal from the transmitter shall be?

9. Draw a diagram showing a radio-frequency carrier 100 per cent modulated, 50 per cent modulated, overmodulated. Which is most desirable?

10. Describe several methods of transmitter modulation.

11. Describe, with the aid of a diagram, two methods of plate modulation.

12. Compare plate modulation and grid modulation as to advantages and disadvantages.

13. Generally speaking, to what stage is it best to couple an audio modulator?

14. What is a buffer amplifier, and what is its purpose?

15. What is the originating source of the radio-frequency portion of a radio-telephone transmitter? Of the audio-frequency portion?

16. Explain the operating principles of the five types of microphones in general use.

17. Give a short description of the form of a frequency-modulated wave.

18. Compare band widths provided for amplitude-modulated stations and frequency-modulated stations.

19. Explain the operation of a discriminator in an FM receiver.

20. Draw the diagram of a ratio detector used in an FM receiver.

21. What is the function of the limiter in the frequency-modulated receiver?

22. In what manner does static affect the radio wave? How does the frequency-modulated receiver eliminate the effects of static?

23. Briefly explain the operation of facsimile transmission.

42

The Cathode-Ray Tube and Its Applications

> **PROBLEM 1.** *What are the principles of the cathode-ray tube?*
>
> **PROBLEM 2.** *How is the cathode ray used in the oscilloscope to show pictures of currents in radio circuits?*
>
> **PROBLEM 3.** *How are television pictures produced?*
>
> **PROBLEM 4.** *How is the radio beam used to detect and range distant objects?*

Geissler Tubes. Up to now we have been considering such applications of the radio tube as the amplifier, the rectifier, and the oscillator. In this chapter, we shall consider a variation of this marvelous device: the cathode-ray tube.

About the year 1874, an English scientist, Sir William Crookes, was experimenting with some Geissler tubes. These are simply long glass tubes into each end of which a metal electrode is sealed. The air inside these tubes is pumped out, and in its place a very small amount of some gas like neon is inserted. When a large voltage is placed across the electrodes, this gas glows just as our present-day neon tubes do.

When the charge on the positive electrode gets great enough, one of the planetary electrons of the gas atom near it is torn away. The gas atom then becomes a positively charged *ion.* As such, it is repelled from the positive electrode (like charges repel), and it rushes toward the negative electrode (unlike charges attract).

As it strikes the negative electrode, the ion regains its missing electron from the great mass of them piled up on this electrode.

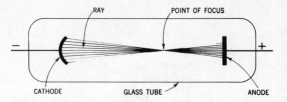

Fig. 42-1. *The cathode rays may be focused like light rays.*

Thus, the gas ion again becomes an atom. In the process of changing from an ion to an atom, energy is given off in the form of light. The color of this light depends upon the kind of gas present in the tube; neon tubes give an orange light.

Crookes Tubes and Cathode Rays. Sir William Crookes did not know all this, but he noticed that if the tube was exhausted to a very high vacuum, the glow of the gas disappeared, and instead, the inside walls of the tube would start to glow with a strange light.

Mysterious rays seemed to shoot out of the negative electrode (the cathode) toward the positive electrode (the anode). If the cathode was made concave, these rays could be focused to a point, just as light is focused to a point by the concave reflector of an automobile headlight (Fig. 42-1).

These rays themselves are invisible, but if a piece of platinum foil is placed at the point of focus, the concentrated energy of the rays is great enough to melt the metal—just as sunlight, focused through a lens, will burn a hole in a piece of paper held at the point of focus.

About 1892, Sir J. J. Thomson, another English scientist, proved that these rays coming from the cathode (and, therefore, called *cathode rays*) are in reality a stream of free electrons. He was able to make the path of this stream visible by placing in the tube, parallel to the electron stream, a strip of mica whose surface was coated with zinc sulphide. This chemical has the property of glowing when struck by electrons. As the electron stream swept

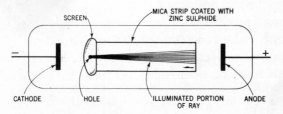

Fig. 42-2. *How the path of the cathode ray is made visible.*

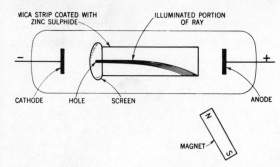

Fig. 42-3. *How the electron stream is deflected by a magnet.*

past this mica strip, the electrons struck against the zinc sulphide. Thus, the path of these electrons was shown clearly (Fig. 42-2).

Deflection of Cathode Rays by a Charged Plate. Thomson discovered another curious thing about these cathode rays. He held a magnet near the glass tube. The path of the rays, as shown on the mica strip, was deflected by the magnet. The stream of electrons was deflected by the magnet, and the stronger the magnet, the more the electrons were deflected (Fig. 42-3). This was because the moving electrons within the tube set up their own magnetic field which interacted with that of the magnet.

It also proved possible to deflect the cathode rays by electrically charged plates. Since the cathode ray consists of a stream of electrons, then if a plate carrying a positive charge is placed parallel to the stream, the ray will be attracted toward that plate. Similarly, if the plate has a negative charge on it, the ray will be repelled from it (Fig. 42-4). Thus, by varying the charge on a third plate other than the cathode and anode, the cathode ray can be bent up or down. This plate is known as a *deflector plate.*

Putting the Cathode Ray to Work. The next step in the direction of making the cathode ray useful was to replace the *cold* cathode described above with a heated filament similar to that

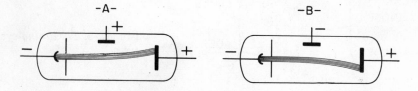

Fig. 42-4. *A—The effect on the electron stream of a positive charge.*
B—The effect on the electron stream of a negative charge.

used in a radio tube. This *hot* cathode, as we have learned in studying radio tubes, is a more practical emitter of electrons than a cold metal plate charged negatively. With such a hot cathode, a smaller positive charge may be used on the anode than with the tube devised by Crookes.

The Tuning-Eye Tube. An ingenious application of the cathode-ray (or electron-ray) tube has been developed to aid us to tune our radio receiver. In a glass bulb from which the air is evacuated, a cathode is mounted in a vertical position. Around it is placed a funnel-shaped anode, tapering down. The inner surface of the anode is coated with a chemical that glows when struck by an electron stream. Electrons streaming off the heated cathode strike the inner surface of the anode (or target), producing a ring of light (Fig. 42-5).

Between the cathode and the anode a vertical deflector plate, consisting of a thin wire, is inserted. If this plate is at the same potential as the anode, it will have little effect on the electron stream, and the glow will be an uninterrupted ring. But if the charge on this deflector plate is less positive than that on the anode, a dielectric field will be set up between it and the anode. This field will repel electrons flowing toward the anode, and thus the portion of the anode in line with the deflector plate will be dark. The greater the potential difference between the anode and the deflector plate, the greater the dark portion of the anode (Fig. 42-6). The electron-ray tube, therefore, can be used as a voltmeter. The dark round spot in the center of this ring of light in most tuning-eye tubes is caused by a cathode light shield so placed as to make the amount of deflection more noticeable.

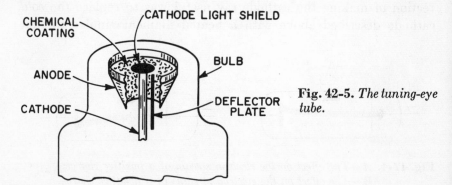

CHEMICAL COATING — CATHODE LIGHT SHIELD — BULB — ANODE — DEFLECTOR PLATE — CATHODE

Fig. 42-5. *The tuning-eye tube.*

Fig. 42-6. *Top view of tuning-eye tube.*

A—Deflector plate at same potential as the anode.

B—Deflector plate at lower potential than the anode.

Now turn to the circuit of the automatic-volume-control circuit (Fig. 24-10). The greater the signal strength in the detector circuit, the greater the negative voltage in the automatic-volume-control system. Thus, when a given station is tuned in at its maximum volume, the automatic-volume-control voltage for that particular station will be at its maximum.

If the deflector plate of our electron-ray tube is connected to this source of automatic-volume-control voltage, the negative charge on this plate will be greatest when the signal is tuned in at its maximum. The dark portion of the ring then will be at its maximum width.

In practice, the reverse of this action is used. The negative automatic-volume-control voltage is placed on the grid of a triode connected to the electron-ray tube, as shown in Figure 42-7. As the grid of the triode becomes more negative (station tuned in at maximum volume), the plate current of the triode gets smaller. The voltage drop across resistor R becomes less ($E = I \times R$), and thus the positive charge on the deflector plate of the electron-ray tube gets nearer to that of the anode. Thus, the dark section of the ring becomes smallest as the station is tuned in to its maximum volume.

This gives us a device for actually "seeing" when the receiver is properly tuned. In modern practice, both the triode and the

Fig. 42-7. *Circuit showing how the tuning-eye is connected to the automatic-volume-control line.*

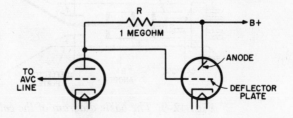

electron-ray tube are placed in one envelope (Fig. 42-8). Such a tube is called a *tuning-eye* tube. Examples are the 6E5 and 6U5/6G5 types.

Modern Cathode-Ray Tubes. Now let us go back to the cathode-ray tube shown in Figure 42-4. We have already learned that if the stream of electrons strikes certain chemicals,

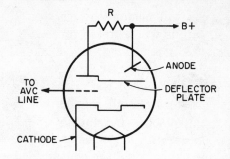

Fig. 42-8. *How the triode and tuning eye are contained in one envelope.*

such as zinc sulphide, it makes them glow. If we erect a screen coated with these chemicals and focus a beam of cathode rays upon it, we can see where the electrons strike it from the point of light which appears. By observing the motion of this point of light toward and away from the deflector plate, we can visualize the varying charges on the deflector plate.

Such a screen may be made by coating the inner side of the end of the tube behind the anode with these chemicals (called *fluorescent* chemicals or *phosphors*). The cathode is a metal tube coated with electron-emitting chemicals. The heater is coiled inside this tube and heats the cathode until it is hot enough to emit a stream of electrons. To enable the electron stream to strike the screen, a hole is cut in the anode plate, and this plate is moved closer to the cathode (Fig. 42-9). Between the cathode and the anode is a control electrode, a tube which is slipped over the cathode. The stream of electrons must pass through the small hole at the end of this electrode. A negative charge on this control elec-

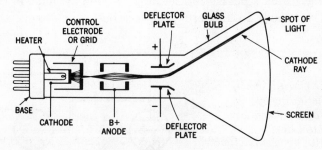

Fig. 42-9. *The basic diagram of the cathode-ray tube.*

trode will narrow the electron stream passing through this hole, and thus will increase the beam density or current. Two deflector plates are inserted, one above the stream and one below. Since one plate is positively charged and the other negatively charged, the deflection of the ray is twice as great as with one plate.

It was found that cathode rays may be focused to a sharp point in somewhat the same way as a light beam may be focused with a lens. The focusing device consists of a second hollow anode inserted between the control electrode and the original anode. The positive charge on this second anode is usually about one fifth of the charge on the original anode. At this value, the cathode ray is focused so that it appears as a pin point of light on the screen. The voltage on this second anode is made variable to provide a means of focusing (Fig. 42-10).

The original anode is called the *accelerating anode,* since its function is to speed up or accelerate the electron stream from the cathode to the screen or target. The second anode is called the *focusing electrode* for obvious reasons. Varying the voltage on this electrode varies the size of the spot of light appearing on the screen. Sometimes a second accelerating anode is inserted between the control electrode and the focusing electrode. The complete assembly of cathode, control electrode, focusing electrode, and accelerating anode is called the *electron gun.*

Placing opposite charges on the deflector plates creates a

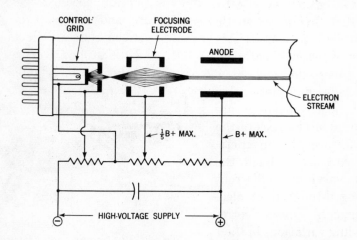

Fig. 42-10. *Voltage relationship between the various portions of the electron gun.*

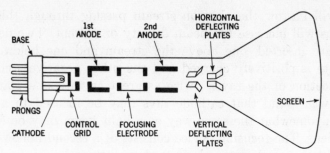

Fig. 42-11. *The cathode-ray tube.*

dielectric or electrostatic field between these plates which tends to deflect the electron stream passing between them toward the positively charged plate. By varying the charges on these plates (and thereby varying the strength of the electrostatic field), the electron beam is moved toward one or the other, and the luminous spot on the screen moves likewise. When they are placed so that the luminous spot moves in a vertical plane (up and down), these plates are called the *vertical deflecting plates.*

By placing two similar plates at the sides of the tube—that is, to the right and left of the electron beam, the luminous spot is also made to move in a horizontal direction or plane. These two plates are called the *horizontal deflecting plates* (Fig. 42-11).

You will recall that the electron beam may also be deflected by a magnetic field (See Figure 42-3). Accordingly, some cathode-ray tubes do not have any deflecting plates. Instead, electromagnets are mounted on the neck of the tube. Since the magnetic field can act through the glass, varying the current flowing through these electromagnets causes corresponding variations in their magnetic fields. As a result, the electron beam is de-

Fig. 42-12. *Commercial 21-inch cathode-ray tube. (Courtesy of Allen B. DuMont Laboratories, Inc.)*

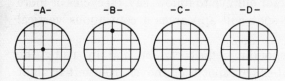

Fig. 42-13. *View of screen of the cathode-ray tube showing the positions of the spot of light.*

flected. This system is called *electromagnetic deflection,* and tubes of this type are widely employed in television receivers.

The Cathode-Ray Oscilloscope. We are now ready to understand how an electric current can be made to draw its picture on the screen of a cathode-ray tube. The machine which pictures the movement of the electric current is called a *cathode-ray oscillograph* or *oscilloscope.* Assume that there is no charge on any of the deflecting plates. The electron stream will be focused to a pin point of light appearing in the center of the screen (Fig. 42-13-A).

If a voltage is placed on the vertical deflecting plates so that the upper plate is positive and the lower is negative, the point of light appears above the center of the tube (Fig. 42-13-B). The distance the point of light is moved above the center of the screen depends upon the voltage on the vertical plates. The *sensitivity* of the tube (that is, the number of volts required to deflect the spot of light one inch) is given by the tube manufacturer. Thus, with a tube that has a deflection sensitivity of 50 volts per inch, if the spot of light has moved, say, an inch and a half above the center position, we know the voltage across the plates is 75 volts. You see that we may use this tube as a voltmeter. For convenience of measurement, a cross-ruled piece of celluloid may be mounted over the screen of the tube.

If our connections are reversed so that the bottom vertical deflection plate is positive, the spot moves below the center of the tube (Fig. 42-13-C). If an alternating voltage is placed on the plates, the spot of light will move up and down in step with the alternations of voltage.

If the frequency of the alternating voltage is low enough, we can actually see the spot move up and down. But if

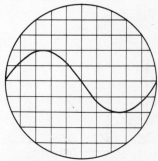

Fig. 42-14. *Trace described by a sine wave.*

the frequency is too high for our eye to follow, say, 60 cycles or more per second, the moving spot will appear as a continuous vertical line (Fig. 42-13-D).

Of course, a corresponding effect can be had by using the horizontal deflecting plates. Our spot then moves from left to right or vice versa.

Assume that we have placed a 60-cycle alternating voltage on the vertical plates. In 1/60 second, the spot will have moved from the center of the screen, up to the top of its path, down to the center again, down to the bottom of its path, and up again to the center. You know, of course, that this sequence represents one complete cycle. Assume that at the same time a constantly increasing voltage is placed on the horizontal plates, which tends to drive the spot from the extreme left of the screen to the right in 1/60 second. As a result of these two voltages, the spot describes a sine curve (Fig. 42-14). The picture appearing on the screen is called a *trace*.

If, at the instant the spot reaches the extreme right of the screen, the voltage on the horizontal deflecting plates drops to zero and starts over again, another sine curve is traced over the original one. This continues, and the effect is as if the curve stood still, enabling us to inspect it.

The Sweep Circuit. The horizontal component of the movement of the spot of light is a continuous, even, left-to-right motion until the extreme right of the screen is reached. At that instant, the spot is returned to its original position at the extreme left of the screen. This motion is described as the *linear sweep* of the cathode-ray tube. The voltage waveform on the horizontal deflecting plates to accomplish this sweep is shown in Figure 42-15. Because of the shape of this waveform, the device that produces it is called a *sawtooth* oscillator. Another name for it is the *linear timing axis* oscillator or *sweep* oscillator.

Neon-Bulb Oscillators. A simple sawtooth oscillator is shown in Figure 42-16.

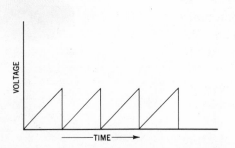

Fig. 42-15. *Waveform of the output of a sawtooth oscillator.*

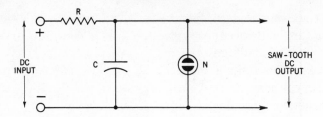

Fig. 42-16. *A sawtooth oscillator using a neon bulb.*

Here, direct current flowing through a resistor (R) charges a fixed capacitor (C). Across the capacitor is a neon bulb (N). This bulb has no effect on the capacitor until a voltage high enough to flash the bulb (about 60 volts) is built up across the plates of the capacitor. When this voltage is reached, the gas within the bulb ionizes. The bulb becomes a conductor, instantly discharging capacitor C.

As the voltage across the capacitor drops to almost zero, the neon gas in the bulb deionizes. This suddenly makes the bulb an insulator, and another cycle begins as the capacitor starts charging up again.

The frequency of these cycles is determined by the length of time it takes to charge the capacitor to the flashing point of the neon bulb. By selecting proper values of capacitance and by making R variable, a sweep of any frequency from a few cycles up to many thousands may be obtained.

Figure 42-17 shows an improvement over the simple neon-bulb oscillator. Substituted for the neon bulb is a tube that looks like an ordinary triode. In this tube, however, a small amount of some such gas as neon is introduced. The action of this tube (which is caller a *thyratron*) is similar to that of the neon bulb, except that its flashing voltage may be set to any predetermined value by using the proper value of grid-bias voltage. The 884 is a tube

Fig. 42-17. *A sawtooth oscillator using a thyratron tube.*

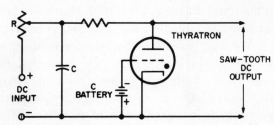

of this type. In these tubes, the discharges will occur when the plate voltage reaches about seven times the grid-bias voltage.

In practice, oscilloscopes are sold in compact units with knobs for control and with means for connection to radio circuits. Amplifiers are usually provided in commercial oscilloscopes to amplify the input voltages to the vertical and horizontal deflecting plates. Our complete oscilloscope then consists of the following parts:

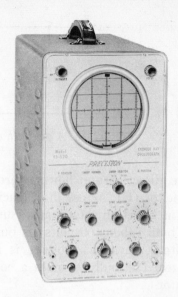

Fig. 42-18. *Cathode-ray oscilloscope. (Courtesy Precision Apparatus Company, Inc.)*

Cathode-ray tube
Vertical amplifier
Horizontal amplifier
Timing-axis oscillator
Power-supply unit

Using the Cathode-Ray Oscilloscope. We cannot discuss here all the tests which can be made with the cathode-ray oscilloscope. Such a discussion is suited to a more advanced text. Indeed, entire volumes have been written about this subject alone. We shall try here to present some simple principles encountered as we operate this marvelous device.

We already know that we can use the oscilloscope to measure alternating and direct voltages. Note that it is the *peak* alternating voltage we measure here, not the root-mean-square voltage (as measured by an alternating-current voltmeter).

We may examine the waveform of an alternating voltage by impressing this voltage on the vertical deflecting plates and impressing the voltage obtained from the sawtooth oscillator on the horizontal plates. If we make the frequency of the horizontal voltage equal to the frequency of the alternating voltage under test, we get the picture of a single cycle of that alternating voltage. This picture, or *trace,* seems to stand still, thus permitting close inspection. Deviations from the true sine curve can be clearly seen.

If we know the frequency of the sawtooth voltage, we can tell the frequency of the alternating voltage. If the frequency of the voltage on the horizontal plates is a *submultiple* of the alternating voltage under test (that is, ½, ⅓, ¼, or the like), we get 2, 3, 4, or a corresponding number of cycles appearing on the screen. As an example, assume we apply a 60-cycle alternating voltage on the vertical plates. If the sawtooth voltage applied to the horizontal plates also has a frequency of 60 cycles per second, we get one cycle on the screen. If it has a frequency of 30 cycles per second (½), we get two cycles on the screen; 20 cycles per second produces 3 cycles, and so forth.

Although the use of the linear timing axis (the sawtooth voltage) is fairly general, there are some applications of the oscilloscope where it is not used. Thus, if we wish to see the phase shift in an electrical device, we can show it pictorially by impressing the input voltage to this device on one set of plates and the output voltage upon the other set of plates.

Graphic pictures of sound waves also may be traced on the screen by using the linear timing axis and connecting the output of a microphone to the vertical plates. As stated, these are but a few of the many applications of the cathode-ray oscilloscope.

Television. The fairy tales of all nations have had some tale of men who could see what was happening at a great distance, far beyond the range of human sight. The twentieth century has seen this tale come true. The invention of television has been one of mankind's greatest achievements. Although the details of television are beyond the scope of an elementary radio text, the principles are quite simple, and we shall present them briefly here.

The eye sees objects by the light reflected from these objects. If an object did not reflect light, it would be invisible. Assume that we have a spot that is illuminated by a bright light. If this spot is light in color, it will reflect a good deal of the light falling on it. If it is dark, it will reflect but little of the light falling on it.

Further, assume that we have a device, such as a photo-electric cell, which can convert light energy into electrical energy. If the reflected light from the light-colored spot falls upon this

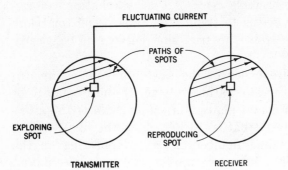

Fig. 42-19. *The basic principle of television. The two spots keep in step with each other.*

device, a large current will flow. If the reflected light from the dark-colored spot strikes this device, less current will flow.

A picture can be broken down into spots of light of varying degrees of light and dark shades. If the device that changes light energy into electrical energy (the *photoelectric* cell) moves from spot to spot successively (we call this *scanning* the picture), the current set flowing in the photoelectric device will vary in step with the light and dark spots.

If this varying current is sent, finally, into a device whose action is the reverse of the photoelectric device—that is, a device whereby electrical energy is changed into light energy, and if this reproducing device moves in step with the photoelectric device, the picture may be reconstructed on a screen (Fig. 42-19).

This explanation covers the principle of television. The varying current may be sent over wires, it may be used to modulate a radio wave and send the variations many miles through space. If the scanning is rapid enough, pictures of moving objects may be shown in rapid succession on the screen of the television receiver, thus giving the illusion of motion just as motion pictures do.

The Iconoscope. There are a number of methods for producing the varying current at the television transmitter. One of these employs our old friend, the cathode ray, in a device called the *iconoscope,* invented by an American scientist, Vladimir K. Zworykin.

There are certain materials, such as the metal *cesium,* which have the

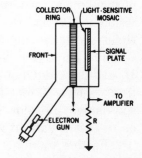

Fig. 42-20. *The iconoscope.*

peculiar property of shooting off electrons when exposed to light. We call such materials *photoelectric* materials. The electrons thus discharged are called *photoelectrons*. The greater the intensity of the light, the greater the number of photoelectrons discharged.

In the iconoscope, a mica sheet is covered with millions of tiny globules of silver, each coated with the photoelectric metal cesium. Each globule, which is called an *element,* is insulated from its neighbors. The mica sheet, with its layer of photelectric globules, is called a *mosaic.* The back of the mica sheet is coated with a metal plate, called the *signal plate.*

The coated side of the mosaic (the *photosensitized* side) faces the front of the bulb and an *electron gun* of the type previously described. In front of the mosaic is mounted a metal ring called the *collecting ring.* Electron gun, mosaic, signal plate, and collecting ring are all mounted in a glass bulb from which the air has been exhausted (Fig. 42-20).

When light strikes an element of the mosaic, photoelectrons are emitted. The greater the intensity of the light, the more electrons are shot off. This illuminated element of the mosaic thus becomes positively charged, the value of this charge depending upon the intensity of the light. Because each element is insulated from its neighbors, its charge remains fixed. Thus the picture appears on the mosaic in terms of varying positive charges. The function of the collecting ring (which is made positive) is to collect the free photoelectrons and drain them out of the bulb.

As each element becomes positively charged, electrons will be attracted and will flow up from ground through resistor R to take their places on the signal plate opposite the charged element. The number of electrons so attracted will depend upon the positive charge on each element, and this depends upon the intensity of the light striking each element. Thus, an electron image of the picture forms on the signal plate.

The mosaic is swept by a thin stream of electrons emitted by the electron gun. As this electron stream strikes a particular element, it supplies the missing electrons, and thus the positive charge is neutralized.

As each element is neutralized, the electrons it held in place on the signal plate are released. These flow back to ground through resistor R. The flow of these electrons sets up a current pulse through the resistor, causing a voltage drop across R. This voltage will depend upon the number of electrons flowing and thus varying voltages are set up as varying numbers of electrons flow through the resistor. As a result, varying voltages are fed to the amplifier. These voltages, fed into the amplifier, are used to modulate a carrier current which, in turn, causes a modulated radio wave to be radiated.

The electron stream from the electron gun sweeps across the charged elements in a horizontal direction, traversing one horizontal row after another. Modern iconoscopes utilize a beam which can sweep or scan 525 rows of elements in 1/30 of a second.

The Television Reproducer. In the television receiver, the cathode-ray tube is used as a reproducer. The tube is adjusted so that the electron beam sweeps across the surface of the screen in step with the beam in the iconoscope. After the modulated wave has been received, amplified, and demodulated, the varying current is fed to the control electrode or grid of the tube. This electrode, you will recall, varies the density of the beam, thus varying the intensity of the light produced on the screen.

For example, if at one instant the beam of the iconoscope discharges an element which has received a large positive charge due to the fact that a bright light had fallen on it, a large current flows from the screen to the modulator of the transmitter. At the receiving end, the beam of the cathode-ray tube is at a position on the screen corresponding to the position of the beam in the iconoscope. The large current flowing into the control grid causes a bright spot to appear on the screen. Thus, dark and bright spots appear on the cathode-ray screen in step with the dark and bright spots of the picture at the transmitting studio. Since these spots constitute the picture, the picture is reproduced on the receiving screen.

These spots merge to produce the picture because of two factors. One is the persistence of human vision. The eye sees a light for a fraction of a second after the light has disappeared. Thus, we get an overlapping of spots which blend to give us the picture. Similar to this is the persistence of glow which the chemicals on the cathode-ray screen possess. The glow persists for a fraction of a second after the electron stream has moved to the next spot. Once again the spots merge to produce the picture. If successive pictures are produced rapidly enough, we get the illusion of motion pictures.

Radar. Radar—RAdio Detection And Ranging—is one of the outstanding electronic developments in recent years. Essentially, it is a device for detecting objects at a considerable distance and for determining the direction and distance between the object and the radar station. Developed for war purposes, radar was quickly adapted to peaceful needs, especially in the field of navigation.

A consideration of the actual circuits employed in radar equipment is beyond the scope of this book. Instead, the general basic principles will be presented.

Assume that an airplane is flying high above the earth on a dark night. A searchlight station on the ground sends out a narrow beam of light. When this beam strikes the airplane, light is reflected from the surface of the plane to the eyes of an observer stationed near the searchlight. The plane is seen or *detected*.

With radar, a narrow radio beam is used instead of the light beam. This invisible beam, striking the plane, is reflected to a radio receiver located near the transmitter, and thus the plane is detected.

Thus far, the radio beam acts like the light beam. However, whereas clouds or fog renders the light beam inoperative, the radio beam easily penetrates these obstacles. Further, the light beam is visible; the radio beam is invisible, and the plane may be detected even though its occupants may not be aware of the fact.

It is not enough to detect the plane. We must know how far away it is, how high up, and its bearing (that is, its compass position in relation to the observer). The searchlight only permits an approximation of the answers to these questions, since it affords no accurate information concerning the distance of the plane from the observer.

With radar equipment, however, we are able to measure the time it takes the radio wave to travel from the transmitter to the plane and back again to the receiver. Knowing the speed at which the radio wave travels (approximately 186,000 miles per second), it is relatively easy to calculate the distance between the plane and the observer at the radar station.

Because of the enormous speed of the radio wave, the time intervals are very small—in the order of *microseconds* (a microsecond is one millionth of a second). The cathode-ray tube is used to measure these small intervals of time.

Assume that at the instant the transmitter sends its radio

beam at the target, the electron stream in the cathode-ray tube is set moving horizontally at a rate which will make the trace move across the face of the tube one inch per 100 microseconds. Further assume that the target is such a distance away from the transmitter that the radio wave, traveling at the rate of about 328 yards per microsecond, requires 100 microseconds to reach it. Since the reflected wave will require the same time to reach the receiver, the round trip will consume 200 microseconds.

During this interval, the trace on the face of the cathode-ray tube will have traveled two inches. If we had some method for marking the trace so that it would record the instant the radio wave was sent out, and the instant it was received, we would then be able to tell the time required for the round trip (in microseconds) by measuring the distance (in inches) between the two marks.

The radio wave is sent out as a short *pulse,* or *burst,* of energy, rather than in a continuous wave. The duration of this pulse usually is only about one microsecond (abbreviated μs). Part of this pulse is sent to the vertical deflecting plates of the cathode-ray tube, and its effect is to produce a sharp bump, or *pip,* on the trace. When the reflected pulse is received, it, too, goes to the vertical deflecting plates of the tube. Thus a second pip appears on the trace (Fig. 42-21).

In the 200 microseconds required for the radio pulse to reach the target and be reflected to the receiver, the trace will have traveled two inches. Thus the two pips will appear two inches apart. By means of a scale printed on the face of the cathode-ray tube, we can translate the distance between the two pips of the trace into distance between the target and the radar station. Since the radio pulse travels at the rate of 328 yards per microsecond, it will require one microsecond for the pulse to reach a target 164 yards away and be reflected to the radar station. Thus, in our example, the distance between the two pips is two inches, the elapsed time for the round trip is 200 microseconds, and the distance between the radar station and the target is 32,800 yards (328×100).

The radio pulses may be sent out several hundred times per second. Since the sweep circuit of the cathode-ray tube is synchronized to start with each transmitted pulse, all the traces will coincide, producing the effect of a single trace.

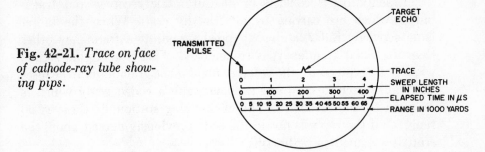

Fig. 42-21. *Trace on face of cathode-ray tube showing pips.*

Also, since the duration of each pulse is extremely brief and the time between pulses relatively great, the average power consumed is small. Thus, small tubes and other components may be employed, even though the power of each pulse is large.

The radio beam must be narrow so that it may be directed toward a particular spot, just as is the light beam of the searchlight. This requires special antenna arrays. To make the equipment portable and to allow the beam to be rotated easily, the antenna array must be quite small. This necessitates the use of very high frequencies—thousands of megacycles. Because of these high frequencies, radar operates on line-of-sight transmissions, similar to light beams.

For peacetime use, radar equipment may be mounted on ships, airplanes, or other vehicles to detect obstacles which normally would not be seen because of darkness or fog.

IFF. It is not enough to detect a target by radar. Before opening fire on it, one should know whether the target is friendly or hostile. To establish this identification, auxiliary apparatus has been developed for use with radar. This apparatus is known as *Identification—Friend or Foe* (IFF).

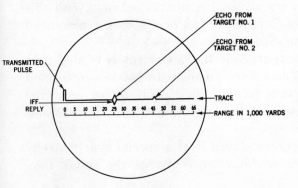

Fig. 42-22. *Trace showing two targets, one of which (the nearest) is friendly, as indicated by the IFF reply.*

Essentially, it consists of an automatic receiver and transmitter which are carried by all friendly craft. When the target is detected by radar, a special coded signal, at a frequency other than the radar frequency, is transmitted. This challenging signal, when it is received by the receiver aboard the friendly craft, causes the transmitter to send out automatically a coded reply which is received by the receiver of the challenging station. If there is no reply, or if the reply is not in the code previously agreed upon, the craft is assumed to be hostile.

The cathode-ray tube is used here, too. If the reply to the challenge is the proper one, a pip appears on the screen. If there is no pip, the craft is hostile. In some installations, the reply signal is superimposed on the radar screen through suitable circuits. In this way it changes the echoing pip produced by the target and thus identifies it as friendly.

In Figure 42-22 there appears a radar screen containing a trace showing two pips, and hence two targets, at different distances from the radar station. The nearest target (No. 1) is friendly, as shown by the downward pip appearing beneath the original pip. This downward pip is produced by the answer to the IFF challenge. The farthest target (No. 2) contains no downward pip and thus is assumed to be hostile.

For peacetime use, the automatic receiver and transmitter may be placed at definite, known points on the ground to serve as beacons for aircraft. As an airplane flies overhead, it may send out a challenging signal. The nearest beacon then would reply. The reply of each beacon would be coded differently for purposes of identification. Since the pilot would know the locations of these beacons from his maps, he thus would know his position.

PPI Radar. More wonderful than the ordinary radar is the *PPI* radar (derived from Plan Position Indicator). With this instrument a radio beam is sent out and brings back a picture of the area surrounding the station.

Assume that a ship containing this apparatus is located near shore (Fig. 42-23-A). The radar antennas are located at the top of a mast and are rotated so that they point at, or *scan,* the horizon. Below deck, and connected to the antennas, is the radar equipment.

The cathode-ray tube employed is of a special type whereby the electron stream sweeps from the center of the tube's face,

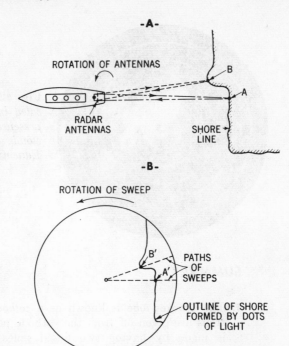

Fig. 42-23. *How the PPI radar operates.*

A—The rotary antennas scan the horizon.

B—How the picture is produced on the face of the cathode-ray tube.

along a radius to the periphery, and back to the center (Fig. 42-23-B). Further, the stream can be rotated around this center. The rotation of this electron stream is synchronized with the rotation of the radar antennas.

As the radar beam is transmitted from the antenna to a point on the horizon, the electron stream of the tube starts from the center toward a corresponding point on the periphery of the tube's face. The trace produced is just too faint to be seen. If the radar beam strikes a reflecting object (A), the echo causes the trace to brighten and a bright spot appears at a corresponding point on the trace (A). Both the antenna and electron stream move to the next angular position. The echo from point B produces a corresponding bright spot on the trace (B).

This continues until a whole series of bright spots, corresponding to the outline of the shore, have appeared on the screen of the tube. Since the screen of the cathode-ray tube is of the high-persistence type, the bright spots will remain for some time after the sweep has moved on to other angular positions. The result then would be a picture of the area surrounding the ship, whose position is indicated by the center of the screen.

Fig. 42-24. *PPI radar screen located in an airplane showing the presence and location of storm clouds ahead. (Courtesy of RCA Educational Services.)*

SUMMARY

1. The **Crookes tube** is known as a **cathode-ray tube** because electrons are given off from the cathode pole of the tube. The tube is made by having two metal poles protrude into a sealed tube from which most of the air has been pumped out. When the ends of the metal electrodes are charged oppositely (by connecting them to a static electric machine or an induction coil) with a high voltage, electrons stream from the cathode to the anode.
2. The deflection of the stream of particles both by magnetic fields and by dielectric fields is evidence that the particles given off by the cathode are electrons.
3. When the cathode is made hot, the principle of the Crookes tube is used as a modern **cathode-ray tube** for radio work.
4. The most important uses in radio for this cathode tube are for the **tuning eye,** the **cathode-ray oscilloscope, television,** and **radar.**
5. The principles of the cathode-ray oscilloscope are that (1) a screen coated with flourescent material glows when bombarded with electrons of the cathode rays. (2) When the cathode rays are focused to a narrow beam, a single point of light is formed on the screen. (3) The beam may be deflected both vertically and horizontally by properly placed **deflecting plates.** (4) When these plates are charged by the varying voltages of radio circuits, the screen may be used to show pictures of the sine curve, of the current in a radio tube, and of other characteristics.
6. **Television,** or the transmission of pictures through space, is a modern application of several principles connected with radio and with electrons: In brief, television depends upon (1) the fact that light causes certain substances to emit electrons pro-

portional to the intensity of the light, (2) the electron impulses can be amplified and transmitted as electromagnetic waves, and (3) electromagnetic waves can be detected, amplified, and transformed into light varying in intensity just as did the original light.

7. *Radar (radio detection and ranging)* employs a cathode-ray tube to measure the time it takes a radio wave to travel from the radar station to the target and back again. Since the speed of the radio wave is known, the distance between the station and the target can be calculated. Also, since the radio wave can be transmitted in the form of a narrow, directional beam, the bearing of the target and its altitude (if it is an airplane) can be determined as well.

8. To identify the target as friendly or hostile, an automatic receiver and transmitter are carried by all friendly craft. When challenged by a specially coded radio signal, the receiver automatically activates the transmitter, causing it to respond with a coded reply signal. This reply signal can be seen on the screen of the cathode-ray tube. Failure to receive a reply to a challenge, or a reply that is improperly coded, indicates a presumably hostile target.

9. By means of the PPI radar equipment it is possible to obtain upon a cathode-ray screen an outline picture of the area surrounding the radar station.

GLOSSARY

Accelerating Electrode: The electrode in the cathode-ray tube which speeds up the stream of electrons from the cathode to the plate.

Cathode Ray: A stream of free electrons.

Cathode-Ray Oscilloscope: A device which traces out on a fluorescent screen a graph, which may be used to interpret the nature of a wave.

Cathode-Ray Tube: A tube in which a stream of electrons is deflected in various directions under the influence of a set of nearby charged plates to produce a trace on a fluorescent screen.

Collecting Ring: A metal ring which collects the electrons emitted by the caesium elements in the iconoscope.

Control Electrode: A tube with a hole at the end of it placed between the anode and cathode which controls the beam density in a cathode-ray tube.

Deflector Plate: A plate in a cathode-ray tube which, by receiving a charge, deflects the cathode ray.

Electron Gun: The complete assembly of cathode, control electrode, focusing electrode, and accelerating electrode in a cathode-ray tube.

Focusing Electrode: An electrode in a cathode-ray tube, used to focus the cathode-ray beam on the screen.

Horizontal Deflecting Plates: Electrodes in a cathode-ray tube which serve to move the focused points from left to right across the screen.

Iconoscope: A tube used in television transmission to pick up light-image impulses and change them into electrical impulses.

IFF: Identification—Friend or Foe. A system for determining whether a target located by radar is friendly or hostile.

Linear Sweep: Movement of the electron beam from left to right and back.

Linear Timing-Axis Oscillator: An oscillator which sweeps the focused dot of an oscilloscope periodically across the screen from left to right.

Mosaic Screen: A screen in which are imbedded photoelectric particles insulated from each other and which change light energy into electrical energy.

Oscillograph: Same as the cathode-ray oscilloscope.

Photoelectric Materials: Materials which convert light energy into electrical energy.

PPI Radar: A radar device for producing an outline picture of the surrounding area on the face of a cathode-ray tube.

Radar: Radio Detection And Ranging. A device for detecting an object by means of a reflected radio wave. Range is determined by measuring the time it takes a radio pulse sent ont by a transmitter to reach the object and be reflected back.

Sawtooth Oscillator, or Sweep Oscillator: Same as a linear timing-axis oscillator.

Television: The process of sending and receiving scenes via radio waves.

Thyratron: A tube used in the oscilloscope to produce sawtooth oscillations.

Tuning-Eye Tube: A cathode-ray tube used for aiding in the tuning of a receiver.

Vertical Deflection Plates: Electrodes in a cathode-ray tube which serve to move the focused dot up and down on the screen.

QUESTIONS AND PROBLEMS

1. What is the nature of the cathode ray in a Crookes tube?
2. Explain the structure and operation of the tuning-eye tube.
3. Explain, with the aid of a diagram, how the tuning-eye tube is connected in a radio receiver to aid in tuning.
4. Why is a triode amplifier used in conjunction with a tuning-eye tube?
5. How are the cathode rays made visible in a cathode-ray tube?

6. How are electrons made to move up and down in a cathode-ray tube? To the right and left?

7. Draw the screen of a cathode-ray oscilloscope and locate the trace for the conditions represented by charges on the deflecting plates:

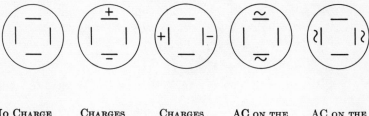

| No Charge on Any Plate | Charges Only on the Vertical Plates | Charges Only on the Horizontal Plates | AC on the Vertical Plates | AC on the Horizontal Plates |

8. How may the cathode-ray oscilloscope be used as a voltmeter?

9. Explain the type of oscilloscope trace that would be obtained if an alternating sine voltage were placed on the vertical plates while an ever-increasing voltage acted to drive the focused light point from left to right under the influence of the horizontal deflecting plates.

10. What is the purpose of a sawtooth oscillator in the oscilloscope?

11. Make the diagram of a simple sawtooth oscillator using a neon tube and explain how it works. How is its timing controlled?

12. List the five essential functional parts of a complete oscilloscope.

13. List several uses to which an oscilloscope may be put.

14. State the general principle of television.

15. Describe the structure of an iconoscope and explain how it works.

16. How many rows of elements are swept per second in modern iconoscopes?

17. Explain how the cathode-ray tube is used in a television receiver to reproduce a scene.

18. How does a series of dots on the cathode-ray tube screen form a total picture as well as show motion?

19. Explain how the cathode-ray tube is used to measure the distance between the station and the target in a radar installation.

20. Explain the IFF method for determining whether a target is friendly or hostile.

21. Explain how the PPI radar produces an outline picture of the surrounding area upon the screen of the cathode-ray tube.

Demonstrations

Demonstrations for Part I

CHAPTER 2

Demonstration 1: *To show how energy is handed on by wave motion.* Set up a row of dominoes, so spaced that when one falls it upsets its neighbor. Tip the first and note how energy is handed down the line without any domino moving more than a small distance (Fig. 2-4). Or perform the experiment shown in Figure 2-5.

CHAPTER 3

Demonstration 1: Light a vacuum-type electric light lamp. Note that heat and light waves pass through the vacuum.

Demonstration 2: Demonstrate the apparatus shown in Figure 3-1.

Demonstration 3: Obtain a number of soft-iron rods about ¼ in. in diameter and 12 in. long. Make a bundle of them about 1½ in. in diameter. Wrap a layer of tape over them. Wind upon this core about 3 lbs of bell wire (No. 18 double cotton covered) making a winding about 6 in. wide. Attach the ends of this coil to the 110-volt alternating-current line. Wind another coil of bell wire consisting of about 30 turns having a diameter of 2 in. Attach a telephone receiver to the ends of this coil. Slip the small coil over the iron core. Note the pickup of the 60-cycle note. Move the small coil farther and farther away from the large coil. Observe that the note falls off. The note is due to magnetic pickup from the energized coil.

CHAPTER 4

Demonstration 1: *To show the need for an antenna.* Set up the following apparatus:

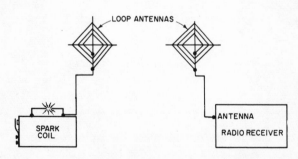

The loop antennas may be made by winding about 15 turns of bell wire on crossed dowel sticks, spacing the turns about 1 in. apart. Place the spark coil in a felt-lined box to absorb the spark noise. The radio receiver will pick up the spark over a fairly large distance.

Disconnect the transmitting antenna. Note that the pickup drops off. Disconnect the receiving antenna. The pickup drops off still more and disappears.

Demonstration 2: *To illustrate the natural period of a wave or vibration.*

(a) Suspend two pendulums, one 2 ft long and the other 3 ft long. Count the number of swings of each in one minute.

(b) Strike various tuning forks of different sizes. Note the different notes characteristic of each fork.

Demonstration 3: *To demonstrate the principle of tuning.* Obtain four tuning blocks having the following frequencies: two of 512 vibrations per second (vps) and two of 256 vps. Strike one 512-vps block. Note that only the other 512-vps block picks up the vibrations. Then strike one 256-vps block. Only the other 256-vps block will pick up these vibrations.

Demonstration 4: Demonstrate the apparatus shown in Figure 4-2 to show how the reproducer changes fluctuating electrical currents into sound.

Demonstration 5: *To show how the detector works.* Connect up a crystal receiver as shown in Figure 8-3 using a fixed crystal, such as the type 1N34 germanium crystal. Short out the crystal. Note how the signal disappears.

CHAPTER 5

Demonstration 1: *To illustrate the behavior of conductors and insulators.*

Arrange the following circuit:

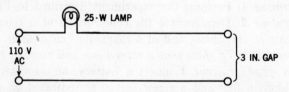

Across the gap in the circuit place, in turn, rods of the following materials: glass, iron, brass, copper, porcelain, carbon, zinc, wood, and the like. The 25-watt lamp lights up when a conductor is placed across the gap.

Demonstration 2: *To construct an antenna.* If the school building is not of the steel-frame type, run a 50-ft piece of bell wire around the molding of the room. Another method of construction is to run a 100-ft length of bell wire from the window to a nearby tree or flag pole. If both of these possibilities are lacking, the wire may be dropped out the window and permitted to hang down, or else run up the side of the building to the roof. Care should be taken that the bare end of the wire does not touch the ground or the side of the building.

CHAPTER 6

Demonstration 1: Show the students various tuning coils from commercial receivers, and explain methods of connecting the windings into the circuit.

Demonstration 2: (a) Open up various fixed capacitors and show their construction. Show the ratings on these capacitors.

(b) Show various variable tuning capacitors. Point out the rotor and stator plates and show their connections.

Demonstration 3: Repeat Demonstration 3, Chapter 4.

Demonstration 4: *To exhibit a mechanical analogy of the fact that for resonance or tuning, the transmitter and receiver need not be physically the same.* Take two tuning forks mounted on resonance boxes, one of 320 vps and the other of 384 vps. Strike one and show that there is no resonance. Then load one or more pinch clamps on the 384-vps fork. By trial and error, find the condition where striking the 320-vps fork results in resonance with the 384-vps fork and its load.

CHAPTER 7

Demonstration 1: Perform the experiment described in Figure 7-1.

Demonstration 2: Demonstrate the construction of a telephone receiver, of a pair of earphones, and of a magnetic loudspeaker.

Demonstration 3: *To show that a reproducer will respond to a varying but not a steady current.* Connect a battery, an ammeter, a magnetic loudspeaker, a file, and a screw driver as indicated on page 615. When the screw driver is in resting contact with the file, a steady current flows through the ammeter, but no sound results. But as the screw driver slides over the file, a fluctuating current flows through the ammeter and a sound is heard coming from the loudspeaker.

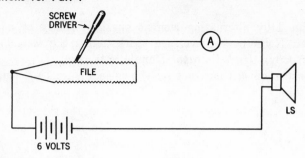

CHAPTER 8

Demonstration 1: Show the students various crystals, of fixed and adjustable types.

Demonstration 2: Connect a type 1N34 crystal detector, 1,000-ohm resistor, a single dry cell, and a sensitive milliammeter in series. Record the milliammeter reading. Now reverse the dry cell. Compare the milliammeter reading with the previous recording.

Demonstration 3: Construct the crystal set described in Demonstration 5, Chapter 4.

CHAPTER 9

Demonstration 1: Show a barograph chart and explain it.

Demonstration 2: Construct a graph on the basis of the time it takes the students to work five problems.

Demonstration 3: If a cathode-ray oscilloscope is available, show an alternating-current sine curve, a direct-current voltage, and an audio-frequency (voice) wave. Interpret them.

CHAPTER 10

Demonstration 1: On a large nail, wind a coil of bell wire consisting of about 25 turns (primary). To the ends of this coil, connect a key and dry cell in series. On the same nail, wind a second coil (secondary) of the same number of turns. Connect a galvanometer to the ends of this coil. Closing the key of the primary coil will send a current flowing in the secondary coil (as shown by the deflection of the galvanometer).

Demonstration 2: *To demonstrate a step-down transformer.* Obtain a bell transformer. Place 110v alternating current on the primary. Attach an electric bell to the secondary.

Demonstration 3: *To demonstrate a step-up transformer.*

(a) Place 6v on the primary of a spark coil and notice the high-voltage spark across the secondary.

(b) Put 110v alternating current on the primary of a neon-sign transformer. Note the high-voltage spark across the secondary (from 5,000 to 15,000v). *High Voltage! Handle with care!*

Demonstration 4: Construct set shown in Figure 10-7, using a type 1N34 crystal.

CHAPTER 11

Demonstration 1: Cut an old dry cell in half. Point out the carbon rod, the zinc shell, and the electrolyte.

Demonstration 2: *To study the law of electric charges.*

(a) Suspend two pith balls from silk strings. Charge them both negatively by touching each with a hard rubber rod that has been stroked on a piece of fur. Now bring the two pith balls near each other. They repel each other. The same experiment may be performed using two inflated balloons that have been rubbed with fur.

(b) Charge one pith ball negatively as above. Charge the other positively by touching it to a glass rod that has been rubbed on silk. Now bring the two pith balls near each other. They attract each other.

Demonstration 3: *To distinguish between alternating current and direct current.* Connect a dry cell to a zero-center ammeter through a 30-ohm resistor. The needle moves to one side and remains stationary. Now replace the dry cell with a hand magneto or a Brownlee generator connected for alternating current. Slowly rotate the handle and note how the needle of the meter fluctuates to either side of the center zero.

CHAPTER 12

Demonstration 1: Inspect the structure of a Leyden jar. Charge it up with an electrostatic machine. Then show the spark as it is discharged with a pair of discharging tongs.

Demonstration 2: Connect a 90-volt battery across a 1-μf capacitor. Disconnect and discharge with a piece of wire, showing the spark.

Demonstration 3: *To exhibit an analogy to the oscillatory discharge of a capacitor.* Suspend a ball from a string about a yard long. Raise the ball to one side and release it. Note that the ball overshoots the center position and swings to the opposite side. Note how long it takes the ball to come to rest.

Demonstration 4: *To note the effect of self-inductance.* Connect a 90-volt battery in series with a 30-henry choke and a key switch. Close the switch. Now open it, and note the spark that jumps across the gap, indicating that current is still flowing for an instant after the key switch is opened.

CHAPTER 13

Demonstration 1: Arrange electric-light lamps in series and parallel circuits and trace the paths of current flow for the students.

Demonstration 2: Repeat Demonstration 4, Chapter 10, placing a 0.006-μf capacitor across the phones.

CHAPTER 14

Demonstration 1: Demonstrate the apparatus shown in Figure 14-1. Instead of an electric lamp, use a type 1H5-GT tube. Connect a dry cell (1½ volts) to tube filament connections Nos. 2 and 7. The meter (which should be a very sensitive milliameter) is connected between diode connection No. 5 and the negative side of the filament. The other tube connections are left free.

Demonstration 2: Demonstrate the apparatus shown in Figures 14-2, 14-3, and 14-4. Use only the diode plate (connection No. 5) and the filament (connections Nos. 2 and 7) of a type 1H5-GT tube. The meter (which should be a 0-10 d-c milliameter) is connected between tube connection No. 5 and the B battery (or alternating-current source). The B battery should be from 45 to 90v. A small hand magneto, turned slowly, will give the alternating-current voltage.

Demonstration 3: *To show how the diode acts as a rectifier.* Arrange the following apparatus:

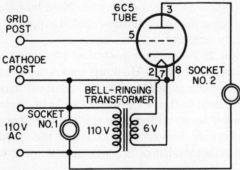

Place a 1 or 2 watt split-plate neon lamp into socket No. 1 to show how both plates are illuminated on alternating current. If direct current is available show how only one plate (the negative) is illuminated. Now place the neon lamp into socket No. 2. Only one of the neon plates lights up, showing that the alternating current has been rectified to direct current by the diode.

Demonstration 4: *To exhibit a working diode detector.* Set up the following apparatus:

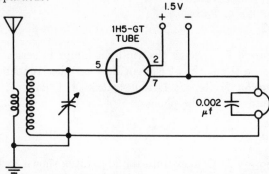

The tuner is the one shown in Figure 10-7 except that the crystal detector has been replaced by a diode (part of the 1H5-GT tube). Only filament connections Nos. 2 and 7 and diode-plate connection No. 5 of the tube are used.

CHAPTER 15

Demonstration 1: *To show how the grid voltage controls plate current.* In the set-up of Demonstration 3, Chapter 14, connect a dry cell between the grid and cathode posts so as to place a positive charge on the grid. Attach more and more cells in series so as to make the grid more and more positive. Note how the plate of the neon lamp glows brighter and brighter, indicating more plate current. Now reverse the cells to place a negative charge on the grid. Note how the brightness of the plate of the neon lamp diminishes and disappears when the grid becomes sufficiently negative.

Demonstration 2: *To compare control of plate current by the plate voltage and by the grid voltage.* Hook up apparatus as shown in Figure 15-3. The tube may be a type 1H5-GT. The filament may be lighted by a single dry cell. The B battery is 90v and should be variable. The meter is a direct-current 0 to 10 milliammeter. Place the charges on the grid by connecting dry cells between the grid and the filament. Vary the grid charges and note the change in plate current for every volt change in grid voltage.

Keep the grid voltage constant and vary the plate voltage. Note the change in plate current for every volt change in plate voltage. Compare the effect on the plate current of the grid voltage and plate voltage. Make graphs.

Demonstration 3: Construct the receiver shown in Figure 15-14. Keep all leads as short as possible. Tune in a station. Remove the grid capacitor. Note the effect. Replace the grid capacitor and remove the grid leak. Note the effect.

Demonstration 4: *To study how a filament rheostat acts as a volume control.* Repeat Demonstration 2, Chapter 15, but include a 30-ohm rheostat in series with the filament and the A battery. Study the effect of changes in rheostat settings upon the plate current.

CHAPTER 16

Demonstration 1: *To show how a varying direct current may operate a transformer.* Obtain a 1:1 or 1:2 audio-frequency transformer. Connect the primary in series with a 6-volt battery and a 30-ohm rheostat. Connect the secondary to a zero-center volt-meter. Move the rheostat arm back and forth and note the variations on the voltmeter. Note that the voltage output of the secondary is alternating in character. Also note that when there is no current variation in the primary, no voltage is produced across the secondary.

Demonstration 2: Repeat Demonstration 3, Chapter 3, holding the smaller coil with its axis the same as the large coil and then with its axis at right angles to the large coil. Note difference.

Demonstration 3: Build the regenerative receiver shown in Figure 16-3. It may be necessary to reverse the tickler-coil terminals if the set fails to operate.

CHAPTER 17

Demonstration 1: Construct the set shown in Figure 17-13. Short out the C battery to show why the grid bias is necessary.

Demonstration 2: Build a public-address system as shown in Figure 17-14.

Demonstration 3: Build an electrical phonograph as shown in Figure 17-17.

Demonstration 4: *To study an analogy of the carbon microphone.* Cut into five pieces the carbon of a dry cell. Line them up in a grooved board. Connect the ends of the carbon in series with a 6-volt battery and a 6-volt 15-watt lamp. Squeeze the carbon pieces together firmly and note the brilliance of the light. Slowly relax the compression and note how the intensity drops off.

Demonstration 5: *To build a simple ac-dc phonograph player.* Construct the circuit shown below. For explanation of the tubes employed, refer to Chapter 27.

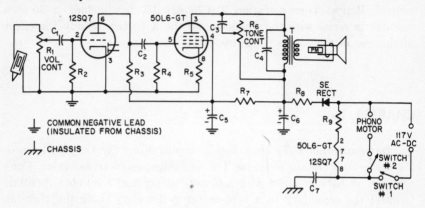

R₁—Volume-control potentiometer, 1 megohm

R₂—4.7 megohms, ½ watt

R₃—100,000 ohms, ½ watt

R₄—470,000 ohms, ½ watt

R₅—150 ohms, ½ watt

R₆—Tone-control potentiometer, 25,000 ohms

R₇—1500 ohms, ½ watt

R₈—22 ohms, ½ watt

R₉—360 ohms, 10 watt

Se Rectifier—75 ma

C₁—0.01 μf, 400 v.

C₂—0.005μf, 400 v.

C₃—0.1 μf, 400 v.

C₄—0.005 μf, 400 v.

C₅,C₆—Dual 30-50 μf electrolytic, 150 v.

C₇—0.1 μf, 400 v.

T—Output transformer, 50L6 to voice coil

Switch #1 SPST mounted on back of R₁

Phono Motor—AC-DC

Switch #2—Phone switch

CHAPTER 18

Demonstration 1: *To show how a tube acts as a rectifier.* Repeat Demonstration 3, Chapter 14.

Demonstration 2: *To explain the component parts of a power transformer.* Repeat Demonstrations 2 and 3, Chapter 10.

Demonstration 3: *To demonstrate the principle of a voltage divider.* Connect a 25,000-ohm potentiometer across a 90-volt battery. Connect a direct-current 0 to 100v voltmeter to one end of the potentiometer and to the sliding arm. Move the sliding arm across the potentiometer and note how the reading of the voltmeter varies.

Demonstration 4: Construct the following apparatus:

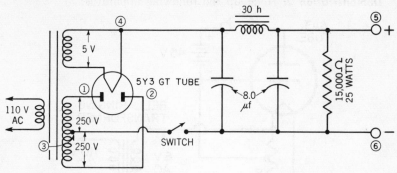

The power transformer should be able to deliver about 250v on either side of the center tap. The rectifier tube is a type 5Y3-GT. The filter capacitors are 8μf at 450v direct-current working voltage. The choke is an ordinary 30-henry choke coil. The voltage divider is 15,000 ohms rated at 25w. Connect a 2-watt split-plate neon lamp in series with a magnetic speaker and test as follows:

1. Open switch. (a) Test from point 3 to point 1. Both plates light up, indicating alternating current. Sixty-cycle hum is heard in the loudspeaker. (b) Test from point 3 to point 2. Both plates light up, as above. (c) Test from point 3 to point 4. One plate lights, indicating direct current. Sixty-cycle hum is heard in the loudspeaker.

2. Close switch. (a) Test from point 5 to point 6. One plate lights, indicating direct current. No hum is heard in the loudspeaker.

Demonstration 5: Repeat above with a cathode-ray oscilloscope.

CHAPTER 19

Demonstration 1: Hook up the apparatus as illustrated. Note the 60-cycle hum in the earphones.

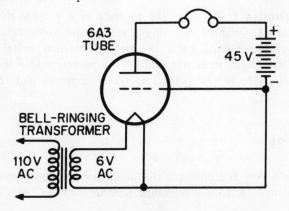

Demonstration 2: Hook up the following apparatus:

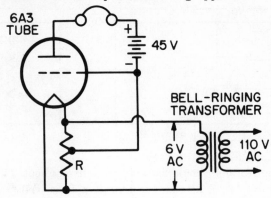

R is a 20- to 40-ohm center-tapped resistor. The hum is nearly gone.

Demonstration 3: Hook up the following apparatus. The hum practically disappears.

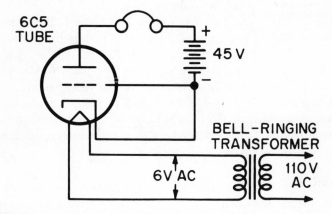

CHAPTER 20

Demonstration 1: *To show the polarity of a voltage drop.* Repeat Demonstration 3, Chapter 18, using a zero-center voltmeter. Leave the slider arm of the potentiometer in one position and switch the other lead of the voltmeter from one end of the potentiometer to the other. Note that one side of the potentiometer is negative and the other is positive.

CHAPTER 21

Demonstration 1: Construct the ac-dc power supply shown on the top of page 623. A 75-ma selenium rectifier is used. The electrolytic

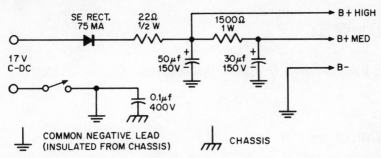

COMMON NEGATIVE LEAD
(INSULATED FROM CHASSIS)   CHASSIS

capacitors are a dual unit (50-30 μf, 150 volts d-c working). The symbol ⊥ represents the common negative line (insulated from the chassis). The symbol 〃 represents the chassis. When using on direct current, reverse the plug to the wall outlet if the power supply fails to work.

CHAPTER 22

Demonstration 1: Construct the following apparatus:

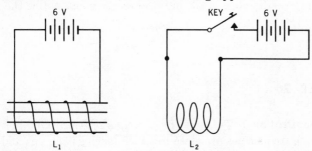

L_1 corresponds to the field coil of the dynamic speaker. It consists of about 300 turns of bell wire wound on a soft-iron core and it is held in a fixed position. L_2 corresponds to the voice coil of the dynamic speaker. It consists of about 30 turns, air wound, with a diameter of about 1 in. It is suspended so that it is free to move.

Close the key. The voice coil moves.

Demonstration 2: Obtain an old electromagnetic dynamic speaker. Open it up to show the field coil, voice coil, and spider. Also examine a permanent-magnet dynamic speaker.

CHAPTER 23

Demonstration 1: Examine a three-gang variable capacitor. Notice how each capacitor moves an equal amount with the rotation of the shaft. Examine the trimmer on each capacitor.

CHAPTER 24

Demonstration 1: Repeat Demonstration 4, Chapter 15.

CHAPTER 25

Demonstration 1: *To show that different sounds may have different pitches.* Strike different types and shapes of materials and note the pitch of each sound produced.

Demonstration 2: *To show how mechanical filters may remove high or low tones.* Talk through a cardboard tube, a megaphone, the cupped hands, and the like.

Demonstration 3: *To show how sounds of different pitches may produce currents of different frequencies.* Connect a telephone receiver to a cathode-ray oscilloscope. Talk into the receiver and notice the wave picture.

CHAPTER 26

Demonstration 1: *To show the principle of beats.* Obtain two tuning forks whose frequencies are close together (such as 320 vps and 384 vps). Strike both and hold them close to each other. Note the beats.

Demonstration 2: Operate an ordinary radio receiver. Near by, operate a regenerative receiver as shown in Figure 16-3. Tune both receivers to the same station. Now adjust the regenerative control until the regenerative receiver oscillates. The second receiver will pick up the radio wave transmitter by the regenerative receiver as a squeal or whistle.

CHAPTER 27

Demonstration 1: Obtain as many different types of burnt-out tubes as possible. Break the glass envelopes and study the electrodes.

Demonstration 2: Build the push-pull audio-frequency amplifier shown on the top of page 625.

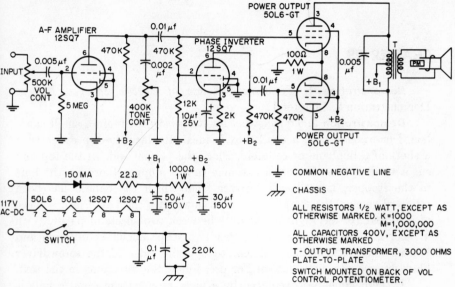

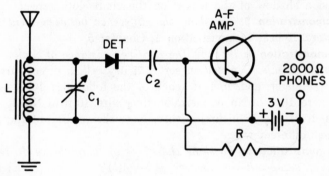

Demonstration 3: Build the transistor radio whose circuit is shown below.

CHAPTER 28

Demonstration 1: Obtain the circuit diagrams of a number of commercial receivers. Trace through these circuits, identifying the purposes of the various components.

Demonstrations for Part II

CHAPTER 29

Demonstration 1: *To show the law of electric charges.* Repeat Demonstration 2, Chapter 11.

Demonstration 2: *To construct an electroscope.* Obtain a small cardboard or wooden box; a chalk box is ideal. Replace the top cover with a sheet of cellophane or celluloid. Place the box on end. In the top end cut a small hole and insert a one-hole rubber stopper. Through the hole in the stopper, insert a screwdriver from which the handle has been removed so that the working end goes down into the box. Place a piece of gold leaf (or any light metal foil) between two sheets of paper. With a razor blade, cut through the paper two strips about ⅜ in. wide and 1¼ in. long. Attach the gold leaf to opposite sides of the screwdriver blade by use of a little saliva. For use, follow the directions in the text.

If the cellophane is replaced by a piece of chart cloth and a hole is cut in the bottom of the box, shining an electric light through this hole will cast a shadow of the leaves on the chart-cloth screen.

Demonstration 3: *To show the difference between insulators and conductors.* Repeat Demonstration 1, Chapter 5.

Demonstration 4: *To show the relative resistance of similar wires of different materials.* Connect, in series, a dry cell, a direct-current 0 to 30-amp ammeter, and, in turn, each of the following: 10 ft of No. 36 copper wire, 10 ft of No. 36 German silver wire, 10 ft of No. 36 soft-iron wire, 10 ft of No. 36 nichrome wire. Note the reading of the ammeter with each different wire.

Demonstration 5: *To show the effect of temperature on resistance.* Connect in series a 6-volt battery, a 6-volt 15-watt lamp, and about 13 in. of No. 28 nichrome wire. The lamp burns faintly. Heat the nichrome wire with a bunsen flame. The lamp goes out. When the wire cools, the lamp lights up again.

Demonstration 6: *To show how resistance varies with the cross-section area of a conductor.* Repeat Demonstration 4 using 10 ft of No. 36 nichrome wire. Note the ammeter reading. Now repeat using 10 ft of No. 18 nichrome wire. Note the ammeter reading.

Demonstration 7: *To show how resistance varies with the length of a conductor.* Repeat Demonstration 4, using 10 ft of No. 36 nichrome wire. Repeat, using 5 ft of wire of the same size. Use 20 ft of wire. Note the ammeter reading in each case.

Demonstration 8: *To show the heating effect of an electric current.* Pass 110v through a heater coil and note the temperature change.

Demonstration 9: *To show how a fuse works.* Connect in series with the 110-volt line a 25-watt lamp and about 2 in. of fuse wire rated at 2 amp. Short out the lamp with a piece of wire. The fuse "pops."

Caution! Place the fuse wire on a piece of asbestos board and use a glass screen around it to avoid being sprayed by the molten metal.

Demonstration 10: *To illustrate the concept of "voltage drop."*

(a) Connect in series a 45-volt battery, a 1,000-ohm resistor, a 2,000-ohm resistor, and a 3,000-ohm resistor. Test the voltage across each resistor with a direct-current 0 to 50v voltmeter.

(b) Substitute for the resistors a 25-watt lamp, a 50-watt lamp, and a 100-watt lamp. For the battery, substitute the 110-volt alternating-current line. Test across the lamps with an alternating-current 0 to 150v voltmeter.

Demonstration 11: *To show the total resistance of resistors in series and parallel.* Hook up the following appartus:

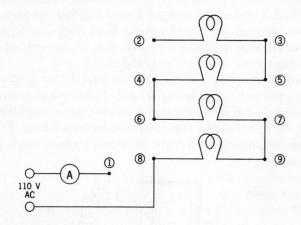

The lamps are each 110-volt, 50-watt. The ammeter is an alternating-current 0 to 5-amp ammeter.

Series connections:

To get current through 1 lamp, connect a wire from 1 to 9. To get current through 2 lamps, connect a wire from 1 to 6. To get current through 3 lamps, connect a wire from 1 to 5. To get current through 4 lamps, connect a wire from 1 to 2. Observe the ammeter reading in each case.

Parallel connections:

Connect wires from 6 to 8, 5 to 7, 2 to 4, and 1 to 9. Remove all the lamps and reinsert them one at a time, taking ammeter readings with each lamp inserted.

Demonstration 12: *To construct a voltaic cell.* Place a strip of zinc and copper in a sulphuric acid solution (1 part acid to 20 parts water). Connect a voltmeter across the two strips.

Caution! In mixing acid with water, use an earthenware or pyrex vessel and always pour the acid *slowly* into the water. If any of the acid spills, neutralize with bicarbonate of soda.

Demonstration 13: *To construct a storage cell.* Place two lead strips in sulphuric acid (one part acid to five parts water). Connect a 6-volt storage battery across the lead strips for about five minutes. Remove the battery and connect a bell or direct-current voltmeter across the lead strips.

CHAPTER 30

Demonstration 1: *To show the magnetic field around a magnet.*

(a) Place a piece of cardboard over a bar magnet. Sprinkle iron filings on the cardboard. Tap gently. The iron filings line up along the lines of force.

(b) Place a piece of magnetized watch spring between two glass plates, then lay them all on an upright delineoscope and project on a screen. Sprinkle the top plate with fine iron filings and tap it gently. This demonstration is good for a classroom.

Demonstration 2: *To illustrate the molecular theory of magnetism.* Magnetize a piece of watch spring. Test its polarity with a compass. Cut the spring in half and test the polarity of each piece. Note that the ends formed by the break at the center have opposite polarity.

Demonstration 3: *To illustrate the Oersted effect.* Hook up the following apparatus:

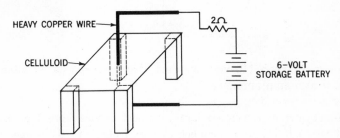

(a) Trace the magnetic lines of force by a small compass moved around on the sheet of celluloid.

(b) Place the whole device on an upright delineoscope, sprinkle with iron filings, and tap gently. Be sure to focus on the plane of the celluloid sheet.

Demonstration 4: *To show the relationship between polarity and direction of current through an electromagnet.* Send direct current through a coil of wire wound on a nail. Test for north and south poles. Reverse the battery and retest for polarity.

Demonstration 5: *To show the effect of an iron core on the strength of an electromagnet.* Wind 50 turns of bell wire on a cardboard tube about 1 in. in diameter. Connect the coil to a battery of four dry cells in series. See if it will pick up any small brads. Now place a soft-iron core in the tube. See how many brads can be picked up now.

Demonstration 6: *To show how the strength of an electromagnet depends upon the ampere-turns.* Wind 25 turns of bell wire on a soft-iron bar. Send 6v through it, and weigh the number of brads that can be picked up. Now rewind the coil with 50 turns of wire. Compare the weight of the brads lifted by the electromagnet. Repeat, using 3v. Compare the results. If a scale is not available, the number of brads lifted in each case may be counted. Care should be taken that all the brads are of the same size.

Demonstration 7: *To show the principle of the motor.* Place two smooth bar magnets with like poles together, one on top of the other. The upper magnet will spin around so that the opposite poles are together.

Demonstration 8: *To illustrate the principle of the electric motor and galvanometer.* Arrange the following apparatus:

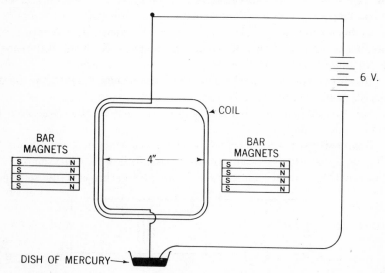

The coil consists of about 25 turns of bell wire. Both ends are bared. One end is connected to a piece of thin copper wire (No. 30 or finer) which suspends the coil. The other end dips into a small dish of mercury. A 6-volt battery is connected to the coil through the thin wire at one end and the mercury at the other.

The field magnets are made up of two sets of four bar magnets arranged as shown. As the current flows through the coil it makes a half turn. A light wooden splint stuck in the coil may simulate the pointer of the galvanometer. Reversing the battery will swing the coil the other way.

Demonstration 9: *To observe how a voltmeter and ammeter are used to determine the wattage of an electrical device.* Connect a lamp of unknown wattage to the 110-volt line. In series with it connect an ammeter. Across the lamp connect a voltmeter. Determine the wattage of the lamp from the following formula:

$$\text{Watts} = E \times I$$

CHAPTER 31

Demonstration 1: Wind 50 turns of bell wire on a cardboard tube 1 in. long and 1 in. in diameter. Connect a sensitive galvanometer to the ends of the coil. Mount a bar magnet in a vertical position. Slip the coil over the magnet. Note the deflection of the meter pointer.

Demonstration 2: Replace the galvanometer in the above demonstration with a zero-center galvanometer. Now move the coil up and down the bar magnet. Observe the movement of the pointer.

Demonstration 3: (a) In the setup for Demonstration 2, use first a weak bar magnet and then a strong bar magnet. Note the difference in the amount of deflection.

(b) Move the coil slowly over the bar magnet. Now move the coil rapidly. Note the greater deflection.

(c) Increase the number of turns of the coil to 100. Now note the greater deflection.

Demonstration 4: *To calculate the power factor.* Connect up the following apparatus. W is an a-c wattmeter, L is a 15-henry choke, A is an alternating-current ammeter, V is an alternating-current voltmeter.

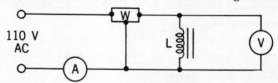

If we multiply the voltage by the current, we get the apparent power. The wattmeter gives us the true power. We can obtain the power factor from the following formula:

$$\text{Power factor} = \frac{\text{true power}}{\text{apparent power}}$$

Demonstration 5: *To illustrate the thermocouple principle.* Connect a demonstration thermocouple (which may be obtained from any scientific supply house) to a direct-current millivoltmeter. Heat the junction point of the thermocouple and note the voltage developed.

CHAPTER 32

Demonstration 1: *To illustrate self-inductance.* Connect up the following apparatus:

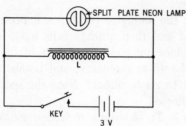

L is a 15- to 30-henry choke. Close the key. Since the neon lamp requires about 70v before it lights up, no light appears. Now open the key quickly. The neon lamp flashes.

Demonstration 2: *To indicate the operation of inductive reactance.* Connect a 1-henry choke in series with the 110-volt direct-current line, a 25-watt lamp, and a 0 to 5-amp direct-current ammeter. (If the choke is not available, the primary of a power transformer may be substituted.) Note the reading of the ammeter. Now replace the direct-current ammeter with an alternating-current ammeter and the 110-volt direct-current line by a 110-volt alternating-current line. Note the difference in ammeter reading.

Demonstration 3: *To show the effect of an iron core on inductive reactance.* Wind about 400 turns of bell wire on a cardboard tube 6 in. long and 1½ in. in diameter. Connect this coil in series with the 110-volt alternating-current line and a 500-watt lamp. Observe the brightness of the lamp. Now place a bundle of soft-iron rods into the core space of the coil. Note how the brightness of the lamp diminishes.

Demonstration 4: *To show how power dissipated in a transformer secondary causes the primary to draw more power from the source.* Connect a 25-watt incandescent lamp in series with the primary of a filament transformer, as shown below.

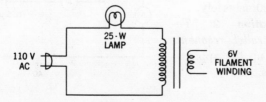

With the secondary open, note that the lamp glows dimly. Now cause the secondary to draw power by shorting its ends. The primary draws more current from the source and the lamp glows brightly.

Caution! The secondary should be shorted for only a short time.

CHAPTER 33

Demonstration 1: *To show the nature of the charge on the plates of a capacitor.* Connect in series a 45-volt battery, a 1-μf capacitor, and a zero-center ammeter.

(a) Note that the ammeter pointer is deflected at the moment the circuit is completed and then quickly falls back to zero. This indicates that the capacitor does not pass direct current.

(b) Remove the 45-volt battery, and touch together the two wires that formerly went to its terminals. Note the spark. Note how the ammeter pointer is deflected.

Demonstration 2: *To show how a capacitor blocks direct current but passes alternating current.* Connect a 10-μf 200-volt paper capacitor in series with a 25-watt lamp and the 110-volt direct-current line. Note that the lamp does not light. Now replace the 110-volt direct current with 110-volt alternating current. The lamp lights up.

Demonstration 3: *To illustrate capacitive reactance.* Connect a 25-watt lamp, an alternating-current ammeter, and a 0.1-μf, 200-volt paper capacitor in series with the 110-volt alternating-current line. Note the ammeter reading. Now replace the 0.1-μf capacitor with capacitors whose values are 0.5μf, 1μf, 2μf, 4μf, 8μf, 12μf. Note the ammeter reading for each capacitor.

CHAPTER 34

Demonstration 1: *To observe the series resonant circuit.* Connect a 30-henry choke, a 10-watt lamp, and an alternating-current ammeter in series with the 110-volt 60-cycle alternating-current line. Note the reading on the ammeter. Replace the choke with a 0.25-μf paper capacitor rated at 600v working voltage. Note the reading of the ammeter. Now connect the lamp, ammeter, choke, and capacitor in series with the 110-volt alternating-current line. Note the ammeter reading.

Caution! The choke should pass 200ma safely.

Demonstration 2: *To study the parallel resonant circuit.* Hook up the apparatus shown here.

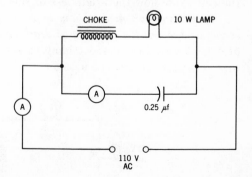

The value of the choke is 30h at 200ma. The capacitor is rated at 600v working voltage. The ammeters are alternating-current meters. Note the readings of the two ammeters.

Demonstration 3: *To derive a resonance curve.* Repeat Demonstration 1, using, one at a time, capacitors of the following values: $0.01\mu f$, $0.05\mu f$, $0.1\mu f$, $0.25\mu f$, $0.5\mu f$, $1\mu f$, $2\mu f$, $4\mu f$. Note the ammeter reading in each case and plot a graph of the amount of current flow (on the Y axis) against the capacitance (on the X axis).

Caution! All of the above capacitors should be rated at 600v working voltage.

Demonstration 4: *Construction of an oscillator and wavemeter.*

C is a 140-$\mu\mu$f variable capacitor. L is 3 turns $\frac{1}{8}$-in. copper tubing, 3 in. in diameter. An insulated wire runs through the tubing and is con-

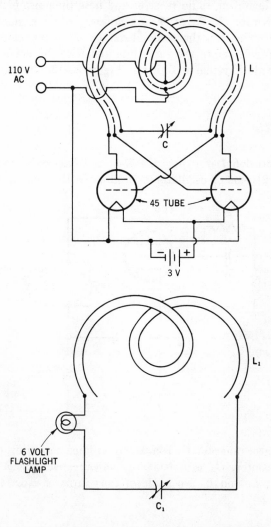

nected to the grids of the tubes. L_1 is the same as L, except that there is no wire running through the tubing. C_1 is the same as C.

When the oscillator is connected up, bring the wavemeter close so that the plane of L_1 is parallel to that of L. Then turn C_1 slowly until the flashlight lamp lights up. The wavemeter is now in resonance with the oscillator. Change C to vary the frequency of the oscillator. The flashlight lamp goes out, and C_1 must be adjusted again before the lamp lights up again.

CHAPTER 35

Demonstration 1: *To illustrate man-made static.* Spark an induction coil near an operating radio receiver and note the noise pickup.

Demonstration 2: *To filter line noises.* Obtain a small motor and place a little grease on the commutator to cause sparking. Connect an electric radio receiver to the same line and note the noise pickup. Now connect up a filter system as shown in Figure 35-12. Note the diminishing of the noise.

CHAPTER 36

Demonstration 1: *To show the node and loop points on an antenna.* Construct a 2½-meter oscillator as follows:

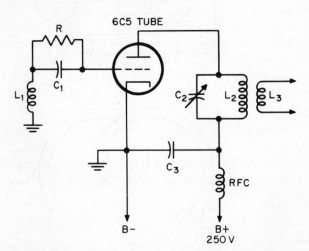

In this oscillator diagram, C_1 is a 0.0001-μf mica capacitor, C_2 is a 15-$\mu\mu$f variable capacitor, C_3 is a 0.0005-μf mica capacitor; R is 10,000 to 50,000 ohms; L_1 and L_2 are made of four turns of No. 14 copper wire wound to make a coil ⅜ in. in diameter and spaced to be ⅝ in. long; L_3 is made of one or two turns of No. 14 copper wire wound to make a coil ⅜ in. in diameter and coupled to the bottom of L_2; RFC is approximately 30 turns of No. 30 wire on a ¼-in. dowel stick.

Note carefully! *It is unlawful for anyone but a licensed operator to transmit a radio signal. In time of war, even licensed amateurs may not transmit. This oscillator is a transmitting set and care should be taken not to connect it to an antenna.*

Having constructed the oscillator, set up the following apparatus (called a Lecher system):

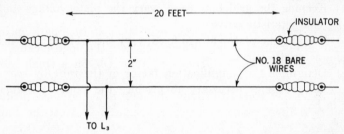

Solder a one-turn loop of wire about ½ inch in diameter to the base terminals of a low-current flashlight lamp. When this loop is brought near or placed over the end of L_2, the lamp should glow. Connect the ends of the Lecher system to L_3. A shorting bar (a metal strip with a knife edge) is slid along the Lecher wires outward from the oscillator until the flashlight shows a sharp dip in brightness. Mark this point on the wires and move on until a second dip is obtained.

The points at which the lamp dips in brightness correspond to the current loops of the wave. Midway between them is a current node. If desired, the frequency and wavelength of the oscillator may be determined. The distance between points is half the wavelength. The frequency may be determined by means of the following formula:

$$f \text{ (megacycles)} = \frac{5905}{\text{distance (inches) between points}}$$

Caution! Mount the Leacher wires clear of obstructions and keep the wires taut. Keep the hands clear of the wires when in use.

CHAPTER 37

Demonstration 1: *To determine the characteristics of a radio tube.* Connect up the following apparatus:

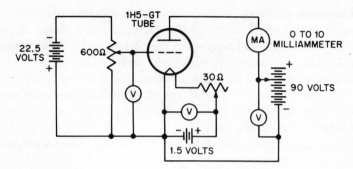

(a) Keeping the grid bias fixed, vary the plate voltage and draw the I_p-E_p characteristic curve.

(b) Keeping the plate voltage fixed, vary the grid bias and draw the E_g-I_p characteristic curve.

(c) Determine the amplification factor of the tube by seeing how great an E_g change is necessary to produce the same I_p change as a change in E_p.

CHAPTER 38

Demonstration 1: *To show conditions for maximum transfer of power.* Calculate the data required from the data given in the following table:

Generator resistance	Generator voltage	External resistance	Current	Power dissipated externally	Voltage across the external resistor
2Ω	10	0.2Ω			
2Ω	10	0.5Ω			
2Ω	10	1Ω			
2Ω	10	2Ω			
2Ω	10	4Ω			
2Ω	10	6Ω			
2Ω	10	8Ω			
2Ω	10	10Ω			

Note when the power dissipated externally is greatest. Note when the voltage across the external resistor is greatest.

CHAPTER 39

Demonstration 1: *To build an oscillator for audio frequencies.* Build an oscillator according to the following diagram:

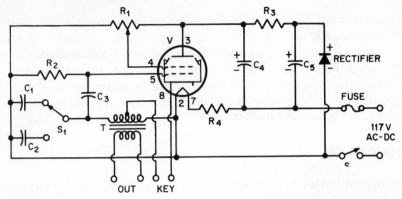

C₁—0.1 μf, 200v, paper capacitor
C₂—0.01 μf, 200v, paper capacitor
C₃—0.05 μf, 200v, paper capacitor
C₄,C₅—Dual 10-10 μf, 150v, electrolytic capacitor
R₁—50K potentiometer with S₂ mounted on back (Volume control)
R₂—33K, 1/2 watt
R₃—500Ω, 5 watt
R₄—400Ω, 10 watt

S₁—S.P.D.T. switch (Tone control)
S₂—S.P.S.T. switch mounted on back of R₁
T—Output transformer, PP50L6 to voice coil
V—50L6-GT tube
Rectifier-Selenium, 75ma
Key
Speaker-Voice coil to match output transformer (T)

This oscillator is suitable for code practice work.

Demonstration 2: *To build a low-power Hartley oscillator for the broadcast frequencies.* Build the set shown in the illustration below.

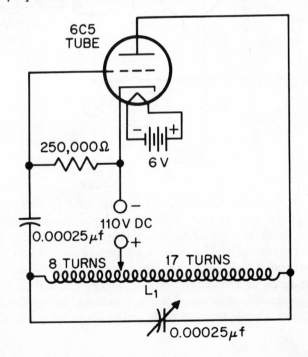

L_1 is 25 turns of No. 14 double-cotton-covered wire on a cardboard tube 3 in. in diameter.

To modulate, wind one turn of No. 14 double-cotton-covered wire over the grid end of L_1. Connect a dry cell and a telephone microphone in series with this one turn. The signal may be picked up on a nearby standard broadcast receiver. *Remember the caution* (p. 635) *against connecting this oscillator to an antenna!*

CHAPTER 40

Demonstration 1: *To construct a simple continuous-wave transmitter for 80 meters.* Build the set shown below.

C_1 is a 0.0001-μf variable capacitor; C is a 0.1-μf 600-volt fixed capacitor; R_1 is 10,000 ohms, 2w; R_2 is 200 ohms, 1w; R_3 is 20,000 ohms, 5w; RFC is 2.5mh; L_1 is 29 turns of No. 18 double-cotton-covered wire on a 1½-in. form; L_2 is 1 turn of No. 18 double-cotton-covered wire; the crystal is an 80-meter crystal.

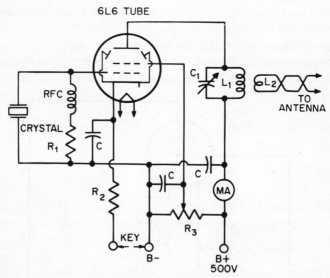

Close the key. The transmitter is now oscillating. This condition is indicated by the drop in plate current as shown on the milliammeter. If a 2-watt lamp is touched to the plate-circuit tank coil, the lamp will glow. *Observe the caution against connecting this set to an antenna.*

Demonstration 2: *To show the use of the dummy antenna.* Wind a coil similar to L_1 of Demonstration 1. Connect this coil in series with a 0.0001-μf variable capacitor, a radio-frequency milliammeter, and a 10-ohm resistor. Couple this coil to L_1 in the above setup and adjust the variable capacitor until resonance is reached. (This condition is shown by the greatest current reading of the milliammeter.) Then calculate the power by the formula $P = I^2 \times R$, where I is the current indicated by the radio-frequency milliammeter and R is 10 ohms.

CHAPTER 41

Demonstration 1: *To construct a simple radio telephone on the broadcast band.* Construct the following apparatus:

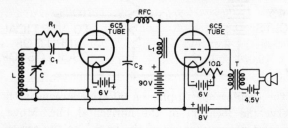

C is a 0.00035-μf variable capacitor; C_1 is a 0.00025-μf fixed capacitor; C_2 is a 0.002-μf fixed capacitor; R_1 is 50,000 ohms; RFC is 33 turns of No. 32 double-cotton-covered wire on a $\frac{1}{2}$-in. dowel; L is a broadcast-band coil; L_1 is a 30-henry choke; T is the microphone transformer.

Test for oscillation by touching a neon lamp to coil L.

Speak into the microphone and tune a nearby broadcast receiver for the signal. Adjust the tap on coil L for best results.

Caution! *Avoid connecting this transmitter to an antenna.*

CHAPTER 42

Demonstration 1: *To show magnetic deflection of a cathode ray.* Connect a Crookes tube with a fluorescent screen to the secondary of an induction coil. Connect the primary of the coil to a 6-volt battery. Observe the path of the cathode ray on the screen. Now bring the north pole of a magnet to the top of the tube. Note the deflection of the ray. Bring the south pole of the magnet to the top of the tube. Note the deflection of the ray.

Demonstration 2: *To operate the cathode-ray oscilloscope.* Plug the oscilloscope into a 110-volt alternating-current outlet and turn on the main power switch. Wait several seconds for the dot to appear on the screen. Keep the intensity control low so that the screen will not be damaged. If the dot is not sharp, adjust the focus control knob. By adjusting the vertical and horizontal centering knobs, get the dot to appear at the center of the screen. You are now ready to make various tests. The general method of employing an oscilloscope is to impress the voltage to be observed on the vertical input and to apply the sweep circuit on the horizontal plates of the cathode-ray tube.

Demonstration 3: *To observe a direct-current voltage on the oscilloscope.* Connect the following hookup directly to the vertical deflection plates of the oscilloscope:

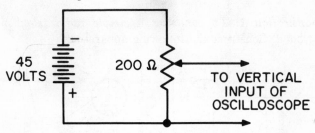

Adjust the oscilloscope to place a 60-cycle sweep on the horizontal plates. Observe the location of the horizontal line. Move the potentiometer arm and notice changes of the image on the screen.

Reverse the battery terminals and note the effect on the position of the image.

Demonstration 4: *To observe an alternating-current voltage on the oscilloscope.* Set the horizontal control on the 60-cycle sweep. Connect the primary of a bell transformer to the 110-volt alternating-current line and connect the output to the vertical input of the oscilloscope. Observe the waveform produced. Note the results when the horizontal and vertical gain controls are turned up. Note the results when the frequency and range controls are varied. The waveform will be a sine curve.

Demonstration 5: Connect the output of an audio-frequency amplifier, shown in Figure 17-14, to the vertical input of the oscilloscope. Set the horizontal sweep at 60 cycles. Speak into the microphone. Observe the waveforms produced.

Demonstration 6: Connect the vertical input terminals of the oscilloscope to the OUT terminals of the code oscillator shown in Demonstration 1, Chapter 39. Set the horizontal sweep at 60 cycles. Close the key and observe the waveforms produced. Observe the results obtained by varying the frequency of the horizontal sweep.

Demonstration 7: Substitute the vertical input posts of the oscilloscope for the neon lamp and speaker in Demonstration 4, Chapter 18. Set the horizontal sweep for 60 cycles and observe the waveforms at different portions of the power supply.

Appendix

Appendix

THE EVENTFUL DATES IN RADIO DEVELOPMENT

1727 Cuneus and Musschenbroek (Dutch) discovered the principle of the capacitor.

1842 Joseph Henry (U. S.) experimented with induced voltages.

1850 Faraday (English) performed experiments similar to those of Joseph Henry.

1867 Clerk Maxwell (Scotch) showed mathematically that light is an electromagnetic wave and predicted that there must be other electromagnetic waves of different frequencies.

1874 Ferdinand Braun (German) discovered the rectifying action of some crystals.

1879 Hughes (English) heard wireless waves but could not explain them to the Royal Society.

1884 Edison (U. S.) observed the Edison effect.

1887-9 Heinrich Hertz (German) developed a spark transmitter using a capacitor with plates fairly wide apart. He developed the first wireless detector.

1889 Sir Oliver Lodge (English) developed the principle of tuning based on the previous work of Michael Pupin (U. S.).

1890 Branly (French) developed the Branly coherer, a form of detector, based on the earlier work of Guitard (French).

1894 Marconi (Italian) developed an antenna and ground system, using the Branly coherer. He radiotelegraphed over a distance of two miles.

1901 Marconi sent a signal from England to Newfoundland, using a detector invented by Lieutenant Solari (Italian).

1902 Fessenden (U. S.) developed the continuous-wave system with radio-frequency alternators. Poulsen (Denmark) worked out another continuous-wave system with an arc.

1904 J. A. Fleming (English) developed the Fleming valve.

1906 General Dunwoody (U. S.) devised a crystal detector.

1907 Lee De Forest (U. S.) developed the triode with a control grid.

1907 E. H. Armstrong (U. S.) developed the regeneration principle for receivers and transmitters.

1909 The steamship *Republic* sank, January 23. People were rescued for the first time through the use of radio. Radio was popularized.

Recent   Hazeltine (U. S.) developed the neutrodyne receiver.

Recent   Armstrong (U. S.) developed the superheterodyne and frequency-modulation receiver.

SCHEMATIC SYMBOLS USED IN CIRCUIT DIAGRAMS

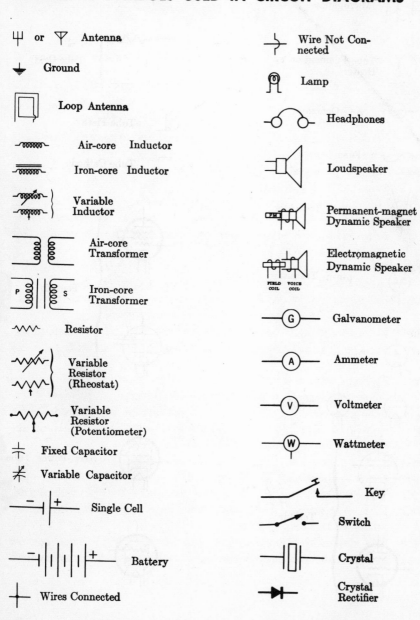

ꟺ or ∀   Antenna

⏚   Ground

Loop Antenna

Air-core   Inductor

Iron-core   Inductor

Variable Inductor

Air-core Transformer

P   S   Iron-core Transformer

Resistor

Variable Resistor (Rheostat)

Variable Resistor (Potentiometer)

Fixed Capacitor

Variable Capacitor

− +   Single Cell

− +   Battery

Wires Connected

Wire Not Connected

Lamp

Headphones

Loudspeaker

Permanent-magnet Dynamic Speaker

Electromagnetic Dynamic Speaker
FIELD COIL   VOICE COIL

G   Galvanometer

A   Ammeter

V   Voltmeter

W   Wattmeter

Key

Switch

Crystal

Crystal Rectifier

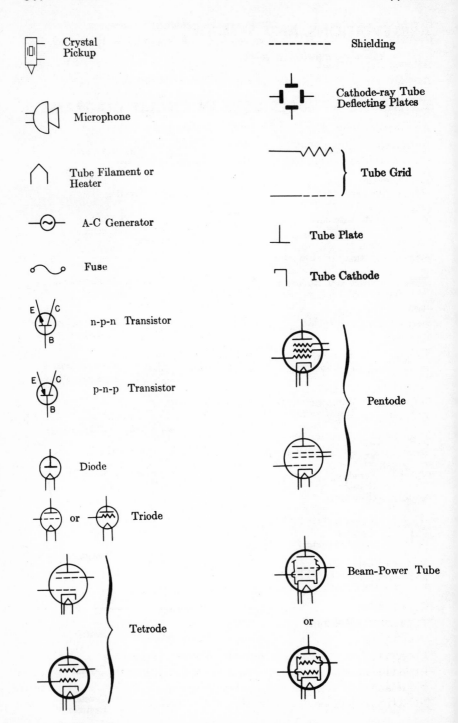

Crystal Pickup

Microphone

Tube Filament or Heater

A-C Generator

Fuse

n-p-n Transistor

p-n-p Transistor

Diode

or   Triode

Tetrode

Shielding

Cathode-ray Tube Deflecting Plates

Tube Grid

Tube Plate

Tube Cathode

Pentode

Beam-Power Tube

or

ABBREVIATIONS AND SYMBOLS

Alternating current	ac	Megohm	$\text{meg}\Omega$
Ampere	amp	Meter (measure of length)	m
Amplitude modulation	AM	Micro (1/1,000,000)	μ
Antenna	ant	Microampere	μamp
Audio frequency	af	Microfarad	μf
Automatic volume control	avc	Microhenry	μh
Beat-frequency oscillator	BFO	Micromicro	
Capacitance	C	(1/1,000,000,000,000)	$\mu\mu$
Capacitive reactance	X_C	Micromicrofarad	$\mu\mu\text{f}$
Centimeter	cm	Microvolt	μv
Continuous waves	cw	Microwatt	μw
Current	I	Milli (1/1,000)	m
Direct current	dc	Milliampere	ma
Electromotive force	emf	Millihenry	mh
Farad	f	Millivolt	mv
Frequency	f	Milliwatt	mw
Frequency modulation	FM	Modulated continuous waves	mcw
Ground	gnd	Ohm	Ω
Henry	h	Power	P
High frequency	hf	Power factor	pf
Impedance	Z	Radio frequency	rf
Inductance	L	Resistance	R
Inductive reactance	X_L	Tuned radio frequency	TRF
Intermediate frequency	if	Ultrahigh frequency	uhf
Interrupted continuous waves	icw	Vibrations per second	vps
Kilocycles	kc	Volt	v
Kilowatt	kw	Watt	w
Megacycles	mc		

ELECTRICAL UNITS

Capacitance	farad	Phase	degree
Capacitive reactance	ohm	Power	watt
Current	ampere	Resistance	ohm
Frequency	cycles per second	Voltage (potential	
Impedance	ohm	difference, emf)	volt
Inductance	henry	Wavelength	meter
Inductive reactance	ohm		

EIA COLOR CODE

To identify the various connections and values of standard radio components, the Electronics Industries Association (EIA) has adopted a color code. Numbers are represented by the following colors:

0	black	5	green
1	brown	6	blue
2	red	7	violet
3	orange	8	gray
4	yellow	9	white

EIA COLOR CODE FOR RESISTORS

The value in ohms of a resistor may be learned from three dots or bands of color. The first color represents the first figure of the resistance value. The second color represents the second figure. The third color represents the decimal multiplier, or number of zeros, following the first two figures. In old-type resistors, the first color usually was the color of the *body* of the resistor. The second color was that of the *tip* of the resistor. The third color was a *dot,* usually at the center of the resistor.

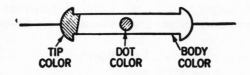

TIP   DOT   BODY
COLOR   COLOR   COLOR

Here is an example. Assume a resistor whose body is yellow, tip blue, and dot red. We thus get yellow, blue, red—which, translated into the code, stands for

4-6-00   or   4,600 ohms.

In the new-type resistors, these colors are shown in bands, with the first band being the one nearest to one end. Sometimes a fourth band of color is shown to indicate the degree of accuracy, or tolerance, of the resistor.

The complete color code for resistors is given in the following table:

Color	1st Figure	2nd Figure	Multiplier	Tolerance
Black..............	..	0	1	....
Brown.............	1	1	10	1%
Red................	2	2	100	2%
Orange............	3	3	1,000	3%
Yellow............	4	4	10,000	4%
Green.............	5	5	100,000	....
Blue...............	6	6	1,000,000	....
Purple............	7	7	10,000,000	....
Gray..............	8	8	100,000,000	....
White.............	9	9	1,000,000,000	....
Silver.............	..	..	....	10%
Gold..............	..	..	....	5%
No Color..........	..	..	....	20%

Let us consider another example. Assume that a resistor shows four bands of color which, starting at one end, appear as yellow, purple, orange, and gold.

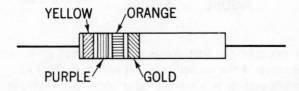

YELLOW   ORANGE

PURPLE   GOLD

From this we may gather that the resistance is 47,000 ohms and the tolerance is 5 per cent.

Flexible resistors are made of resistance wire wound on a flexible insulating core and the whole covered with a braided sleeve. The first

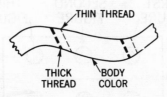

THIN THREAD

THICK
THREAD   BODY
COLOR

figure of the resistance is obtained from the body color of the sleeve. The second figure is shown by the color of a thick thread woven into the sleeve. The multiplier is obtained from the color of a thin thread woven into the sleeve.

EIA COLOR CODE FOR MICA CAPACITORS

A good deal of confusion arises from the fact that different manufacturers employ different color codes to identify the values of mica capacitors. In an attempt to dispel this confusion, the EIA has introduced two systems of color coding.

One is a three-dot code to be applied to mica capacitors rated at 500 volts, direct-current working voltage and ±20 % tolerance only. The first dot indicates the first figure, the second dot the second figure, and the third dot indicates the multiplier. The value is read in micromicrofarads ($\mu\mu$f), and the sequence of the dots is indicated by an arrow.

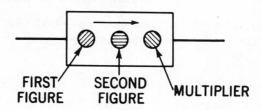

FIRST FIGURE   SECOND FIGURE   MULTIPLIER

If, for example, the first dot is red, the second green, and the third brown, the value of the capacitor is 250 $\mu\mu$f, or 0.00025 μf.

The other system is a six-dot color code with three dots along the top and three dots at the bottom. Again the value is read in micromicrofarads, and the sequence is shown by means of an arrow. As you can see, we may determine from this code the first three figures, the multiplier, the tolerance, and the direct-current working voltage.

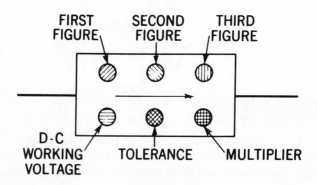

FIRST FIGURE   SECOND FIGURE   THIRD FIGURE

D-C WORKING VOLTAGE   TOLERANCE   MULTIPLIER

The complete color code for mica capacitors is as follows:

Color	Figures	Multiplier	D-c Working Voltage	Tolerance
Black................	0	1	.....	...
Brown...............	1	10	100	1%
Red.................	2	100	200	2%
Orange..............	3	1,000	300	3%
Yellow..............	4	10,000	400	4%
Green...............	5	100,000	500	...
Blue................	6	1,000,000	600	6%
Violet..............	7	10,000,000	700	7%
Gray................	8	100,000,000	800	8%
White...............	9	1,000,000,000	900	9%
Gold................	..	0.1	1,000	5%
Silver..............	..	0.01	2,000	10%
No color............	..	....	500	20%

EIA COLOR CODE FOR POWER TRANSFORMERS

To identify the various leads the following color code has been adopted:

1. Primary leads—black. If tapped: common—black; tap—black and yellow striped; finish—black and red striped.

2. High-voltage plate winding—red. Center tap—red and yellow striped.

3. Rectifier filament winding—yellow. Center tap—yellow and blue striped.

4. Filament winding No. 1—green. Center tap—green and yellow striped.

5. Filament winding No. 2—brown. Center tap—brown and yellow striped.

6. Filament winding No. 3—slate. Center tap—slate and yellow striped.

EIA COLOR CODE FOR AUDIO-FREQUENCY TRANSFORMERS

Blue—Plate (finish) lead of the primary.
Red—B+ lead (this applies whether the primary is plain or center-tapped).

Brown—Plate (start) lead on center-tapped primaries. (Blue may be used for this lead if polarity is not important.)

Green—Grid (finish) lead to secondary.

Black—Grid return (this applies whether the secondary is plain or center-tapped).

Yellow—Grid (start) lead on center-tapped secondaries. (Green may be used for this lead if polarity is not important.)

Note: These markings apply also to line-to-grid, and tube-to-line transformers.

EIA COLOR CODE FOR INTERMEDIATE-FREQUENCY TRANSFORMERS

Blue—Plate lead.
Red—B+ lead.
Green—Grid (or diode) lead.
Black—Grid (or diode) return.

Note: If the secondary of the intermediate-frequency transformer is center-tapped, the second diode plate lead is green and black striped, and black is used for the center-tap lead.

EIA COLOR CODE FOR LOUDSPEAKER VOICE COILS

Green—finish   Black—start

EIA COLOR CODE FOR LOUDSPEAKER FIELD COILS

Black and red striped—start
Yellow and red striped—finish
Slate and red striped—tap (if any)

WAVELENGTH—FREQUENCY CONVERSIONS

$$\text{Wavelength (in meters)} = \frac{300{,}000{,}000}{\text{frequency (in cycles per second)}}$$

Velocity of a radio wave = 300,000,000 meters per second.

BY PROHIAS

THE RESONANT WAVELENGTH

Wavelength (in meters) = $1{,}885 \sqrt{L \times C}$,

where L is in microhenrys and C is in microfarads.

INTERNATIONAL MORSE CODE TABLE

Prohias

A · —	J · — — —	S · · ·
B — · · ·	K — · —	T —
C — · — ·	L · — · ·	U · · —
D — · ·	M — —	V · · · —
E ·	N — ·	W · — —
F · · — ·	O — — —	X — · · —
G — — ·	P · — — ·	Y — · — —
H · · · ·	Q — — · —	Z — — · ·
I · ·	R · — ·	

1 · — — — —	6 — · · · ·
2 · · — — —	7 — — · · ·
3 · · · — —	8 — — — · ·
4 · · · · —	9 — — — — ·
5 · · · · ·	0 — — — — —

Period · — · — · —	Wait · — · · ·
Interrogation · · — — · ·	End of message ·
Break — · · · —	End of transmission · · · — · —

HOW TO SOLDER

There are three essentials to successful soldering: cleanliness, flux, and heat.

1: *Cleanliness.* Be sure that the surfaces to be soldered are perfectly clean. Scrape the surfaces with a knife or rub with sandpaper or steel wool wherever possible.

2. *Flux.* Use a rosin flux. An acid flux may corrode the wires. Use flux sparingly—enough to flow thinly over the surfaces, not to drown them. After soldering, wipe off any excess flux.

3. *Heat.* Heat the surfaces to be soldered until the solder flows over them. If possible, keep the hot iron on the joint even after the solder has flowed so as to be sure there is enough heat. For ordinary radio work a 65- to 75-watt soldering iron is sufficient. Larger soldered surfaces require greater heat.

4. Keep the soldering iron clean by removing any oxide that may form on it. Tin the iron by scraping it clean, dipping the point into the flux, and then applying solder to the tip.

PRACTICAL DATA

1. Make connections as short as possible.

2. Shield as many grid leads as you can.

3. The rotor of a variable capacitor is usually grounded to eliminate body capacitance.

4. Pushback wire will be found convenient for wiring.

5. In electrolytic capacitors, the black wire is usually the negative wire, and the red wire usually the positive wire.

6. For shielding purposes, in using paper capacitors, the end which is marked by a black band is usually the grounded or negative end.

7. To calculate a line-cord resistance:

R (ohms) =

$$\frac{110 - \text{sum of all the filament voltages of the tubes in series}}{\text{current through the tube filaments}}$$

HOW TO READ THE BASE PINS OF TUBES

With the pins held facing you, the pin numbers appear as follows:

OCTAL TUBE

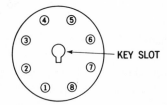

7-PIN MINIATURE TUBE

9-PIN MINIATURE TUBE

Index